CASE STUDIES

ESSAYS

HAVE YOU EVER WONDERED?

PEARSON

ALWAYS LEARNING

Teresa Audesirk • Gerald Audesirk • Bruce E. Byers

Biology
Life on Earth with Physiology

Custom Edition for Portland Community College for Biology 101

Taken from:
Biology: Life on Earth with Physiology, Eleventh Edition
by Teresa Audesirk, Gerald Audesirk, and Bruce E. Byers

Cover Art: Courtesy of Photodisc/Getty Images.

Taken from:

Biology: Life on Earth with Physiology, Eleventh Edition
by Teresa Audesirk, Gerald Audesirk, and Bruce E. Byers
Copyright © 2017, 2014, 2011 by Pearson Education, Inc.
New York, New York 10013

Pearson Education, Inc., 330 Hudson Street, New York, New York 10013
A Pearson Education Company
www.pearsoned.com

Printed in the United States of America

000200010272108686

CM

ISBN 10: 1-323-75709-0
ISBN 13: 978-1-323-75709-3

ABOUT THE AUTHORS

TERRY AND GERRY AUDESIRK grew up in New Jersey, where they met as undergraduates, Gerry at Rutgers University and Terry at Bucknell University. After marrying in 1970, they moved to California, where Terry earned her doctorate in marine ecology at the University of Southern California and Gerry earned his doctorate in neurobiology at the California Institute of Technology. As postdoctoral students at the University of Washington's marine laboratories, they worked together on the neural bases of behavior, using a marine mollusk as a model system.

They are now emeritus professors of biology at the University of Colorado Denver, where they taught introductory biology and neurobiology from 1982 through 2006. In their research, funded primarily by the National Institutes of Health, they investigated the mechanisms by which neurons are harmed by low levels of environmental pollutants and protected by estrogen.

Terry and Gerry are long-time members of many conservation organizations and share a deep appreciation of nature and of the outdoors. They enjoy hiking in the Rockies, walking and horseback riding near their home outside Steamboat Springs, and singing in the community chorus. Keeping up with the amazing and endless stream of new discoveries in biology provides them with a continuing source of fascination and stimulation. They are delighted that their daughter Heather has become a teacher and is inspiring a new generation of students with her love of chemistry.

BRUCE E. BYERS is a Midwesterner transplanted to the hills of western Massachusetts, where he is a professor in the biology department at the University of Massachusetts Amherst. He has been a member of the faculty at UMass (where he also completed his doctoral degree) since 1993. Bruce teaches courses in evolution, ornithology, and animal behavior, and does research on the function and evolution of bird vocalizations.

With love to Jack, Lori, and Heather and in loving memory of Eve and Joe

— T. A. & G. A.

In memory of Bob Byers, a biologist at heart.

—B. E. B.

ABOUT THE COVER A young boreal owl (*Aegolius funereus*) peers out of a cavity. Boreal owls take their name from the boreal forest, the vast, northern coniferous forest in which they live. The owls inhabit boreal forest in Scandinavia, Siberia, Canada, and Alaska, as well as mountain forests a bit further south. Boreal owls hunt at night, using their keen hearing to find the mice, voles, and other small mammals that make up most of their diet. The owls do not build nests. Instead, a female lays her eggs in a cavity in a tree, often one excavated and abandoned by a woodpecker. About a month later, the eggs hatch. For another month or so, the young owls remain in the cavity, subsisting on food brought by their parents. Eventually, though, a young owl ventures to the mouth of the cavity and prepares to take flight. It will live out its life in a corner of the boreal forest, which is also home to endangered species such as the Amur tiger and the Siberian crane. Unfortunately, the boreal forest biome is threatened by widespread logging and a warming climate.

BRIEF CONTENTS

DETAILED CONTENTS

UNIT 1

The Life of the Cell   17

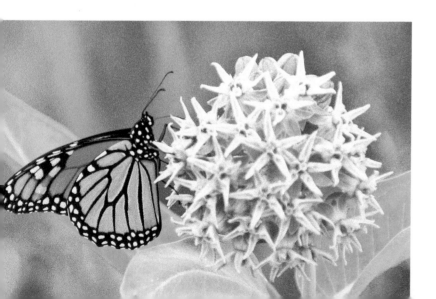

PREFACE

THE CASE FOR SCIENTIFIC LITERACY

Climate change, biofuels versus food and forests, bioengineering, stem cells in medicine, potential flu pandemics, the plight of polar bears and pandas, human population growth and sustainability: these are just some of the very real, urgent, and interrelated concerns sweeping our increasingly connected human societies. The Internet places a wealth of information—and a flood of misinformation—at our fingertips. Never have scientifically literate students been more important to humanity's future. As educators, we feel humbled before this massive challenge. As authors, we feel hopeful that the Eleventh Edition of *Biology: Life on Earth* will help lead introductory biology students along paths to understanding.

Scientific literacy requires a foundation of factual knowledge that provides a solid and accurate cognitive framework into which new information can be integrated. But more importantly, it endows people with the mental tools to separate the wealth of data from the morass of misinformation. Scientifically literate citizens are better able to evaluate facts and to make informed choices in both their personal lives and the political arena.

This Eleventh Edition of *Biology: Life on Earth* continues our tradition of:

- Helping instructors present biological information in a way that will foster scientific literacy among their students.
- Helping to inspire students with a sense of wonder about the natural world, fostering an attitude of inquiry and a keen appreciation for the knowledge gained through science.
- Helping students to recognize the importance of what they are learning to their future roles in our rapidly-changing world.

WHAT'S NEW IN THIS EDITION?

Each new edition gives the authors a fresh opportunity to ponder: "What can we do better?" With extensive help from reviewers, development editors, and our coauthors, we've answered this question with the following changes organized around three major goals:

Highlight an Inquiry-Driven Approach to Learning

- **Probing questions at the end of the extensively revised "Case Study Continued" segments** help students anticipate what they will learn.
- **Three unique question types in essays and figure captions** encourage students to think critically about the content: "Think Critically" questions focus on solving

problems, thinking about scientific data, or evaluating a hypothesis; "Evaluate This" questions ask students to interpret or draw conclusions from a hypothetical scenario; and "Consider This" questions invite students to form an opinion or pose an argument for or against an issue, based on valid scientific information. Answers to "Think Critically" and "Evaluate This" questions are included in the back of the book; hints for "Consider This" questions are included on MasteringBiology.

- **New multiple choice questions at the end of every chapter** address students' recall and comprehension and help them prepare for tests.

Create Connections for Students

- **"Health Watch" essays often include an "Evaluate This" question,** encouraging students to connect health topics to practical, real-world examples.
- **"Threads of Life" themes** in pertinent chapters weave together what may otherwise appear to be unrelated fields within the uniquely diverse science of biology. These threads—identified in our list of changes by chapter below—are the unifying theme of *Evolution*, the exploding science of *Biotechnology*, our increasing recognition of the impacts of *Climate Change*, and our emerging understanding of the importance of *Microbiomes* throughout the living world.
- **Dozens of entirely new and revised figures** illustrate concepts more clearly and engagingly than ever before. For example, negative feedback cycles are now illustrated in a consistent manner that allows students to instantly recognize the chain of events and relate it to negative feedback events in other chapters.

Encourage Critical Thinking

- **New "How Do We Know That?" essays** show students the process of science in a simple way, emphasizing the process and method to what scientists do. Essays go into the details of experiments, highlighting exciting technology and data. "How Do We Know That?" features include "Think Critically" or "Consider This" questions, encouraging students to analyze data or engage with the topics presented in the essay.
- **"Earth Watch" essays include more data.** Students will find more examples of real scientific data in the form of graphs and tables; the data are accompanied by "Think Critically" questions that challenge students to interpret the data, fostering increased understanding of how science is communicated.

In addition, **mitosis and meiosis are now covered in separate chapters** (Chapters 9 and 10, respectively), so students gain a stronger foundational understanding of some of the toughest topics in biology.

BIOLOGY: LIFE ON EARTH, ELEVENTH EDITION

... Is Organized Clearly and Uniformly

Navigational aids help students explore each chapter. An important goal of this organization is to present biology as a hierarchy of closely interrelated concepts rather than as a compendium of independent topics.

- Major sections are introduced as broad questions that stimulate students to think about the material to follow; subheadings are statements that summarize their specific content.
- A "Summary of Key Concepts" section ends each chapter, providing a concise, efficient review of the chapter's major topics.

... Engages and Motivates Students

Scientific literacy cannot be imposed on students—they must actively participate in acquiring the necessary information and skills. To be inspired to accomplish this, they must first recognize that biology is about their own lives. For example, we help students acquire a basic understanding and appreciation of how their own bodies function by including information about diet and weight, cancer, and lower back pain.

We fervently hope that students who use this text will come to see their world through keener eyes. For example, they will perceive forests, fields, and ponds as vibrant and interconnected ecosystems brimming with diverse life-forms rather than as mundane features of their everyday surroundings. If we have done our job, students will also gain the interest, insight, and information they need to look at how humanity has intervened in the natural world. If they ask the question, "Is this activity sustainable?" and then use their new knowledge and critical thinking skills to seek some answers, we can be optimistic about the future.

In support of these goals, the Eleventh Edition has updated features that make Biology more engaging and accessible.

- **Case Studies** Each chapter opens with an attention-grabbing "Case Study" that highlights topics of emerging relevance in today's world. Case Studies, including "Unstable Atoms Unleashed" (Chapter 2), "New Parts for Human Bodies" (Chapter 4), and "Unwelcome Dinner Guests" (Chapter 20), are based on news events, personal interest stories, or particularly fascinating biological topics. "Case Study Continued" segments weave the topic throughout the chapter, whereas "Case Study Revisited" completes the chapter, exploring the topic further in light of the information presented.

- **Boxed Essays** Four categories of essays enliven this text. "Earth Watch" essays explore pressing environmental issues; "Health Watch" essays cover important or intriguing medical topics; "How Do We Know That?" essays explain how scientific knowledge is acquired; and "In Greater Depth" essays make this text versatile for in-depth levels of instruction.
- **"Have You Ever Wondered" Questions** These popular features continue to demystify common and intriguing questions, showing the application of biology in the real world.
- **End-of-Chapter Questions** The questions that conclude each chapter allow students to review the material in different formats—multiple choice, fill-in-the-blank, and essay—that help them to study and test what they have learned. Answers to the multiple choice and fill-in-the-blank questions are included in the back of the book. Answers or hints for the essay questions are included on MasteringBiology.
- **Key Terms and a Complete Glossary** Boldfaced key terms are defined clearly within the text as they are introduced. These terms are also listed at the end of each chapter, providing users with a quick reference to the chapter's important vocabulary. The glossary, carefully written by the authors, provides exceptionally complete definitions for all key terms, as well as for many other important biological terms.

... Is a Comprehensive Learning Package

The Eleventh Edition of *Biology: Life on Earth* is a complete learning package, providing updated and innovative teaching aids for instructors and learning aids for students.

CHAPTER-BY-CHAPTER SUMMARY OF IMPORTANT CHANGES

Following the revision of chapters in response to reviews by instructors and experts, the text and artwork were carefully reviewed by each of the other two authors and the development editors. The coauthors provided valuable insights to one another, integrating the chapters more thoroughly, improving consistency between chapters, and explaining complex concepts more clearly. Our development editors brought trained eyes for order and detail to our work, helping us make the writing even more student-friendly. Following this intense scrutiny, each initial revision underwent a second, sometimes extensive revision. Specific changes include the following:

- **Chapter 1: An Introduction to Life on Earth** includes an entirely updated Case Study to reflect the recent Ebola epidemic. A new "Have You Ever Wondered: Why Scientists Study Obscure Organisms?" highlights unforeseen benefits that have emerged from investigating different organisms. Our *Evolution* "Thread of Life" is emphasized throughout and *Climate Change* is noted in the context of evolution.

UNIT 1 The Life of the Cell

- **Chapter 2: Atoms, Molecules, and Life** offers improved coverage of the unique properties of water. The essay "How Do We Know That? Radioactive Revelations" includes new PET images. The essay "Health Watch: Free Radicals—Friends and Foes?" incorporates new findings on antioxidant supplements. Figures 2-1, 2-2, 2-3, 2-4, 2-5, and 2-6 have been revised for greater clarity and consistency.

- **Chapter 3: Biological Molecules** now covers lipids last, because they are distinct in their structural diversity and in not forming polymers. The discussion of protein structure and intrinsically disordered proteins has been extensively revised. The "Health Watch" essay on trans fats and cholesterol has been extensively updated and rewritten, as has the "Have You Ever Wondered" essay on hair structure. Figures 3-1 and 3-3 and Table 3-2 have undergone major revisions.

- **Chapter 4: Cell Structure and Function** features an entirely new Case Study supporting our *Biotechnology* thread. There is new art for relative sizes as well as enhanced coverage and new art of the extracellular matrix and cytoskeleton (Figures 4-1, 4-6, and 4-7, respectively). Prokaryotic cells are now covered before eukaryotic cells. A new "Earth Watch" essay discusses the environmental impact of raising livestock and the culturing of cow muscle in the lab. "Have You Ever Wondered" has been revised and introduces our *Microbiome* thread.

- **Chapter 5: Cell Membrane Structure and Function** includes upgraded figures of the plasma membrane (Figure 5-1), phospholipids (Figure 5-2), membrane receptors (Figure 5-3), osmosis (Figure 5-6), and surface/volume relationship (Figure 5-13). Added micrographs illustrate cell junctions (Figure 5-14). The "How Do We Know That?" essay on aquaporins has been updated and now includes a data figure. Membrane fluidity has now been incorporated into a "Health Watch" essay, and there is a new "Have You Ever Wondered" essay describing how antibiotics destroy bacteria and supporting our *Evolution* thread.

- **Chapter 6: Energy Flow in the Life of a Cell** includes an updated Case Study, as well as revised art of coupled reactions (Figure 6-7), feedback inhibition (Figure 6-12), and regenerative braking (Figure E6-1). There are new images for entropy (Figure 6-3), activation energy (Figure 6-5b), and food preservation (Figure 6-14). Our explanation of the second law of thermodynamics now uses the phrase "isolated system." The section on solar energy incorporates the *Climate Change* thread. The revised "Health Watch" essay on lactose intolerance supports our *Evolution* thread and a revised "Have You Ever Wondered" about glowing plants supports our *Biotechnology* thread.

- **Chapter 7: Capturing Solar Energy: Photosynthesis** has a revised and updated Case Study, a new overview figure (Figure 7-1), and a chloroplast micrograph added to the figure illustrating photosynthetic structures (Figure 7-3). Figures describing energy transfer in the light reactions (Figure 7-7) and the C_4 and CAM pathways (Figures E7-1 and E7-2) have been significantly improved. The section The Calvin Cycle Captures Carbon Dioxide incorporates the *Biotechnology* thread. The "Earth Watch" essay on biofuels has been updated and supports our *Climate Change* thread.

- **Chapter 8: Harvesting Energy: Glycolysis and Cellular Respiration** features an entirely new Case Study on on the use of mitochondrial DNA in the identification of King Richard III of England. The essay "Health Watch: How Can You Get Fat by Eating Sugar?" has new art showing the conversion of sugar to fat. A micrograph of the mitochondrion has been added to Figure 8-4; the electron transport chain in Figure 8-6 has been redrawn; a new Figure 8-8 illustrates energy extraction from foods; and a new Table 8-1 summarizes glucose breakdown.

UNIT 4 Behavior and Ecology

- **Chapter 26: Animal Behavior** has been extensively revised and updated, including new material and many new figures.

- **Chapter 27: Population Growth and Regulation** opens with a new Case Study on the crash and subsequent regrowth of populations of northern elephant seals. Figure 27-1, illustrating exponential growth, has been revised. Section 27.3 offers a new discussion of life history strategies and their evolution, which also supports our *Evolution* thread. The chapter has been updated with current statistics and figures related to the growth of the human population.

- **Chapter 28: Community Interactions** begins with a new Case Study about endangered Channel Island foxes. Section 28.1 has been expanded to describe the different types of community interactions. Section 28.3 has been extensively revised to describe consumer–prey interactions as a general category that includes all situations in which one organism (the consumer) feeds on another (the prey), and encompasses predation (including herbivory) and parasitism. A new "Have You Ever Wondered" essay explains why rattlesnakes rattle. A new "Health Watch" essay explores how coevolution between parasites and their hosts can produce a range of outcomes, supporting our *Microbiome* thread.

- **Chapter 29: Energy Flow and Nutrient Cycling in Ecosystems** includes updated information on atmospheric carbon dioxide and supports our *Climate Change* thread. A new "How Do We Know That?" essay explores the ways in which scientists monitor Earth's conditions. The "Health Watch" essay on biological magnification includes a new figure.

- **Chapter 30: Earth's Diverse Ecosystems** provides a clear explanation of why global average temperature decreases with latitude, including a new illustration in Figure 30-2a. Descriptions of monsoons and the El Nino/Southern Oscillation have been added to Section 30.2.

- **Chapter 31: Conserving Earth's Biodiversity** opens with a new Case Study of the effects of extirpating, and then reintroducing, wolves in Yellowstone National Park. The description of ecosystem services is now organized into the four categories used by the *Millennium Ecosystem Assessment* and The Economics of Ecosystems and Biodiversity (TEEB). There are new images of rain-forest destruction (Figure 31-4) and wildlife corridors (Figure 31-8).

ACKNOWLEDGMENTS

Biology: Life on Earth enters its 11th edition invigorated by the oversight of the excellent team at Pearson. Beth Wilbur, our Editor-in-Chief, continues to oversee the huge enterprise with the warmth and competence that makes her such an excellent leader. Ginnie Simione Jutson, Executive Development Manager, and Leata Holloway, Program Manager, coordinated this complex and multifaceted endeavor. Senior Acquisitions Editor Star Burruto Mackenzie did a great job of helping us form a revision plan that even further expanded the text's appeal and its ability to convey fascinating information in a user-friendly manner. She listened and responded helpfully to our questions and suggestions—all while traveling extensively to share her enthusiasm for the text and its extensive ancillary resources with educators across the country. Mae Lum, as Project Manager, has done a marvelous job of keeping everything—especially the authors—on track and on schedule, not to mention helping us through the complexities of a rigorously upgraded permissions process. Erin Schnair carefully reviewed every word of the manuscript, making sure the sometimes extensive revisions and rearrangements flowed smoothly into the existing text. Her attention to detail and thoughtful suggestions have contributed significantly to the text's organization and clarity. Our outstanding copyeditor, Joanna Dinsmore, not only negotiated the intricacies of grammar and formatting, but also caught inconsistencies that we had overlooked. Erin and Joanna also looked carefully at the art, checking each piece for consistency with the text and helping us with instructions to the artists. As production advanced, Kari Hopperstead contributed her first-rate formatting skills to meld images and text into an integrated whole. The book boasts a large number of excellent new photos, tracked down with skill and persistence by Kristin Piljay. Kristin was always cheerfully responsive to our requests for still more photos when nothing in the first batch would do.

We are grateful to Imagineering Art, under the direction of Project Manager Wynne Au-Yeung, for deciphering our art instructions and patiently making new adjustments to already outstanding figures. We owe our beautifully redesigned text and delightful new cover to Elise Lansdon.

The production of this text would not have been possible without the considerable efforts of Norine Strang, Senior Project Manager at Cenveo Publisher Services. Norine brought the art, photos, and manuscript together into a seamless and beautiful whole, graciously handling last-minute changes. We thank Lauren Harp, Executive Marketing Manager, for making sure the finished product reached your desk.

In her role as Manufacturing Buyer, Stacey Weinberger's expertise has served us well. The ancillaries are an endeavor fully as important as the text itself. Mae Lum skillfully coordinated the enormous effort of producing a truly outstanding package that complements and supports the text, while Eddie Lee took the lead on the Instructor Resource DVD. Finally, thanks to Chloé Veylit for developing the outstanding MasteringBiology Web site that accompanies this text.

We are extremely fortunate to be working with the Pearson team. This Eleventh Edition of *Biology: Life on Earth* reflects their exceptional abilities and dedication.

With gratitude,

TERRY AUDESIRK, GERRY AUDESIRK,
AND BRUCE BYERS

Eleventh Edition Reviewers

Aekam Barot,
Lake Michigan College
Mark Belk,
Brigham Young University
Karen Bledsoe,
Western Oregon University
Christine Bozarth,
Northern Virginia Community College
Britt Canada,
Western Texas College
Reggie Cobb,
Nash Community College
Rachel Davenport,
Texas State University, San Marcos
Diane Day,
Clayton State University

Lewis Deaton,
University of Louisiana at Lafayette
Peter Ekechukwu,
Horry-Georgetown Technical College
Janet Gaston,
Troy University
Mijitaba Hamissou,
Jacksonville State University
Karen Hanson,
Carroll Community College
Brian Ingram,
Jacksonville State University
Karen Kendall-Fite,
Columbia State Community College

Neil Kirkpatrick,
Moraine Valley Community College
Damaris-Lois Lang,
Hostos Community College
Tiffany McFalls-Smith,
Elizabethtown Community and Technical College
Mark Meade,
Jacksonville State University
Samantha Parks,
Georgia State University
Indiren Pillay,
Georgia College
John Plunket,
Horry-Georgetown Technical College
Cameron Russell,
Tidewater Community College

Roger Sauterer,
Jacksonville State University
Terry Sellers,
Spartanburg Methodist College
David Serrano,
Broward College
Philip Snider,
Gadsden State Community College
Judy Staveley,
Carroll Community College
Katelynn Woodhams,
Lake Michigan College
Min Zhong,
Auburn University
Deborah Zies,
University of Mary Washington

Previous Edition Reviewers

Mike Aaron,
Shelton State Community College
Kammy Algiers,
Ventura College
W. Sylvester Allred,
Northern Arizona University
Judith Keller Amand,
Delaware County Community College
William Anderson,
Abraham Baldwin Agriculture College
Steve Arch,
Reed College
George C. Argyros,
Northeastern University
Kerri Lynn Armstrong,
Community College of Philadelphia
Ana Arnizaut-Vilella,
Mississippi University for Women

Dan Aruscavage,
State University of New York, Potsdam
G. D. Aumann,
University of Houston
Vernon Avila,
San Diego State University
J. Wesley Bahorik,
Kutztown University of Pennsylvania
Peter S. Baletsa,
Northwestern University
Isaac Barjis,
New York City College of Technology
John Barone,
Columbus State University
Bill Barstow,
University of Georgia–Athens
Mike Barton,
Centre College

Erin Baumgartner,
Western Oregon University
Michael C. Bell,
Richland College
Colleen Belk,
University of Minnesota, Duluth
Robert Benard,
American International College
Heather Bennett,
Illinois College
Gerald Bergtrom,
University of Wisconsin
Arlene Billock,
University of Southwestern Louisiana
Brenda C. Blackwelder,
Central Piedmont Community College
Melissa Blamires,
Salt Lake Community College

Karen E. Bledsoe,
Western Oregon University
Bruno Borsari,
Winona State University
Raymond Bower,
University of Arkansas
Robert Boyd,
Auburn University
Michael Boyle,
Seattle Central Community College
Marilyn Brady,
Centennial College of Applied Arts and Technology
David Brown,
Marietta College
Virginia Buckner,
Johnson County Community College
Arthur L. Buikema, Jr.,
Virginia Polytechnic Institute
Diep Burbridge,
Long Beach City College

Jamie Burchill,
Troy University
J. Gregory Burg,
University of Kansas
William F. Burke,
University of Hawaii
Robert Burkholter,
Louisiana State University
Matthew R. Burnham,
Jones County Junior College
Kathleen Burt-Utley,
University of New Orleans
Linda Butler,
University of Texas–Austin
W. Barkley Butler,
Indiana University of Pennsylvania
Jerry Button,
Portland Community College
Bruce E. Byers,
University of Massachusetts Amherst
Anne Casper,
Eastern Michigan University
Sara Chambers,
Long Island University
Judy A. Chappell,
Luzerne County Community College
Nora L. Chee,
Chaminade University
Joseph P. Chinnici,
Virginia Commonwealth University
Dan Chiras,
University of Colorado–Denver
Nicole A. Cintas,
Northern Virginia Community College
Bob Coburn,
Middlesex Community College
Joseph Coelho,
Culver Stockton College
Martin Cohen,
University of Hartford
Mary Colavito,
Santa Monica College
Jay L. Comeaux,
Louisiana State University
Walter J. Conley,
State University of New York at Potsdam
Mary U. Connell,
Appalachian State University
Art Conway,
Randolph-Macon College
Jerry Cook,
Sam Houston State University
Sharon A. Coolican,
Cayuga Community College
Clifton Cooper,
Linn-Benton Community College
Joyce Corban,
Wright State University
Brian E. Corner,
Augsburg College
Ethel Cornforth,
San Jacinto College–South
David J. Cotter,
Georgia College

Lee Couch,
Albuquerque Technical Vocational Institute
Donald C. Cox,
Miami University of Ohio
Patricia B. Cox,
University of Tennessee
Peter Crowcroft,
University of Texas–Austin
Carol Crowder,
North Harris Montgomery College
Mitchell B. Cruzan,
Portland State University
Donald E. Culwell,
University of Central Arkansas
Peter Cumbie,
Winthrop University
Robert A. Cunningham,
Erie Community College, North
Karen Dalton,
Community College of Baltimore County-Catonsville Campus
Lydia Daniels,
University of Pittsburgh
David H. Davis,
Asheville-Buncombe Technical Community College
Jerry Davis,
University of Wisconsin, LaCrosse
Douglas M. Deardon,
University of Minnesota
Lewis Deaton,
University of Louisiana–Lafayette
Fred Delcomyn,
University of Illinois–Urbana
Joe Demasi,
Massachusetts College
David M. Demers,
University of Hartford
Kimberly Demnicki,
Thomas Nelson Community College
Lorren Denney,
Southwest Missouri State University
Katherine J. Denniston,
Towson State University
Charles F. Denny,
University of South Carolina–Sumter
Jean DeSaix,
University of North Carolina–Chapel Hill
Ed DeWalt,
Louisiana State University
Daniel F. Doak,
University of California-Santa Cruz
Christy Donmoyer,
Winthrop University
Matthew M. Douglas,
University of Kansas
Ronald J. Downey,
Ohio University
Ernest Dubrul,
University of Toledo

Michael Dufresne,
University of Windsor
Susan A. Dunford,
University of Cincinnati
Mary Durant,
North Harris College
Ronald Edwards,
University of Florida
Rosemarie Elizondo,
Reedley College
George Ellmore,
Tufts University
Joanne T. Ellzey,
University of Texas–El Paso
Wayne Elmore,
Marshall University
Thomas Emmel,
University of Florida
Carl Estrella,
Merced College
Nancy Eyster-Smith,
Bentley College
Gerald Farr,
Texas State University
Rita Farrar,
Louisiana State University
Marianne Feaver,
North Carolina State University
Susannah Feldman,
Towson University
Linnea Fletcher,
Austin Community College–Northridge
Doug Florian,
Trident Technical College
Charles V. Foltz,
Rhode Island College
Dennis Forsythe,
The Citadel
Douglas Fratianne,
Ohio State University
Scott Freeman,
University of Washington
Donald P. French,
Oklahoma State University
Harvey Friedman,
University of Missouri–St. Louis
Don Fritsch,
Virginia Commonwealth University
Teresa Lane Fulcher,
Pellissippi State Technical Community College
Michael Gaines,
University of Kansas
Cynthia Galloway,
Texas A&M University–Kingsville
Irja Galvan,
Western Oregon University
Gail E. Gasparich,
Towson University
Janet Gaston,
Troy University
Farooka Gauhari,
University of Nebraska–Omaha
John Geiser,
Western Michigan University

Sandra Gibbons,
Moraine Valley Community College
George W. Gilchrist,
University of Washington
David Glenn-Lewin,
Iowa State University
Elmer Gless,
Montana College of Mineral Sciences
Charles W. Good,
Ohio State University–Lima
Joan-Beth Gow,
Anna Maria College
Mary Rose Grant,
St. Louis University
Anjali Gray,
Lourdes College
Margaret Green,
Broward Community College
Ida Greidanus,
Passaic Community College
Mary Ruth Griffin,
University of Charleston
Wendy Grillo,
North Carolina Central University
David Grise,
Southwest Texas State University
Martha Groom,
University of Washington
Lonnie J. Guralnick,
Western Oregon University
Martin E. Hahn,
William Paterson College
Madeline Hall,
Cleveland State University
Georgia Ann Hammond,
Radford University
Blanche C. Haning,
North Carolina State University
Richard Hanke,
Rose State College
Helen B. Hanten,
University of Minnesota
Rebecca Hare,
Cleveland County Community College
John P. Harley,
Eastern Kentucky University
Robert Hatherill,
Del Mar College
William Hayes,
Delta State University
Kathleen Hecht,
Nassau Community College
Stephen Hedman,
University of Minnesota
Jean Helgeson,
Collins County Community College
Alexander Henderson,
Millersville University
Wiley Henderson,
Alabama A&M University
Timothy L. Henry,
University of Texas–Arlington
James Hewlett,
Finger Lakes Community College

Alison G. Hoffman,
*University of Tennessee–
Chattanooga*

Kelly Hogan,
*University of North Carolina–
Chapel Hill*

Leland N. Holland,
*Paso-Hernando Community
College*

Laura Mays Hoopes,
Occidental College

Dale R. Horeth,
Tidewater Community College

Harriette Howard-Lee Block,
Prairie View A&M University

Adam Hrincevich,
Louisiana State University

Michael D. Hudgins,
Alabama State University

David Huffman,
*Southwest Texas State
University*

Joel Humphrey,
Cayuga Community College

Donald A. Ingold,
East Texas State University

Jon W. Jacklet,
*State University of New York–
Albany*

Kesmic Jackson,
Georgia State University

Rebecca M. Jessen,
Bowling Green State University

J. Kelly Johnson,
University of Kansas

James Johnson,
*Central Washington
University*

Kristy Y. Johnson,
The Citadel

Ross Johnson,
Chicago State University

Florence Juillerat,
*Indiana University–Purdue
University at Indianapolis*

Thomas W. Jurik,
Iowa State University

Ragupathy Kannan,
*University of Arkansas, Fort
Smith*

A. J. Karpoff,
University of Louisville

L. Kavaljian,
California State University

Joe Keen,
*Patrick Henry Community
College*

Jeff Kenton,
Iowa State University

Hendrick J. Ketellapper,
*University of California,
Davis*

Jeffrey Kiggins,
*Blue Ridge Community
College*

Michael Koban,
Morgan State University

Aaron Krochmal,
*University of Houston–
Downtown*

Harry Kurtz,
Sam Houston State University

Kate Lajtha,
Oregon State University

Tom Langen,
Clarkson University

Patrick Larkin,
Santa Fe College

Stephen Lebsack,
*Linn-Benton Community
College*

Patricia Lee-Robinson,
*Chaminade University of
Honolulu*

David E. Lemke,
Texas State University

William H. Leonard,
Clemson University

Edward Levri,
*Indiana University of
Pennsylvania*

Graeme Lindbeck,
University of Central Florida

Jerri K. Lindsey,
*Tarrant County Junior
College–Northeast*

Mary Lipscomb,
*Virginia Polytechnic Institute
and State University*

Richard W. Lo Pinto,
*Fairleigh Dickinson
University*

Jonathan Lochamy,
Georgia Perimeter College

Jason L. Locklin,
Temple College

John Logue,
*University of South Carolina–
Sumter*

Paul Lonquich,
*California State University
Northridge*

William Lowen,
*Suffolk Community
College*

Ann S. Lumsden,
Florida State University

Steele R. Lunt,
*University of Nebraska–
Omaha*

Fordyce Lux,
*Metropolitan State College of
Denver*

Daniel D. Magoulick,
*The University of Central
Arkansas*

Bernard Majdi,
Waycross College

Cindy Malone,
*California State University–
Northridge*

Paul Mangum,
Midland College

Richard Manning,
*Southwest Texas State
University*

Mark Manteuffel,
St. Louis Community College

Barry Markillie,
*Cape Fear Community
College*

Ken Marr,
*Green River Community
College*

Kathleen A. Marrs,
*Indiana University–Purdue
University Indianapolis*

Michael Martin,
University of Michigan

Linda Martin-Morris,
University of Washington

Kenneth A. Mason,
University of Kansas

Daniel Matusiak,
*St. Charles Community
College*

Margaret May,
*Virginia Commonwealth
University*

D. J. McWhinnie,
De Paul University

Gary L. Meeker,
*California State University,
Sacramento*

Thoyd Melton,
*North Carolina State
University*

Joseph R. Mendelson III,
Utah State University

Karen E. Messley,
Rock Valley College

Timothy Metz,
Campbell University

Steven Mezik,
*Herkimer County Community
College*

Glendon R. Miller,
Wichita State University

Hugh Miller,
East Tennessee State University

Neil Miller,
Memphis State University

Jeanne Minnerath,
*St. Mary's University of
Minnesota*

Christine Minor,
Clemson University

Jeanne Mitchell,
Truman State University

Lee Mitchell,
*Mt. Hood Community
College*

Jack E. Mobley,
University of Central Arkansas

John W. Moon,
Harding University

Nicole Moore,
Austin Peay University

Richard Mortenson,
Albion College

Gisele Muller-Parker,
*Western Washington
University*

James Mulrooney,
*Central Connecticut State
University*

Kathleen Murray,
University of Maine

Liz Nash,
*California State University,
Long Beach*

Robert Neill,
University of Texas

Russell Nemecek,
*Columbia College,
Hancock*

Harry Nickla,
Creighton University

Daniel Nickrent,
Southern Illinois University

Jane Noble-Harvey,
University of Delaware

Murad Odeh,
South Texas College

David J. O'Neill,
*Community College of
Baltimore County–Dundalk
Campus*

James T. Oris,
Miami University of Ohio

Marcy Osgood,
University of Michigan

C. O. Patterson,
Texas A&M University

Fred Peabody,
*University of South
Dakota*

Charlotte Pedersen,
Southern Utah University

Harry Peery,
*Tompkins-Cortland
Community College*

Luis J. Pelicot,
*City University of New York,
Hostos*

Rhoda E. Perozzi,
*Virginia Commonwealth
University*

Gary B. Peterson,
*South Dakota State
University*

Bill Pfitsch,
Hamilton College

Ronald Pfohl,
Miami University of Ohio

Larry Pilgrim,
Tyler Junior College

Therese Poole,
Georgia State University

Robert Kyle Pope,
*Indiana University South
Bend*

Bernard Possident,
Skidmore College

Ina Pour-el,
DMACC–Boone Campus

Elsa C. Price,
*Wallace State Community
College*

Marvin Price,
Cedar Valley College

Kelli Prior,
*Finger Lakes Community
College*

Jennifer J. Quinlan,
Drexel University

James A. Raines,
North Harris College

Paul Ramp,
*Pellissippi State Technical
College*

Robert N. Reed,
Southern Utah University

Wenda Ribeiro,
*Thomas Nelson Community
College*

Elizabeth Rich,
Drexel University

Mark Richter,
University of Kansas
Robert Robbins,
Michigan State University
Jennifer Roberts,
Lewis University
Frank Romano,
Jacksonville State University
Chris Romero,
Front Range Community College
David Rosen,
Lee College
Paul Rosenbloom,
Southwest Texas State University
Amanda Rosenzweig,
Delgado Community College
K. Ross,
University of Delaware
Mary Lou Rottman,
University of Colorado-Denver
Albert Ruesink,
Indiana University
Cameron Russell,
Tidewater Community College
Connie Russell,
Angelo State University
Marla Ruth,
Jones County Junior College
Christopher F. Sacchi,
Kutztown University
Eduardo Salazar,
Temple College
Doug Schelhaas,
University of Mary
Brian Schmaefsky,
Kingwood College
Alan Schoenherr,
Fullerton College
Brian W. Schwartz,
Columbus State University
Edna Seaman,
University of Massachusetts, Boston
Tim Sellers,
Keuka College
Patricia Shields,
George Mason University
Marilyn Shopper,
Johnson County Community College
Jack Shurley,
Idaho State University
Bill Simcik,
Lonestar College
Rick L. Simonson,
University of Nebraska, Kearney
Howard Singer,
New Jersey City University
Anu Singh-Cundy,
Western Washington University
Linda Simpson,
University of North Carolina-Charlotte

Steven Skarda,
Linn-Benton Community College
Russel V. Skavaril,
Ohio State University
John Smarelli,
Loyola University
Mark Smith,
Chaffey College
Dale Smoak,
Piedmont Technical College
Jay Snaric,
St. Louis Community College
Phillip J. Snider,
University of Houston
Shari Snitovsky,
Skyline College
Gary Sojka,
Bucknell University
John Sollinger,
Southern Oregon University
Sally Sommers Smith,
Boston University
Jim Sorenson,
Radford University
Anna Bess Sorin,
University of Memphis
Mary Spratt,
University of Missouri, Kansas City
Bruce Stallsmith,
University of Alabama-Huntsville
Anthony Stancampiano,
Oklahoma City University
Theresa Stanley,
Gordon College
Benjamin Stark,
Illinois Institute of Technology
William Stark,
Saint Louis University
Barbara Stebbins-Boaz,
Willamette University
Mary-Pat Stein,
California State University, Northridge
Kathleen M. Steinert,
Bellevue Community College
Barbara Stotler,
Southern Illinois University
Nathaniel J. Stricker,
Ohio State University
Martha Sugermeyer,
Tidewater Community College
Gerald Summers,
University of Missouri-Columbia
Marshall Sundberg,
Louisiana State University
Bill Surver,
Clemson University
Eldon Sutton,
University of Texas-Austin
Peter Svensson,
West Valley College

Dan Tallman,
Northern State University
Jose G. Tello,
Long Island University
Julienne Thomas-Hall,
Kennedy King College
David Thorndill,
Essex Community College
William Thwaites,
San Diego State University
Professor Peter Tobiessen,
Union College
Richard Tolman,
Brigham Young University
Sylvia Torti,
University of Utah
Dennis Trelka,
Washington and Jefferson College
Richard C. Tsou,
Gordon College
Sharon Tucker,
University of Delaware
Gail Turner,
Virginia Commonwealth University
Glyn Turnipseed,
Arkansas Technical University
Lloyd W. Turtinen,
University of Wisconsin, Eau Claire
Robert Tyser,
University of Wisconsin, La Crosse
Robin W. Tyser,
University of Wisconsin, La Crosse
Kristin Uthus,
Virginia Commonwealth University
Rani Vajravelu,
University of Central Florida
Jim Van Brunt,
Rogue Community College
F. Daniel Vogt,
State University of New York-Plattsburgh
Nancy Wade,
Old Dominion University
Susan M. Wadkowski,
Lakeland Community College
Jyoti R. Wagle,
Houston Community College-Central
Jerry G. Walls,
Louisiana State University, Alexandria
Holly Walters,
Cape Fear Community College
Winfred Watkins,
McLennan Community College
Lisa Weasel,
Portland State University

Janice Webster,
Ivy Tech Community College
Michael Weis,
University of Windsor
DeLoris Wenzel,
University of Georgia
Jerry Wermuth,
Purdue University-Calumet
Diana Wheat,
Linn-Benton Community College
Richard Whittington,
Pellissippi State Technical Community College
Jacob Wiebers,
Purdue University
Roger K. Wiebusch,
Columbia College
Carolyn Wilczynski,
Binghamton University
Lawrence R. Williams,
University of Houston
P. Kelly Williams,
University of Dayton
Roberta Williams,
University of Nevada-Las Vegas
Emily Willingham,
University of Texas-Austin
Sandra Winicur,
Indiana University-South Bend
Bill Wischusen,
Louisiana State University
Michelle Withers,
Louisiana State University
Chris Wolfe,
North Virginia Community College
Stacy Wolfe,
Art Institutes International
Colleen Wong,
Wilbur Wright College
Wade Worthen,
Furman University
Robin Wright,
University of Washington
Taek H. You,
Campbell University
Brenda L. Young,
Daemen College
Cal Young,
Fullerton College
Tim Young,
Mercer University
Marty Zahn,
Thomas Nelson Community College
Izanne Zorin,
Northern Virginia Community College-Alexandria
Michelle Zurawski,
Moraine Valley Community College

Hallmark Case Studies place biology in a real-world context

A **Case Study** describing a true and relevant event or phenomenon runs throughout each chapter, tying biological concepts to the real world.

10 MEIOSIS: THE BASIS OF SEXUAL REPRODUCTION

The Giddings family is a rainbow of colors.

All chapters open with a Case Study, a true yet extraordinary story that relates to the science presented in the chapter. The **Eleventh Edition** explores several new Case Study topics including the Ebola epidemic (Chapter 1), DNA Identification (Chapter 8), and Biotechnology (Chapter 14).

NEW! Chapter 9 now covers only mitotic cell division and the control of the cell cycle. Meiotic cell division and its importance in sexual reproduction are discussed in Chapter 10.

CASE STUDY CONTINUED
The Rainbow Connection

The genetic variability of the Giddings children started out as mutations that occurred thousands of years ago. Take hair color: Our distant ancestors probably all had dark hair, its color controlled by multiple genes located on several different chromosomes. The alleles that produced Tess's blond hair originated as mutations in genes that control the amount and type of hair pigment. Tess probably inherited only "pale hair" alleles of all of these genes, so for any given hair color gene, she has the same pale hair allele on both homologous chromosomes. Chris, on the other hand, inherited both dark and pale hair alleles for at least some of the genes, so his homologues have different alleles. As we will see in Chapter 11, in many cases one allele (in this case, the dark hair allele) overrides the effects of the other allele (the pale hair allele), so Chris has black hair. What combinations of alleles might have been packaged in Tess's eggs and Chris's sperm, which would combine to produce their diverse children?

Every chapter contains Case Study Continued sections that appear when you are well into the chapter. These sections expand on the Chapter Opening Case Studies and connect to biological concepts you will have learned.

CASE STUDY
The Rainbow Connection

FIRST CAME JACOB, WHO HAS BLUE EYES like his mom, Tess, but curly brown hair and olive skin. Next came Savannah, who looks a lot like Jacob, though her hair is perhaps more dark blond than brown. Amiah, however, was truly a surprise when she was born—she has very pale skin, with straight, sandy-brown hair. Zion, the youngest child, has dark skin, black curly hair, and brown eyes, similar to his father, Chris. Even in today's multicultural England, a family like that is unusual.

Tess and Chris Giddings are as surprised as everyone else by their rainbow family. In fact, when Amiah was born, she had low blood sugar and needed to be checked out by a specialist right away. She was whisked away so fast that the hospital staff hadn't put an ID wristband on her yet. When she was returned to her parents a little while later, they were astounded at how white her skin was. They asked the inevitable question: Was she switched with another baby by mistake? Just to be sure, the Giddings agreed to a DNA test. The results showed that Tess and Chris were indeed Amiah's parents. When Zion was born a few years later, Chris burst out, "Oh my God, he's black!" To which the astounded midwife could only reply, "You do know you're a black man, don't you?"

How could one couple have such a diverse family? As we will see in this chapter, sexual reproduction can mix inherited characteristics from the parents into a remarkable variety of different offspring. How does sexual reproduction produce genetic diversity? And why would natural selection favor seemingly random shuffling of traits?

156

CASE STUDY REVISITED
The Rainbow Connection

Many people are astounded by the diversity of the Giddings children. Basic biology, however, easily explains how such diversity arises. Most genes have multiple alleles, meiotic cell division separates homologous chromosomes—and the alleles they carry—into different sperm and eggs, and the sperm and eggs unite at random. From a biological perspective, perhaps the more interesting question is this: Why do alleles for dark pigmentation occur most frequently in people whose ancestors lived in equatorial regions, and alleles for pale pigmentation in people of northern European ancestry?

Natural selection probably favored different skin colors because of the differing amount of sunlight in equatorial versus northern regions and the importance of vitamin D and vitamin B9 (folate) in human health. Vitamin D is needed for many physiological functions, including the absorption of calcium and other minerals by the digestive tract. Folate is also essential for many of otherwise dark-haired people. Novel appearance, within limits, is often attractive to members of the opposite sex. Some anthropologists have speculated that, a few thousand years ago, high-status men (proficient hunters or chieftains of small tribes, for example) preferentially chose blond-haired women as mates. Therefore, blond women produced more offspring than dark-haired women did. The result is that more than half the people in parts of Scandinavia have blond hair.

Ultraviolet rays in sunlight stimulate the synthesis of vitamin D, but they break down folate. In the fierce sunlight of equatorial regions, dark skin still allows for plenty of vitamin D production, while protecting against too much depletion of folate. In northern Europe, with far weaker sunlight and often cloudy skies, paler skin boosts vitamin D production, while folate levels remain adequate.

The selective advantage of blond hair in northern Europe is more uncertain. Some of the same genes contribute to hair and skin color, so selection for pale skin may have selected for pale hair as well. Another hypothesis is that the first few people with blond hair were very conspicuous in a population

CONSIDER THIS Ultraviolet rays in sunlight cause skin cancer. In today's world, people of all skin colors, but especially pale-skinned people, are often urged to stay out of the sun and get their vitamin D from food or supplements. In the past, do you think that the risk of skin cancer selected against pale-skinned people, partially counterbalancing selection in favor of pale skin for vitamin D production?

A Case Study Revisited section wraps up the narrative of each chapter by connecting the biological themes described throughout the chapter with the everyday science brought out in the Case Study. The accompanying Consider This question allows further reflection on how the biology in the Case Study can be applied to a new situation.

NEW! Three-pronged taxonomy of questions in each chapter

Each chapter is organized around a consistent framework of questions that encourage students to look forward, look back, or dig deeper.

AT A GLANCE

14.1 What Is Biotechnology?
14.2 What Natural Processes Recombine DNA Between Organisms and Between Species?
14.3 How Is Biotechnology Used in Forensic Science?

14.4 How Is Biotechnology Used to Make Genetically Modified Organisms?
14.5 How Are Transgenic Organisms Used?
14.6 How Is Biotechnology Used to Learn About the Genomes of Humans and Other Organisms?

14.7 How Is Biotechnology Used for Medical Diagnosis and Treatment?
14.8 What Are the Major Ethical Issues of Modern Biotechnology?

CASE STUDY

Guilty or Innocent?

IMAGINE SPENDING WELL OVER for crimes you didn't commit. For real life for Thomas Haynesworth

The section headings and case study sections give a preview of questions that will be addressed in the chapter.

CHECK YOUR LEARNING

Can you ...

- explain why people might be opposed to the use of genetically modified organisms in agriculture?
- envision circumstances in which it would be ethical to modify the genome of a human fertilized egg?

The Check Your Learning and End of Chapter questions ask students to look back, recall, and reinforce their comprehension of biology concepts.

Thinking Through the Concepts

Multiple Choice

1. Which of the following is *not* true of a single nucleotide polymorphism?
   a. It is usually caused by a translocation mutation.
   b. It is usually caused by a nucleotide substitution mutation.
   c. It may change the phenotype of an organism.
   d. It is inherited from parent to offspring.
2. Imagine you are looking at a DNA profile that shows an STR pattern of a mother's DNA and her child's DNA. Will all of the bands of the child's DNA match those of the mother?
   a. Yes, because the mother's DNA and her child's DNA are identical.
   b. Yes, because the child developed from her mother's egg.
   c. No, because half of the child's DNA is inherited from its father.
   d. No, because the child's DNA is a random sampling of its mother's.
3. Which of the following is *not* a commonly used method of modifying the DNA of an organism?
   a. crossbreeding two plants of the same species
   b. crossbreeding two plants of different species
   c. the polymerase chain reaction
   d. genetic engineering
4. A restriction enzyme
   a. cuts DNA at a specific nucleotide sequence.
   b. cuts DNA at a random nucleotide sequence.
   c. splices pieces of DNA together at a specific nucleotide sequence.
   d. splices pieces of DNA together without regard to the nucleotide sequence.
5. DNA cloning is
   a. making multiple genetically identical cells.
   b. making multiple copies of a piece of DNA.
   c. inserting DNA into a cell.
   d. changing the nucleotide sequence of a strand of DNA.

CONSIDER THIS Genetic engineering is used both in food crops and in medicine. Golden Rice and almost all the corn and soybeans grown in the United States contain genes from other species. The he[...] by inserting a gene from th[...] The antibodies in ZMapp, [...] Ebola therapy, are part mo[...] scientifically important diff[...] engineering for food or for [...]

EVALUATE THIS In January 2012, the Pittsburgh Steelers football team played against the Denver Broncos in the "Mile-High City" (Denver's altitude is a mile above sea level). Steelers head coach Mike Tomlin did not allow safety Ryan Clark to play, because Clark has sickle-cell trait. What can happen when someone with sickle cell trait exercises at high [...] right call in bench-[...]

Applying the Concepts

1. As you may know, many insects have evolved resistance to common pesticides. Do you think that insects might evolve resistance to *Bt* crops? If this is a risk, do you think that *Bt* crops should be planted anyway? Why or why not?
2. All children born with X-linked SCID are boys. Can you [...]

THINK CRITICALLY There are many other applications in which DNA barcoding might be useful. For example, how might ecologists use DNA barcoding to find out what species are present in a rain forest, or what kinds of animals a predator eats?

Consider This, Think Critically, Evaluate This and Applying the Concepts ask students to dig deeper, reflect, and think critically about the chapter material.

NEW! Think Critically questions challenge readers to apply their knowledge to information presented in a photo, figure, graph, or table.

NEW! Evaluate This questions present a brief, realistic health care scenario and ask the reader to evaluate information before forming an opinion or making a decision.

NEW! Revised Art and Content Throughout

Improved Figures and Photos appear throughout the text and include easy-to-follow process diagrams with labeled steps and a clearer use of color for distinguishing different structures.

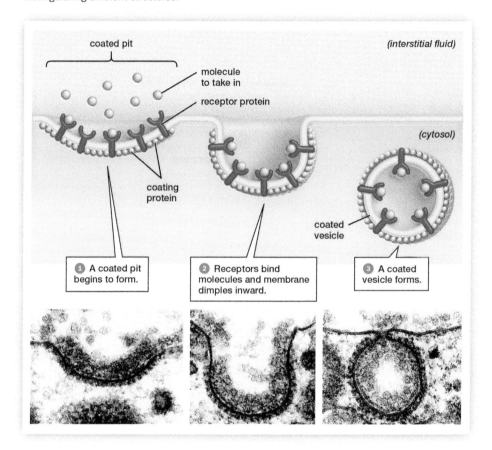

coated pit   (interstitial fluid)

molecule to take in

receptor protein

(cytosol)

coating protein

coated vesicle

① A coated pit begins to form.

② Receptors bind molecules and membrane dimples inward.

③ A coated vesicle forms.

NEW! How Do We Know That? Essays explore the process of scientific discovery, experimental design, and exciting new biotechnology techniques, explaining how scientists know what they know about biology.

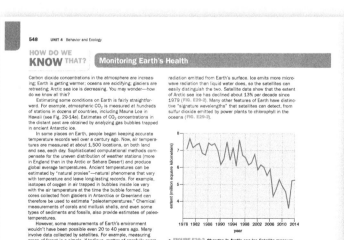

HOW DO WE KNOW THAT? Monitoring Earth's Health

Carbon dioxide concentrations in the atmosphere are increasing; Earth is getting warmer; oceans are acidifying; glaciers are retreating; Arctic sea ice is decreasing. You may wonder—how do we know all this?

Estimating some conditions on Earth is fairly straightforward. For example, atmospheric CO_2 is measured at hundreds of stations in dozens of countries, including Mauna Loa in Hawaii (see Fig. 29-14a). Estimates of CO_2 concentrations in the distant past are obtained by analyzing gas bubbles trapped in ancient Antarctic ice.

In some places on Earth, people began keeping accurate temperature records well over a century ago. Now, air temperatures are measured at about 1,500 locations, on both land and sea, each day. Sophisticated computational methods compensate for the uneven distribution of weather stations (more in England than in the Arctic or Sahara Desert) and produce global average temperatures. Ancient temperatures can be estimated by "natural proxies"—natural phenomena that vary with temperature and leave long-lasting records. For example, isotopes of oxygen in air trapped in bubbles inside ice vary with the air temperature at the time the bubble formed. Ice cores collected from glaciers in Antarctica or Greenland can therefore be used to estimate "paleotemperatures." Chemical measurements of corals and mollusk shells, and even some types of sediments and fossils, also provide estimates of paleotemperatures.

However, some measurements of Earth's environment wouldn't have been possible even 20 to 40 years ago. Many involve data collected by satellites. For example, measuring areas of forest is a simple, if tedious, matter of carefully examining satellite photos. Other measurements are much more sophisticated. Accurate estimates of Arctic sea ice started in 1979, with the launch of satellites that measure microwave

radiation emitted from Earth's surface. Ice emits more microwave radiation than liquid water does, so the satellites can easily distinguish the two. Satellite data show that the extent of Arctic sea ice has declined about 13% per decade since 1979 (FIG. E29-2). Many other features of Earth have distinctive "signature wavelengths" that satellites can detect, from sulfur dioxide emitted by power plants to chlorophyll in the oceans (FIG. E29-3).

▲ **FIGURE E29-2 Changes in Arctic sea ice** Satellite measurements of Arctic sea ice began in 1979. By 2014, the area covered by ice at the end of the summer (September) had declined by more than a third.

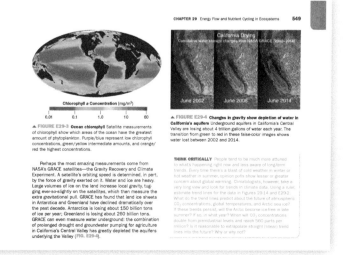

Chlorophyll a Concentration (mg/m³)

0.01   0.1   1.0   60

▲ **FIGURE E29-3 Ocean chlorophyll** Satellite measurements of chlorophyll show which areas of the ocean have the greatest amount of phytoplankton. Purple/blue represent low chlorophyll concentrations, green/yellow intermediate amounts, and orange/red the highest concentrations.

Perhaps the most amazing measurements come from NASA's GRACE satellites—the Gravity Recovery and Climate Experiment. A satellite's orbiting speed is determined, in part, by the force of gravity exerted on it. Water and ice are heavy. Large volumes of ice on the land increase local gravity, tugging ever-so-slightly on the satellites, which then measure the extra gravitational pull. GRACE has found that land ice sheets in Antarctica and Greenland have declined dramatically over the past decade. Antarctica is losing about 150 billion tons of ice per year; Greenland is losing about 260 billion tons. GRACE can even measure water underground: the combination of prolonged drought and groundwater pumping for agriculture in California's Central Valley has greatly depleted the aquifers underlying the Valley (FIG. E29-4).

California Drying
Cumulative water storage changes from NASA GRACE (2002–2014)

June 2002   June 2008   June 2014

▲ **FIGURE E29-4 Changes in gravity show depletion of water in California's aquifers** Underground aquifers in California's Central Valley are losing about 4 trillion gallons of water each year. The transition from green to red in these false-color images shows water lost between 2002 and 2014.

THINK CRITICALLY People tend to be much more attuned to what's happening right now and less aware of long-term trends. Every time there's a blast of cold weather in winter or hot weather in summer, opinion polls show lesser or greater concern about global warming. Climatologists, however, take a very long view and look for trends in climate data. Using a ruler, estimate trend lines for the data in Figures 29-14 and E29-2. What do the trend lines predict about the future of atmospheric CO_2 concentrations, global temperatures, and Arctic sea ice? If these trends persist, will the Arctic become ice free in late summer? If so, in what year? When will CO_2 concentrations double from preindustrial levels and reach 560 parts per million? Is it reasonable to extrapolate straight (linear) trend lines into the future? Why or why not?

Improve your grade—and your learning—with MasteringBiology®

Mastering is the most effective and widely used online homework and assessment system for the sciences. It delivers self-paced tutorials that focus on your course objectives, provide individualized coaching, and respond to your progress. Mastering motivates you to learn outside of class and arrive prepared for lecture or lab.

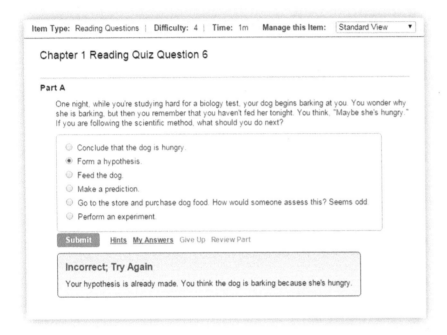

Reading Quizzes keep you on track with reading assignments. The quizzes require only 5–8 minutes for you to complete and make it possible for your instructor to understand your misconceptions before you arrive for class.

EXPANDED! Building Vocabulary Exercises help you learn the meaning of common prefixes, suffixes, and word roots, and then ask you to apply your knowledge to learn unfamiliar biology terms.

NEW! Working with Data activities ask students to analyze and apply their knowledge of biology to a graph or a set of data.

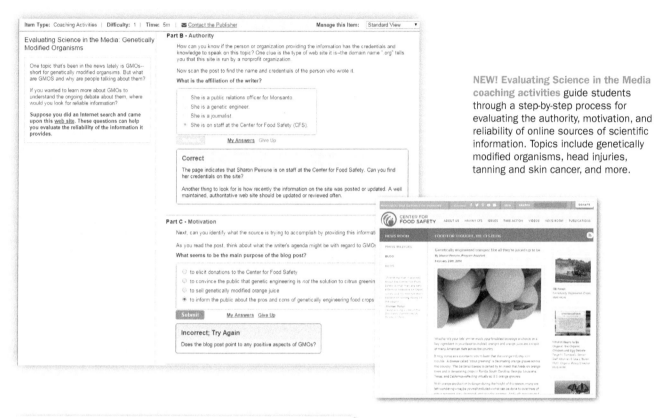

Evaluating Science in the Media: Genetically Modified Organisms

One topic that's been in the news lately is GMOs-- short for genetically modified organsims. But what are GMOS and why are people talking about them?

If you wanted to learn more about GMOs to understand the ongoing debate about them, where would you look for reliable information?

Suppose you did an Internet search and came upon this web site. These questions can help you evaluate the reliability of the information it provides.

Part B - Authority

How can you know if the person or organization providing the information has the credentials and knowledge to speak on this topic? One clue is the type of web site it is--the domain name ".org" tells you that this site is run by a nonprofit organization.

Now scan the post to find the name and credentials of the person who wrote it.

What is the affiliation of the writer?

- She is a public relations officer for Monsanto.
- She is a genetic engineer.
- She is a journalist.
- ◉ She is on staff at the Center for Food Safety (CFS).

My Answers Give Up

Correct

The page indicates that Sharon Perrone is on staff at the Center for Food Safety. Can you find her credentials on the site?

Another thing to look for is how recently the information on the site was posted or updated. A well maintained, authoritative web site should be updated or reviewed often.

Part C - Motivation

Next, can you identify what the source is trying to accomplish by providing this information?

As you read the post, think about what the writer's agenda might be with regard to GMOs.

What seems to be the main purpose of the blog post?

- to elicit donations to the Center for Food Safety
- to convince the public that genetic engineering is *not* the solution to citrus greening
- to sell genetically modified orange juice
- ◉ to inform the public about the pros and cons of genetically engineering food crops

Submit   My Answers Give Up

Incorrect; Try Again

Does the blog post point to any positive aspects of GMOs?

NEW! Evaluating Science in the Media coaching activities guide students through a step-by-step process for evaluating the authority, motivation, and reliability of online sources of scientific information. Topics include genetically modified organisms, head injuries, tanning and skin cancer, and more.

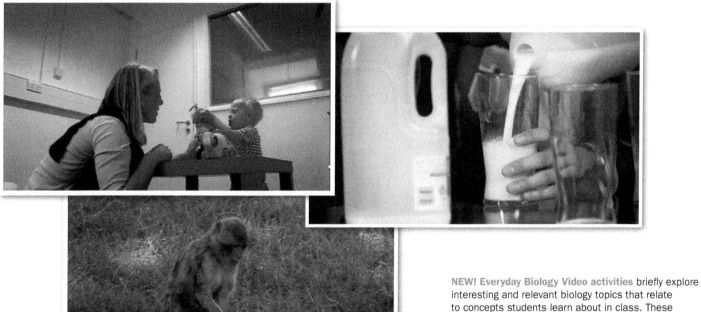

NEW! Everyday Biology Video activities briefly explore interesting and relevant biology topics that relate to concepts students learn about in class. These 20 videos, produced by the BBC, can be assigned in MasteringBiology with assessment questions.

For Students:
Study Anytime, Anywhere

MasteringBiology®

is an online homework, tutorial, and assessment program that helps you quickly master biology concepts and skills. Self-paced tutorials provide immediate wrong-answer feedback and hints to help keep you on track to succeed in the course.

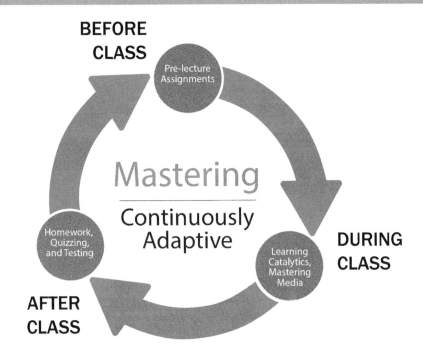

BEFORE CLASS

Pre-lecture Assignments

Mastering
Continuously Adaptive

DURING CLASS

Learning Catalytics, Mastering Media

AFTER CLASS

Homework, Quizzing, and Testing

BEFORE CLASS

NEW! Dynamic Study Modules help you acquire, retain, and recall information faster and more efficiently than ever before. These convenient practice questions and detailed review explanations can be accessed using a smartphone, tablet, or computer.

NEW! eText 2.0 allows students to access the text anytime, anywhere using a smartphone, tablet, or computer. The new eText is fully accessible and ready to use with screen-readers, re-sizable type, and more.

Which of the following is in the correct order?

○ Kingdom, Domain, Phylum, Family, Order, Class, Genus, Species

○ Domain, Kingdom, Phylum, Class, Order, Family, Genus, Species

○ Domain, Kingdom, Phylum, Family, Order, Class, Genus, Species

○ Kingdom, Domain, Phylum, Class, Family, Order, Genus, Species

○ Kingdom, Domain, Phylum, Class, Order, Family, Genus, Species

9.3
Skeletal muscle fibers contain calcium-regulated molecular motors

Learning Objectives

• Describe the microscopic structure and functional roles of the myofibrils, sarcoplasmic reticulum, and T tubules of skeletal muscle fibers.
• Describe the sliding filament model of muscle contraction.

Each skeletal muscle fiber is a long cylindrical cell with multiple oval nuclei just beneath its sarcolemma or plasma membrane (Figure 9.2b). Skeletal muscle fibers are huge cells. Their diameter typically ranges from 10 to 100 μm —up to ten times that of an average body cell—and their length is phenomenal, some up to 30 cm

DYNAMIC STUDY MODULES

ETEXT 2.0

DURING CLASS

NEW!

Learning Catalytics is an assessment and classroom activity system that works with any web-enabled device and facilitates collaboration with your classmates. Your MasteringBiology subscription with eText includes access to Learning Catalytics.

AFTER CLASS

A wide range of question types and activities are available for homework assignments, including the following NEW assignment options for the Eleventh Edition:

- **EXPANDED! Building Vocabulary activities** help you learn the meaning of common prefixes, suffixes, and word roots, and then ask you to apply your knowledge to learn unfamiliar biology terms.
- **NEW! Working with Data questions** require you to analyze and apply your knowledge of biology to a graph or set of data.
- **NEW! Evaluating Science in the Media** challenge you to evaluate various information from websites, articles, and videos.

For Instructors: New Resources for Flipped Classrooms and More

New resources save valuable time both during course prep and during class.

NEW!

Learning Catalytics is a "bring your own device" assessment and classroom activity system that expands the possibilities for student engagement. Using Learning Catalytics, instructors can deliver a wide range of auto-gradable or open-ended questions that test content knowledge and build critical thinking skills. Eighteen different answer types provide great flexibility, including:

SKETCH/DIRECTION

MANY CHOICE

REGION

MasteringBiology®

MasteringBiology users may select from Pearson's library of Learning Catalytics questions, including questions developed specifically for *Biology: Life on Earth* 11e.

1 AN INTRODUCTION TO LIFE ON EARTH

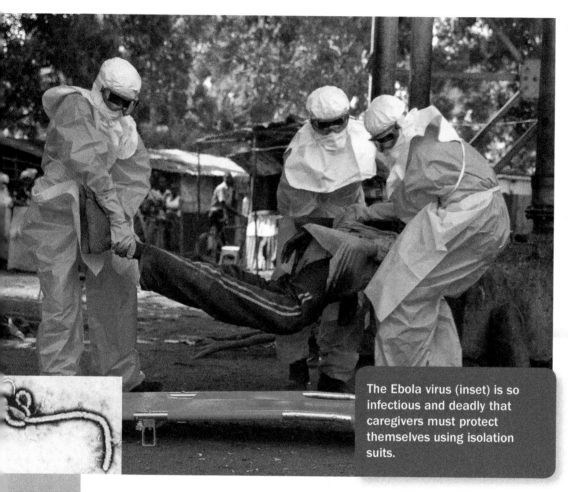

The Ebola virus (inset) is so infectious and deadly that caregivers must protect themselves using isolation suits.

The Boundaries of Life

IN A SMALL VILLAGE in Guinea, a huge, hollow tree housed thousands of bats. The tree was a magnet for local children, who loved to play inside it and catch the bats. Scientists hypothesize that this is where two-year-old Emile Ouamouno, the first victim of the recent massive Ebola epidemic, may have become infected. Emile died in December 2013, followed by his mother and siblings. This set off a chain of transmission that has since killed more than 10,500 people, roughly half of those who became infected. The Ebola virus (see the inset photo) can lurk in rain-forest animals including certain types of bats, porcupines, chimpanzees, gorillas, and antelope—all of which are consumed in parts of Africa.

The threat of Ebola virus disease ("Ebola") strikes fear in anyone familiar with its symptoms, which often begin with fever, headache, joint and muscle aches, and stomach pains and progress to vomiting, bloody diarrhea, and organ failure. Internal hemorrhaging can leave victims bleeding from nearly every orifice. Death usually occurs within 7 to 16 days after the onset of symptoms, and there is no cure; the death rate ranges from 25% to 90%. Ebola is so contagious that caregivers wear "moon suits" to avoid contact with any body fluids from their patients.

Ebola is one of many diseases caused by viruses. Although some viral diseases, such as smallpox and polio, have been largely eradicated, others, like the common cold and influenza (flu), continue to make us miserable. Most alarming are the contagious and deadly viruses that have emerged in recent history. AIDS (caused by the human immunodeficiency virus, HIV) was first documented in 1981 in San Francisco, and Ebola was first identified in 1976 (and named after Africa's Ebola River, where one of the first outbreaks occurred). New types of flu virus emerge regularly; a few of these cause a very high mortality rate and raise fears of a widespread epidemic.

No matter how you measure it, viruses are enormously successful. Although many consist only of a small amount of genetic material surrounded by protein, viruses infect every known form of life and are the most abundant biological entity on the planet. Viruses can rapidly increase in number and spread among organisms they infect. Yet in spite of these lifelike qualities, not all scientists agree about whether to classify viruses as living organisms or as inert parasitic biological particles. The basis for this argument may surprise you: There is no universally accepted scientific definition of life. What is life, anyway?

AT A GLANCE

1.1 WHAT IS LIFE?

The word **biology** comes from the Greek roots "bio" meaning "life" and "logy" meaning "the study of" (see Appendix I for more word roots). But what is life? If you look up "life" in a dictionary, you will find definitions such as "the quality that distinguishes a vital and functioning being from a dead body," but you won't discover what that "quality" is. Life is intangible and defies simple definition, even by biologists. However, most agree that living things, or **organisms,** all share certain characteristics that, taken together, define life:

- Organisms acquire and use materials and energy.
- Organisms actively maintain organized complexity.
- Organisms sense and respond to stimuli.
- Organisms grow.
- Organisms reproduce.
- Organisms, collectively, evolve.

Nonliving objects may possess some of these attributes. Crystals can grow, and a desk lamp acquires energy from electricity and converts it to heat and light, but only living things can do them all.

The **cell** is the basic unit of life. A plasma membrane separates each cell from its surroundings, enclosing a huge variety of structures and chemicals in a fluid environment. The plasma membranes of many types of cells, including those of microorganisms and plants, are enclosed in a protective cell wall (FIG. 1-1). Although the most abundant organisms on Earth are unicellular (exist as single cells), the qualities of life are more easily visualized in **multicellular** organisms such as the water flea in FIGURE 1-2, an animal smaller than this letter "o." In the sections below, we introduce the characteristics of life.

▲ **FIGURE 1-1 The cell is the smallest unit of life** This artificially colored micrograph of a plant cell (a eukaryotic cell) shows a supporting cell wall (blue) that surrounds plant cells. Just inside the cell wall, the plasma membrane (found in all cells) has control over which substances enter and leave. Cells also contain several types of specialized organelles, including the nucleus, suspended within a fluid environment (orange).

cell wall

plasma membrane

nucleus

organelles

▶ **FIGURE 1-2 Properties of life** The water flea uses energy from photosynthetic organisms that it consumes (green material in its gut) to maintain its amazing complexity. Eyes and antennae respond to stimuli. This adult female is reproducing, and she herself has grown from an egg like those she now carries. All the adaptations that allow this water flea to survive, grow, and reproduce have been molded by evolution.

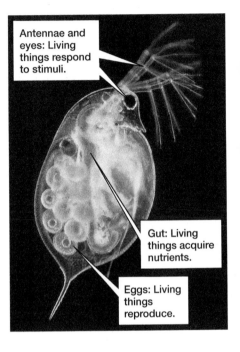

Antennae and eyes: Living things respond to stimuli.

Gut: Living things acquire nutrients.

Eggs: Living things reproduce.

Organisms Acquire and Use Materials and Energy

Organisms obtain the materials that make up their bodies—such as minerals, water, and other simple chemical building blocks—from the air, water, soil, and, in some cases, the bodies of other living things. Because life neither creates nor destroys matter, materials are continuously exchanged and recycled among organisms and their nonliving surroundings (FIG. 1-3).

Organisms use energy continuously to remain alive. For example, energy is needed to move and to construct the complex molecules that make up an organism's body. Essentially all the energy that sustains life comes from sunlight. Some organisms capture solar energy directly through a process called **photosynthesis.** Photosynthetic organisms (plants and many single-celled organisms) trap and store the sun's energy for their own use. The energy stored in their bodies also powers all nonphotosynthetic organisms. So energy flows in a one-way path from the sun to photosynthetic organisms to all other forms of life (see Fig. 1-3). Some energy is lost as heat at each transfer from one organism to another, making less energy available with each transfer.

Organisms Actively Maintain Organized Complexity

For both the books and papers on your desk and the fragile and dynamic intricacy of a cell, organization tends to disintegrate unless energy is used to maintain it (see Chapter 6). Living things, representing the ultimate in organized complexity, continuously use energy to maintain themselves.

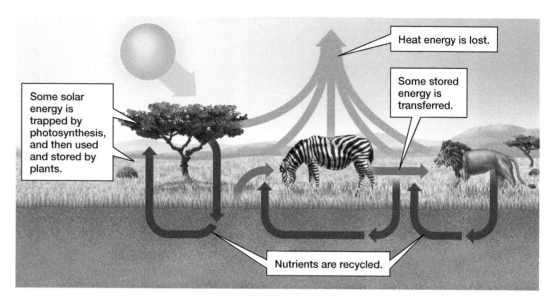

Some solar energy is trapped by photosynthesis, and then used and stored by plants.

Heat energy is lost.

Some stored energy is transferred.

Nutrients are recycled.

◀ FIGURE 1-3 **The flow of energy and the recycling of nonliving nutrients**

THINK CRITICALLY
Describe the source of the energy stored in the meat and the bun of a hamburger, and explain how the energy got from the source to the two foodstuffs.

◀ FIGURE 1-4 **Organisms maintain relatively constant internal conditions** Evaporative cooling by water, both from sweat and from a bottle, helps this athlete maintain his body temperature during vigorous exercise.

The ability of an organism to maintain its internal environment within the limits required to sustain life is called **homeostasis.** To maintain homeostasis, cell membranes constantly pump specific substances in and others out. People and other mammals use both physiological and behavioral mechanisms to maintain the narrow temperature range that allows life-sustaining reactions to occur in their cells (FIG. 1-4). Life, then, requires very precise internal conditions maintained by a continuous expenditure of energy.

Organisms Sense and Respond to Stimuli

To obtain energy and nutrients, organisms must sense and respond to stimuli in their environments. Animals use specialized cells to detect light, temperature, sound, gravity, touch, chemicals, and many other stimuli from their external and internal surroundings. For example, when your brain detects a low level of sugar in your blood (an internal stimulus), it causes your mouth to water at the smell of food (an external stimulus). Plants, fungi, and single-celled organisms use very different mechanisms that are equally effective for their needs (FIG. 1-5). Even many bacteria, the smallest and simplest life-forms, can move toward favorable conditions and away from harmful substances.

Organisms Grow

At some time in its life, every organism grows. The water flea in Figure 1-2 grew from the size of one of the eggs you see in its body. Single-celled organisms such as bacteria grow to about double their original size, copy their genetic material, and then divide in half to reproduce. Animals and plants use a similar process to produce more cells within their bodies, repeating the sequence until growth stops. Individual cells can also contribute to the growth of an organism by increasing in size, as occurs in muscle and fat cells in animals and in food storage cells in plants.

Organisms Reproduce

Organisms reproduce in a variety of ways (FIG. 1-6). These include dividing in half, producing seeds, bearing live young, and producing eggs (see Fig. 1-2). The end result is always the same: new versions of the parent organisms that inherit the instructions for producing and maintaining their particular form of life. These instructions—copied in every cell and passed on to descendants—are carried in the unique structure

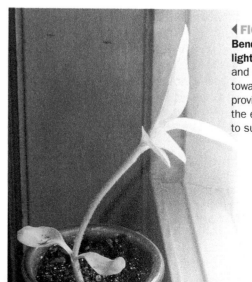

◀ FIGURE 1-5
Bending toward the light Plants perceive and often bend toward light, which provides them with the energy they need to survive.

(a) Dividing *Streptococcus* bacterium   (b) Dandelion producing seeds   (c) Panda with its baby

▲ FIGURE 1-6 **Organisms reproduce**

of the hereditary molecule **deoxyribonucleic acid (DNA)** (FIG. 1-7; see Chapter 12). The complete set of DNA molecules contained in each cell provides a detailed instruction manual for life, much like an architectural blueprint provides instructions for constructing a building.

▲ FIGURE 1-7 **DNA** As James Watson, the codiscoverer of the structure of DNA, stated: "A structure this pretty just had to exist."

Organisms, Collectively, Have the Capacity to Evolve

A simple definition of **evolution** is the change in DNA that occurs in a population over time. Through the course of generations, changes in DNA within any **population** (a group of the same type of organism inhabiting the same area) are inevitable. In the words of biologist Theodosius Dobzhansky, "Nothing in biology makes sense except in the light of evolution." The next section provides a brief introduction to evolution—the unifying concept of biology.

CHECK YOUR LEARNING
Can you ...
- explain the characteristics that define life?
- explain why these characteristics are necessary to sustain life?
- describe how reproduction allows evolution to occur?

CASE STUDY \ **CONTINUED**
The Boundaries of Life

Are viruses alive? Viruses release their genetic material inside cells and then hijack the infected cell's energy supplies and biochemical machinery, turning the cell into a kind of factory that churns out many copies of viral parts. These parts assemble into an army of virus particles. The newly formed viruses then emerge from the host cell, often rupturing it in the process. Some types of viruses, including HIV and the Ebola virus, acquire an outer envelope made of the infected cell's plasma membrane as they emerge. Viruses do not obtain or use their own energy or materials, maintain themselves, or grow. Therefore, viruses do not meet our criteria for life. They do, however, possess a few characteristics of life: Viruses respond to stimuli by binding to specific sites on the cells they attack, and some scientists consider viral replication a form of reproduction. Viruses also evolve, often with stunning speed. How does evolution occur in viruses and other biological entities?

1.2 WHAT IS EVOLUTION?

Evolution is genetic change in a population over time. Cumulative changes over vast stretches of time explain the amazing diversity of organisms that now share this planet. The scientific theory of evolution was formulated in the mid-1800s by two English naturalists, Charles Darwin and Alfred Russel Wallace. Since that time, it has been supported by fossils, geological studies, radioactive dating of rocks, genetics, molecular biology, biochemistry, and breeding experiments. Evolution not only explains the enormous diversity of life, but also accounts for the remarkable similarities among different types of organisms. For example, people share many features with chimpanzees, and the sequence of our DNA is nearly identical to that of chimpanzees. This similarity is

◀ **FIGURE 1-8 Chim-panzees and people are closely related**

strong evidence that people and chimps descended from a common ancestor, but the obvious differences (**FIG. 1-8**) reflect the differences in our evolutionary paths.

Three Natural Processes Underlie Evolution

Evolution is an automatic and inevitable outcome of three natural occurrences: (1) differences among members of a population, (2) inheritance of these differences by offspring, and (3) natural selection, the process by which individuals that inherit certain characteristics tend to survive and reproduce better than other individuals. Let's take a closer look at these three factors.

Mutations Are the Source of Differences in DNA

Look around at your classmates and notice how different they are, or observe how dogs differ in size, in shape, and in the color, length, and texture of their coats. Although some of this variation (particularly among your classmates) is due to differences in environment and lifestyle, much of it results from differences in genes. **Genes,** which are specific segments of DNA, are the basic units of heredity. Before a cell divides, all of its DNA is copied, allowing its genes to be passed along to both resulting cells. Just as you would make mistakes if you tried to copy a blueprint by hand, cells make some errors as they copy their DNA. Changes in genes, such as those caused by these random copying errors, are called **mutations.** Mutations can also result from damage to DNA, caused, for example, by ultraviolet rays from sunlight, radiation released from a damaged nuclear power plant, or toxic chemicals from cigarette smoke. Just as changes to a blueprint will cause changes in the structure built from it, so may a new cell with altered DNA differ from its parent cell.

Some Mutations Are Inherited

Mutations that occur in sperm or egg cells may result in transmission of altered DNA from parent to offspring. Each cell in the offspring will carry the inherited mutation. Most mutations to genes are either harmful or neutral. For example, genetic diseases such as hemophilia, sickle-cell anemia, and cystic fibrosis are caused by harmful mutations. Other mutations have no observable effect or change the organism in a way that

is *neutral,* neither harmful nor beneficial. Almost all of the inherited variability among traits—such as human eye color—is caused by neutral mutations that occurred in the distant past and have been passed along harmlessly through generations. On rare occasions, however, an inherited mutation changes a gene in a way that helps offspring to survive and reproduce more successfully than those lacking the mutation. These infrequent events provide the raw material for evolution.

Some Inherited Mutations Help Individuals Survive and Reproduce

The most important process in evolution is natural selection, which acts on the natural variability in traits. **Natural selection** is the process by which organisms with certain inherited traits survive and reproduce better than others in a given environment. As a result, the advantageous inherited traits become increasingly common in the population as generations pass. Because these traits are caused by differences in genes, the genetic makeup of the population as a whole will change over time; that is, the population will evolve. Consider a likely scenario of natural selection. Imagine that ancient beavers had short front teeth like most other mammals. If a mutation caused one beaver's offspring to grow longer front teeth, these offspring would have gnawed down trees more efficiently, built bigger dams and lodges, and eaten more bark than beavers that lacked the mutation. These long-toothed beavers would have been better able to survive and would have raised more offspring that would inherit the genes for longer front teeth. Over time, long-toothed beavers would have become increasingly common; after many generations, all beavers would have long front teeth.

Structures, physiological processes, or behaviors that help an organism survive and reproduce in a particular environment are called **adaptations.** Most of the features that we admire so much in other life-forms, such as the fleet, agile limbs of deer, the broad wings of eagles, and the mighty trunks of redwood trees, are adaptations. Adaptations help organisms escape predators, capture prey, reach the sunlight, or accomplish other feats that help ensure their survival and reproduction. The huge array of adaptations found in living things today was molded by natural selection acting on random mutations.

But how did life's diversity, including deer, eagles, redwoods, and people, all arise from the first single-celled life that appeared billions of years ago? Natural selection is not uniform; a trait that is adaptive in one environment may not be helpful (or may even be a hindrance) in a different setting. After Darwin observed different but closely related organisms on clusters of islands, he hypothesized that different forms of life may evolve if a population becomes fragmented and groups of individuals are subjected to different environments. For example, a violent storm may carry some individuals from the mainland to an offshore island. The mainland and the island populations will initially consist of the same **species** (organisms of the same type that can interbreed). But if the island's environment differs from that of

◀ **FIGURE 1-9 A fossil from a newly discovered dinosaur, *Titanosaurus*** The most widely accepted hypothesis for the extinction of dinosaurs about 65 million years ago is a massive meteorite strike that rapidly and radically altered their environment. This thigh bone, estimated to be 95 million years old, is from a plant-eating giant with an estimated length of 130 feet (40 meters) and a weight of about 176,000 pounds (80 metric tons).

THINK CRITICALLY The largest dinosaurs were plant-eaters. Based on Figure 1-3, can you suggest a reason why?

the mainland, the newcomers will be subjected to different forces of natural selection; as a result, they will evolve different adaptations. These differences may eventually become great enough that the two populations can no longer interbreed; a new species will have evolved.

What helps an organism survive today may become a liability in the future. If environments change—for example, as global climate change occurs—the traits that best adapt organisms to their environments will change as well. In the case of global climate change, if a random mutation helps an organism survive and reproduce in a warmer climate, the mutation will be favored by natural selection and will become more common in the population with each new generation.

If mutations that help an organism to adapt do not occur, a changing environment may doom a species to **extinction**—the complete elimination of this form of life. Dinosaurs flourished for 100 million years, but because they did not evolve fast enough to adapt to rapidly changing conditions, they became extinct (**FIG. 1-9**). In recent decades, human activities such as burning fossil fuels and converting tropical forests to farmland have drastically accelerated the rate of environmental change. Mutations that better adapt organisms to these altered environments are quite rare, and consequently the rate of extinction has increased dramatically.

CHECK YOUR LEARNING

Can you ...

- explain what mutations are, how they occur, what allows them to be inherited, and what general types of changes mutations can produce?
- explain how natural processes lead inevitably to evolution?
- describe how a new species can be produced by natural selection?

CASE STUDY \ **CONTINUED**

The Boundaries of Life

One lifelike property of viruses is their capacity to evolve. Through evolution, viruses sometimes become more infectious or more deadly, or they may gain the ability to infect new hosts. Certain types of viruses, including Ebola, HIV, and flu, are very sloppy in copying their genetic material and mutate about 1,000 times as often as the average animal cell. One consequence is that viruses such as flu evolve rapidly; flu shots must immunize you against different types of flu every year. Likewise, more than 200 different viruses can cause symptoms of the "common cold," explaining why you keep getting new colds throughout life. HIV in an infected person can produce up to 10 billion new viruses daily, with 10 million of these carrying a random mutation. Inevitably, some of these mutations will produce resistance to an antiviral drug. Therefore, antiviral drugs act as agents of natural selection that promote the survival and successful replication of drug-resistant viruses. For this reason, HIV victims are given "cocktails" of three or four different drugs; resistance to all of them would require multiple specific mutations to occur in the same virus, an enormously unlikely event.

1.3 HOW DO SCIENTISTS STUDY LIFE?

The science of biology encompasses many different areas of inquiry, each requiring different types of specialized knowledge. In fact, biology is not a single field, but many—linked by the amazing complexity of life.

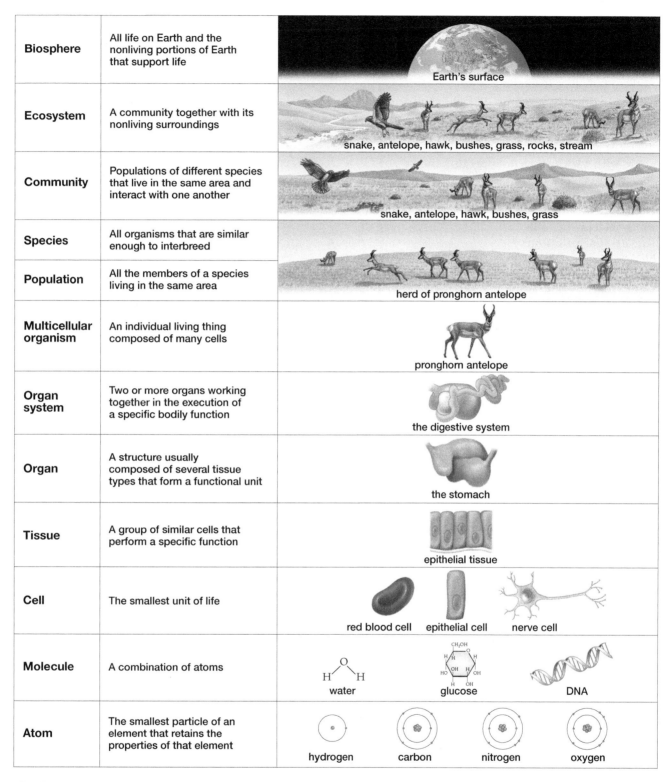

Biosphere	All life on Earth and the nonliving portions of Earth that support life	Earth's surface
Ecosystem	A community together with its nonliving surroundings	snake, antelope, hawk, bushes, grass, rocks, stream
Community	Populations of different species that live in the same area and interact with one another	snake, antelope, hawk, bushes, grass
Species	All organisms that are similar enough to interbreed	herd of pronghorn antelope
Population	All the members of a species living in the same area	
Multicellular organism	An individual living thing composed of many cells	pronghorn antelope
Organ system	Two or more organs working together in the execution of a specific bodily function	the digestive system
Organ	A structure usually composed of several tissue types that form a functional unit	the stomach
Tissue	A group of similar cells that perform a specific function	epithelial tissue
Cell	The smallest unit of life	red blood cell epithelial cell nerve cell
Molecule	A combination of atoms	water glucose DNA
Atom	The smallest particle of an element that retains the properties of that element	hydrogen carbon nitrogen oxygen

▲ **FIGURE 1-10 Levels of biological organization** Each level provides building blocks for the one above it, which has new properties that emerge from the interplay of the levels below.

THINK CRITICALLY What current, ongoing environmental change is likely to affect the entire biosphere?

Life May Be Studied at Different Levels

Let's look at the levels of organization that comprise life on Earth (FIG. 1-10). Biologists conduct research at nearly every level, from complex biological molecules such as DNA to entire ecosystems (for example, how forest ecosystems may be altered by climate change).

Each level of organization provides a foundation for the one above it, and each higher level has new, more inclusive properties. All matter consists of **elements,** substances that cannot be broken down or converted into simpler substances. An **atom** is the smallest particle of an element that retains all the properties of that element. For example, a diamond is a form of the element carbon. The smallest possible unit of a diamond is an individual carbon atom. Atoms may combine in specific ways to form **molecules;** for example, one oxygen atom can combine with two hydrogen atoms to form a molecule of water. Complex biological molecules containing carbon atoms—such as proteins and DNA—form the building blocks of cells, which are the basic units of life. Although many organisms exist as single cells, in multicellular organisms, cells of a similar type may combine to form **tissues,** such as the epithelial tissue that lines the stomach. Different types of tissues, in turn, unite to form functional units called **organs,** such as the entire stomach. The grouping of two or more organs that work together to perform a specific body function is called an **organ system;** for example, the stomach is part of the digestive system. Organ systems combine within complex multicellular organisms to carry out the activities of life.

Levels of organization also extend to groups of organisms. A population is a group of organisms of the same type (the same species) that live in a defined area where they interact and interbreed with one another. A species consists of all organisms that are similar enough to interbreed, no matter where they are found. A **community** is formed by populations of different species that live in the same area and interact with one another. An **ecosystem** consists of a community and the nonliving environment that surrounds it. Finally, the **biosphere** includes all life on Earth and the nonliving portions of Earth that support life.

▲ FIGURE 1-11 The domains of life

Biologists Classify Organisms Based on Their Evolutionary Relationships

Although all forms of life share certain characteristics, evolution has produced an amazing variety of life-forms. Scientists classify organisms based on their evolutionary relatedness, placing them into three major groups, or **domains:** Bacteria, Archaea, and Eukarya (FIG. 1-11).

This classification reflects fundamental differences among cell types. Members of both Bacteria and Archaea consist of a single, simple cell. At the molecular level, however, there are fundamental differences between them that indicate that they are only distantly related. In contrast to the simple cells of Bacteria and Archaea,

members of Eukarya have bodies composed of one or more extremely complex cells. The domain Eukarya includes a diverse collection of organisms collectively known as *protists* and the fungi, plants, and animals. (You will learn far more about life's incredible diversity and how it evolved in Unit 3.)

Cell Type Distinguishes the Bacteria and Archaea from the Eukarya

All cells are surrounded by a thin sheet of molecules called the **plasma membrane** (see Fig. 1-1). All contain the hereditary material DNA. Cells also contain **organelles,** structures specialized to carry out specific functions such as helping to synthesize large molecules, digesting food molecules, or obtaining energy.

There are two fundamentally different types of cells: eukaryotic and prokaryotic. **Eukaryotic** cells are extremely complex and contain a variety of organelles, many of which are surrounded by membranes. The term "eukaryotic" comes from Greek words meaning "true" ("eu") and "nucleus" ("kary"). As the name suggests, the **nucleus,** a membrane-enclosed organelle that contains the cell's DNA, is a prominent feature of eukaryotic cells (see Fig. 1-1). All members of the Eukarya are composed of eukaryotic cells. **Prokaryotic** cells, which comprise the domains Bacteria and Archaea, are far simpler and generally much smaller than eukaryotic cells, and they lack organelles enclosed by membranes. As their name—meaning "before" ("pro") the nucleus—suggests, the DNA of prokaryotic cells is not confined within a nucleus. Although they are invisible to the naked eye, the most abundant forms of life are found in the domains Bacteria and Archaea, which consist entirely of prokaryotic cells.

Multicellularity Occurs Only Among the Eukarya

Members of the domains Bacteria and Archaea are unicellular. Although some form strands, mats, or biofilms (thin layers of bacteria), there is relatively little communication, cooperation, or organization among them compared to multicellular organisms—which are only found among the Eukarya. Although protists are eukaryotic and many are unicellular, all plants and animals and nearly all fungi are multicellular; their lives depend on intimate communication and cooperation among numerous specialized cells.

Biologists Use the Binomial System to Name Organisms

To provide a unique scientific name for each form of life, biologists use a **binomial system** (literally "two names") consisting of the genus (a group of closely related species) and the species. The genus name is capitalized, and both names are italicized and based on Latin or Greek word roots. The animal in Figure 1-2 has the common name "water flea," but there are many types of water fleas, and people who study them need to be precise. So this water flea has been given the scientific name *Daphnia longispina,* placing it in the genus *Daphnia* (which includes many similar species of water fleas) and the species *longispina* (referring to its long spine). People are classified as *Homo sapiens;* we are the only surviving members of our genus.

CHECK YOUR LEARNING
Can you ...
- describe the levels of biological organization?
- explain how scientists name and categorize diverse forms of life?
- describe the fundamental differences between prokaryotic and eukaryotic cells?

1.4 WHAT IS SCIENCE?

Science can be defined as the systematic inquiry—through observation and experiment—into all aspects of the physical universe.

Science Is Based on General Underlying Principles

Three basic principles provide the foundation for scientific inquiry. The first is that all events can be traced to natural causes. In ancient times—in contrast—it was common to believe that supernatural forces were responsible for natural events that seemed to defy explanation. Ancient Greeks explained lightning bolts as weapons hurled by the god Zeus and attributed epileptic seizures to a visitation from the gods. Today, science tells us that lightning is a massive electrical discharge, and epilepsy is a brain disorder caused by uncontrolled firing of nerve cells. Science is an unending quest to discover the causes of phenomena that we don't yet understand.

The second principle of science is that natural laws do not change over time or distance. The laws of gravity, for example, are the same today as they were 10 billion years ago, and they apply everywhere in our universe.

The third principle is that scientific findings are "value neutral." Science, in its ideal form, provides us with facts that are independent of subjective values; in other words, scientific data exist outside of any belief system. For example, science can describe in detail the events that occur when a human egg is fertilized, but cannot tell us whether a fertilized egg is a person.

The Scientific Method Is an Important Tool of Scientific Inquiry

To learn about the world, scientists in many disciplines, including biology, use some version of the **scientific method.** This consists of six interrelated elements: *observation, question, hypothesis, prediction, experiment,* and *conclusion.* Scientific inquiry begins with an **observation** of a specific phenomenon. The observation, in turn, leads to a **question:** "What caused this?" After carefully studying earlier investigations, thinking, and often conversing with colleagues, the investigator forms a hypothesis. A **hypothesis** is a proposed explanation for the phenomenon, based on available evidence. To be useful, the hypothesis must lead to a **prediction,** which is the expected outcome of testing if the hypothesis is correct. The prediction is tested by carefully designed additional observations or carefully controlled manipulations called **experiments.** Experiments produce results that either support or refute the hypothesis, allowing the scientist to reach a **conclusion** about whether the hypothesis is valid or not. For the conclusion to be valid, the experiment and its results must be repeatable not only by the original researcher but also by others.

We use less formal versions of the scientific method in our daily lives. For example, suppose you are late for an important date, so you rush to your car, turn the ignition key, and make the *observation* that the car won't start. Your *question,* "Why won't the car start?" leads to a *hypothesis:* The battery is dead. This leads to the *prediction* that a jump-start will solve the problem. You *experiment* by attaching jumper cables from your roommate's car battery to your own. The result? Your car starts immediately, leading to the *conclusion* that your experiment supported your hypothesis about the dead car battery.

Biologists Test Hypotheses Using Controlled Experiments

In controlled experiments, two types of situations are established. One is a baseline, or **control,** situation, in which all possible factors are held constant. The other is the experimental situation, where one factor, the **variable,** is manipulated to test the hypothesis that this variable is the cause of an observation. Often, the manipulation inadvertently changes more than one factor. In the preceding car example, jump-starting the car might have both delivered a charge to the battery and knocked some corrosion off the battery terminal that was preventing the battery from delivering power—your battery might actually have been fully charged. In real experiments, scientists must control for all the possible effects of any manipulation they perform, so frequently more than one control is needed.

Valid scientific experiments must be repeatable by the researcher and by other scientists. To help ensure this, a researcher performs multiple repetitions of an experiment, setting up several replications of each control group and an equal number of experimental groups. Data from control and experimental situations are often compared using *statistics,* mathematical formulas that can help interpret and draw conclusions from various types of numerical measurements. Statistics can determine the likelihood that the difference between control and experimental groups arose by random chance. If statistical tests show chance to be sufficiently unlikely, the difference between the groups is described as *statistically significant.*

Science must also be communicated, or it is useless. Good scientists publish their results, explaining their methods in detail so others can repeat and build on their experiments. Francesco Redi recognized this in the 1600s when he carefully recorded the methods of his classic controlled experiment testing the hypothesis that flies caused maggots to appear on rotting meat (see "How Do We Know That? Controlled Experiments Provide Reliable Data" on page 12).

Experimentation using variables and controls is powerful, but it is important to recognize its limitations. In particular, scientists can seldom be sure that they have controlled for *all* possible variables or performed all the manipulations that could possibly refute their hypothesis. Therefore, science mandates that conclusions are always subject to revision if new experiments or observations contradict them.

HAVE YOU EVER WONDERED ...

Fruit flies, bacteria from hot springs, sea jellies, Gila monsters, burdock burrs—why study these obscure forms of life? In fact, research on these organisms, and a host of others, has improved people's lives.

> *Why Scientists Study Obscure Organisms?*

Fruit flies, for example, have been used for over 100 years to study how genes influence traits. Their genes are similar enough to ours that many human genetic diseases can be investigated to some extent in these flies—a pair of which can produce several hundred genetically identical offspring in a few weeks. An obscure bacterium from a hot spring in Yellowstone National Park is the source of a protein crucial to a process that rapidly copies DNA. Thanks to this discovery, the amount of DNA in a few skin cells left at a crime scene can now generate a sample large enough

Gila monster

to be compared to the DNA of a suspect. A fluorescent green protein discovered in a sea jelly can be attached to a gene, protein, or virus, making it glow and allowing researchers to monitor its activity. A protein found in the Gila monster's venomous saliva was approved in 2005 as a drug to help diabetics maintain more constant blood sugar levels. And what did microscopic examination of a burr lead to? The inspiration for Velcro.

Some people criticize governments for funding research into topics that seem obscure, like what makes a jellyfish glow. But no one can predict where such studies will lead; even lines of research that appear to be dead ends can provide unexpected and valuable insights.

Scientific Theories Have Been Thoroughly Tested

Scientists use the word "theory" in a way that differs from its everyday usage. If Dr. Watson asked Sherlock Holmes, "Do you have a theory as to the perpetrator of this foul deed?" in scientific terms, he would be asking Holmes for a hypothesis—a proposed explanation based on clues that provide incomplete evidence. A **scientific theory,** in contrast, is a general and reliable explanation of important natural phenomena that has been developed through extensive and reproducible observations and experiments. In short, a scientific theory is best described as a **natural law,** a basic principle derived from the study of nature that has never been disproven by scientific inquiry. For example, scientific theories such as the atomic theory (that all matter is composed of atoms) and the theory of gravitation (that objects exert attraction for one another) are fundamental to the science of physics. Likewise, the **cell theory** (that all living organisms are composed of cells) and the theory of evolution are fundamental to the study of biology.

Scientists describe fundamental principles as "theories" rather than "facts" because even scientific theories can potentially be disproved, or falsified. If compelling evidence arises that renders a scientific theory invalid, that theory must be modified or discarded. A modern example of the need to modify basic principles in the light of new scientific evidence is the discovery of prions, which are infectious proteins (see Chapter 3). Before the early 1980s, all known infectious disease agents copied themselves using instructions from genetic material. Then in 1982, neurologist Stanley Prusiner published evidence that scrapie (an infectious disease of sheep that causes brain degeneration) is actually triggered and transmitted by a protein and has no genetic material. Infectious proteins were unknown to science, and Prusiner's results were met with widespread disbelief. It took nearly two decades of further research to convince most of the scientific community that a protein alone could act as an infectious disease agent. Prions are now known to cause mad cow disease and two fatal human brain disorders. Stanley Prusiner was awarded the Nobel Prize in Physiology or Medicine for his pioneering work. Science is based on the premise that even basic scientific principles can be modified in light of new data. By accepting prions as infectious proteins, scientists maintained the integrity of the scientific process while expanding our understanding of how diseases can occur.

Ongoing scientific inquiry continuously tests scientific theories. This is a major difference between scientific principles and faith-based doctrines (such as creationism), which are impossible to prove or disprove and thus fall outside the scope of science.

Scientific Theories Involve Both Inductive and Deductive Reasoning

Scientific theories arise through **inductive reasoning**, the process of creating a broad generalization based on many observations that support it and none that contradict it. For example, the cell theory arises from the observation that all organisms that possess the characteristics of life are composed of one or more cells and that nothing that is not composed of cells shares all of these attributes.

Once a scientific theory has been formulated, it can be used to support deductive reasoning. In science, **deductive reasoning** starts with a well-supported generalization and uses it to generate hypotheses about how a specific experiment or observation will turn out. For example, based on the cell theory, if a scientist discovers a new entity that exhibits all the characteristics of life, she can confidently hypothesize that it will be composed of cells. Of course, the new organism must then be carefully examined to confirm its cellular structure.

Science Is a Human Endeavor

Scientists are people, driven by the pride, fears, and ambition common to humanity. Accidents, lucky guesses, controversies with competing scientists, and, of course, the intellectual curiosity of individual scientists all contribute to scientific advances. Even mistakes can play a role. Let's consider an actual case.

Microbiologists often study pure cultures—a single type of bacterium grown in sterile, covered dishes free from contamination by other bacteria and molds. At the first sign of contamination, a culture is usually thrown out, often with mutterings about sloppy technique. In the late 1920s, however, Scottish bacteriologist Alexander Fleming turned a ruined bacterial culture into one of the greatest medical advances in history.

One of Fleming's cultures became contaminated with a mold (a type of fungus) called *Penicillium*. But instead of discarding the dish, Fleming observed that no bacteria were growing near the mold (FIG. 1-12). He asked the question "Why aren't bacteria growing in this region?" Fleming then formulated the hypothesis that *Penicillium* releases a substance that kills bacteria, and he predicted that a solution in which the mold had grown would contain this substance and kill bacteria. To test this hypothesis, Fleming performed an experiment. He grew *Penicillium* in a liquid nutrient broth, and then filtered out the mold and poured some of the mold-free broth on a plate with a pure bacterial culture. Sure enough, something in the liquid killed the bacteria, supporting his hypothesis. This (and more experiments that confirmed his results) led to the conclusion that *Penicillium* secretes a substance that kills bacteria. Further research into these mold extracts resulted in the production of the first antibiotic—penicillin.

Fleming's experiments are a classic example of the scientific method, but they would never have happened without the combination of a mistake, a chance observation, and the curiosity to explore it. The outcome has saved millions of

Bacteria grow in a film on solid culture medium.

pellet of penicillin

Penicillin diffusing outward inhibits bacterial growth.

▲ **FIGURE 1-12 Penicillin kills bacteria** Alexander Fleming observed similar inhibition of bacterial growth around colonies of *Penicillium* mold.

HOW DO WE KNOW THAT?

Controlled Experiments Provide Reliable Data

A classic experiment by the Italian physician Francesco Redi (1621–1697) beautifully demonstrates the scientific method and helps to illustrate the basic scientific principle that all events can be traced to natural causes. Redi investigated why maggots (fly larvae) appear on spoiled meat. In Redi's time, refrigeration was unknown, and meat was stored in the open. Many people of that time believed that the appearance of maggots on meat was evidence of **spontaneous generation,** the emergence of life from nonliving matter.

Redi *observed* that flies swarm around fresh meat and that maggots appear on meat left out for a few days. He *questioned* where the maggots came from. He then formed a testable *hypothesis:* Flies produce maggots. This led to the *prediction* that keeping flies off the meat would prevent maggots from appearing. In his *experiment,* Redi wanted to test one variable—the access of flies to the meat. Therefore, he placed similar pieces of meat in each of two clean jars. He left one jar open (the control jar) and covered the other with gauze to keep out flies (the experimental jar). He did his best to keep all the other conditions the same (for example, the type of jar, the type of meat, and the temperature). After a few days, he observed maggots on the meat in the open jar but saw none on the meat in the covered jar. Redi *concluded* that his hypothesis was correct and that maggots are produced by flies, not by the nonliving meat (**FIG. E1-1**). Only through this and other controlled experiments could the age-old belief in spontaneous generation be laid to rest.

Today, more than 300 years later, the scientific method is still used. Consider the experiments of Malte Andersson, who investigated the mating choices of female widowbirds. Andersson *observed* that male, but not female, widowbirds have extravagantly long tails, which they display while flying across African grasslands. Andersson asked the *question:* Why do male birds have such long tails? His *hypothesis* was that females prefer to mate with long-tailed males, and so these males have more offspring, who inherit their genes for long tails. Andersson *predicted* that if

Observation:	Flies swarm around meat left in the open; maggots appear on the meat.
Question:	Where do maggots on the meat come from?
Hypothesis:	Flies produce the maggots.
Prediction:	IF the hypothesis is correct, THEN keeping the flies away from the meat will prevent the appearance of maggots.

Experiment:

Obtain identical pieces of meat and two identical jars

Place meat in each jar

Leave the jar uncovered

Experimental variable: gauze prevents the entry of flies

Cover the jar with gauze

Leave exposed for several days

Controlled variables: time, temperature, place

Leave covered for several days

Flies swarm around and maggots appear

Results

Flies are kept from the meat; no maggots appear

Control situation

Experimental situation

Conclusion:	The experiment supports the hypothesis that flies are the source of maggots and that spontaneous generation of maggots does not occur.

▲ **FIGURE E1-1 The experiment of Francesco Redi illustrates the scientific method**

his hypothesis were true, more females would build nests on the territories of males with artificially lengthened tails than on the territories of males with artificially shortened tails. To test this, he captured some males, trimmed their tails to about half their original length, and released them (*experimental* group 1). He

took another group of males and glued on the tail feathers that he had removed from the first group, creating exceptionally long tails (*experimental* group 2). Then, in *control* group 1, he cut the tail feathers but then glued them back in place (to control for the effects of capturing the birds and manipulating their feathers). In *control* group 2, he simply captured and released a group of male birds to control for behavioral changes caused by the stress of being caught and handled. Later, Andersson counted the number of nests that females had built on each male's territory, which indicated how many females had mated with that male. He found that males with lengthened tails had the most nests on their territories, males with shortened tails had the fewest, and control males (with normal-length tails, either untouched or cut and glued together) had an intermediate number (**FIG. E1-2**). Andersson *concluded* that his results supported the hypothesis that female widowbirds prefer to mate with long-tailed males.

THINK CRITICALLY Did Redi's experiment (Fig. E1-1) convincingly demonstrate that flies produce maggots? What kind of follow-up experiment would help confirm the source of maggots?

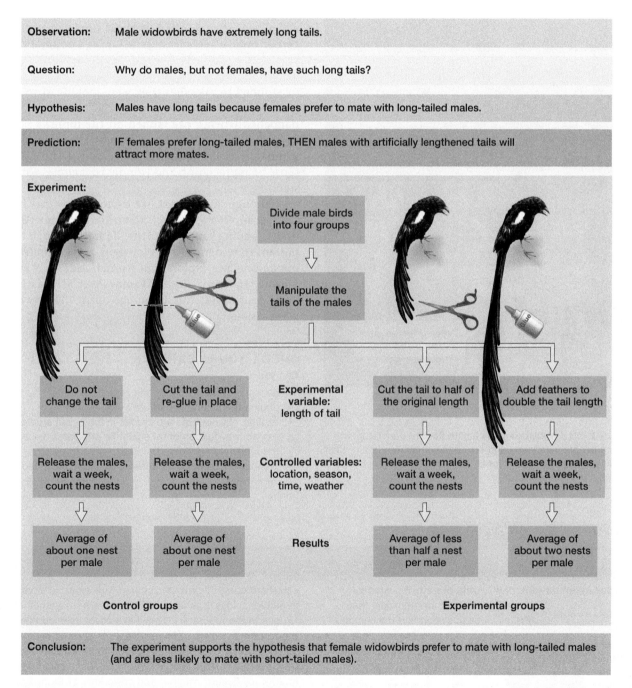

Observation:	Male widowbirds have extremely long tails.
Question:	Why do males, but not females, have such long tails?
Hypothesis:	Males have long tails because females prefer to mate with long-tailed males.
Prediction:	IF females prefer long-tailed males, THEN males with artificially lengthened tails will attract more mates.

Experiment:

Divide male birds into four groups

Manipulate the tails of the males

| Do not change the tail | Cut the tail and re-glue in place | Experimental variable: length of tail | Cut the tail to half of the original length | Add feathers to double the tail length |

| Release the males, wait a week, count the nests | Release the males, wait a week, count the nests | Controlled variables: location, season, time, weather | Release the males, wait a week, count the nests | Release the males, wait a week, count the nests |

| Average of about one nest per male | Average of about one nest per male | Results | Average of less than half a nest per male | Average of about two nests per male |

Control groups   Experimental groups

| Conclusion: | The experiment supports the hypothesis that female widowbirds prefer to mate with long-tailed males (and are less likely to mate with short-tailed males). |

▲ **FIGURE E1-2 The experiment of Malte Andersson**

lives. As French microbiologist Louis Pasteur said, "Chance favors the prepared mind."

Knowledge of Biology Illuminates Life

Some people regard science as a dehumanizing activity, thinking that too deep an understanding of the world robs us of wonder and awe. Nothing could be further from the truth. For example, let's look at lupine flowers. Their two

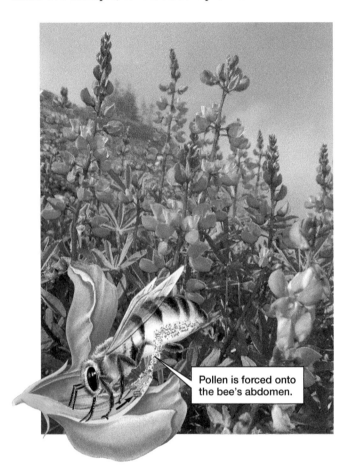

▲ **FIGURE 1-13 Adaptations in lupine flowers** Understanding life helps people notice and appreciate the small wonders at their feet. (Inset) A lupine flower deposits pollen on a foraging bee's abdomen.

lower petals form a tube surrounding both male and female reproductive parts (FIG. 1-13). In young flowers, the weight of a bee on this tube forces pollen (carrying sperm) out of the tube onto the bee's abdomen. In older lupine flowers that are ready to be fertilized, the female part grows and emerges through the end of the tube. When a pollen-dusted bee visits, it deposits some pollen on the female organ, allowing the lupine to produce the seeds of its next generation.

Do these insights detract from our appreciation of lupines? Far from it. There is added delight in watching and understanding the intertwined form and function of bee and flower that resulted as these organisms evolved together. Soon after learning the lupine's pollination mechanism, two of the authors of this text crouched beside a wild lupine to watch it happen. An elderly man passing by stopped to ask what they were looking at so intently. He listened with interest as they explained about what happened when a bee landed on the lupine's petals and immediately went to observe another patch of lupines where bees were foraging. He, too, felt the heightened sense of appreciation and wonder that comes with understanding.

Throughout this text, we try to convey that biology is not just another set of facts to memorize. It is a pathway to understanding yourself and the life around you. It is also important to recognize that biology is not a completed work, but an ongoing exploration. As Alan Alda, best known for playing "Hawkeye" in the TV show *M*A*S*H,* stated: "With every door into nature we nudge open, 100 new doors become visible."

CHECK YOUR LEARNING

Can you ...

- describe the principles underlying science?
- outline the scientific method?
- explain why controls are crucial in biological studies?
- explain why fundamental scientific principles are called theories?
- distinguish between inductive and deductive reasoning?

CASE STUDY   REVISITED

The Boundaries of Life

If viruses aren't a form of life, what are they? A virus by itself is an inert particle that doesn't approach the complexity of a cell. The simplest virus, such as that causing smallpox (FIG. 1-14), consists of a protein coat that surrounds genetic material. The uncompli-

protein coat

genetic material

▲ **FIGURE 1-14 A smallpox virus**

cated structure of viruses, coupled with amazing advances in biotechnology, has allowed researchers to synthesize viruses in the laboratory. They have accomplished this using the blueprint contained in viral genetic material and readily purchased chemicals. The first virus to be synthesized was the small, simple poliovirus. This feat was accomplished in 2002 by Eckard Wimmer and coworkers at Stony Brook University, who titled their work "The Test-Tube Synthesis of a Chemical Called Poliovirus."

Did these researchers create life in the laboratory? A few scientists would say "yes," defining life by its ability to copy itself and to evolve. Wimmer himself describes viruses as entities that switch between a nonliving phase outside the cell and a living phase inside. Although most scientists agree that viruses aren't alive and support the definition of life presented in this text, the controversy continues. As virologist Luis Villarreal puts it, "Viruses are parasites that skirt the boundaries between life and inert matter."

CONSIDER THIS When Wimmer and coworkers announced that they had synthesized the poliovirus, they created considerable controversy. Some people feared that deadly and highly contagious viruses might be synthesized by bioterrorists. The researchers responded that they were merely applying current knowledge and techniques to demonstrate the principle that viruses are basically chemical entities that can be synthesized in the laboratory. Do you think scientists should synthesize viruses or other agents that can cause infectious disease? What are the implications of forbidding such research?

CHAPTER REVIEW

 Go to **MasteringBiology** for practice quizzes, activities, eText, videos, current events, and more.

Answers to Think Critically, Evaluate This, Multiple Choice, and Fill-in-the-Blank questions can be found in the Answers section at the back of the book.

Summary of Key Concepts

1.1 What Is Life?

Organisms acquire and use materials and energy. Materials are obtained from other organisms or the nonliving environment and are repeatedly recycled. Energy must be continuously captured from sunlight by photosynthetic organisms, whose bodies supply energy to all other organisms. Organisms also actively maintain organized complexity, perceive and respond to stimuli, grow, reproduce, and, collectively, evolve.

1.2 What Is Evolution?

Evolution is the scientific theory that modern organisms descended, with changes, from earlier organisms. Evolution occurs as a consequence of (1) genetic differences, originally arising as mutations, among members of a population; (2) inheritance of these differences by offspring; and (3) natural selection of the differences that produce the best adaptations to the organisms' environment.

1.3 How Do Scientists Study Life?

Scientists identify a hierarchy of levels of organization, each more encompassing than those beneath (see Fig. 1-10). Biologists categorize organisms into three domains: Archaea, Bacteria, and Eukarya. Members of Archaea and Bacteria consist of single prokaryotic cells, but fundamental molecular differences distinguish them. Members of Eukarya are composed of one or more eukaryotic cells. Organisms are assigned scientific names that identify each as a unique species within a specific genus.

1.4 What Is Science?

Science is based on three principles: (1) all events can be traced to natural causes that can be investigated; (2) the laws of nature are unchanging; and (3) scientific findings are independent of values except honesty in reporting data. Knowledge in biology is acquired through the scientific method, in which an observation leads to a question that leads to a hypothesis. The hypothesis generates a prediction that is then tested by controlled

experiments or precise observation. The experimental results, which must be repeatable, lead to a conclusion that either supports or refutes the hypothesis. A scientific theory is a general explanation of natural phenomena developed through extensive and reproducible experiments and observations.

Key Terms

adaptation 5	mutation 5
atom 8	natural law 10
binomial system 9	natural selection 5
biology 2	nucleus 9
biosphere 8	observation 9
cell 2	organ 8
cell theory 10	organ system 8
community 8	organelle 9
conclusion 9	organism 2
control 10	photosynthesis 2
deductive reasoning 11	plasma
deoxyribonucleic acid (DNA) 4	membrane 8
domain 8	population 4
ecosystem 8	prediction 9
element 8	prokaryotic 9
eukaryotic 9	question 9
evolution 4	science 9
experiment 9	scientific method 9
extinction 6	scientific theory 10
gene 5	species 5
homeostasis 3	spontaneous
hypothesis 9	generation 12
inductive reasoning 11	tissue 8
molecule 8	unicellular 2
multicellular 2	variable 10

Thinking Through the Concepts

Multiple Choice

1. Evolution is
   a. a belief.
   b. a scientific theory.
   c. a hypothesis.
   d. never observed in the modern world.

2. Which of the following is *not* true of science?
   a. Science is based on the premise that all events can be traced to natural causes.
   b. Important science can be based on chance observations.
   c. A hypothesis is basically a wild guess.
   d. Scientific theories can potentially be disproved.

3. Which of the following does *not* apply to mutations?
   a. They occur to cause adaptive changes in response to the environment.
   b. They are usually either harmful or neutral.
   c. They are only inherited if they occur in a sperm or egg cell.
   d. They often occur when DNA is copied.

4. Viruses
   a. have DNA confined in a nucleus.
   b. are relatively rare compared to living organisms.
   c. do not evolve.
   d. may be surrounded by plasma membrane from their host cell.

5. Which one of the following is True?
   a. The presence of a cell nucleus distinguishes Bacteria from Archaea.
   b. All cells are surrounded by a plasma membrane.
   c. All members of Eukarya are multicellular.
   d. Viruses are the simplest cells.

Fill-in-the-Blank

1. Organisms respond to _____. Organisms acquire and use _____ and _____ from the environment. Organisms are composed of cells whose structure is both _____ and _____. Collectively, organisms _____ over time.

2. The smallest particle of an element that retains all the properties of that element is a(n) _____. The smallest unit of life is the _____. Cells of a specific type within multicellular organisms combine to form _____. A(n) _____ consists of all of the same type of organism within a defined area. A(n) _____ consists of all the interacting populations within the same area. A(n) _____ consists of the community and its nonliving surroundings.

3. A(n) _____ is a general explanation of natural phenomena supported by extensive, reproducible tests and observations. In contrast, a(n) _____ is a proposed explanation for observed events. To answer specific questions about life, biologists use a general process called the _____.

4. An important scientific theory that explains why organisms are at once so similar and so diverse is the theory of _____. This theory explains life's diversity as having originated primarily through the process of _____.

5. The molecule that guides the construction and operation of an organism's body is called (complete term) _____, abbreviated as _____. This large molecule contains discrete segments with specific instructions; these segments are called _____.

Review Questions

1. What properties are shared by all forms of life?

2. Why do organisms require energy? Where does the energy come from?

3. Define *evolution,* and explain the three natural occurrences that make evolution inevitable.

4. What are the three domains of life?

5. What are some differences between prokaryotic and eukaryotic cells? In which domain(s) is each found?

6. What basic principles underlie scientific inquiry?

7. What is the difference between a scientific theory and a hypothesis? Why do scientists refer to basic scientific principles as "theories" rather than "facts"?

8. What factors did Redi control for in his open jar of meat? What factors did Andersson control for?

9. Explain the differences between inductive and deductive reasoning. Which of these processes generates scientific theories?

10. List the steps in the scientific method with a brief description of each step.

Applying the Concepts

1. What misunderstanding causes some people to dismiss evolution as "just a theory"?

2. How would this textbook's definition of life need to be changed to allow viruses to qualify as life-forms? For prions to be considered alive?

3. Review Alexander Fleming's experiment that led to the discovery of penicillin. What would be an appropriate control for the experiment in which Fleming applied filtered medium from a *Penicillium* culture to plates of bacteria?

4. Explain an instance in which your own understanding of a phenomenon enhances your appreciation of it.

5. In using the scientific method to help start your car, if jump-starting didn't work, what hypothesis would you test next?

UNIT 1
The Life of the Cell

Single cells can be complex, independent organisms such as this freshwater protist of the genus *Dendrocometes*. A rounded attachment region anchors the cell firmly to the gills of freshwater fish or crustaceans. Tentacles, resembling microscopic antlers, snare food as water passes over them.

"Any living cell carries with it the experiences of a billion years of experimentation by its ancestors." — MAX DELBRÜCK

2 ATOMS, MOLECULES, AND LIFE

The aftermath of explosions at the Fukushima nuclear power plant in Japan.

CASE STUDY

Unstable Atoms Unleashed

AN EARTHQUAKE OF EPIC MAGNITUDE—9.0 on the Richter scale—shook the northeast coast of Japan on March 11, 2011. It was the most violent earthquake in Japan's history, and one of the most powerful ever recorded worldwide. Soon after, a tsunami caused by the quake slammed into the Fukushima Daiichi nuclear power plant on Japan's eastern coast. Towering waves nearly 50 feet high flooded the plant and knocked out its main electrical power supply and backup generators, which caused its cooling system to fail.

The cores of nuclear reactors like those in the Fukushima plant contain thousands of fuel rods consisting of zirconium metal tubes filled with uranium fuel. Two thick steel containment vessels surround the nuclear core, and water is pumped continuously around the vessels to absorb the intense heat generated by the nuclear reactions within them. The heated water produces steam, which then expands, driving turbines that generate electricity.

When the power loss shut down the plant's water pumps, operators used firefighting equipment to inject seawater into the inner containment vessel in a desperate attempt to cool it. But their efforts failed; heat and pressure cracked the inner containment vessel, allowing water and steam to escape. The core temperature rose to over 1,800°F (about 1,000°C), melting the zirconium tubes and releasing the radioactive fuel into the inner vessel.

Because of the incredibly high temperatures, the zirconium reacted with the steam to generate hydrogen gas. As the pressure of the steam and hydrogen gas increased, it threatened to rupture the outer containment vessel. To prevent this, plant operators vented the mixture—which also contained radioactive elements from the melted fuel rods—into the atmosphere. As the hot hydrogen gas encountered oxygen in the atmosphere, the two combined explosively, destroying parts of the buildings housing the containment vessels (see the photo above). Despite venting, the intense heat and the pressure it generated eventually caused the outer containment structure to leak and disgorge contaminated water into the ocean for months following the disaster. Officials evacuated tens of thousands of people living within 12 miles of the plant, and many nearby villages remain uninhabitable.

Why were people evacuated from their homes when radioactive gases were released into the atmosphere? What are atoms composed of? How do the atoms of radioactive elements differ from non-radioactive elements?

AT A GLANCE

2.1 What Are Atoms?

2.2 How Do Atoms Interact to Form Molecules?

2.3 Why Is Water So Important to Life?

2.1 WHAT ARE ATOMS?

If you write "atom" with a pencil, you are forming the letters with graphite, a form of carbon. Now imagine cutting up the carbon into finer and finer particles, until all you have left is a substance split into its basic subunits: individual carbon atoms, each with the structure unique to carbon. A carbon atom is so small that 100 million of them placed in a row would span less than half an inch (1 centimeter).

Atoms Are the Basic Structural Units of Elements

Carbon is an example of an **element**—a substance that can neither be separated into simpler substances nor converted into a different substance by ordinary **chemical reactions** (processes that form or break bonds between atoms). Elements, both alone and combined with other elements, form all matter. An **atom** is the smallest unit of an element, and each atom retains all the chemical properties of that element.

Ninety-two different elements occur in nature. Each is given an abbreviation, its *atomic symbol,* based on its name (sometimes in Latin; e.g., lead is Pb, for *plumbum*). Most elements are present in only small quantities in the biosphere, and relatively few are essential to life on Earth. **TABLE 2-1** lists the most common elements in living things.

TABLE 2-1	Common Elements in Living Organisms		
Element	**Atomic Number[1]**	**Mass Number[2]**	**% by Weight in the Human Body**
Oxygen (O)	8	16	65.0
Carbon (C)	6	12	18.5
Hydrogen (H)	1	1	9.5
Nitrogen (N)	7	14	3.0
Calcium (Ca)	20	40	1.5
Phosphorus (P)	15	31	1.0
Potassium (K)	19	39	0.35
Sulfur (S)	16	32	0.25
Sodium (Na)	11	23	0.15
Chlorine (Cl)	17	35	0.15
Magnesium (Mg)	12	24	0.05
Iron (Fe)	26	56	Trace
Fluorine (F)	9	19	Trace
Zinc (Zn)	30	65	Trace

[1]Atomic number: number of protons in the atomic nucleus.
[2]Mass number: total number of protons and neutrons.

TABLE 2-2	Mass and Charge of Subatomic Particles	
Subatomic Particle	**Mass (in atomic mass units)**	**Charge**
Neutron (n)	1	0
Proton (p^+)	1	+1
Electron (e^-)	0.00055	−1

Atoms Are Composed of Still Smaller Particles

Atoms are composed of *subatomic particles:* **neutrons** (n), which have no charge; **protons** (p^+), each of which carries a single positive charge; and **electrons** (e^-), each of which carries a single negative charge. An atom as a whole is uncharged, or *neutral,* because it contains equal numbers of protons and electrons, whose positive and negative charges electrically balance each other. Subatomic particles are assigned their own unit of mass, measured in *atomic mass units.* As you can see in **TABLE 2-2**, each proton and neutron has a mass unit of 1, while the mass of an electron is negligible compared to these larger particles. The **mass number** of an atom is the total number (which equals the total mass) of the protons and neutrons in its nucleus.

Protons and neutrons cluster together in the center of each atom, forming its **atomic nucleus.** An atom's tiny electrons are in continuous rapid motion around its nucleus within a large, three-dimensional space, as illustrated by the two simplest atoms, hydrogen and helium, in **FIG. 2-1**. These *orbital models* of

(a) Hydrogen (H)
1 proton

(b) Helium (He)
2 protons
2 neutrons

▲ **FIGURE 2-1 Atomic models** Orbital models of **(a)** hydrogen (the only atom with no neutrons) and **(b)** helium. In these simplified models, the electrons (pale blue) are represented as miniature planets, orbiting around a nucleus that contains protons (brown) and neutrons (olive green).

THINK CRITICALLY What is the mass number of hydrogen? Of helium?

atomic structure are extremely simplified to make atoms easy to imagine. Atoms are never drawn to scale; if they were, and if this dot • were the nucleus, the electrons would be somewhere in the next room (or outside)—roughly 30 feet away!

Elements Are Defined by Their Atomic Numbers

The number of protons in the nucleus—called the **atomic number**—is the feature that defines each element, making it distinct from all others. For example, every hydrogen atom has one proton, every carbon atom has six, and every oxygen atom has eight, giving these atoms atomic numbers of 1, 6, and 8, respectively. The **periodic table** in Appendix II organizes the elements according to their atomic numbers (rows) and their general chemical properties (columns).

Isotopes Are Atoms of the Same Element with Different Numbers of Neutrons

Although every atom of an element has the same number of protons, the atoms of that element may have different numbers of neutrons. Atoms of the same element with different numbers of neutrons are called **isotopes.** Isotopes can be distinguished from one another because each has a different mass number, which is written as a superscript preceding the atomic symbol.

Some Isotopes Are Radioactive

Most isotopes are stable; their nuclei do not change spontaneously. A few, however, are **radioactive,** meaning that their nuclei spontaneously break apart, or decay. Radioactive decay always emits energy and often subatomic particles as well. The decay of radioactive nuclei may form different elements. For example, nearly all carbon exists as stable ^{12}C. But a radioactive isotope called carbon-14 (^{14}C; 6 protons + 8 neutrons; 1 in every trillion carbon atoms) is produced continuously by atmospheric reactions involving cosmic rays. ^{14}C atoms disintegrate spontaneously at a slow, predictable rate. When one decays, energy is released and a neutron is converted to a proton, producing a stable nitrogen atom (^{14}N; 7 protons + 7 neutrons).

Radioactive Isotopes Are important in Scientific Research and Medicine

Scientists often make use of radioactive isotopes. For example, archeologists take advantage of the fact that after an organism dies, the ratio of ^{14}C to ^{12}C in its body declines predictably as the ^{14}C decays. By measuring this ratio in artifacts such as mummies, ancient trees, skeletons, or tools made of wood or bone, researchers can accurately assess the age of artifacts up to about 50,000 years old.

In laboratory research, scientists often expose organisms to radioactive isotopes and trace the isotopes' movements during physiological processes. For example, experiments with radioactively labeled DNA and protein

allowed scientists to conclude that DNA is the genetic material of cells (described in Chapter 12).

Modern medicine also makes extensive use of radioactive isotopes. For example, radiation therapy is frequently used to treat cancer. DNA can be destroyed by radiation, so rapidly dividing cancer cells (which require intact DNA to copy themselves) are particularly vulnerable. A radioactive isotope may be introduced into the bloodstream or implanted in the body near the cancer, or radiation may be directed into the tumor by an external device. The radiation that kills cancer cells can also cause mutations in the DNA of healthy cells. This slightly increases the chance that the patient will develop cancer again in the future, but most patients consider this a risk worth taking. You'll learn more uses for radioactive isotopes in "How Do We Know That? Radioactive Revelations" on page 22.

CASE STUDY \ **CONTINUED**
Unstable Atoms Unleashed

Because exposure to radioactivity can cause cancer, Japanese authorities have performed regular cancer screenings on hundreds of thousands of children exposed to radioactivity by the Fukushima power plant disaster. Fortunately, recent surveys have found no evidence of increased cancer rates.

But months after the meltdown, engineers at the Fukushima power plant—using specialized cameras located outside the plant—discovered hot spots of radiation so intense that a person exposed for an hour would be dead within a few weeks. How could death come so fast? Extremely high doses of radiation damage DNA and other biological molecules so badly that cells—particularly those that divide rapidly—can no longer function. Skin cells are destroyed. Cells lining the stomach and intestine break down, causing nausea and vomiting. Bone marrow, where blood cells and platelets are produced, is destroyed. Lack of white blood cells allows infections to flourish, and the loss of platelets crucial for blood clotting leads to internal bleeding.

Fortunately, radioactive substances such as those released by the Fukushima disaster are rare in nature. Why do most elements remain stable?

Electrons Are Responsible for the Interactions Among Atoms

Nuclei and electrons play complementary roles in atoms. Nuclei (unless they are radioactive) provide stability; they remain unchanged during ordinary chemical reactions. Electrons, in contrast, are dynamic; they can capture and release energy, and as we describe later, they form the bonds that link atoms together into molecules.

Electrons Occupy Shells of Increasing Energy

Electrons occupy **electron shells,** complex three-dimensional regions around the nucleus. For simplicity, we will depict these shells as increasingly large, concentric

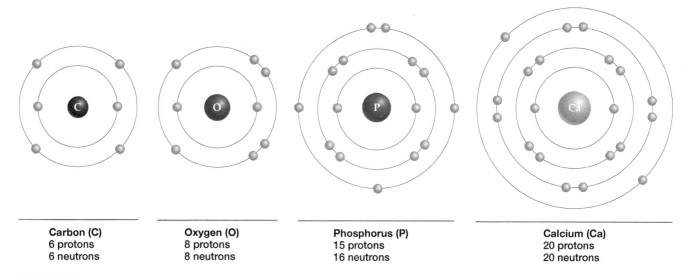

Carbon (C)
6 protons
6 neutrons

Oxygen (O)
8 protons
8 neutrons

Phosphorus (P)
15 protons
16 neutrons

Calcium (Ca)
20 protons
20 neutrons

▲ FIGURE 2-2 **Electron shells in atoms** Most biologically important atoms have two or more shells of electrons. The shell closest to the nucleus can hold two electrons; the next three shells can each contain eight electrons.

THINK CRITICALLY Why do atoms with unfilled outer electron shells tend to react with one another?

rings around the nucleus where electrons travel like planets orbiting the sun (FIG. 2-2). Each shell has a specific energy associated with it. The farther away from the nucleus, the greater the amount of energy stored in the electrons occupying the shell.

Electrons Can Capture and Release Energy

When an atom is excited by energy, such as heat or light, this energy can cause an electron to jump from a lower-energy electron shell to a higher-energy shell. Soon afterward, the electron spontaneously falls back into its original electron shell and releases its extra energy, some in the form of heat, and often in the form of light as well (FIG. 2-3).

We make use of the ability of electrons to capture and release energy every time we switch on a light bulb. Although

incandescent bulbs are rapidly becoming obsolete, they are the easiest type to understand. Electricity flows through a thin wire, heating it to around 4,500°F (about 2,500°C) for a 100-watt bulb. The heat energy bumps some electrons in the wire into higher-energy electron shells. As the electrons drop back down into their original shells, they emit some of the energy as light. Unfortunately, more than 90% of the energy absorbed by the wire is re-emitted as heat rather than light, making an incandescent bulb an extremely inefficient light source.

As Atomic Number Increases, Electrons Fill Shells Increasingly Distant from the Nucleus

Each electron shell can hold a specific number of electrons; the shell nearest the nucleus can hold only two, and more

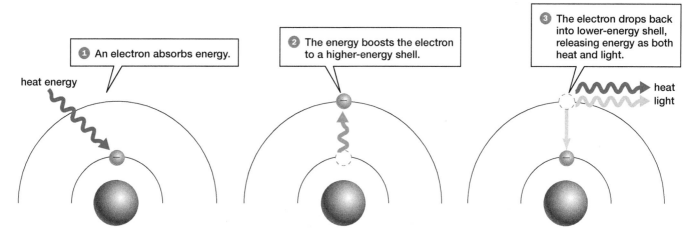

1 An electron absorbs energy.

2 The energy boosts the electron to a higher-energy shell.

3 The electron drops back into lower-energy shell, releasing energy as both heat and light.

heat energy

heat
light

▲ FIGURE 2-3 **Energy capture and release in an incandescent bulb.**

THINK CRITICALLY What causes the coals of a campfire to glow?

How do doctors know the location and size of a cancerous brain tumor? Or how brain activity diminishes with Alzheimer's disease? Or what brain regions are active when a person performs a math problem? These and many more questions can be investigated using positron emission tomography (PET) scans. To perform PET scans, sugar molecules tagged with a radioactive isotope are injected into a patient's bloodstream. More metabolically active regions of the body use more sugar for energy, accumulating larger amounts of radioactivity. To identify these regions, the person's body is moved through a ring of detectors that respond to the energetic particles (positrons) emitted as the isotope decays. A powerful computer then uses these data

(a) Alzheimer's patient   (b) Healthy brain

▲ FIGURE E2-2 **PET reveals differences in brain function** Brain activity is rainbow color-coded, with red indicating the highest activity and blue the lowest; black areas are fluid-filled.

to calculate precisely where the decays occurred and generates a color-coded map of the frequency of decays within each "slice" of body passing through the detector ring (FIG. E2-1a). PET can be used to study the working brain, because regions activated by a specific mental task—such as a math problem—will have increased energy needs and will "light up" as they accumulate more radioactive glucose. Cancerous tumors show up in PET scans as "hot spots" because their rapid cell division uses large amounts of glucose (FIG. E2-1b). PET also reveals that the brain of an Alzheimer's patient is far less active than that of a healthy individual (FIG. E2-2).

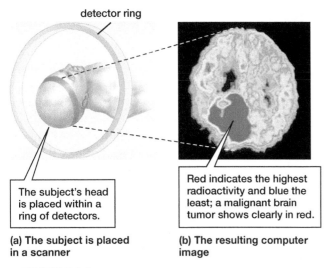

The subject's head is placed within a ring of detectors.

Red indicates the highest radioactivity and blue the least; a malignant brain tumor shows clearly in red.

(a) The subject is placed in a scanner

(b) The resulting computer image

▲ FIGURE E2-1 **Positron emission tomography**

THINK CRITICALLY In addition to lower brain activity, what other problem has occurred in the Alzheimer's victim's brain as shown by the images in Fig. E2-2?

distant shells can hold eight or more. Electrons always fill the lowest-energy shell (the shell nearest the nucleus) first, and then fill higher-energy shells. Elements with increasingly large numbers of protons in their nuclei require more electrons to balance these protons, so their electrons will occupy shells at increasing distances from the nucleus. For example, the two electrons in helium (He) occupy the first electron shell (see Fig. 2-1b). A carbon atom (C) with six electrons will have two electrons filling its first shell and four occupying its second shell, which can contain a total of eight electrons (see Fig. 2-2).

CHECK YOUR LEARNING

Can you ...

- define *element* and *atom*?
- name and describe the *subatomic particles* that make up the atom?
- explain atomic number and mass number?
- explain radioactivity and its dangers and benefits?
- describe electron shells?

2.2 HOW DO ATOMS INTERACT TO FORM MOLECULES?

Most forms of matter that we encounter in our daily lives consist of atoms of the same or different elements linked together to form **molecules.** Simple examples are oxygen gas (O_2; two oxygen atoms) and water (H_2O; two hydrogen atoms and one oxygen atom). How and why do molecules form?

Atoms Form Molecules by Filling Vacancies in Their Outer Electron Shells

In most elements, the electrons needed to balance the protons fill one or more inner shells, but they do not completely fill the outer shell. Atoms generally behave according to two basic principles:

- An atom whose outermost electron shell is completely full will not react with other atoms. Such an atom (e.g., helium in Fig. 2-1b) is extremely stable and is described as *inert*.

TABLE 2-3	Common Types of Bonds in Biological Molecules	
Type	**Type of Interaction**	**Example**
Ionic bond	An electron is transferred between atoms, creating positive and negative ions that attract one another.	Occurs between the sodium (Na^+) and chloride (Cl^-) ions of table salt (NaCl)
Covalent bond	Electrons are shared between atoms.	
Nonpolar	Electrons are shared equally between atoms.	Occurs between the two hydrogen atoms in hydrogen gas (H_2)
Polar	Electrons are shared unequally between atoms.	Occurs between hydrogen and oxygen atoms of a water molecule (H_2O)
Hydrogen bond	Attractions occur between polar molecules in which hydrogen is bonded to oxygen or nitrogen. The slightly positive hydrogen attracts the slightly negative oxygen or nitrogen of a nearby polar molecule.	Occurs between water molecules, where slightly positive charges on hydrogen atoms attract slightly negative charges on oxygen atoms of nearby molecules

- An atom whose outermost electron shell is only partially full will react readily with other atoms. Such an atom (e.g., hydrogen in Fig. 2-1a) is described as *reactive*.

Among atoms and molecules with unfilled outer shells, some—called **free radicals**—are so reactive that they can tear other molecules apart. Free radicals are produced in large numbers in the body by reactions that make energy available to cells. Although these reactions are essential for life, over time, the stress that free radicals place on living cells may contribute to aging and eventual death. Learn more in "Health Watch: Free Radicals—Friends and Foes?" on page 25.

Chemical Bonds Hold Atoms Together in Molecules

Reactive atoms form **chemical bonds,** which are attractive forces that hold atoms together in molecules. Bonds are formed when atoms acquire, lose, or share electrons to gain stability. There are three major types of bonds: *ionic bonds, covalent bonds,* and *hydrogen bonds* (TABLE 2-3).

Ionic Bonds Form Among Ions

Atoms, including those that are reactive, have equal numbers of protons and electrons. The equal number of protons and electrons gives atoms an overall neutral charge, but that does not make them stable. An atom with an almost empty outermost electron shell can become more stable by losing electrons and completely emptying the outer shell; this gives it a positive charge. An atom with a nearly full outer shell can become more stable by gaining electrons and filling the shell completely, giving it a negative charge.

When an atom becomes stable by losing or gaining one (or a few) electrons and thus acquiring an overall positive or negative charge, it becomes an **ion** (FIG. 2-4). Ions with

An electron is transferred.

Oppositely charged ions attract.

Sodium atom (neutral)
11 protons
11 neutrons

Chlorine atom (neutral)
17 protons
17 neutrons

Sodium ion (+1)
11 protons
10 neutrons

Chloride ion (−1)
17 protons
18 neutrons

(a) The formation of ions from atoms

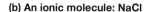

(b) An ionic molecule: NaCl

◀ **FIGURE 2-4 Ions and ionic bonds (a)** Stable ions form when sodium loses an electron (Na^+) and chlorine gains an electron (Cl^-). **(b)** Sodium and chloride ions nestle closely together in cubic crystals of table salt (NaCl).

opposite charges attract one another, and the electrical attraction between positively and negatively charged ions forms **ionic bonds.** For example, the white crystals in your salt shaker are sodium and chloride ions linked by ionic bonds. Sodium (Na) has only one electron in its outermost electron shell, so it can become stable by losing this electron, forming the ion Na^+. Chlorine (Cl) has seven electrons in its outer shell, which can hold eight electrons. So chlorine can become stable by gaining an electron (in this case from sodium), forming the ion Cl^- (FIG. 2-4a) and producing an ionic bond between Na^+ and Cl^-. These ionic bonds result in crystals composed of a repeating, orderly array of Na^+ and Cl^- (FIG. 2-4b). As we describe later, water is attracted to ions and can break ionic bonds, as occurs when water dissolves salt. Because biological molecules function in a watery environment, most are held tightly together by covalent bonds.

Covalent Bonds Form When Atoms Share Electrons

Atoms with partially full outermost electron shells can become stable by sharing electrons with one another, filling both of their outer shells and forming **covalent bonds.** The atoms in most biological molecules, such as proteins, sugars, and fats, are joined by covalent bonds (TABLE 2-4).

▲ FIGURE 2-5 **Nonpolar covalent bonds** A hydrogen molecule (H_2) is formed when an electron from each of two hydrogen atoms is shared equally, forming a single nonpolar covalent bond.

Because the two H nuclei are identical, their electrons spend equal time near each, and so neither end, or *pole,* of the molecule is charged. Other examples of nonpolar molecules include oxygen gas (O_2), nitrogen gas (N_2), carbon dioxide (CO_2), and certain biological molecules such as oils and fats (described in Chapter 3). In each of these molecules, the nuclei exert a roughly equal pull on the shared electrons.

Some covalently bonded atoms share electrons unequally, because the nucleus of one molecule attracts the electrons more strongly than the nucleus of the other. Unequally shared electrons produce **polar covalent bonds** in molecules, which are then described as *polar molecules.* Although the molecule as a whole is electrically neutral, a polar molecule has charged poles. In water (H_2O), for example, each hydrogen atom shares an electron with the single oxygen atom (FIG. 2-6). The oxygen nucleus exerts a stronger attraction on the electrons than does either hydrogen nucleus. By attracting electrons, the oxygen pole of a water molecule becomes slightly negative, leaving each hydrogen atom slightly positive.

TABLE 2-4	Electrons and Bonds in Atoms Common in Biological Molecules		
Atom	Capacity of Outer Electron Shell	Electrons in Outer Shell	Number of Covalent Bonds Usually Formed
Hydrogen (H)	2	1	1
Carbon (C)	8	4	4
Nitrogen (N)	8	5	3
Oxygen (O)	8	6	2
Sulfur (S)	8	6	2

Covalent Bonds May Produce Nonpolar or Polar Molecules

In all covalent bonds between atoms of the same element, and in covalent bonds between some pairs of atoms of different elements, the participating atoms share electrons equally or nearly equally. This creates **nonpolar covalent bonds** in which there is no charge on any part of the molecule. For example, two hydrogen atoms can become more stable if they share their outer electrons, allowing each to behave almost as if it had two electrons in its outer shell (FIG. 2-5). This reaction forms hydrogen gas (H_2).

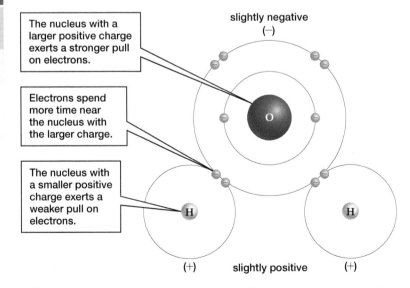

▲ FIGURE 2-6 **Polar covalent bonds** Oxygen (O) needs two electrons to fill its outer shell, allowing it to form covalent bonds with two hydrogen atoms (H), which produces water (H_2O). The oxygen atom exerts a greater pull on the electrons than do the hydrogen atoms, producing a slight negative charge near the oxygen and a slight positive charge near the two hydrogens.

Health WATCH

Free Radicals—Friends and Foes?

Any atom with a partially full outer electron shell will be reactive, but this reactivity increases dramatically if the unfilled shell also contains an uneven number of electrons. Like people, electrons like to pair up. Free radicals are molecules containing atoms with unpaired electrons in their outer shells. They react vigorously with other molecules, capturing or releasing electrons to achieve a more stable arrangement. Such reactions may result in damage to crucial biological molecules, including proteins and DNA.

Our bodies continuously produce oxygen-containing free radicals, such as hydrogen peroxide (H_2O_2), as a by-product of reactions that generate cellular energy. Free radicals are also formed when our cells are bombarded by sunlight, X-rays, radioactive isotopes, and various toxic chemicals in the environment. Our bodies counteract free radicals by generating **antioxidants,** molecules that react with free radicals and render them harmless. We also obtain antioxidants in our diets, since they occur naturally in many plant-derived foods. But when free radicals are produced that overwhelm the body's ability to counteract them, the resulting *oxidative stress* can injure cells. For example, free radicals generated by ultraviolet rays can damage DNA and promote skin cancer. Oxidative stress contributes to cardiovascular disease, lung disorders such as asthma, and neurological diseases, including Alzheimer's. The most visible signs of aging—graying hair from free radical damage to hair follicles and wrinkles that occur when ultraviolet rays from sunlight damage proteins in skin—are a result of oxidative stress (FIG. E2-3).

Strong evidence suggests that diets high in antioxidant-containing fruits and vegetables are associated with a lower incidence of cardiovascular disease and some cancers. Many people have concluded that a shortcut to health can be provided by antioxidant supplements such as vitamins C and E and beta-carotene (found in many fruits and vegetables). But an analysis that combined numerous studies using large groups of people showed no health benefits from taking these supplements and suggested that beta-carotene and vitamin E supplements may in some cases have adverse health effects. Why might this be?

During the course of evolution, organisms have continuously been exposed to free radicals and have evolved ways to both use them constructively and deactivate them. Free radicals are involved in regulating blood pressure, wound healing, and defense against disease-causing microbes. Growing evidence supports the hypothesis that health requires a complex balance of free radicals

and antioxidants and that the high doses of purified antioxidants in supplements can upset this delicate equilibrium. Fruits and vegetables contain natural antioxidants at levels generally well below those found in supplements, so it is most prudent to obtain antioxidants from a diet rich in fruits and vegetables (unless a medical condition requires using supplements).

What types of fruits and vegetables should you eat? While it's a stretch to put chocolate in the fruit or vegetable category, cocoa (a powder made from the cacao bean; FIG. E2-4) is especially rich in natural plant molecules called *flavonols*. Flavonols—also found in green tea, cranberries, apples, onions, kale, and other plant foods—possess antioxidant and other beneficial properties. Although it sounds almost too good to be true, controlled studies have reported beneficial effects of consuming dark chocolate (with a high percentage of cocoa) on risk factors for cardiovascular disease including high blood pressure. Several large studies on human populations have also found a correlation between higher consumption of chocolate and other flavonol-rich foods and a reduced incidence of cardiovascular disease, including high blood pressure, strokes, and heart attacks (correlation studies provide suggestive evidence, but are far less rigorous than controlled studies).

EVALUATE THIS At a physical exam, Thomas, a sedentary individual, was warned of dangerously high blood pressure. After reading that chocolate is good for cardiovascular health, he immediately stocked up on 6-oz dark chocolate bars and resolved to add one daily to his regular diet. Predict some results of his next annual physical exam and provide him with some good health advice.

▲ FIGURE E2-4 **Chocolate** This substance comes from cacao beans found inside pods (inset) that grow from the trunks of trees native to South America.

◀ FIGURE E2-3 **Free-radical damage** Free radicals interfere with the production of hair pigment and damage proteins that give skin its elasticity. The results? Gray or white hair and wrinkled skin.

Hydrogen Bonds Are Attractive Forces Between Certain Polar Molecules

Biological molecules, including sugars, proteins, and nucleic acids, often have many polar covalent bonds between either hydrogen and oxygen or hydrogen and nitrogen. In these cases, the hydrogen is slightly positive and the oxygen or nitrogen is slightly negative. As you know, opposite charges attract. A **hydrogen bond** is the attraction between the slightly positive and slightly negative regions of polar molecules. Hydrogen bonding occurs in water molecules between their slightly positive hydrogen poles and slightly negative oxygen poles, linking water molecules into a loosely connected, ever-changing network (**FIG. 2-7**). As you will see shortly, hydrogen bonds among water molecules give it several unusual properties that make water crucial for life as we know it.

CHECK YOUR LEARNING

Can you ...

- explain what makes an atom reactive?
- define *molecules* and *chemical bonds*?
- describe and provide examples of ionic, covalent, and hydrogen bonds?

2.3 WHY IS WATER SO IMPORTANT TO LIFE?

As naturalist Loren Eiseley eloquently stated, "If there is magic on this planet, it is contained in water." Water has many special properties that all result from the polarity of its molecules and the hydrogen bonds that form among them. What makes water unique?

Water Molecules Attract One Another

Hydrogen bonds interconnect water molecules. But, like square dancers continually moving from one partner to

▲ **FIGURE 2-7 Hydrogen bonds in water** The slight charges on opposite poles of water molecules (shown in parentheses) produce hydrogen bonds (dotted lines) between the oxygen and hydrogen atoms in adjacent water molecules. Each water molecule can form up to four hydrogen bonds. In liquid water, these bonds constantly break as new ones form.

the next, joining and releasing hands as they go, hydrogen bonds in liquid water constantly break and re-form, allowing water to flow. Hydrogen bonds among water molecules cause **cohesion,** the tendency for molecules of a single type to stick together; this causes water to form droplets (**FIG. 2-8a**). Cohesion also produces **surface tension,** the tendency for a water surface to resist being broken. Surface water molecules have nothing above them to bond with, so they are attracted more strongly to one another and to the water molecules

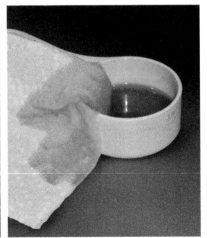

(a) Cohesion and adhesion   (b) Cohesion causes surface tension   (c) Capillary action

▲ FIGURE 2-8 **Water molecules have cohesive and adhesive properties (a)** Cohesion causes water to form droplets; adhesion sticks them to spiderweb silk. **(b)** This basilisk lizard uses surface tension as it races across the water's surface to escape a predator. **(c)** Cohesion and adhesion work together in capillary action, which draws water into narrow spaces among charged surfaces.

beneath them. For example, water brimming slightly above the top of a glass just before it overflows is caused by surface tension. Surface tension in a pond can support water insects and even a running basilisk lizard (**FIG. 2-8b**).

Water also exhibits **adhesion,** the tendency for different surfaces to cling to one another. Water adheres to substances whose molecules contain charged regions; these substances include glass, the cellulose in wood and paper, and the silk of spiderwebs (see Fig. 2-8a).

When water is attracted onto a surface by adhesion and then draws more water molecules along by cohesion, this produces **capillary action.** During capillary action, water moves spontaneously into very narrow spaces, such as those between the cellulose fibers of a paper towel (**FIG. 2-8c**).

The strong cohesion among polar water molecules plays a crucial role in the life of land plants. How does nutrient-laden water absorbed by a plant's roots ever reach its leaves, especially if the plant is a 300-foot-tall redwood tree? Water fills tubes that connect the roots, stem, and leaves. As water molecules continuously evaporate from leaves, each pulls the water molecule below it to the leaf's surface, much like a chain being dragged up from the top. The hydrogen bonds that link water molecules are stronger than the downward pull of gravity, so the water chain doesn't break. In addition, water adheres to the walls of the conducting tubes, which are composed of cellulose and are microscopically narrow. These properties allow capillary action to contribute to the transport of water from roots to leaves. Without the cohesion of water, there could be no large land plants, and life on Earth would be radically different.

Water Interacts with Many Other Molecules

A **solvent** is a substance that completely surrounds and disperses the individual atoms or molecules of another substance. When this occurs, the solvent is said to **dissolve** the substance it disperses. A solvent that contains one or more dissolved substances is called a **solution.** The positive and negative poles of water are attracted to charges on other polar molecules and ions, making water an excellent solvent. Polar molecules and ions are described as **hydrophilic** (Gk. *hydro,* water, and *phylos,* loving) because they are attracted to (and dissolve in) water.

A crystal of table salt, for example, is held together by ionic bonds between positively charged sodium ions (Na^+) and negatively charged chloride ions (Cl^-; see Fig. 2-4b). When a salt crystal is dropped into water, the positively charged hydrogen poles of water molecules are attracted to the Cl^-, and the negatively charged oxygen poles are attracted to the Na^+. As water molecules surround the ions, shielding them from interacting with each other, the ions separate from the crystal and drift away in the water—thus, the salt dissolves (**FIG. 2-9**).

Gases such as oxygen and carbon dioxide also dissolve in water even though they are nonpolar. How? These molecules are so small that they fit into the spaces between water

▲ **FIGURE 2-9 Water as a solvent** When a salt crystal (NaCl) is dropped into water, the water surrounds the sodium and chloride ions, with positive poles of water molecules facing the Cl^-, and the negative poles facing the Na^+. The ions disperse as the surrounding water molecules isolate them from one another, dissolving the salt crystal.

THINK CRITICALLY If you placed a salt crystal in a nonpolar liquid (like oil), would it dissolve?

molecules without disrupting the hydrogen bonds. The ability of water to dissolve oxygen allows fish to flourish, even when swimming under a layer of ice.

Larger molecules with nonpolar covalent bonds, such as fats and oils, are **hydrophobic** (Gk. *phobic,* fearing) and do not dissolve in water. Nevertheless, water has an important effect on such molecules. By sticking together, water molecules exclude oil molecules. The nonpolar oil molecules are forced together into drops, surrounded by water molecules that form hydrogen bonds with one another but not with the oil (**FIG. 2-10**).

◀ **FIGURE 2-10 Oil and water don't mix** Yellow oil poured into water remains in discrete droplets as it rises to the surface. Oil floats because it is less dense than water.

THINK CRITICALLY
Predict how a drop of water on an oil-coated surface would differ in shape from a drop on a clean glass surface.

HAVE YOU EVER WONDERED...

The slap of a belly flop provides firsthand experience of the power of cohesion among water molecules. Because of the hydrogen bonds that interconnect its molecules, the water surface resists being broken. When you suddenly force a large number of water molecules apart with your belly, the result can be a bit painful. Do you think that belly-flopping into a pool of (nonpolar) vegetable oil would hurt as much? If you encountered a deep pool filled with vegetable oil, could you float or swim in it?

> ### Why It Hurts So Much to Do a Belly Flop?

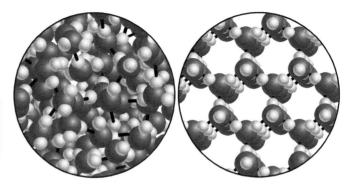

▲ **FIGURE 2-11** Liquid water (left) and ice (right)

THINK CRITICALLY How do these configurations explain why ice floats?

Water Moderates the Effects of Temperature Changes

The hydrogen bonds linking water molecules (see Fig. 2-7) allow water to moderate temperature changes.

It Takes a Lot of Energy to Heat Water

The energy required to heat 1 gram of a substance by 1°C is called its **specific heat.** The specific heat of water is far higher than that of any other common substance. Why? At any temperature above absolute zero (−459°F or −273°C), all molecules are in constant motion. The warmer the substance, the faster its molecules move. But forcing water molecules to speed up requires breaking their hydrogen bonds more frequently. Breaking the bonds consumes a considerable amount of energy, and so less energy is available to raise the water's temperature. In contrast, when substances lack hydrogen bonds, a greater proportion of added energy is available to raise their temperatures. For example, a given amount of energy would increase the temperature of granite rock (which lacks hydrogen bonds) about five times as much as it would the same weight of water.

Because of its high specific heat, water moderates temperature changes. One reason you can sit on hot sand in the hot sun without instantly overheating is that your body is about 60% water, which must absorb considerable heat to change its temperature.

It Takes a Lot of Energy to Evaporate Water

Overheating still poses a real threat, however, because the molecules in our bodies function only within a narrow range of temperatures. We use another property of water when we perspire to maintain our body temperature in hot conditions. Water has an extremely high **heat of vaporization,** which is the amount of heat needed to cause a substance to evaporate (change from a liquid to a vapor). Because of the polar nature of water molecules, water must absorb enough energy to break the hydrogen bonds that interconnect its molecules before the molecules can move fast enough to escape and evaporate into the air. Water in sweat absorbs a great deal of body heat, and it cools us as its fastest-moving molecules vaporize.

Water Forms an Unusual Solid: Ice

Even solid water is unusual. Most liquids become denser when they solidify, but ice is actually less dense than liquid water. When water freezes, each molecule forms stable hydrogen bonds with four other water molecules, creating an open, hexagonal (six-sided) arrangement (FIG. 2-11). This keeps the water molecules farther apart than their average distance in liquid water. Thus, ice is less dense than liquid water, which is why icebergs and ice cubes float.

This property of water is crucial to the distribution of aquatic life. When a pond or lake starts to freeze in winter, the floating ice forms an insulating layer that delays the freezing of the rest of the water. This insulation allows fish and other aquatic organisms to survive in the liquid water below (FIG. 2-12). If ice were to sink, many ponds and lakes around the world would freeze solid from the bottom up during the winter, killing most of their inhabitants. The ocean floor at higher latitudes would be covered with extremely thick layers of ice that would never melt.

Water-Based Solutions Can Be Acidic, Basic, or Neutral

At any given time, a tiny fraction of water molecules (H_2O) will have split into hydroxide ions (OH^-) and hydrogen ions (H^+) (FIG. 2-13). Pure water contains equal concentrations of each.

CASE STUDY \ CONTINUED
Unstable Atoms Unleashed

The high specific heat of water makes it an ideal coolant for nuclear power plants. Compared to nonpolar liquids like alcohol, a great deal of heat is required to raise the temperature of water. The tsunami that hit the Fukushima power plant disrupted the electrical supply running the pumps that kept water circulating over the fuel rods. Without enough water to absorb the excess heat, the metal tubes surrounding the fuel rods melted.

◀ FIGURE 2-12 **Ice floats**
The floating ice insulates the water beneath it, helping to protect bodies of water from freezing solid and allowing fish and other organisms to survive beneath it.

water
(H₂O)

hydroxide ion
(OH⁻)

hydrogen ion
(H⁺)

▲ FIGURE 2-13 **Some water is always ionized**

When ion-forming substances that release OH⁻ or H⁺ are added to water, the solution no longer has equal concentrations of OH⁻ and H⁺. If the concentration of H⁺ exceeds the concentration of OH⁻, the solution is **acidic.** An **acid** is a substance that releases hydrogen ions when it dissolves in water. For example, when hydrochloric acid (HCl) is added to pure water, almost all of the HCl molecules separate into H⁺ and Cl⁻. Therefore, the concentration of H⁺ exceeds the concentration of OH⁻, and the resulting solution is acidic. Acidic substances—think lemon juice (containing citric acid) or vinegar (acetic acid)—taste sour because sour receptors on your tongue respond to excess H⁺.

If the concentration of OH⁻ is greater than the concentration of H⁺, the solution is **basic.** A **base** is a substance that

combines with hydrogen ions, reducing their number. If, for instance, sodium hydroxide (NaOH) is added to water, the NaOH molecules separate into Na⁺ and OH⁻. Some OH⁻ ions combine with H⁺ to produce H₂O, reducing the number of H⁺ ions and creating a basic solution. Bases are used in many cleaning solutions. Bases are also in many antacids like Tums to neutralize heartburn caused by excess hydrochloric acid in the stomach.

The **pH scale** of 0 to 14 measures how acidic or basic a solution is (**FIG. 2-14**). Neutral pH (equal concentrations of H⁺ and OH⁻) is 7. Pure water has a pH of 7, acids have a pH below 7, and bases have a pH above 7. Each unit on the pH scale represents a tenfold change in the concentration of H⁺. Thus, the concentration of H⁺ is 10,000 times greater in a soft drink with a pH of 3 than in water (pH 7).

A **buffer** is a molecule that tends to maintain a solution at a nearly constant pH by accepting or releasing H⁺ in response to small changes in H⁺ concentration. In the presence of excess H⁺, a buffer combines with the H⁺, reducing its concentration. In the presence of excess OH⁻, buffers release H⁺, which

▲ FIGURE 2-14 **The pH scale** The pH scale reflects the concentration of hydrogen ions in a solution. Notice that pH (upper scale; 0–14) is the negative log of the H⁺ concentration (lower scale). Each unit on the scale represents a tenfold change. Lemon juice, for example, is about 10 times more acidic than orange juice.

combines with the OH⁻ to form H_2O. Humans and other mammals maintain a pH in body fluids that is just slightly basic (about 7.4). If your blood became as acidic as 7.0 or as basic as 7.8, you would likely die because even small changes in pH cause drastic changes in both the structure and function of biological molecules. Nevertheless, living cells seethe with chemical reactions that take up or release H^+. The pH of body fluids remains remarkably constant because it is controlled by several different buffers.

CHECK YOUR LEARNING

Can you ...

- describe the unique properties of water and the importance of these properties to life?
- explain how polar covalent and hydrogen bonds contribute to the unique properties of water?
- explain the concept of pH and how acids, bases, and buffers affect solutions?

CASE STUDY \ REVISITED

Unstable Atoms Unleashed

Scientists believe that the isotopes of uranium were forged in the explosion of a star and became incorporated into Earth as our solar system formed. Today, the radioactive form of this rare element is mined and concentrated to help satisfy humanity's unquenchable desire for energy.

The chain reaction that generates heat in nuclear power plants begins when neutrons are released from radioactive uranium. These bombard other uranium atoms and cause them to split, in a self-sustaining chain reaction. When the tsunami struck the Fukushima plant, neutron-absorbing rods were immediately lowered around the fuel, halting the chain reaction. But the breakdown of uranium generates additional radioactive isotopes, and these continued to spontaneously decay and generate heat. This caused the disastrous breach that released these isotopes into the environment. One isotope of particular concern is radioactive iodine.

Iodine enters the body in food and water. It becomes concentrated in the thyroid gland, which uses iodine to synthesize thyroid hormone. Unfortunately, the thyroid gland does not distinguish between radioactive and non-radioactive iodine. Children exposed

to radioactive iodine are at increased risk for thyroid cancer, which may occur decades after exposure. To help protect them, Japanese authorities distributed iodine tablets to children near the failed reactor. This non-radioactive iodine saturates the thyroid, which then does not take up the radioactive form. Only time will reveal the full health effects of the fallout from Fukushima.

CONSIDER THIS The Fukushima disaster led to a reassessment of safety precautions in nuclear power plants and a worldwide dialogue about the dangers of nuclear power, which also generates waste that remains radioactive for thousands of years. How can societies evaluate and compare the safety of nuclear power versus the safety of burning fossil fuels, from which humanity currently gets most of its energy? How can one compare the possibility of events that might cause a nuclear disaster—such as a magnitude 9 earthquake or the accidental escape of radioactive waste—with the certainty of continued carbon dioxide emissions and global climate change resulting from fossil fuel use? To what extent should societies invest in renewable energy, including wind and solar power?

CHAPTER REVIEW

 Go to **MasteringBiology** for practice quizzes, activities, eText, videos, current events, and more.

Answers to Think Critically, Evaluate This, Multiple Choice, and Fill-in-the-Blank questions can be found in the Answers section at the back of the book.

Summary of Key Concepts

2.1 What Are Atoms?

An element is a substance that can neither be broken down nor converted to different substances by ordinary chemical reactions. The smallest particle of an element is the atom, which is composed of positively charged protons, uncharged neutrons, and negatively charged electrons. All atoms of a given element have the same unique number of protons. Neutrons and protons cluster to form atomic nuclei. Electrons orbit the nucleus within regions called electron shells. Shells at increasing distances from the nucleus contain electrons with increasing amounts of energy. Each shell can contain a fixed maximum number of electrons. An atom is most stable when its outermost shell is full. Isotopes are atoms of the same element with different numbers of neutrons. Nuclei of

radioactive isotopes spontaneously break down, forming new elements and releasing energy and often subatomic particles.

2.2 How Do Atoms Interact to Form Molecules?

Atoms gain stability by filling or emptying their outer electron shells. They do this by acquiring, losing, or sharing electrons during chemical reactions. This produces attractive forces called chemical bonds, which link atoms to form molecules.

There are three types of bonds: ionic, covalent, and hydrogen. Ions are atoms that have lost or gained electrons. Ionic bonds link negatively and positively charged ions in crystals. Covalent bonds form when atoms fill their outer electron shells by sharing electrons. In a nonpolar covalent bond, the two atoms share electrons equally. In a polar covalent bond, one atom attracts electrons more strongly than the other atom does, giving the molecule slightly positive and negative poles. Polar covalent bonds allow hydrogen bonding, the attraction between the slightly positive hydrogen of one molecule and the slightly negative regions of other polar molecules.

2.3 Why Is Water So Important to Life?

Water's unique properties allowed life as we know it to evolve. Water is polar and dissolves polar substances and ions. Water forces nonpolar substances, such as oil, to form clumps. Water molecules cohere to each other using hydrogen bonds, producing surface tension. Water also adheres to other polar surfaces. Water's extremely high specific heat and high heat of vaporization function in some animals to maintain relatively stable body temperatures despite large outside temperature fluctuations. Water is unusual in being less dense in its frozen than in its liquid state.

Pure water contains equal numbers of H^+ and OH^- (pH 7), but dissolved substances can make solutions acidic (more H^+ than OH^-) or basic (more OH^- than H^+). Buffers help maintain a constant pH.

Key Terms

acid *29*	heat of vaporization *28*
acidic *29*	hydrogen bond *26*
adhesion *27*	hydrophilic *27*
antioxidant *25*	hydrophobic *27*
atom *19*	ion *23*
atomic nucleus *19*	ionic bond *24*
atomic number *20*	isotope *20*
base *29*	mass number *19*
basic *29*	molecule *22*
buffer *29*	neutron *19*
capillary action *27*	nonpolar covalent bond *24*
chemical bond *23*	periodic table *20*
chemical reaction *19*	pH scale *29*
cohesion *26*	polar covalent bond *24*
covalent bond *24*	proton *19*
dissolve *27*	radioactive *20*
electron *19*	solution *27*
electron shell *20*	solvent *27*
element *19*	specific heat *28*
free radical *23*	surface tension *26*

Thinking Through the Concepts

Multiple Choice

1. Which of the following is False?
   a. An element is defined by its atomic number.
   b. Ninety-two elements occur naturally.
   c. An atom consists of subatomic particles.
   d. Electron shells increase in energy closer to the nucleus.

2. The mass number of an element is equal to
   a. the mass of its atom's protons and neutrons.
   b. the mass of its atom's neutrons.
   c. the mass of its atom's protons.
   d. its atomic number.

3. Isotopes are defined as atoms of
   a. the same element with different numbers of protons.
   b. radioactive elements.
   c. stable elements.
   d. the same element with different numbers of neutrons.

4. Molecules
   a. always consist of different elements bonded together.
   b. may be polar or nonpolar.
   c. may be held together entirely by hydrogen bonds.
   d. cannot be held together by ionic bonds.

5. Covalent bonds
   a. link water molecules in ice.
   b. create only nonpolar molecules.
   c. bind sodium and chlorine in table salt.
   d. link hydrogen to oxygen in water.

Fill-in-the-Blank

1. An atom consists of an atomic nucleus composed of positively charged _____ and uncharged _____. Orbiting around the nucleus are _____ that occupy discrete spaces called _____.

2. An atom that has lost or gained one or more electrons is called a(n) _____. If an atom loses an electron it takes on a(n) _____ charge. Atoms with opposite charges attract one another, forming _____ bonds.

3. Atoms of the same element that differ in the number of neutrons in their nuclei are called _____. Some of these atoms spontaneously break apart, and in this process, they sometimes become different _____. Atoms that behave this way are described as being _____.

4. An atom with an outermost electron shell that is either completely full or empty is described as _____. Atoms with partially full outer electron shells are _____. Covalent bonds are formed when atoms _____ electrons, filling their outer shells.

5. Water is described as _____ because each water molecule has slightly negative and positive poles. This property allows water molecules to form _____ bonds with one another. The bonds between water molecules give water a high _____ that produces surface tension.

Review Questions

1. Based on Table 2-1, how many neutrons are there in oxygen? In hydrogen? In nitrogen?

2. Distinguish between atoms and molecules and among protons, neutrons, and electrons.

3. Compare and contrast covalent bonds and ionic bonds.

4. Explain how polar covalent bonds allow hydrogen bonds to form, and provide an example.

5. Why can water absorb a great amount of heat with little increase in its temperature? What is this property called?

6. Describe how water dissolves a salt.

7. Define *pH scale, acid, base,* and *buffer.* How do buffers reduce changes in pH when hydrogen ions or hydroxide ions are added to a solution? Why is this phenomenon important in organisms?

Applying the Concepts

1. Detergents help clean by dispersing fats and oils in water so that they can be rinsed away. What general chemical structures (for example, polar or nonpolar parts) must a soap or detergent have, and why?

2. What do people mean when they say, "It's not the heat, it's the humidity"? Why does high humidity make a hot day less bearable?

3. Artificial ice cubes ("whiskey stones") made of granite can be cooled in your freezer and used in drinks. Would these cool drinks more or less effectively than an equal weight of ice cubes from the same freezer? Explain.

3

BIOLOGICAL MOLECULES

Friends don't eat friends. Mad cow disease may have emerged as a result of cows eating feed containing protein from the remains of sheep infected with scrapie.

Puzzling Proteins

"YOU KNOW, LISA, I think something is wrong with me," Charlene Singh told her sister. The vibrant 22-year-old scholarship winner had begun to lose her memory and experience mood swings. During the next 3 years, her symptoms worsened. Singh's hands shook, she was subject to uncontrollable episodes of biting and striking people, and she became unable to walk or swallow. Ultimately, Charlene Singh became the first U.S. resident to die of the human form of mad cow disease, which she had almost certainly contracted more than 10 years earlier while living in England.

It was not until the mid-1990s that health officials recognized that mad cow disease, or BSE (bovine spongiform encephalitis), could spread to people who ate meat from infected cattle. Although millions of people may have eaten tainted beef, fewer than 200 people worldwide have contracted the human version of BSE, called vCJD (variant Creutzfeldt-Jakob disease; CJD is a human genetic disorder with similar symptoms). For those infected, however, the disease is always fatal, riddling the brains of people and cows with microscopic holes that give the brain a spongy appearance.

Where did mad cow disease come from? One hypothesis is that it was derived from a disease in sheep called scrapie, whose symptoms are almost identical to those of BSE. Scrapie was named after the tendency of infected sheep to scrape off their wool. They also lose weight and coordination and may become nervous or aggressive, and their brains become spongy. A mutated form of scrapie may have become capable of infecting cattle, perhaps in the early 1980s. At that time, cattle feed often included parts from sheep, some of which may have harbored scrapie. BSE was first identified in British cattle in 1986, and the use of sheep, cow, and goat parts in cattle feed was banned in 1988. In 1996 British beef exports were temporarily halted after experts confirmed that the disease could spread to people who ate infected meat. As a precautionary measure at that time, more than 4.5 million cattle in Britain were slaughtered and their bodies were burned—a tragedy for British farmers.

Why is mad cow disease particularly fascinating to scientists? In the early 1980s, Dr. Stanley Prusiner, a researcher at the University of California–San Francisco, provided evidence that a protein caused scrapie and that this protein could transmit the disease to experimental animals. He dubbed the infectious proteins "prions" (pronounced PREE-ons). No entity lacking genetic material (DNA or RNA) had ever been shown to be contagious before, and Prusiner's results were initially met with skepticism. But after other scientists confirmed them, his findings expanded our understanding of the importance of proteins.

What are proteins? How do they differ from DNA and RNA? How can a protein infect another organism, increase in number, and produce a fatal disease? Are BSE and vCJD still a threat?

AT A GLANCE

3.1 WHY IS CARBON SO IMPORTANT IN BIOLOGICAL MOLECULES?

You have probably seen fruits and vegetables in the supermarket labeled as "organic," meaning that they were grown without synthetic fertilizers or pesticides. But in chemistry, the word **organic** describes molecules that always contain carbon and usually contain oxygen and hydrogen. Many organic molecules are synthesized by organisms, hence the name organic. In contrast, **inorganic** molecules lack carbon atoms (examples are water and salt). Inorganic molecules, such as those that make up Earth's rocks and metal deposits, are far less diverse and generally much simpler than organic molecules.

Life is characterized by an amazing variety of **biological molecules,** which we define as all molecules produced by living things. Nearly all of these are based on the carbon atom. Biological molecules interact in dazzlingly complex ways that are governed by the chemical properties that arise from their structures. As molecules within cells interact with one another, their structures and chemical properties change. Collectively, these precisely orchestrated changes give cells the ability to acquire and use nutrients, eliminate wastes, move and grow, and reproduce. This complexity is made possible by the versatile carbon atom.

The Bonding Properties of Carbon Are Key to the Complexity of Organic Molecules

As described in Chapter 2, atoms whose outermost electron shells are only partially filled tend to react with one another, gaining stability by filling their shells and forming covalent bonds. Depending on the number of vacancies in their outer shells, two atoms can share two, four, or six electrons—forming a single, double, or triple covalent bond (**FIG. 3-1**). The bonding patterns in the four most common types of atoms found in biological molecules are shown in **FIGURE 3-2**. Covalent bonds are represented by solid lines drawn between atomic symbols.

The bonding versatility of the carbon atom is key to the tremendous variety of biological molecules that make life on Earth possible. The carbon atom (C) has four electrons in its outermost shell, which can accommodate eight electrons. Carbons readily form single or double bonds with each other,

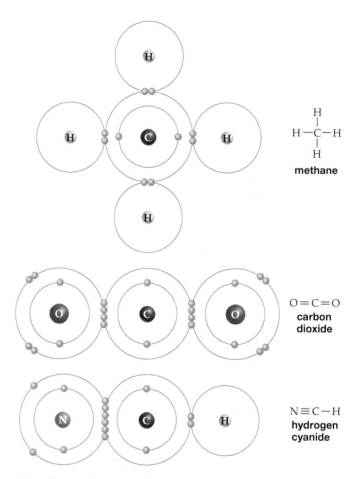

▲ **FIGURE 3-1 Covalent bonding by carbon atoms** Carbon must form four covalent bonds to fill its outer electron shell and become stable. It can do this by forming single, double, or triple covalent bonds. In these examples, carbon forms methane (CH_4), carbon dioxide (CO_2), and hydrogen cyanide (HCN).

THINK CRITICALLY Which of these is/are polar molecules? (You may need to refer back to Chapter 2.)

▶ **FIGURE 3-2 Bonding patterns** The bonding patterns of the four most common atoms in biological molecules. Each line indicates a covalent bond.

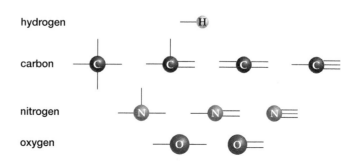

but can also bond with two, three, or four other atoms (see Fig. 3-1). Additional diversity arises from the range of complex shapes that organic molecules can assume, including branched chains, rings, sheets, and helices.

Functional Groups Attach to the Carbon Backbone of Organic Molecules

Functional groups are commonly occurring atoms or groups of atoms that are attached to the carbon backbone of organic molecules. Functional groups are less stable than the carbon backbone and are more likely to participate in chemical reactions. The functional groups in biological molecules endow them with unique properties and tendencies to react with other molecules. TABLE 3-1 describes seven functional groups that are important in biological molecules.

CHECK YOUR LEARNING

Can you ...

- define *organic* molecules and explain why carbon is so important to life?
- explain why functional groups are important in biological molecules?
- name and describe the properties of seven functional groups?

3.2 HOW ARE LARGE BIOLOGICAL MOLECULES SYNTHESIZED?

Although a complex molecule could be made by laboriously attaching one atom after another, the machinery of life works far more efficiently by preassembling molecular subunits and hooking them together. Just as trains are made by joining a series of train cars, small organic molecules (for example, sugars or amino acids) are joined to form large biological molecules (for example, starches or proteins). The individual subunits are called **monomers** (Gk. *mono,* one); chains of monomers are called **polymers** (Gk. *poly,* many).

Biological Polymers Are Formed by the Removal of Water and Broken Down by the Addition of Water

The subunits of large biological molecules are usually joined by a chemical reaction called **dehydration synthesis,** literally meaning "removing water to put together." In dehydration synthesis, a hydrogen ion (H^+) is removed from one subunit and a hydroxyl ion (OH^-) is removed from a second subunit, leaving openings in the

---

TABLE 3-1	Important Functional Groups in Biological Molecules		
Group	**Structure**	**Properties**	**Found In**
Hydroxyl	—O—H	Polar; involved in dehydration and hydrolysis reactions; forms hydrogen bonds	Sugars, polysaccharides, nucleic acids, alcohols, some amino acids, steroids
Carbonyl	O / C	Polar; makes parts of molecules hydrophilic (water soluble)	Sugars (linear forms), steroid hormones, peptides and proteins, some vitamins
Carboxyl (ionized form)	O / C / O	Polar and acidic; the negatively charged oxygen may bond H^+, forming carboxylic acid (—COOH); involved in peptide bonds	Amino acids, fatty acids, carboxylic acids (such as acetic and citric acids)
Amino	H / N \ H	Polar and basic; may become ionized by binding a third H^+; involved in peptide bonds	Amino acids, nucleic acids, some hormones
Sulfhydryl	—S—H	Nonpolar; forms disulfide bonds in proteins	Cysteine (an amino acid), many proteins
Phosphate (ionized form)	O / O—P—O / O	Polar and acidic; links nucleotides in nucleic acids; forms high-energy bonds in ATP (ionized form occurs in cells)	Phospholipids, nucleotides, nucleic acids
Methyl	H / H—C—H / H	Nonpolar; may be attached to nucleotides in DNA (methylation), changing gene expression	Steroids, methylated nucleotides in DNA

(a) Dehydration synthesis

(b) Hydrolysis

▲ **FIGURE 3-3 Dehydration synthesis and hydrolysis** Biological polymers are formed by **(a)** linking monomer subunits in a reaction that removes H_2O from polar functional groups. These polymers may be broken apart by adding the atoms in H_2O **(b)**, which recreates the subunits.

outer electron shells of atoms in the two subunits. These openings are filled when the subunits share electrons, creating a covalent bond that links them. The hydrogen ion

and the hydroxyl ion combine to form a molecule of water (H_2O), as shown in **FIGURE 3-3a**.

The reverse reaction is hydrolysis (Gk. *hydro,* water, and *lysis,* break apart). **Hydrolysis** breaks apart the molecule into its original subunits, with water donating a hydrogen ion to one subunit and a hydroxyl ion to the other (**FIG. 3-3b**). Digestive enzymes use hydrolysis to break down food. For example, enzymes in our saliva and small intestines promote hydrolysis of starch, which consists of a chain of sugar molecules, into individual sugar molecules that can be absorbed into the body.

Although there is a tremendous diversity of biological molecules, nearly all fall into one of four general categories: carbohydrates, proteins, nucleic acids, and lipids (**TABLE 3-2**).

CHECK YOUR LEARNING
Can you ...
- name and describe the reactions that create and break apart biological polymers?

TABLE 3-2	Four Principal Classes of Biological Molecules		
Name and General Structure	**Types**	**Example(s)**	**Typical Function**
Carbohydrates: Molecules composed primarily of C, H, and O in the ratio $(CH_2O)_n$, where *n* is the number of C's in the molecule's backbone. **Subunit:** Monosaccharide	**Monosaccharides:** Simple sugars	Glucose, fructose	Short-term energy storage in plants
	Disaccharides: Two linked monosaccharides	Sucrose	
	Polysaccharides: Polymers of monosaccharides	Starch, glycogen	Long-term energy storage in plants and animals, respectively
		Cellulose, chitin	Structural support in plants and arthropods, respectively
Proteins: Molecules with one or more chains of amino acids. Proteins have up to four levels of structure. **Subunit:** Amino acid	**Peptides:** Short chains of amino acids	Insulin, oxytocin	Hormones involved in blood sugar regulation and reproduction, respectively
	Polypeptides: Long chains (polymers) of amino acids	Hemoglobin	Oxygen transport
		Keratin	Structural component of hair
Nucleic acids: Molecules composed of polymers of nucleotides, each consisting of a simple sugar, an N-containing base, and a phosphate group. **Subunit:** Nucleotide	**Deoxyribonucleic acid (DNA):** A polymer of nucleotides whose simple sugar is deoxyribose	DNA	Codes for genetic information
	Ribonucleic acids (RNA): Polymers of nucleotides whose simple sugar is ribose	Messenger RNA, transfer RNA, ribosomal RNA	Work together to form proteins from amino acids based on nucleotide sequences in DNA
Lipids: Diverse group of molecules containing non-polar (hydrophobic) regions that make them insoluble in water. **Subunit:** No consistent subunit; not polymers	**Fats, oils, and waxes:** Contain one or more fatty acids, hydrophobic chains of carbon atoms that terminate in a carboxylic acid functional group	Animal fats, vegetable oils	Long-term energy storage in animals and plants, respectively
		Beeswax	Structural component of bee hives
	Phospholipids: Contain two fatty acids (hydrophobic) and two hydrophilic functional groups, one of which is phosphate	Lecithin	Structural component of cell membranes
	Steroids: Contain four rings of carbon atoms, with different functional groups attached	Cholesterol	Component of cell membranes
		Testosterone, estrogen	Male and female sex hormones, respectively

3.3 WHAT ARE CARBOHYDRATES?

Carbohydrate molecules are composed of carbon, hydrogen, and oxygen in the approximate ratio of 1:2:1. This ratio explains the origin of the word "carbohydrate," which literally means "carbon plus water." All carbohydrates are either small, water-soluble **sugars** or polymers of sugar, such as starch. If a carbohydrate consists of just one sugar molecule, it is called a **monosaccharide** (Gk. *mono,* one, and *saccharum,* sugar). When two monosaccharides are linked, they form a **disaccharide.** For example, sucrose, or table sugar, is a disaccharide composed of fructose and glucose. If you've stirred sugar into coffee, you know that sugar dissolves in water. Sugar molecules are hydrophilic; their hydroxyl functional groups are polar and form hydrogen bonds with polar water molecules (**FIG. 3-4**).

▼ FIGURE 3-4 **Sugar dissolving in water** Glucose dissolves as the polar hydroxyl groups of each sugar molecule form hydrogen bonds with nearby water molecules.

Different Monosaccharides Have Slightly Different Structures

Monosaccharides have a backbone of three to seven carbon atoms. Most of these carbon atoms have both a hydrogen (—H) and a hydroxyl group (—OH) attached to them; therefore, carbohydrates generally have the approximate chemical formula $(CH_2O)_n$, where n is the number of carbons in the backbone. When a sugar molecule is dissolved in water, such as inside a cell, its carbon backbone usually forms a ring.

Glucose is the most common monosaccharide in organisms and the primary energy source of cells. Glucose has six carbons, so its chemical formula is $C_6H_{12}O_6$. Figure 3-4 and **FIGURE 3-5** show various ways of depicting the chemical structure of glucose; keep in mind that any unlabeled "joint" in a ring or chain actually represents a carbon atom.

Many organisms synthesize other monosaccharides that have the same chemical formula as glucose but slightly different structures. For example, some plants store energy in *fructose* (L. *fruct,* fruit), which we consume in fruits, juices, honey, corn syrup, and soft drinks. *Galactose* is secreted by mammals in their milk as an energy source for their young (**FIG. 3-6**). Fructose and galactose must be converted to glucose before cells can use them as a source of energy.

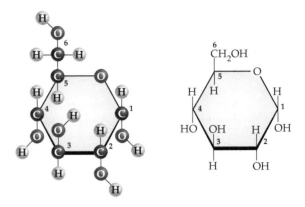

▲ FIGURE 3-5 **Depictions of chemical structures** The molecule glucose ($C_6H_{12}O_6$) can be drawn as (left) a ball-and-stick model showing each atom or (right) a simplified version in which each unlabeled joint is a carbon atom. The carbon atoms are numbered for reference. The space-filling structure of glucose is shown in Figure 3-4.

▲ FIGURE 3-6 **Some six-carbon monosaccharides**

Other common monosaccharides, such as ribose and deoxyribose (found in the nucleic acids of RNA and DNA, respectively), have five carbons. Notice in **FIGURE 3-7** that deoxyribose has one fewer oxygen atom than ribose because one of the hydroxyl groups in ribose is replaced by a hydrogen atom in deoxyribose.

▲ FIGURE 3-7 **Some five-carbon monosaccharides**

Disaccharides Consist of Two Monosaccharides Linked by Dehydration Synthesis

Monosaccharides can be linked by dehydration synthesis to form disaccharides or polysaccharides (**FIG. 3-8**). Disaccharides are often used for short-term energy storage in plants. When energy is required, the disaccharides are broken apart by hydrolysis into their monosaccharide

▲ FIGURE 3-8 **Synthesis of a disaccharide** Sucrose is synthesized by a dehydration reaction in which a hydrogen is removed from glucose and a hydroxyl group is removed from fructose. This forms water and leaves the two monosaccharide rings joined by single bonds to the remaining oxygen atom.

THINK CRITICALLY Describe hydrolysis of this molecule.

subunits (see Fig. 3-3) and converted to glucose, which is broken down further to release energy stored in its chemical bonds. Perhaps you had toast and coffee with cream and sugar for breakfast. You stirred *sucrose* (glucose plus fructose) into your coffee and then added cream containing *lactose* (glucose plus galactose). The disaccharide *maltose* (glucose plus glucose) is rare in nature, but it is formed when enzymes in your digestive tract hydrolyze starch, such as the wheat starch in your toast. Other digestive enzymes then hydrolyze each maltose into two glucose molecules that cells can absorb and break down to liberate energy.

If you've ever added Splenda or Equal to your coffee instead of sugar, you know that these artificial sweeteners contain few calories. How is this possible? We discuss artificial sweeteners and artificial fats in "Health Watch: Fake Foods" on page 38.

Polysaccharides Are Chains of Monosaccharides

A polymer of many monosaccharides is called a **polysaccharide.** Most polysaccharides do not dissolve in water at body temperatures because the polar hydroxyl groups of their sugars have been lost during dehydration synthesis, which links the monomers together and releases water (see Fig. 3-8). Despite their lack of solubility, polysaccharides can be hydrolyzed under the right conditions. For example, if you take a bite of a bagel and chew it for a minute or so, you may notice that it gradually tastes sweeter. This is because enzymes in saliva cause hydrolysis of the **starch** (a polysaccharide) in the bagel into its component glucose molecules, which dissolve in your saliva and stimulate receptors on your tongue that respond to sweetness. Plants often use starch (FIG. 3-9) as an energy-storage molecule. Starch, which

(a) Potato cells

(b) A starch molecule

(c) Detail of a starch molecule

▲ FIGURE 3-9 **Starch structure and function (a)** Starch grains inside potato cells store energy that will allow the potato to generate new plants in the spring. **(b)** A section of a single starch molecule. Starches consist of branched chains of up to half a million glucose subunits. **(c)** The precise structure of the circled portion of the starch molecule in (b). Notice the linkage between the individual glucose subunits for comparison with cellulose (Fig. 3-10).

Health WATCH

Fake Foods

People evolved to enjoy sweets and fats because they are high in the calories we need to survive. But in societies blessed with an overabundance of food, obesity is a serious health problem. In response, food scientists have modified biological molecules to make them noncaloric (FIG. E3-1). How are these fake food molecules made?

The artificial oil olestra, used in fat-free potato chips, tastes and feels similar to oil. The olestra molecule has a core of sucrose, but with six to eight fatty acids attached to its carbon atoms, which prevent digestive enzymes from breaking it down. Fat-soluble vitamins (A, D, E, and K) dissolve in olestra, so foods containing olestra are supplemented with small amounts of these vitamins to compensate. After its initial debut on grocery shelves, olestra became unpopular with consumers and has been largely phased out.

The sweetener sucralose (Splenda) is a modified sucrose molecule in which three hydroxyl groups are replaced with chlorine atoms. Aspartame (Equal, NutraSweet) is a combination of the amino acids aspartic acid and phenylalanine (see Figs. 3-14a, b). Both taste hundreds of times as sweet as the same amount of sugar.

High-fructose corn syrup is a fake food often substituted for sucrose in soft drinks because it is easier for manufacturers to work with. Although it does not occur in nature, high-fructose corn syrup very closely resembles sucrose (50% fructose + 50% glucose) but with fructose increased to 55%.

Are fake foods bad for you? Olestra interferes with the absorption of carotenoids (pigments with antioxidant properties) from fruits and vegetables, a possible drawback to eating it frequently. Products containing aspartame carry a warning for people with the rare genetic disorder phenylketonuria, which prevents them from metabolizing phenylalanine. There is no good scientific evidence that high-fructose corn syrup is more detrimental to health than the equivalent amount of sucrose, despite numerous popular press reports.

But our understanding of the health effects of fake foods is limited. Controlled studies of human nutrition are notoriously difficult to design and interpret correctly. Hundreds of recent nutritional studies have reached conclusions that differ considerably and often seem contradictory, due to differences in study groups, sample sizes, methods, controls, and interpretation of the results. The ways in which the human body processes food are staggeringly complex and differ among individuals. Although studies using laboratory animals can be far better controlled, their results may not directly apply to people. Nonetheless, the popular press often pounces on conclusions that can be stated most dramatically in headlines, often omitting important caveats by the investigators. The bottom line? Get your health information from reliable sources and be aware that even expert opinions in this field often change. There is no magic bullet for weight loss, and everything you eat has consequences for your body. The safest approach is to use moderation in consuming natural sugars and fats as well as the fake foods that might replace them.

▲ FIGURE E3-1 Artificial foods Products made with artificial sweeteners and olestra are marketed to people trying to control their weight.

EVALUATE THIS A 19-year-old 6′ 2″ male weighing 297 pounds comes to his doctor's office with high blood sugar, a symptom of adult-onset diabetes (often associated with obesity), and claims to have an insatiable sweet tooth. He proposes to switch to sugar-free cakes and donuts. What advice should the doctor give him?

---

is commonly formed in roots and seeds, consists of branched chains of up to half a million glucose subunits. **Glycogen,** a short-term energy-storage molecule in animals (including people), is also a chain of glucose subunits but is much more highly branched than starch. Glycogen is stored primarily in the liver and muscles.

Many organisms use polysaccharides as structural materials. One of the most important structural polysaccharides is **cellulose,** which makes up most of the walls of the living cells of plants, the fluffy white bolls of cotton plants, and about half the dry weight of tree trunks (FIG. 3-10). Scientists estimate that plants synthesize about a trillion tons

of cellulose each year, making it the most abundant organic molecule on Earth.

Cellulose, like starch, is a polymer of glucose, but in cellulose, every other glucose is "upside down," as you will see when you compare Figure 3-9c with Figure 3-10d. Although most animals easily digest starch, no vertebrates synthesize an enzyme that can attack the bonds between glucose molecules in cellulose. A few animals, such as cows and termites, harbor cellulose-digesting microbes in their digestive tracts and can benefit from the glucose subunits that the microbes release. In humans, cellulose fibers pass intact through the digestive system; cellulose supplies no

(a) Cellulose is a major component of wood

(b) A plant cell with a cell wall

(c) A close-up of cellulose fibers in a cell wall

Hydrogen bonds cross-linking cellulose molecules.

Alternating bond configuration differs from starch.

bundle of cellulose molecules

cellulose fiber

(d) Detail of a cellulose molecule

▲ FIGURE 3-10 **Cellulose structure and function (a)** Wood in this 3,000-year-old bristlecone pine is primarily cellulose. **(b)** Cellulose forms the cell wall that surrounds each plant cell. **(c)** Plant cell walls often consist of cellulose fibers in layers that run at right angles to each other to resist tearing in both directions. **(d)** Cellulose is composed of up to 10,000 glucose subunits. Compare this structure with Figure 3-9c and notice that every other glucose molecule in cellulose is "upside down."

nutrients but provides roughage with several digestive benefits.

Another supportive polysaccharide is **chitin,** which makes up the outer coverings (exoskeletons) of insects, crabs, and spiders. Chitin also stiffens the cell walls of many fungi, including mushrooms. Chitin is similar to cellulose, except the glucose subunits bear a nitrogen-containing functional group (FIG. 3-11).

Carbohydrates may also form parts of larger molecules; for example, the plasma membrane that surrounds each cell

▶ FIGURE 3-11 **Chitin structure and function** Chitin has the same glucose bonding configuration as cellulose, but the glucose subunits have a nitrogen-containing functional group replacing one of the hydroxyls. Chitin supports the otherwise soft bodies of arthropods (including spiders such as this one, insects, and crabs and their relatives) as well as most fungi.

is studded with proteins to which carbohydrates are attached. Nucleic acids (discussed later) also contain sugar molecules.

CHECK YOUR LEARNING

Can you ...

- describe the major types of carbohydrates?
- provide examples of each type of carbohydrate and explain how organisms use them?

3.4 WHAT ARE PROTEINS?

Like starches, **proteins** are biological polymers synthesized by linking simple subunits. Scientists estimate that the human body has between 250,000 and 1 million different proteins (**TABLE 3-3**). Most cells contain hundreds of different **enzymes,** which are proteins that promote specific chemical reactions. Other proteins are structural. *Keratin,* for example, forms hair, horns, nails, scales, and feathers (**FIG. 3-12**). Silk proteins are secreted by silk moths and spiders to make cocoons and webs, respectively. Nutritional proteins, such as albumin in egg white and casein in milk, provide amino acids to developing animals. The protein hemoglobin transports oxygen in the blood. Actin and myosin in muscle are contractile proteins that allow animal bodies to move. Some proteins are hormones (insulin and growth hormone, for example), others are antibodies (which help fight disease and infection), and a few are toxins (such as rattlesnake venom).

Proteins Are Formed from Chains of Amino Acids

The subunits of proteins are **amino acids.** There are 20 different amino acids commonly found in proteins, all of which have the same basic structure. A central carbon is bonded to a hydrogen atom and to three functional groups: a nitrogen-containing amino group ($-NH_2$), a

TABLE 3-3	Functions of Proteins
Function	**Example(s)**
Structural	Keratin (forms hair, nails, scales, feathers, and horns); silk (forms webs and cocoons)
Movement	Actin and myosin (found in muscle cells; allow contraction)
Defense	Antibodies (found in the bloodstream; fight disease organisms; some neutralize venoms); venoms (found in venomous animals; deter predators and disable prey)
Storage	Albumin (in egg white; provides nutrition for an embryo)
Signaling	Insulin (secreted by the pancreas; promotes glucose uptake into cells)
Catalyzing reactions	Amylase (found in saliva and the small intestine; digests carbohydrates)

▲ **FIGURE 3-13 Amino acid structure**

carboxylic acid group ($-COOH$), and an "R" group that varies among different amino acids (**FIG. 3-13**). The R group gives each amino acid distinctive properties (**FIG. 3-14**). Some amino acids are hydrophilic and water soluble because their R groups are polar. Others are hydrophobic, with nonpolar R groups that are insoluble in water. The amino acid cysteine (Fig. 3-14c) is unique in having a sulfur-containing (sulfhydryl) R group that can form covalent **disulfide bonds** with the sulfur of another cysteine molecule. These disulfide bonds play important roles in proteins, as described later.

(a) Hair

(b) Horn

(c) Silk

▲ **FIGURE 3-12 Structural proteins** Keratin is a common structural protein. It is the predominant protein found in **(a)** hair, **(b)** horn, and **(c)** the silk of a spiderweb.

O=C—OH | CH₂ | CH₂ | H₂N—C—C—OH | H O
glutamic acid (glu)

OH | C=O | CH₂ | H₂N—C—C—OH | H O
aspartic acid (asp)

⬡ | CH₂ | H₂N—C—C—OH | H O
phenylalanine (phe)

CH₃ CH₃ | CH | CH₂ | H₂N—C—C—OH | H O
leucine (leu)

SH | CH₂ | H₂N—C—C—OH | H O
cysteine (cys)

(a) Hydrophilic functional groups   **(b) Hydrophobic functional groups**   **(c) Sulfur-containing functional group**

▲ **FIGURE 3-14 Amino acid diversity** The diversity of amino acids is caused by the different R functional groups (green backgrounds), which may be **(a)** hydrophilic or **(b)** hydrophobic. **(c)** The R group of cysteine has a sulfur atom that can form covalent bonds with the sulfur in other cysteines.

THINK CRITICALLY Look up the rest of the amino acids and, based on their structures, identify three others that have hydrophobic functional groups.

Like polysaccharides and lipids, proteins are formed by dehydration synthesis. In proteins, the nitrogen in the amino group of one amino acid is joined to the carbon in the carboxylic acid group of another amino acid by a single covalent bond, and water is liberated (**FIG. 3-15**). This process forms a **peptide bond,** and the resulting chain of two amino acids is called a **peptide,** a term used for relatively short chains of amino acids (up to 50 or so). Additional amino acids are added, one by one, until a long *polypeptide* chain is completed. Polypeptide chains in cells can be up to thousands of amino acids in length. A protein consists of one or more polypeptide chains.

A Protein Can Have up to Four Levels of Structure

Interactions among amino acids and their R groups cause twists, folds, and interconnections that give proteins their three-dimensional structure. Up to four levels of well-defined protein structure are possible: primary, secondary, tertiary, and quaternary. The first three structures are characteristic of many proteins, and the fourth level occurs in proteins such as hemoglobin that include two or more polypeptide chains (**FIG. 3-16**). The sequence of amino acids in a protein is called its **primary structure** and is specified by genetic instructions in a cell's DNA (see Fig. 3-16a). The positions of specific amino acids in the sequence allow hydrogen bonds to form at particular sites within the polypeptide, causing it to assume a **secondary structure,** which is most commonly either a helix or a pleated sheet. These hydrogen bonds do not involve the R groups, but form between the slightly negative C=O (carbonyl) group in one amino acid and the slightly positive N—H group from an amino acid farther along the peptide chain (see the carbonyl group in Table 3-1 and on the right side of Figure 3-15). When such hydrogen bonds form between every fourth amino acid, they create the coils of the spring-like **helix** found in the polypeptide subunits of the hemoglobin molecule (see Fig. 3-16b). The keratin protein of hair also forms helices. Other proteins, such as silk, contain polypeptide chains that repeatedly fold back upon themselves, anchored by hydrogen bonds in

▲ **FIGURE 3-15 Protein synthesis** A dehydration reaction forms a peptide bond between the carbon of the carboxylic acid group of one amino acid and the nitrogen of the amino group of a second amino acid.

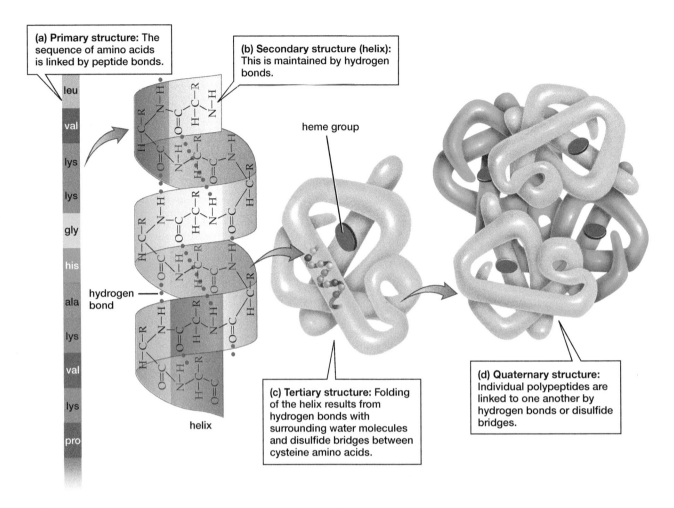

(a) Primary structure: The sequence of amino acids is linked by peptide bonds.

(b) Secondary structure (helix): This is maintained by hydrogen bonds.

heme group

hydrogen bond

helix

leu
val
lys
lys
gly
his
ala
lys
val
lys
pro

(c) Tertiary structure: Folding of the helix results from hydrogen bonds with surrounding water molecules and disulfide bridges between cysteine amino acids.

(d) Quaternary structure: Individual polypeptides are linked to one another by hydrogen bonds or disulfide bridges.

▲ **FIGURE 3-16 The four levels of protein structure** Hemoglobin is the oxygen-carrying protein in red blood cells. Red disks represent the iron-containing heme group that binds oxygen.

THINK CRITICALLY Why do many proteins, when heated excessively, lose their ability to function?

a **pleated sheet** arrangement (**FIG. 3-17a**). Silk proteins also contain disordered segments with no defined secondary structure that link their pleated sheets and allow silk to stretch (**FIG. 3-17b**).

CASE STUDY **CONTINUED**

Puzzling Proteins

Infectious prions such as those that cause mad cow disease are abnormally folded versions of a protein that is found throughout the body. The secondary structure of the normal prion protein is primarily helical. Infectious prions, however, fold into pleated sheets. The pleated sheets are so stable they are unaffected by the enzymes that break down normal prion protein. As a result, infectious prions accumulate destructively in the brain.

Helices and pleated sheets are the two major secondary structures of proteins. What do protein tertiary and quaternary structures look like?

Each protein also contorts into a **tertiary structure** (see Fig. 3-16c) determined by the protein's primary and secondary structure and also by its environment. For example, a protein in the watery interior of a cell folds in a roughly spherical way that exposes its hydrophilic amino acids to the water and buries its hydrophobic amino acids deeper within the molecule. These somewhat water-soluble *globular proteins* include hemoglobin, enzymes, and albumin in eggs. Tertiary structure also forms fibrous proteins such as the keratin in hair, hoofs, horns, and fingernails. Fibrous proteins are insoluble in water and contain many hydrophobic amino acids. In keratin, tertiary structure consists of paired helical strands held together by disulfide bonds that form between cysteines of each helical polypeptide (see Fig. E3-2 on page 44). The more disulfide bonds, the stiffer the keratin; for example, keratin in fingernails has more cysteine and more disulfide bonds than keratin in hair.

A fourth level of protein organization, called **quaternary structure,** occurs in proteins that contain individual polypeptides linked by hydrogen bonds, disulfide bonds, or attractions between oppositely charged portions of

▼ FIGURE 3-17 **The pleated sheet and the structure of silk protein (a)** In a pleated sheet, a single polypeptide chain is folded back upon itself repeatedly (the loops formed by these folds are not shown). Adjacent segments of the folded polypeptide are linked by hydrogen bonds (dotted lines). The R groups (green) project alternately above and below the sheet. **(b)** Silk protein contains stacks of pleated sheets connected by intrinsically disordered protein segments, which allow silk to stretch.

hydrogen bond

stack of pleated sheets   intrinsically disordered segment   strand of silk

(a) Secondary structure (pleated sheet)

(b) Structure of silk

different amino acids. Hemoglobin, for example, consists of four polypeptide chains held together by hydrogen bonds (see Fig. 3-16d). Each of the four polypeptides holds an iron-containing organic molecule called a heme group that can bind one molecule of oxygen. In keratin, quaternary structure links paired helical subunits into groups of eight.

Protein Function Is Determined by Protein Structure

The highly organized structures of many proteins are essential for their ability to function. Various enzymes, for example, fold in ways that only allow very specific molecules to interact with them, fitting together like a lock and key, as described in Chapter 6. Primary protein structure specifies the location of amino acids bearing specific R groups. In hemoglobin, for example, specific R groups must occur in precisely the right places to hold the heme group that binds oxygen. Interactions of hydrophilic and hydrophobic R groups with their watery environment are important in determining whether and how a protein will fold and what other molecules it can react with. A mutation that replaces a hydrophilic with a hydrophobic amino acid can sometimes cause significant distortion of the protein. For example, this type of mutation in hemoglobin causes the genetic disorder sickle-cell anemia (described in Chapters 11 and 13).

Many proteins, notably enzymes, hemoglobin, and structural proteins such as keratin, rely on a precise three-dimensional structure to perform their functions in the body. But there has recently been an explosion of interest and research into proteins or segments of protein with very flexible structures. These **intrinsically disordered proteins** have a precisely ordered primary structure dominated by hydro-

philic amino acids that float rather freely in their watery surroundings. As a result, they lack stable secondary and tertiary structure. Intrinsically disordered proteins are flexible and versatile; some can fold in various ways that allow them to interact with several different molecules, like master keys that fit several locks. But unlike rigid keys, intrinsically disordered proteins change their configuration as they bind different targets. For example, the protein p53 (see Chapter 9) has disordered segments that can bind multiple target molecules. This allows the p53 protein to regulate such diverse processes as cell division and the repair of defective DNA molecules.

A protein is described as **denatured** when its normal three-dimensional structure is destroyed, leaving its primary structure intact. For example, egg white consists of albumin protein, which is normally transparent and relatively fluid. But the heat of a frying pan rips its hydrogen bonds apart, destroying the albumin's secondary and tertiary structure and causing it to become opaque, white, and solid (FIG. 3-18). Keratin in hair is denatured by a permanent wave, as described in "Have You Ever Wondered: Why a Perm Is (Temporarily) Permanent?" on page 44. Bacteria and viruses can be destroyed by denaturing their proteins using heat, ultraviolet light, or solutions that are highly salty or acidic. Water is sometimes sterilized with ultraviolet light, and dill pickles are preserved from bacterial attack by their salty, acidic brine.

▲ FIGURE 3-18 **Heat denatures albumin**

HAVE YOU EVER
WONDERED...

Whether your hair is naturally straight or curly is determined by the properties of your hair follicles and the shape of the hair shafts they produce. The follicles of straight hair are round in cross section, whereas the follicles of curly hair are flatter. But genes are not destiny! You can create curls chemically.

Each hair consists of bundles within bundles of keratin (**FIG. E3-2**). Keratin's helical, spring-like secondary structure is created by hydrogen bonds, which are easily disrupted by the attraction of polar water molecules. So if you let wet straight hair dry on curlers, as the water disappears, new hydrogen bonds form among the keratin molecules in different places because of the distortion caused by the curler. But if it's rainy (or even humid), you can say goodbye to your hydrogen-bonded curls as the moisture disrupts them and your hair reverts to its natural straightness.

How is a permanent wave created? Keratin has lots of cysteine amino acids, and a perm alters the locations of the strong covalent disulfide bonds between cysteines. First, the hair is soaked in a solution that breaks the natural disulfide bonds linking adjacent keratin molecules. Set on curlers, the hair is then saturated with a different solution that causes disulfide bonds to re-form. The curlers force these bonds to form in new locations, and the strong disulfide bonds permanently maintain the curl (see Fig. E3-2). Genetically straight hair has been transformed into artificially curly hair—until new hair grows in.

> *Why a Perm Is (Temporarily) Permanent?*

▲ **FIGURE E3-2 A permanent distortion** A perm changes the location of covalent disulfide bonds between adjacent keratin molecules throughout the hair shaft, making it curl.

straight hair

permed hair

CHECK YOUR LEARNING

Can you ...

- describe protein subunits and how proteins are synthesized?
- explain the four levels of protein structure and why a protein's three-dimensional structure is important?
- list several functions of proteins and provide examples of proteins that perform each function?
- describe the properties of intrinsically disordered proteins?

3.5 WHAT ARE NUCLEOTIDES AND NUCLEIC ACIDS?

A **nucleotide** is a molecule with three parts: a five-carbon sugar, a phosphate functional group, and a nitrogen-containing **base.** The sugar may be either ribose or deoxyribose (see Fig. 3-7). The bases are composed of carbon and nitrogen atoms linked together in either a single ring (in the bases thymine, uracil, and cytosine) or double rings (in the bases adenine and guanine). A deoxyribose nucleotide with the adenine base is illustrated in **FIGURE 3-19**. Nucleotides may function as energy-carrier molecules, intracellular messenger molecules, or subunits of polymers called nucleic acids.

Some Nucleotides Act As Energy Carriers or Intracellular Messengers

Adenosine triphosphate (ATP) is a ribose nucleotide with three phosphate functional groups (**FIG. 3-20**). This molecule is formed in cells by reactions that release energy, such as the reaction that breaks down a sugar molecule. ATP stores energy in bonds between its phosphate groups and releases energy when the bond linking the last phosphate to the ATP molecule is broken. This energy is then available to drive energy-demanding reactions, such as linking amino acids to form proteins.

▲ **FIGURE 3-19 A deoxyribose nucleotide**

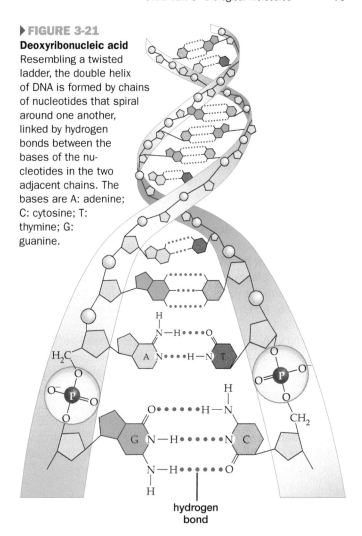

▲ **FIGURE 3-20** **The energy-carrier molecule adenosine triphosphate (ATP)**

The ribose nucleotide cyclic adenosine monophosphate (cAMP) acts as a messenger molecule in cells. Many hormones exert their effects by stimulating cAMP to form within cells, where it initiates a series of biochemical reactions (see Chapter 38).

Other nucleotides (such as NAD^+ and FAD) are known as *electron carriers* because they transport energy in the form of high-energy electrons. Their energy and electrons are used in ATP synthesis, for example, when cells break down sugar (see Chapter 8).

DNA and RNA, the Molecules of Heredity, Are Nucleic Acids

Single nucleotides (monomers) may be strung together in long chains by dehydration synthesis, forming polymers called **nucleic acids.** In nucleic acids, an oxygen atom in the phosphate functional group of one nucleotide is covalently bonded to the sugar of the next. The polymer of deoxyribose nucleotides, called **deoxyribonucleic acid (DNA),** can contain millions of nucleotides. A DNA molecule consists of two strands of nucleotides entwined in the form of a double helix and linked by hydrogen bonds (FIG. 3-21). DNA forms the genetic material of all cells. Its sequence of nucleotides, like the letters of a biological alphabet, spells out the genetic information needed to construct the proteins of each organism. Single-stranded chains of ribose nucleotides, called **ribonucleic acid (RNA),** are copied from the DNA and direct the synthesis of proteins (see Chapters 11 and 12).

▶ **FIGURE 3-21**
Deoxyribonucleic acid
Resembling a twisted ladder, the double helix of DNA is formed by chains of nucleotides that spiral around one another, linked by hydrogen bonds between the bases of the nucleotides in the two adjacent chains. The bases are A: adenine; C: cytosine; T: thymine; G: guanine.

hydrogen bond

CHECK YOUR LEARNING
Can you ...
- describe the general structure of nucleotides?
- list three different functions of nucleotides?
- explain how nucleic acids are synthesized?
- give two examples of nucleic acids and their functions?

CASE STUDY \ CONTINUED
Puzzling Proteins

All cells use DNA as a blueprint for producing more cells, and viruses use either DNA or RNA. Before the discovery of prions, however, no infectious agent had ever been discovered that completely lacked genetic material composed of nucleic acids. Scientists were extremely skeptical of the hypothesis that prion proteins could reproduce themselves, until repeated studies found no trace of genetic material associated with prions.

In addition to lacking genetic material, prions also lack another component that all other infectious agents possess: a surrounding membrane. What kinds of molecules are involved in the construction of membranes?

3.6 WHAT ARE LIPIDS?

Lipids are a diverse group of molecules that contain regions composed almost entirely of hydrogen and carbon, with nonpolar carbon–carbon and carbon–hydrogen bonds. These regions are hydrophobic, which makes lipids insoluble in water. Unlike carbohydrates, proteins, and nucleic acids, lipids are not formed by linking monomer subunits into polymers. Lipids can store energy, provide waterproof coatings on plants, form major components of cell membranes, or function as hormones. Lipids fall into three major groups: (1) oils, fats, and waxes, (2) phospholipids, and (3) steroids.

Oils, Fats, and Waxes Contain Only Carbon, Hydrogen, and Oxygen

Oils, fats, and waxes are built from only three types of atoms: carbon, hydrogen, and oxygen. Each contains one or more **fatty acids,** long chains of carbon and hydrogen with a carboxylic acid functional group (—COOH) at one end. Fats and oils are formed by dehydration synthesis linking three fatty acid subunits to one molecule of *glycerol,* a three-carbon molecule (**FIG. 3-22**). This structure gives fats and oils their chemical name: **triglycerides.**

Fats and **oils** are used primarily as energy-storage molecules; they contain more than twice as many calories per gram as do carbohydrates and proteins. Fats (such as butter and lard) are produced primarily by animals, whereas oils (found in corn, canola, olives, and avocados) are produced primarily by plants (**FIG. 3-23**). The difference between fats, which are solid at room temperature, and oils, which are liquid at room temperature, lies in the structure of their fatty acid subunits.

In fats, the carbons of fatty acids are linked entirely by single bonds, and the fatty acids are described as **saturated,** because they contain as many hydrogen atoms as possible. Saturated fatty acid chains are straight and can pack closely together, thus forming a solid at room temperature (**FIG. 3-24a**). If, however, some of the carbons are linked by double bonds and the fatty acids consequently contain fewer hydrogens, the fatty acids are **unsaturated.** The double

(a) Fat is stored prior to hibernation.   **(b) Avocado flesh is rich in oil.**

▲ FIGURE 3-23 **Energy storage (a)** A grizzly bear stores fat to provide both insulation and energy as he prepares to hibernate. If he stored the same amount of energy in carbohydrates, he would probably be unable to walk. **(b)** Oily avocado flesh likely originally evolved to entice enormous seed-dispersing mammals (such as giant ground sloths, extinct for about 10,000 years), which would swallow the seeds and excrete them intact.

bonds produce kinks in the fatty acid chains, which prevent oil molecules from packing closely together (**FIG. 3-24b**). The commercial process of hydrogenation—which breaks some of the double bonds and adds hydrogens to the carbons—can convert liquid oils to solids, but with health consequences (see "Health Watch: Cholesterol, *Trans* Fats, and Your Heart" on page 48).

▲ FIGURE 3-22 **Synthesis of a triglyceride** Dehydration synthesis links a single glycerol molecule with three fatty acids to form a triglyceride and three water molecules.

THINK CRITICALLY What kind of reaction breaks this molecule apart?

(a) A fat

(b) An oil

▲ FIGURE 3-24 **Fats and oils (a)** Fats have straight chains of carbon atoms in their fatty acid tails. **(b)** The fatty acid tails of oils have double bonds between some of their carbon atoms, creating kinks in the chains. Oils are liquid at room temperature because their kinky tails keep the molecules farther apart.

▲ **FIGURE 3-25 Waxes** Waxes are highly saturated lipids that remain solid at outdoor temperatures. Bees form wax into the hexagons of this honeycomb.

Although **waxes** are chemically similar to fats, humans and most other animals do not have the appropriate enzymes to break them down. Waxes are highly saturated and are solid at outdoor temperatures. They form a water repellent coating on the leaves and stems of land plants, and birds distribute waxy secretions over their feathers, causing them to shed water. Honey bees use waxes to build intricate honeycomb structures, where they store honey and lay their eggs (**FIG. 3-25**).

Phospholipids Have Water-Soluble "Heads" and Water-Insoluble "Tails"

The plasma membrane that surrounds each cell contains several types of **phospholipids.** A phospholipid resembles an oil with one of its three fatty acids replaced by a phosphate group. The phosphate is linked to one of several polar functional groups that typically contain nitrogen (**FIG. 3-26**). A phospholipid molecule has two dissimilar ends. At one end are the two nonpolar fatty acid "tails," which are insoluble in water. At the other end is the phosphate–nitrogen "head," which is polar and water soluble. These properties of phospholipids are crucial to the structure and function of cell membranes (see Chapter 5).

Steroids Contain Four Fused Carbon Rings

All **steroids** are composed of four rings of carbon atoms. As shown in **FIGURE 3-27**, the rings share one or more sides, with various functional groups protruding from them. One steroid, *cholesterol*, is a vital component of the membranes

▲ **FIGURE 3-27 Steroids** All steroids have a similar, nonpolar molecular structure with four fused carbon rings. Differences in steroid function result from differences in functional groups attached to the rings. **(a)** Cholesterol, the molecule from which other steroids are synthesized; **(b)** the female sex hormone estrogen (estradiol); **(c)** the male sex hormone testosterone. Note the similarities in structure between the sex hormones.

THINK CRITICALLY Why are steroid hormones able to diffuse through cell membranes to exert their effects?

◀ **FIGURE 3-26 Phospholipids** Phospholipids have two hydrophobic fatty acid tails attached to the three-carbon glycerol backbone. The third position on glycerol is occupied by a polar head (left) consisting of a phosphate group to which a second (usually nitrogen-containing) variable functional group is attached. The phosphate group bears a negative charge, and the nitrogen-containing functional group bears a positive charge, making the head hydrophilic.

Cholesterol, *Trans* Fats, and Your Heart

Why are so many foods advertised as "cholesterol free" or "low in cholesterol"? Cholesterol is crucial to life, so what makes it bad?

Cholesterol molecules are insoluble and are transported in the bloodstream as microscopic particles surrounded by hydrophilic phospholipids and proteins. These *lipoprotein* (lipid plus protein) particles differ considerably in their relative amounts of cholesterol and protein. Those with less cholesterol and more protein are described as *high-density lipoprotein* (HDL), because proteins are denser than lipids. Those with more cholesterol and less protein are *low-density lipoprotein* (LDL).

Blood tests can identify the levels of HDL and LDL present in the body. Why is this important to know? Because elevated HDL is associated with a reduced risk of heart disease and stroke, whereas elevated LDL is a risk factor for cardiovascular disease. LDL deposits cholesterol in artery walls, where it participates in the formation of complex fatty deposits called *plaques* (FIG. E3-3). Blood clots may form around the plaques. If a clot breaks loose and blocks an

artery supplying blood to the heart muscle or brain, it can cause a heart attack or a stroke. In contrast to the damaging effects of LDL, HDL particles can absorb cholesterol from plaque accumulating in artery walls and transport it to the liver, which uses cholesterol to synthesize bile. The bile is secreted into the small intestine to aid in fat digestion.

Most cholesterol is synthesized by the body. Saturated fats (such as those in dairy and red meat) stimulate the liver to churn out more LDL cholesterol. Foods containing cholesterol, which include egg yolks, sausages, bacon, whole milk, and butter, typically only contribute about 15% to 20% of our blood cholesterol, but diets in which unsaturated fats (found in fish, nuts, and most vegetable oils) replace saturated fats are associated with a decreased risk of heart disease. Lifestyle also contributes: Exercise tends to increase HDL, whereas obesity and smoking increase LDL cholesterol levels.

The worst dietary fat is **trans fat,** made artificially when hydrogen atoms are added to oil in a configuration that causes the kinky fatty acid tails to straighten and the oil to become solid at room temperature. Because they are very stable, *trans* fats extend the shelf life and help retain the flavor of processed foods such as margarine, cookies, crackers, and fried foods. *Trans* fat, also called "partially hydrogenated oil," simultaneously decreases HDL and increases LDL and so places consumers at a higher risk of heart disease. Since 2006, when the danger was clearly recognized and new laws required that the *trans* fat content of foods be specified, most manufacturers and fast food chains have greatly reduced or eliminated *trans* fats from their products. In 2015, based on the scientific evidence, the FDA concluded that *trans* fats are "not generally recognized as safe" and gave food manufacturers three years to eliminate them.

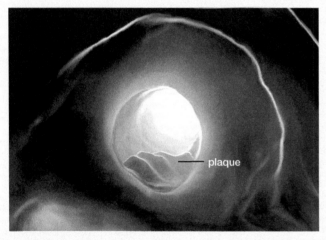

plaque

▲ **FIGURE E3-3 Plaque** A plaque deposit (rippled structure) partially blocks this carotid artery.

EVALUATE THIS An obese 55-year-old woman consults her physician about minor chest pains during exercise. Explain the physician's preliminary diagnosis, list the questions she should ask her patient, describe the tests she would perform, and provide the advice she should give.

of animal cells. It makes up about 2% of the human brain, where it is an important component of the lipid-rich membranes that insulate nerve cells. Cholesterol is also used by cells to synthesize other steroids, such as the female and male sex hormones *estrogen* and *testosterone*. Too much of the wrong form of cholesterol is linked to cardiovascular disease, as explained in "Health Watch: Cholesterol, *Trans* Fats, and Your Heart."

CHECK YOUR LEARNING

Can you ...

- compare and contrast the structure and synthesis of fats and oils?
- describe the functions of fats, oils, and waxes?
- provide two reasons why cholesterol is important in the body?

Puzzling Proteins

Stanley Prusiner and his associates coined the term "prion" to refer to the misfolded version of a normal protein called PrP^c, found on cell membranes. But how do prions replicate themselves? Researchers have discovered that prions interact with normal helical PrP^c proteins, forcing segments of them to change into the pleated sheet configuration of the infectious form. These new "prion converts" then go on to transform other normal PrP^c proteins in an ever-expanding chain reaction. The chain reaction apparently occurs slowly enough that, as in Charlene Singh's case, it can be a decade or more after infection before disease symptoms occur. Fortunately, both vCJD and BSE have been nearly eradicated worldwide. However, there is evidence that the gene coding for PrP^c can mutate in extremely rare cases, causing cows that have not been exposed to BSE prions to develop the disease. Careful surveillance of cattle continues.

Recognition of the prion as the disease agent in vCJD has focused attention on the role of the normal PrP^c protein. It is found in cell membranes throughout the body and in relatively high levels in the brain, a prime target of infectious prions. Preliminary evidence suggests that PrP^c has diverse functions, which include protecting cells from oxidative stress, contrib-

uting to the growth of neurons, and helping to maintain the new connections between neurons that form when an animal learns.

In 1997, when accepting the Nobel Prize for his prion research, Prusiner predicted that our understanding of this novel disease process could lead to insights into the prevention and treatment of other neurodegenerative disorders. Researchers are now exploring the hypothesis that diseases including Alzheimer's, Parkinson's, and amyotrophic lateral sclerosis (ALS) may arise from misfolded proteins that propagate and accumulate within the nervous system.

CONSIDER THIS A disorder called CWD (chronic wasting disease) of deer and elk, first identified in the late 1960s, has now been reported in at least 20 U.S. states. Like scrapie and BSE, CWD is a fatal brain disorder caused by prions. The disease spreads among animals by contact with saliva, urine, and feces, which may contain prions. Prions have also been found in the muscles of deer with CWD. There is no evidence that CWD can be transmitted to people or domestic livestock. If you were a hunter in an affected region, would you continue to hunt? Would you eat deer or elk meat? Explain why or why not.

CHAPTER REVIEW

(MB) Go to **MasteringBiology** for practice quizzes, activities, eText, videos, current events, and more.

Answers to Think Critically, Evaluate This, Multiple Choice, and Fill-in-the-Blank questions can be found in the Answers section at the back of the book.

Summary of Key Concepts

3.1 Why Is Carbon So Important in Biological Molecules?

Organic molecules have a carbon backbone. They are so diverse because the carbon atom is able to form bonds with up to four other molecules. This allows organic molecules to form complex shapes, including branched chains, helices, pleated sheets, and rings. The presence of functional groups produces further diversity among biological molecules (see Table 3-1).

3.2 How Are Large Biological Molecules Synthesized?

Most large biological molecules are polymers synthesized by linking many smaller monomer subunits using dehydration

synthesis. Hydrolysis reactions break these polymers apart. The most important organic molecules fall into four classes: carbohydrates, lipids, proteins, and nucleotides/nucleic acids (see Table 3-2).

3.3 What Are Carbohydrates?

Carbohydrates include sugars, starches, cellulose, and chitin. Sugars include monosaccharides and disaccharides. They are used for temporary energy storage and the construction of other molecules. Starches and glycogen are polysaccharides that provide longer-term energy storage in plants and animals, respectively. Cellulose forms the cell walls of plants, and chitin strengthens the exoskeletons of many invertebrates and the cell walls of fungi.

3.4 What Are Proteins?

Proteins consist of one or more amino acid chains called polypeptides with up to four levels of structure. Primary structure is the sequence of amino acids; secondary structure consists of helices or pleated sheets. These may fold to produce tertiary structure.

Proteins with two or more linked polypeptides have quaternary structure. Some proteins or parts of proteins are disordered and lack a stable secondary or tertiary structure. The function of a protein is determined by its shape and by how its amino acids interact with their surroundings and with each other. See Table 3-3 for protein functions and examples.

3.5 What Are Nucleotides and Nucleic Acids?

A nucleotide is composed of a phosphate group, a five-carbon sugar (ribose or deoxyribose), and a nitrogen-containing base. Molecules formed from single nucleotides include energy-carrier molecules (ATP) and messenger molecules (cyclic AMP). Nucleic acids are chains of nucleotides. DNA carries the hereditary blueprint, and RNA is copied from DNA and directs the synthesis of proteins.

3.6 What Are Lipids?

Lipids are nonpolar, water-insoluble molecules. Oils, fats, waxes, and phospholipids all contain fatty acids, which are chains of carbon and hydrogen atoms with a carboxylic acid group at the end. Steroids all have four fused rings of carbon atoms with functional groups attached. Lipids are used for energy storage (oils and fats), as waterproofing for the outside of many plants and animals (waxes), as the principal component of cellular membranes (phospholipids and cholesterol), and as hormones (steroids).

Key Terms

adenosine triphosphate
   (ATP)   *44*
amino acid   *40*
base   *44*
biological molecules   *33*
carbohydrate   *36*
cellulose   *38*
chitin   *39*
dehydration synthesis   *34*
denatured   *43*
deoxyribonucleic
   acid (DNA)   *45*
disaccharide   *36*
disulfide bond   *40*
enzyme   *40*
fat   *46*
fatty acid   *46*
functional group   *34*
glucose   *36*
glycogen   *38*
helix   *41*
hydrolysis   *35*
inorganic   *33*
intrinsically disordered
   protein   *43*
lipid   *45*
monomer   *34*

monosaccharide   *36*
nucleic acid   *45*
nucleotide   *44*
oil   *46*
organic   *33*
peptide   *41*
peptide bond   *41*
phospholipid   *47*
pleated sheet   *42*
polymer   *34*
polysaccharide   *37*
primary structure   *41*
protein   *40*
quaternary structure   *42*
ribonucleic acid
   (RNA)   *45*
saturated   *46*
secondary
   structure   *41*
starch   *37*
steroid   *47*
sugar   *36*
tertiary structure   *42*
trans fat   *48*
triglyceride   *46*
unsaturated   *46*
wax   *47*

Thinking Through the Concepts

Multiple Choice

1. Polar molecules
  a.   dissolve in lipids.
  b.   are hydrophobic.
  c.   form covalent bonds.
  d.   form ionic bonds.

2. Which match is correct?
  a.   monosaccharide–sucrose
  b.   polysaccharide–maltose
  c.   disaccharide–lactose
  d.   disaccharide–glycogen

3. Which of the following statements is False?
  a.   In starch breakdown, water is formed.
  b.   In chitin, glucoses are linked as in cellulose.
  c.   Peptide bonds determine primary peptide structure.
  d.   Disulfide bridges are formed by covalent bonds.

4. Which of the following is *not* composed of repeating subunits?
  a.   starch
  b.   protein
  c.   nucleic acid
  d.   lipid

5. Which of the following statements is False?
  a.   Carbohydrates are the most efficient energy-storage molecules by weight.
  b.   Intrinsically disordered protein segments have mostly hydrophilic amino acids.
  c.   Nucleotides may act as energy-carrier molecules.
  d.   Very acidic or salty solutions may denature proteins.

Fill-in-the-Blank

1. In organic molecules made of chains of subunits, each subunit is called a(n) _____, and the chains are called _____. Carbohydrates consisting of long chains of sugars are called _____. These sugar chains can be broken down by _____ reactions. Three types of carbohydrates consisting of long glucose chains are _____, _____, and _____.

2. Fill in the following with the specific bond(s): Maintain(s) the helical structure of many proteins: _____; link(s) polypeptide chains and can cause proteins to bend: _____ and _____; join(s) the two strands of the double helix of DNA: _____; link(s) amino acids to form the primary structure of proteins: _____.

3. Proteins are synthesized by a reaction called _____ synthesis, which releases _____. Subunits of proteins are called _____. The sequence of protein subunits is called the _____ structure of the protein. Two regular configurations of secondary protein structure are _____ and _____. When a protein's secondary or higher-order structure is destroyed, the protein is said to be _____.

4. A nucleotide consists of three parts: _____, _____, and _____. A nucleotide that acts as an energy carrier is _____. The four bases found in deoxyribose nucleotides are _____, _____, _____, and _____. Two important nucleic acids are _____ and _____. The functional group that joins nucleotides in nucleic acids is _____.

5. Fill in the following with the appropriate type of lipid: Unsaturated, liquid at room temperature: _____; bees use to make honeycombs: _____; stores energy in animals: _____; sex hormones are synthesized from these: _____; the LDL form of this contributes to heart disease: _____; a major component of cell membranes that has polar heads: _____.

Review Questions

1. What does the term "organic" mean to a chemist?
2. List the four principal classes of biological molecules and give an example of each.
3. What roles do nucleotides play in living organisms?

4. How are fats and oils similar? How do they differ, and how do their differences explain whether they are solid or liquid at room temperature?
5. Describe and compare dehydration synthesis and hydrolysis. Give an example of a substance formed by each chemical reaction, and describe the specific reaction in each instance.
6. Describe the synthesis of a protein from amino acids. Then describe the primary, secondary, tertiary, and quaternary structures of a protein.
7. Where in nature do we find cellulose? Where do we find chitin? In what way(s) are these two polymers similar? How are they different?

Applying the Concepts

1. Based on their structure, sketch and explain how phospholipids would organize themselves in water.
2. Compare the way fat and carbohydrates interact with water, and explain why this interaction gives fat an extra advantage for weight-efficient energy storage.
3. In an alternate universe where people could digest cellulose molecules, how might this affect our way of life?

4 CELL STRUCTURE AND FUNCTION

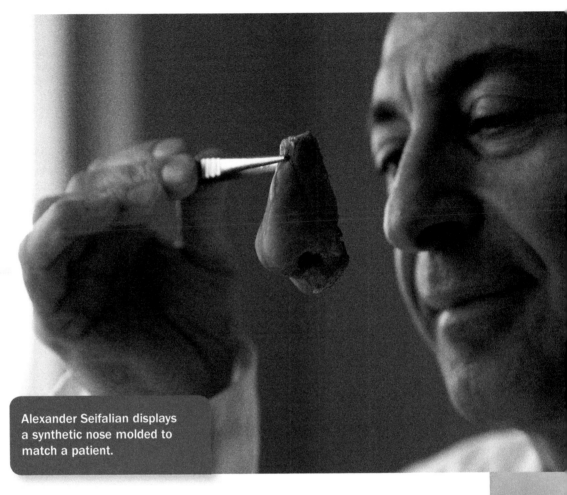

Alexander Seifalian displays a synthetic nose molded to match a patient.

CASE STUDY

New Parts for Human Bodies

ANDEMARIAM BEYENE, A STUDENT FROM AFRICA, was pursuing a postgraduate degree at the University of Iceland when he developed a tracheal tumor that persisted despite surgery and radiation therapy. No donor windpipe was available, so Beyene agreed to become the first person to receive an artificial body part embedded with his own cells.

An international team overseen by a Swedish thoracic surgeon collaborated to create Beyene's artificial trachea. In England, researchers used a CT scan (a series of X-rays combined by computer to generate a three-dimensional image) to create an exact glass replica of Beyene's trachea. The replica formed a mold for a plastic scaffolding material with microscopic pores that could be infiltrated with human cells. In Sweden, the plastic trachea scaffold was placed in a temperature-controlled "bioreactor" that had been specially designed in the United States to seed cells onto artificial scaffolds. Doctors isolated stem cells (which are capable of forming a variety of adult cell types) from Beyene's bone marrow and placed them in a nutrient broth in the bioreactor. The plastic trachea scaffold was rotated within the bioreactor, allowing the stem cells to attach. Doctors then replaced Beyene's cancerous trachea with the newly-constructed bio-artificial organ. The new trachea bought time for Beyene. He resumed his studies and graduated in 2012 with a Master's degree. But in 2014, the bioartificial trachea loosened and Beyene died.

The hope, hype, and ultimate failure of the first human biosynthetic organ underscores both the immense possibilities and the practical challenges facing bioengineered human body parts. At the Royal Free Hospital in London, Professor Alexander Seifalian and his team have been working to grow noses, ears, and blood vessels in an endeavor that may eventually transform thousands of lives. The body parts with the greatest immediate promise are the simple ones, which don't move or perform complex functions. When a British businessman lost his nose to cancer, the group molded him a new one, slanted slightly to the left, just like the original. The structure was seeded with the patient's stem cells and incubated in a nutrient solution formulated to stimulate the stem cells to develop into cartilage. It was then implanted under the skin of his forearm to acquire blood vessels, nerves, and a coating of skin in preparation for transfer to his face.

Bioengineering simple human organs demonstrates our rapidly-expanding ability to manipulate cells, the fundamental units of life. What structures make up cells? What new bioengineering techniques involving human or animal cells are being developed and tested?

AT A GLANCE

4.1 WHAT IS THE CELL THEORY?

Because cells are so small, no one had ever seen them until the first microscope was invented in the mid-1600s (see "How Do We Know That? The Search for the Cell" on page 54). But seeing cells was only the first step toward understanding their importance. In 1838, the German botanist Matthias Schleiden concluded that cells and substances produced by cells form the basic structure of plants and that plant growth occurs by adding new cells. In 1839, German biologist Theodor Schwann (Schleiden's friend and collaborator) drew similar conclusions about animal cells. The work of Schleiden and Schwann provided a unifying theory of cells as the fundamental units of life. In 1855, the German physician Rudolf Virchow completed the **cell theory**—a fundamental concept of biology—by concluding that all cells come from previously existing cells.

The cell theory consists of three principles:

1. Every organism is made up of one or more cells.
2. The smallest organisms are single cells, and cells are the functional units of multicellular organisms.
3. All cells arise from preexisting cells.

CHECK YOUR LEARNING

Can you ...

- trace the historical development of the cell theory?
- list the three principles of the cell theory?

4.2 WHAT ARE THE BASIC ATTRIBUTES OF CELLS?

All living things, from microscopic bacteria to a giant sequoia tree, are composed of cells. Cells perform an enormous variety of functions, including obtaining energy and nutrients, synthesizing biological molecules, eliminating wastes, interacting with other cells, and reproducing.

Most cells range in size from about 1 to 100 micrometers (μm; millionths of a meter) in diameter (**FIG. 4-1**). Why are most cells so small? The answer lies in the need for cells to exchange nutrients and wastes with their external environment through the plasma membrane. Many nutrients and wastes move into, through, and out of cells by **diffusion**, the process by which molecules dissolved in fluids disperse

▲ **FIGURE 4-1 Relative sizes** Dimensions encountered in biology range from about 100 meters (the height of the tallest redwood trees) to a few nanometers (the diameter of many large molecules).

HOW DO WE KNOW THAT?

The Search for the Cell

Although cells form the basis of life, they're so small that it wasn't until we could actually see them that we realized they existed. In 1665, the English scientist and inventor Robert Hooke aimed his primitive light microscope at an "exceeding thin ... piece of Cork" and saw "a great many little Boxes" (**FIG. E4-1a**). Hooke called the boxes "cells," because he thought they resembled the tiny rooms (called cells) occupied by monks in a monastery. Cork comes from the dry outer bark of the cork oak, and we now know that he was looking at the nonliving cell walls that surround all plant cells. Hooke wrote that in the living oak and other plants, "These cells [are] fill'd with juices."

In the 1670s, Dutch microscopist Anton van Leeuwenhoek constructed his own simple light microscopes and observed a previously unknown living world (**FIG. E4-1b**). Although van Leeuwenhoek's microscopes appear much more primitive than Hooke's, their superior lenses provided clearer images and

higher magnification, down to almost 1 micron (1 µm; see Fig. 4-1). A self-taught amateur scientist, van Leeuwenhoek's descriptions of myriad "animalcules" (mostly single-celled organisms) in rain, pond, and well water were greeted with amazement. Over the years, he described an enormous range of microscopic specimens, including blood cells, sperm cells, and the eggs of aphids and fleas, helping overturn the belief that these insects emerged spontaneously from dust or grain. Observing white matter scraped from his teeth, van Leeuwenhoek saw swarms of cells that we now recognize as bacteria. Disturbed by these animalcules in his mouth, he tried to kill them with vinegar and hot coffee—but with little success.

Since the pioneering efforts of early microscopists, biologists, physicists, and engineers have collaborated to develop a variety of advanced microscopes to view the cell and its components. *Light microscopes* use lenses made of

(b) van Leeuwenhoek's light microscope

(a) Robert Hooke's light microscope and his drawing of cork cells

(c) Electron microscope

▲ **FIGURE E4-1 Microscopes yesterday and today (a)** Robert Hooke saw the walls of cork cells through his elegant light microscope, and drew them with great skill. **(b)** Hooke and van Leeuwenhoek were contemporaries. Hooke admitted that van Leeuwenhoek's microscopes produced better images, but described these extremely simple microscopes as "offensive to my eye." **(c)** This modern machine is both a transmission electron microscope (TEM) and a scanning electron microscope (SEM).

glass or quartz to bend, focus, and transmit light rays that have passed through or bounced off a specimen. The light microscope produces images depending on how the specimen is illuminated and how it has been stained. Fluorescent stains targeted to specific molecules and viewed under specific wavelengths of light are now revolutionizing our view of cells. The resolving power (the smallest structure distinguishable under ideal conditions) of modern light microscopes is about 200 nanometers (nm; see Fig. 4-1). This is sufficient to see most prokaryotic cells, some structures inside eukaryotic cells, and living cells such as a swimming *Paramecium* (FIG. E4-2a).

Electron microscopes (FIG. E4-1c) use beams of electrons focused by magnetic fields rather than light focused by lenses. *Transmission electron microscopes* pass electrons through a thin specimen and can reveal the details of interior cell structure (FIG. E4-2b). Some modern transmission electron microscopes can resolve structures as small as 0.05 nanometer, allowing scientists to see molecules such

as DNA and even individual carbon atoms (seen here forming a six-carbon ring).

TEM of carbon atoms

Scanning electron microscopes bounce electrons off specimens that are dry and hard (such as shells) or that have been covered with an ultrathin coating of metal such as gold. Scanning electron microscopes can be used to view the three-dimensional surface details of structures that range in size from entire small insects down to cells and their components, with a maximum resolution of about 1.5 nanometers (FIGS. E4-2c, d).

THINK CRITICALLY Based on the images in Fig. E4-2, what advantages are there in visualizing microscopic structures using each of these techniques?

(a) Light micrograph (*Paramecium*)

(b) Transmission electron micrograph

(c) Scanning electron micrograph (*Paramecia*)

(d) Scanning electron micrograph

▲ FIGURE E4-2 **A comparison of microscope images (a)** A living *Paramecium* (a single-celled freshwater protist) photographed through a light microscope. **(b)** A transmission electron micrograph (TEM) showing mitochondria. **(c)** A scanning electron micrograph (SEM) of two *Paramecia*. **(d)** An SEM showing mitochondria and smooth endoplasmic reticulum. All colors in electron micrographs (SEMs or TEMs) have been added artificially.

from regions where their concentration is higher to regions where their concentration is lower (see Chapter 5). Diffusion is a relatively slow process, so to meet the constant metabolic demands of cells, even their innermost parts must remain close to the external environment. Thus, cells maintain a very small diameter, whether they are round or elongated.

All Cells Share Common Features

All cells arose from a common ancestor that evolved about 3.5 billion years ago. Modern cells include the simple prokaryotic cells of bacteria and archaea and the complex eukaryotic cells of protists, fungi, plants, and animals. All cells, whether simple or complex, share some important features.

The Plasma Membrane Encloses the Cell and Allows Interactions Between the Cell and Its Environment

Each cell is surrounded by an extremely thin, rather fluid membrane called the **plasma membrane** (FIG. 4-2). The plasma membrane, like all membranes in and around cells, contains proteins embedded in a double layer, or *bilayer*, of phospholipids interspersed with cholesterol molecules.

The phospholipid and protein components of cellular membranes play very different roles. The phospholipid bilayer helps isolate the cell from its surroundings, allowing the

▲ **FIGURE 4-2 The plasma membrane** The plasma membrane encloses the cell in a double layer of phospholipids associated with a variety of proteins. The membrane is supported by the cytoskeleton.

cell to maintain essential differences in the concentrations of materials inside and out. In contrast, the huge variety of proteins within the bilayer facilitate communication between the cell and its environment. For example, *channel proteins* allow passage of specific molecules or ions into or out of the cell (see Fig. 4-2). *Glycoproteins*, which have short carbohydrate chains extending outside the cell, both facilitate interactions between cells and respond to external signaling molecules that promote chemical reactions within the cell (described in Chapter 5).

All Cells Contain Cytoplasm

The **cytoplasm** consists of all the fluid and structures that lie inside the plasma membrane but outside of the nucleus (see Figs. 4-4 and 4-5). The fluid portion of the cytoplasm in both prokaryotic and eukaryotic cells, called the **cytosol,** contains water, salts, and an assortment of organic molecules, including proteins, lipids, carbohydrates, sugars, amino acids, and nucleotides (described in Chapter 3). Most of the cell's metabolic activities—the biochemical reactions that support life—occur in the cell cytoplasm.

The **cytoskeleton** consists of a variety of protein filaments within the cytoplasm. These provide support, transport structures within the cell, aid in cell division, and allow cells to move and change shape (see Figs. 4-2 and 4-7).

All Cells Use DNA As a Hereditary Blueprint and RNA to Copy the Blueprint and Guide Construction of Cell Parts

The genetic material in all cells is **deoxyribonucleic acid (DNA),** an inherited blueprint consisting of segments called genes. Genes store the instructions for making all the parts of the cell and for producing new cells (see Chapter 12). **Ribonucleic acid (RNA),** which is chemically similar to DNA, copies the genes of DNA and helps construct proteins based on this genetic blueprint. The construction of protein from RNA in all cells occurs on **ribosomes,** cellular workbenches composed of a specialized type of RNA called *ribosomal RNA.*

There Are Two Basic Types of Cells: Prokaryotic and Eukaryotic

All forms of life are composed of one of two types of cells. **Prokaryotic** cells (Gk. *pro*, before, and *kary*, nucleus) form the bodies of **bacteria** and **archaea,** the simplest forms of life. **Eukaryotic** cells (Gk. *eu*, true) are far more complex and make up the bodies of animals, plants, fungi, and protists. As their names suggest, one striking difference between prokaryotic and eukaryotic cells is that the genetic material of eukaryotic cells is contained within a membrane-enclosed nucleus. **TABLE 4-1** summarizes the principal features of prokaryotic and eukaryotic cells.

TABLE 4-1	Functions and Distribution of Cell Structures			
Structure	Function	Prokaryotes	Eukaryotes: Plants	Eukaryotes: Animals
Cell Surface				
Extracellular matrix	Surrounds cells, providing biochemical and structural support	Absent	Present	Present
Cilia	Move the cell through fluid or move fluid past the cell surface	Absent	Absent (in most)	Present
Flagella	Move the cell through fluid	Present[1]	Absent (in most)	Present
Plasma membrane	Isolates the cell contents from the environment; regulates movement of materials into and out of the cell; allows communication with other cells	Present	Present	Present
Organization of Genetic Material				
Genetic material	Encodes the information needed to construct the cell and to control cellular activity	DNA	DNA	DNA
Chromosomes	Contain and control the use of DNA	Single, circular	Many, linear	Many, linear
Nucleus[2]	Contains chromosomes and nucleoli	Absent	Present	Present
Nuclear envelope	Encloses the nucleus; regulates movement of materials into and out of the nucleus	Absent	Present	Present
Nucleolus	Synthesizes ribosomes	Absent	Present	Present
Cytoplasmic Structures				
Ribosomes	Provide sites for protein synthesis	Present	Present	Present
Mitochondria[2]	Produce energy by aerobic metabolism	Absent	Present	Present
Chloroplasts[2]	Perform photosynthesis	Absent	Present	Absent
Endoplasmic reticulum[2]	Synthesizes membrane components, proteins, and lipids	Absent	Present	Present
Golgi apparatus[2]	Modifies, sorts, and packages proteins and lipids	Absent	Present	Present
Lysosomes[2]	Contain digestive enzymes; digest food and worn-out organelles	Absent	Absent (in most)	Present
Plastids[2]	Store food, pigments	Absent	Present	Absent
Central vacuole[2]	Contains water and wastes; provides turgor pressure to support the cell	Absent	Present	Absent
Other vesicles and vacuoles[2]	Transport secretory products; contain food obtained through phagocytosis	Absent	Present	Present
Cytoskeleton	Gives shape and support to the cell; positions and moves cell parts	Present	Present	Present
Centrioles	Produce the basal bodies of cilia and flagella	Absent	Absent (in most)	Present

[1]Some prokaryotes have structures called flagella, which lack microtubules and move in a fundamentally different way than do eukaryotic flagella.
[2]Indicates organelles, which are surrounded by membranes and found only in eukaryotic cells.

CASE STUDY CONTINUED
New Parts for Human Bodies

Why was Beyene's bioartificial trachea considered a scientific breakthrough? One reason is that the patient's own cells were used to grow the new body part, so his immune system was unlikely to reject the cells. The plasma membranes of all cells bear surface molecules called glycoproteins that are unique to the individual and allow the person's immune system to recognize the cells as "self." Cells from any other person (except an identical twin), however, bear different glycoproteins. The immune system will identify the different cells as foreign and attack them, which can cause rejection of a transplanted organ. To prevent organ rejection, physicians must find donor cells that match the patient's as closely as possible. But even then, the patient must take drugs that suppress the immune system, which increases vulnerability to cancers and infections that the immune system would normally target and destroy. The cells most likely to cause problems for immune-suppressed patients are prokaryotic. What are the features of these simple cells?

CHECK YOUR LEARNING
Can you ...
- describe the structure and features shared by all cells?
- distinguish prokaryotic from eukaryotic cells?

4.3 WHAT ARE THE MAJOR FEATURES OF PROKARYOTIC CELLS?

Prokaryotic cells have a relatively simple internal structure and are generally less than 5 micrometers in diameter (in comparison, eukaryotic cells range from 10 to 100 micrometers in diameter). Prokaryotes also lack the complex internal membrane-enclosed structures that are the most prominent features of eukaryotic cells.

Single prokaryotic cells make up two of life's domains: Archaea and Bacteria. Many Archaea inhabit extreme environments, such as hot springs and cow stomachs, but Archaea are increasingly being discovered in more familiar

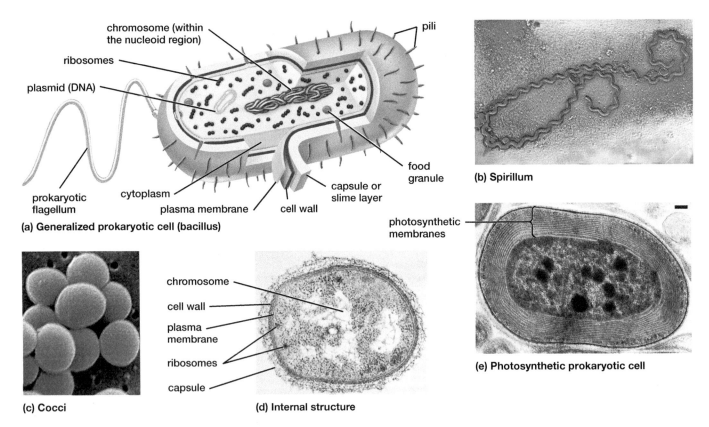

chromosome (within the nucleoid region)

ribosomes

plasmid (DNA)

pili

food granule

(b) Spirillum

prokaryotic flagellum

cytoplasm

capsule or slime layer

plasma membrane   cell wall

(a) Generalized prokaryotic cell (bacillus)

photosynthetic membranes

chromosome

cell wall

plasma membrane

ribosomes

capsule

(e) Photosynthetic prokaryotic cell

(c) Cocci   **(d) Internal structure**

▲ **FIGURE 4-3** **Prokaryotic cells** Prokaryotes come in different shapes, including **(a)** rod-shaped bacilli, **(b)** spiral-shaped spirilla, and **(c)** spherical cocci. Internal structures are revealed in the TEMs in **(d)** and **(e)**. Some photosynthetic bacteria have internal membranes where photosynthesis occurs, as shown in **(e)**.

locales, such as the soil and oceans. None are known to cause disease. In this chapter, we focus on the more familiar bacteria as representative prokaryotic cells (**FIG. 4-3**).

Prokaryotic Cells Have Specialized Surface Features

Nearly all prokaryotic cells are surrounded by a **cell wall,** which is a relatively stiff coating that the cell secretes around itself to provide protection and help maintain its shape. The cell walls of bacteria are composed of *peptidoglycan* (a unique molecule consisting of short peptides that link chains of sugar molecules which have amino functional groups). Bacteria include rod-shaped *bacilli*, spherical *cocci*, and spiral-shaped *spirilla* (see Figs. 4-3a, b, c).

Many bacteria secrete polysaccharide coatings called *capsules* and *slime layers* outside their cell walls (see Fig. 4-3a). In bacteria such as those that cause tooth decay, diarrhea, pneumonia, or urinary tract infections, capsules and slime layers help them adhere to specific host tissues, such as the surface of a tooth or the lining of the small intestine, lungs, or bladder. Capsules and slime layers allow some bacteria to form surface films (such as those that may coat unbrushed teeth or unwashed toilet bowls). They also protect the bacteria and help keep them moist.

Pili (singular, pilus; meaning "hairs") are surface proteins that project from the cell walls of many bacteria (see Fig. 4-3a). There are two types of pili: attachment pili and sex pili. Short,

abundant *attachment pili* may work on their own or with capsules and slime layers to help bacteria adhere to structures. For example, various types of *Streptococcus* bacteria (which can cause strep throat, skin infections, pneumonia, and toxic shock syndrome) use pili to help them infect their victims. Many bacteria form *sex pili*, which are few in number and quite long. A sex pilus from one bacterium binds to a nearby bacterium of the same type and draws them together. The two bacteria form a short bridge that links their cytoplasm and allows them to transfer small rings of DNA called **plasmids.**

Some bacteria and archaea possess **flagella** (singular, flagellum; "whip"), which extend from the cell surface and rotate to propel these cells through a fluid environment (see Fig. 4-3a). Prokaryotic flagella differ from those of eukaryotic cells, which are described later in this chapter.

Prokaryotic Cells Have Specialized Cytoplasmic Structures

The cytoplasm of a typical prokaryotic cell contains several specialized structures. A distinctive region called the **nucleoid** (meaning "like a nucleus"; see Fig. 4-3a) contains a single circular chromosome that consists of a long, coiled strand of DNA that carries essential genetic information. Unlike the nucleus of a eukaryotic cell, the nucleoid is not separated from the cytoplasm by a membrane. Most prokaryotic cells also contain plasmids outside the nucleoid. Plasmids usually carry genes that give the cell special properties; for example, some disease-causing bacteria possess plasmids that encode proteins that inactivate antibiotics, making the bacteria much more difficult to kill. Bacterial cytoplasm also includes ribosomes, where proteins are synthesized, as well as food granules that store energy-rich molecules, such as glycogen.

Although prokaryotic cells lack internal structures surrounded by membranes, some bacteria use internal membranes to organize enzymes. These enzymes facilitate biochemical processes requiring several reactions, and they are situated in a specific sequence along the membrane that corresponds to the sequence in which the reactions must occur. For example, photosynthetic bacteria possess extensive internal membranes where light-capturing proteins and enzymes are embedded, allowing the bacteria to harness the energy of sunlight to synthesize high-energy molecules (Fig. 4-3e).

Prokaryotes also contain an extensive cytoskeleton that includes some proteins that resemble those of the eukaryotic cytoskeleton (see Fig. 4-7) and others that are unique. The prokaryotic and eukaryotic cytoskeletons serve many similar functions; for example, both are essential for cell division and contribute to regulating the shape of the cell.

CHECK YOUR LEARNING
Can you ...
- describe the structure and function of the major features of prokaryotic cells?
- describe the internal features of bacteria, including how some bacteria utilize internal membranes?

4.4 WHAT ARE THE MAJOR FEATURES OF EUKARYOTIC CELLS?

Eukaryotic cells make up the bodies of organisms in the domain Eukarya: animals, plants, protists, and fungi. As you might imagine, these cells are extremely diverse. The cells that form the bodies of unicellular protists can perform all the activities necessary for independent life. Within the body of any multicellular organism, cells are specialized to perform a variety of functions. Here, we focus on plant and animal cells.

Unlike prokaryotic cells, eukaryotic cells (FIG. 4-4) have **organelles** ("little organs"), membrane-enclosed structures specialized for a specific function (see Table 4-1). Organelles contribute to the complexity of eukaryotic cells. Figure 4-4

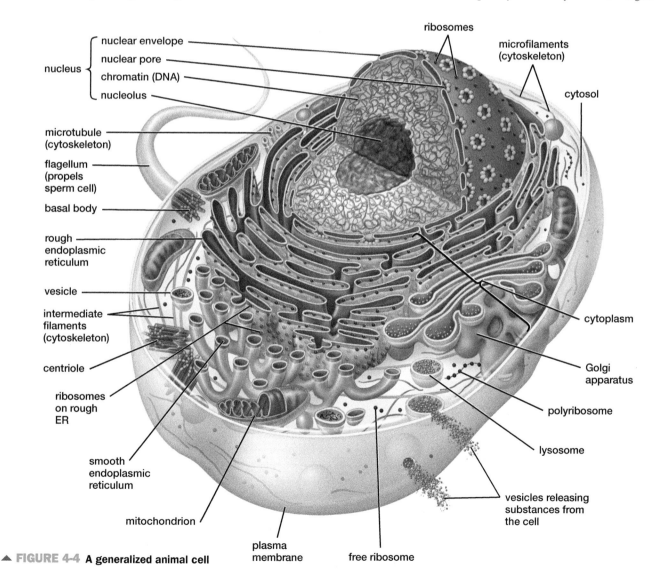

▲ **FIGURE 4-4 A generalized animal cell**

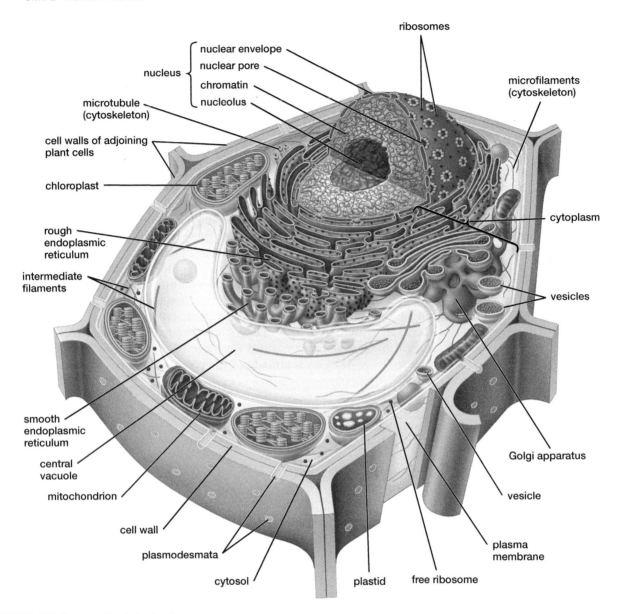

▲ FIGURE 4-5 **A generalized plant cell**

illustrates a generalized animal cell, and FIGURE 4-5 illustrates a generalized plant cell, each with some distinctive structures. Animal cells have centrioles, lysosomes, cilia, and flagella, which are not found in the most common plant cells, and plant cells have cell walls, central vacuoles, and plastids (including chloroplasts), which are absent in animal cells.

Extracellular Structures Surround Animal and Plant Cells

The plasma membrane, which is only about two molecules thick and has the consistency of viscous oil, would be torn apart without reinforcing structures. The reinforcing structure for animal cells is the complex **extracellular matrix (ECM),** secreted by the cell. The ECM includes an array of supporting and adhesive proteins embedded in a gel composed of polysaccharides that are linked together by proteins (FIG. 4-6a). The

ECM (which differs among cell types) provides both structural and biochemical support, including proteins called growth factors, which promote cell survival and growth. The ECM attaches adjacent cells, transmits molecular signals between cells, and guides cells as they migrate and differentiate during development. It anchors cells within tissues and provides a supporting framework within tissues; for example, a stiff extracellular matrix forms the scaffolding for bone and cartilage (FIG. 4-6b).

The extracellular matrix of plant cells is the cell wall, which protects and supports each cell. Plant cell walls, composed mainly of overlapping cellulose fibers, are porous and allow oxygen, carbon dioxide, and water with its dissolved substances to flow through them. Cell walls attach adjacent plant cells to one another and are perforated by plasma membrane-lined openings called *plasmodesmata* that connect the cytoplasm of adjacent cells (see Fig. 4-5).

(a) The extracellular matrix

(b) Extracellular matrix of a cartilage cell

▲ FIGURE 4-6 **The extracellular matrix (a)** Extracellular proteins perform a variety of functions.
(b) An SEM of a cartilage cell surrounded by its extracellular matrix.

CASE STUDY \ CONTINUED

New Parts for Human Bodies

Besides tracheas and noses, researchers are working on growing bioartificial muscles as well. In the past, major muscle injuries could mean amputation and a prosthetic limb, because muscles have limited ability to regenerate, and scar tissue forms and interferes with their function. But Stephen Badylak and colleagues at the McGowen Institute for Regenerative Medicine are investigating the use of the ECM to help muscles heal and even regenerate.

After 28-year-old Marine Ron Strang's quadriceps muscle was almost ripped from his leg by a roadside bomb in Afghanistan, he volunteered for a new bioartificial muscle treatment developed by Badylak. Badylak used ECM from pig bladders with the cells removed (which prevents tissue rejection) to recreate Strang's muscle. Badylak's team then cut away scar tissue from the Marine's thigh muscle and placed the pig matrix in the resulting cavity. There, its unique combination of natural scaffolding proteins and growth factors recruited muscle stem cells and worked a major transformation. After 6 months, the pig matrix was broken down and replaced by healthy human tissue, and Strang went from hobbling to hiking and riding a bike.

Strang's treatment worked in part because the ECM helps support tissues and facilitates communication between cells. Which structures provide support and facilitate communication within a cell?

The Cytoskeleton Provides Shape, Support, and Movement

The cytoskeleton is a dynamic network of protein fibers within the cytoplasm (FIG. 4-7). Cytoskeletal proteins come in three major types: thin **microfilaments** (composed of actin protein), medium-sized **intermediate filaments** (composed of various proteins), and thick **microtubules** (composed of tubulin protein). Cytoskeletal proteins provide the cell with both internal support and the ability to change shape and divide, directed by signals from the ECM. The cytoskeleton is important in regulating the following properties of cells:

- *Cell Shape*   Cytoskeletal proteins can alter the shapes of cells using energy released from ATP, either by changing their length (by adding or removing subunits) or by sliding past one another. In animal cells, a scaffolding of intermediate filaments supports the cell, helps determine its shape, and links cells to one another and to the ECM. An array of microfilaments concentrated just inside the plasma membrane provides additional support and also connects with the surrounding ECM.
- *Cell Movement*   Cell movement can occur in animal cells as microtubules and microfilaments extend by adding subunits at one end and releasing subunits at the other end. Microtubules and intermediate filaments may be associated with *motor proteins,* which are specialized to release energy stored in ATP and use it to generate molecular movement. Another form of movement is generated as motor proteins cause actin microfilaments

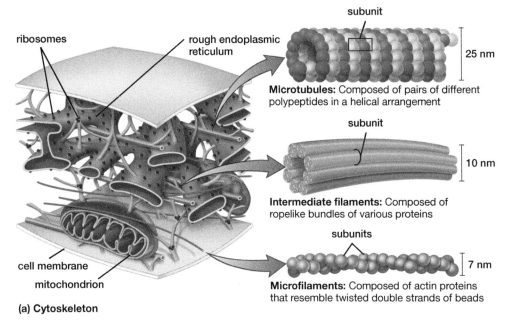

Microtubules: Composed of pairs of different polypeptides in a helical arrangement

25 nm

Intermediate filaments: Composed of ropelike bundles of various proteins

10 nm

Microfilaments: Composed of actin proteins that resemble twisted double strands of beads

7 nm

ribosomes
rough endoplasmic reticulum
subunit
subunit
subunits
cell membrane
mitochondrion

(a) Cytoskeleton

microfilaments (red)
DNA in nucleus (blue)
microtubules (green)

(b) Light micrograph showing the cytoskeleton

▲ **FIGURE 4-7 The eukaryotic cytoskeleton (a)** Three types of protein strands form the cytoskeleton. **(b)** In this light micrograph, cells treated with fluorescent stains reveal microtubules, microfilaments, and nuclei.

to slide past one another; a well-known example occurs during the contraction of muscle cells. Muscle cells must contract to increase in size, as scientists discovered when they attempted to grow muscle protein in the laboratory for possible human consumption. Learn more in "Earth Watch: Would You Like Fries with Your Cultured Cow Cells?" on page 65.

- *Organelle Movement* Motor proteins use microfilaments and microtubules as "railroad tracks" to transport organelles within the cell.
- *Cell Division* Microtubules guide chromosome movements, and microfilaments in animal cells pinch the dividing cell into two daughter cells. (Cell division is covered in Chapter 9.)

Cilia and Flagella May Move Cells Through Fluid or Move Fluid Past Cells

Both **cilia** (singular, cilium; "eyelash") and eukaryotic **flagella** are beating hair-like structures covered by plasma membrane that extend outward from some cell surfaces. They are supported and moved by microtubules of the cytoskeleton. Each cilium or flagellum contains a ring of nine fused pairs of microtubules surrounding an unfused pair (FIG. 4-8). Cilia and flagella beat almost continuously, powered by motor proteins that extend like tiny arms and attach neighboring pairs of microtubules (see Fig. 4-8a). These sidearms use ATP energy to slide the microtubules past one another, causing the cilium or flagellum to bend.

In general, cilia are shorter and more numerous than flagella. Cilia beat in unison to produce a force on the

surrounding fluid that is similar to that created by oars on a rowboat. A flagellum, in contrast, rotates in a corkscrew motion that propels a cell through fluid, acting somewhat like the propeller on a motorboat. Cells with flagella usually have only one or two of them.

HAVE YOU EVER WONDERED...

Over the years, scientists have wondered how many cells are in the human body. They don't yet agree, but 10 trillion seems a reasonable estimate. There is a consensus, however, that there are at least 10 times as many prokaryotic cells associated with the body, residing in a community called the microbiome. We each host a unique community consisting of about 3 pounds (1.4 kilograms) of prokaryotic life, which includes roughly 100 different types of bacteria. These cells colonize the nose, skin, vagina, and the digestive tract from mouth to anus.

How Many Cells Form the Human Body?

Because the digestive tract is a tube open to the outside at both ends, our microbiome occupies a unique niche that is simultaneously integral to—yet outside of—our bodies. With recent advances allowing identification of microorganisms by their unique DNA sequences, scientists are increasingly studying our relationships with our microbial residents. Our gut microbiome helps digest food and synthesize vitamins, and it allows the immune system to develop properly. Even though our bacterial populations changes in response to food intake and states of disease and health, one thing is clear: We would not be ourselves without them.

protein
sidearms

fused
microtubule
pair

central pair of
microtubules

TEM showing cross-
section

plasma
membrane

basal body (extends
into cytoplasm)

(a) Internal structure of cilia and flagella

cilia lining
trachea

(b) Cilia

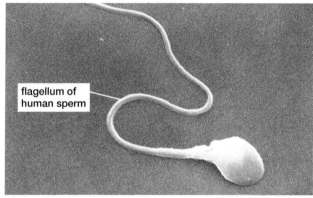

flagellum of
human sperm

(c) Flagellum

▲ **FIGURE 4-8 Cilia and flagella (a)** These structures are filled with microtubules produced by the basal body. **(b)** Cilia, shown in this SEM, line the trachea and sweep out debris. **(c)** A human sperm cell, shown in this SEM, uses its flagellum to swim to the egg.

THINK CRITICALLY What problems would arise if the trachea were lined with flagella instead of cilia?

Protists use cilia or flagella to swim through water; the *Paramecium* in Figures E4-2a, c (see "How Do We Know That? The Search for the Cell" on page 54) uses cilia. In animals, cilia usually move fluids past a surface. Ciliated cells line such diverse structures as the gills of oysters (where they circulate water rich in food and oxygen), the female reproductive tract of vertebrates (where cilia transport the egg cell to the uterus), and the respiratory tracts of most land vertebrates (where cilia convey mucus that carries debris and microorganisms out of the air passages; see Fig. 4-8b). Flagella propel the sperm cells of nearly all animals (see Fig. 4-8c).

Each cilium or flagellum arises from a **basal body** just beneath the plasma membrane. Basal bodies are produced by **centrioles,** and, like centrioles, they differ from the outer portion of flagella and microtubules in having fused triplets and no central pair of microtubules (see Fig. 4-8a). A single pair of centrioles is found in animal cells (see Fig. 4-4), and these play a role in organizing cytoskeletal proteins during cell division (described in Chapter 9).

The Nucleus, Containing DNA, Is the Control Center of the Eukaryotic Cell

A cell's DNA stores all the information needed to construct the cell and direct the countless chemical reactions necessary for life and reproduction. A cell uses only a portion of the instructions in DNA at any given time, depending on the cell's stage of development, its environment, and its function in a multicellular body. In eukaryotic cells, DNA is housed within the nucleus. The **nucleus** is a large organelle with three major parts: the nuclear envelope, chromatin, and the nucleolus (**FIG. 4-9**).

The Nuclear Envelope Allows Selective Exchange of Materials

The nucleus is isolated from the rest of the cell by a double membrane, the **nuclear envelope,** which is perforated by protein-lined nuclear pores. Water, ions, and small molecules can pass freely through the pores, but the passage of large molecules—particularly proteins, parts of ribosomes, and RNA—is regulated by gatekeeper proteins called the **nuclear pore complex** (see Fig. 4-9) that line each nuclear pore. Ribosomes stud the outer

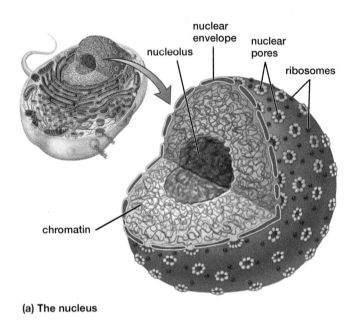

nuclear
envelope
nucleolus   nuclear
pores
ribosomes

chromatin

(a) The nucleus

nucleus

nuclear pores with
nuclear pore complex

(b) Nucleus of a yeast cell

▲ FIGURE 4-9 **The nucleus (a)** The nucleus is bounded by a double outer membrane perforated by pores. **(b)** SEM of the nucleus of a yeast cell.

nuclear membrane, which is continuous with membranes of the rough endoplasmic reticulum, described later.

Chromatin Consists of Strands of DNA Associated with Proteins

Early observers of the nucleus noted that it was darkly colored by the stains used in light microscopy and named the nuclear material **chromatin** (meaning "colored substance"). Biologists have since learned that chromatin consists of **chromosomes** (literally, "colored bodies") made of DNA molecules and their associated proteins. When a cell is not dividing, the chromosomes are extended into extremely long strands that are so thin that they cannot be distinguished from one another with a light microscope. During cell division, the individual chromosomes become condensed and are easily visible with a light microscope (FIG. 4-10).

The genes of DNA, consisting of specific sequences of nucleotides, provide a molecular blueprint for the synthesis of proteins and ribosomes. Some proteins form structural components of the cell, others regulate the movement of materials through cell membranes, and still others are enzymes that promote chemical reactions within the cell.

Proteins are synthesized in the cytoplasm, but DNA is confined to the nucleus. This means that copies of the genetic code for proteins must be ferried from the nucleus into the cytoplasm. To accomplish this, the genetic information is copied from DNA in the nucleus into molecules of *messenger RNA* (mRNA). The mRNA then moves through the nuclear pores into the cytosol. In the cytosol, the sequence of nucleotides in mRNA is used to direct protein synthesis, a process that

occurs on ribosomes (see Fig. 4-11). (Protein synthesis is described in Chapter 13.)

The Nucleolus Is the Site of Ribosome Assembly

Eukaryotic nuclei contain at least one **nucleolus** (plural, **nucleoli;** meaning "little nuclei") (see Fig. 4-9). The nucleolus is the site of ribosome synthesis. It consists of *ribosomal RNA* (rRNA), parts of chromosomes that carry genes coding for rRNA, proteins, and ribosomes in various stages of synthesis.

Ribosomes are small particles composed of ribosomal RNA combined with proteins. A ribosome serves as a kind

chromatin

chromosome

▲ FIGURE 4-10 **Chromosomes** Chromosomes, seen in a light micrograph of a dividing cell (center) in an onion root tip. Chromatin is visible in adjacent cells.

THINK CRITICALLY Why do the chromosomes in chromatin condense in dividing cells?

Earth WATCH

Would You Like Fries with Your Cultured Cow Cells?

What do you get when you combine 20,000 paper-thin yellowish-pink strips of cells, some lab-grown fat cells, beet coloring, egg powder, bread crumbs, and a dash of salt? These unlikely ingredients make up the world's first lab-grown hamburger (**FIG. E4-3**). To create it, cow muscle stem cells were allowed to multiply in a nutrient broth. The cells were then seeded into strips of gel and stimulated repeatedly by pulses of electricity. This caused their actin-based filaments to contract and the cells to "bulk up," much as human muscle cells do when exercised. The resulting artificial burger made up of 20,000 cells cost roughly $425,000 to produce, and its flavor was found to be somewhat lacking by fast-food aficionados. So what was the point?

Demand for meat is growing, fuelled partly by an expanding population, but also by increasing incomes and appetite for meat (**FIG. E4-4**). This is particularly true in China, whose meat consumption between 1971 and 2011 increased at 10 times the rate of its population growth (from 841 million to 1.3 billion people. The Food and Agriculture Organization of the UN estimates that world meat production in 2050 will be 500 million tons (compared to about 350 million tons in in 2016).

To accommodate our increasing demand for meat, we are stripping Earth of its natural ecosystems and altering its climate. Grazing and growing food for livestock already require about 30% of Earth's total land (compared to about 6% used for growing crops directly for human consumption), and meat production accounts for roughly 18% of human-caused greenhouse gas emissions. Cattle have by far the greatest environmental impact among meat-producing livestock; raising beef cattle requires about three times as much land per pound of protein as does raising chicken or pork. Increasing beef production occurs primarily at the expense of rain forest, which is cleared to provide low-quality land for cattle grazing.

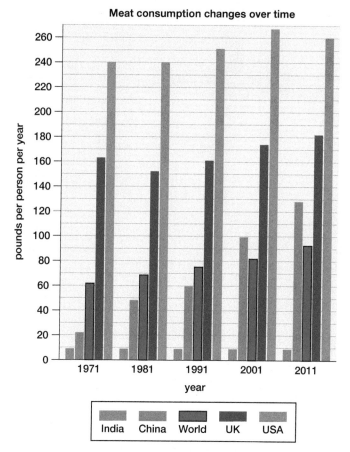

Meat consumption changes over time

India   China   World   UK   USA

▲ **FIGURE E4-4 Changes in meat consumption in selected countries**
Source: FAOSTAT (Food and Agricultural Organization of the United Nations), Food Supply

▲ **FIGURE E4-3 Will hamburger of the future be grown in a lab?**

As livestock compete for Earth's limited resources, beef is likely to become an expensive luxury in the relatively near future. Clearly, our present course is unsustainable. Scientists growing "test-tube beef" argue that if their techniques could be refined and scaled up, meat would require almost no killing of animals and use 99% less land. It would also greatly reduce greenhouse gas emissions and energy and water use.

THINK CRITICALLY Using Fig. E4-4, plot the changes in each country over the 40-year period shown and use a ruler to create a trend line to predict the meat consumption per person in each country in the years 2020, 2030, 2040, and 2050 if the current trends continue. Would the ranking of the countries change over this period? Now look up the current population of each of these countries and determine which is the largest total meat consumer. Was this true in 1980?

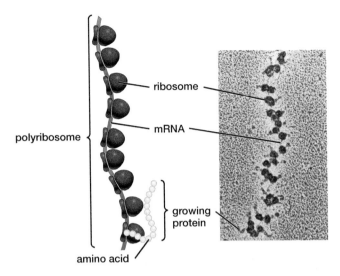

polyribosome

ribosome

mRNA

growing protein

amino acid

▲ **FIGURE 4-11 A polyribosome** Ribosomes strung along a messenger RNA molecule form a polyribosome. In the TEM (right), individual ribosomes are synthesizing multiple copies of a protein, visible as strands projecting from some of the ribosomes.

of workbench for the synthesis of proteins within the cell cytoplasm. Just as a workbench can be used to construct many different objects, a ribosome can be used to synthesize a multitude of different proteins (depending on the mRNA to which it attaches). In electron micrographs of cells, ribosomes appear as dark granules; they may appear singly, may stud the membranes of the nuclear envelope and rough endoplasmic reticulum (see Fig. 4-4), or may be present as *polyribosomes* (GK. *poly,* many) strung along strands of mRNA within the cytoplasm (**FIG. 4-11**).

Eukaryotic Cytoplasm Contains Membranes That Compartmentalize the Cell

All eukaryotic cells contain internal membranes that create loosely connected compartments within the cytoplasm. These membranes, collectively called the **endomembrane system,** segregate molecules from the surrounding cytosol and ensure that biochemical processes occur in an orderly fashion. The endomembrane system encloses regions within which an enormous variety of molecules are synthesized, broken down, and transported for use inside the cell or export outside the cell. This system of intracellular membranes includes the nuclear envelope (described earlier), vesicles, the endoplasmic reticulum, the Golgi apparatus, and lysosomes.

Vesicles Bud from the Endomembrane System and the Plasma Membrane

Vesicles are temporary sacs that bud from parts of the endomembrane system and from the plasma membrane to ferry biological molecules throughout the cell. The fluid property of membranes permits vesicles to fuse with and release their contents into different endomembrane compartments for processing. Vesicles may also fuse with the plasma membrane, exporting

their contents outside the cell, a process called *exocytosis* (Gk. *exo,* outside). Conversely, the plasma membrane may extend and surround material just outside the cell and then fuse and pinch off to form a vesicle inside the cell, a process called *endocytosis* (Gk. *endo,* inside). As they move about the cells, vesicles not only transport their cargo but also transport their membranes, which become integrated into the membranes that they fuse with.

The vesicles are transported within the cell by motor proteins running along tracks of microtubules. How do the vesicles know where to go? Proteins embedded in vesicle membranes contain specific sequences of amino acids that serve as "mailing labels," providing the address for delivery of the vesicle and its payload. Membrane proteins and proteins exported from the cell are synthesized in the rough endoplasmic reticulum, described in the next section.

The Endoplasmic Reticulum Forms Membrane-Enclosed Channels Within the Cytoplasm

The **endoplasmic reticulum (ER)** (endoplasmic, "inside the cytoplasm," and reticulum, "network") is a labyrinth of narrow channels that form interconnected sacs and tubules throughout the cytosol. The ER typically makes up at least 50% of the total cellular membrane (**FIG. 4-12**). This organelle plays a major role in synthesizing, modifying, and transporting biological molecules throughout the cell. Some of these molecules are incorporated into the ER membranes; others are processed within the ER channels and tubules. The ER has both rough and smooth membranes, which are continuous with one another.

Rough Endoplasmic Reticulum Rough ER emerges from the ribosome-covered outer nuclear membrane (see Fig. 4-4). Ribosomes studding the outer surface make it appear rough under the electron microscope. These ribosomes are the most important sites of protein synthesis in the cell. As they are synthesized, some proteins on ER ribosomes are inserted into the ER membrane. Some remain there, whereas others become part of vesicle membranes budded from the ER. Proteins destined to be secreted from the cell or used in lysosomes are inserted into the interior of the ER, where they are chemically modified and folded into their proper three-dimensional structures (see Chapter 3). Eventually, the proteins accumulate in pockets of ER membrane that pinch off as vesicles and travel to the Golgi apparatus. Proteins produced by the rough ER for export differ with cell type; they include digestive system enzymes, infection-fighting antibodies, and proteins that form the extracellular matrix. Proteins that remain in the cell include the digestive enzymes within lysosomes (described later) and plasma membrane proteins.

Enzymes produced for the synthesis of membrane phospholipids are located on the outer surfaces of ER membranes. Phospholipids become incorporated into the ER membrane as they are formed, along with membrane proteins synthesized in the rough ER. Thus, the ER produces new membrane that, through vesicle fusion, becomes distributed throughout the endomembrane system.

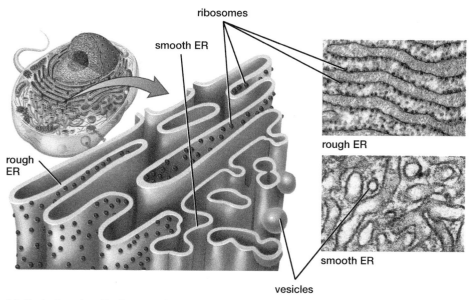

ribosomes

smooth ER

rough ER

rough ER

smooth ER

vesicles

(a) Endoplasmic reticulum may be rough or smooth

(b) Smooth and rough ER

◄ FIGURE 4-12 Endoplasmic reticulum (a) Ribosomes (black dots) stud the outside of the rough ER membrane. Rough ER is continuous with the outer nuclear envelope. Smooth ER is less flattened and more cylindrical than rough ER and may be continuous with rough ER. (b) TEMs of rough and smooth ER with vesicles.

Smooth Endoplasmic Reticulum Smooth ER, which lacks ribosomes, is also involved in the synthesis of cell membrane phospholipids. It is scarce in most cell types, but abundant and specialized in others. For example, smooth ER packs the cells of vertebrate reproductive organs that synthesize steroid sex hormones. Membranes of smooth ER of liver cells have a variety of enzymes embedded within them. Some participate in converting stored glycogen into glucose to provide energy. Others promote the synthesis of the lipid portion of lipoproteins. Finally, smooth ER enzymes break down metabolic wastes such as ammonia, drugs such as alcohol, and poisons such as certain pesticides. In muscle cells, smooth ER is specialized to store calcium ions, which play a central role in muscle contraction.

The Golgi Apparatus Modifies, Sorts, and Packages Important Molecules

Named for the Italian physician and cell biologist Camillo Golgi, who discovered it in 1898, the **Golgi apparatus** (or simply **Golgi**) is a specialized set of membranes resembling a stack of flattened and interconnected sacs (FIG. 4-13). The compartments of the Golgi act like the finishing rooms of a factory, where final touches are added to products to be packaged and exported. Vesicles from the rough ER fuse with the receiving side of the Golgi apparatus, adding their membranes to the Golgi and emptying their contents into the Golgi sacs. Within the Golgi compartments, some of the proteins synthesized in the rough ER are modified further; many are tagged with molecules that specify their destinations in the cell. Finally, vesicles bud off from the "shipping" face of the Golgi, carrying away finished products for use in the cell or export out of the cell.

The Golgi apparatus performs the following functions:

• The Golgi modifies some molecules; an important role of the Golgi is to add carbohydrates to proteins to make glycoproteins. Some of these carbohydrates

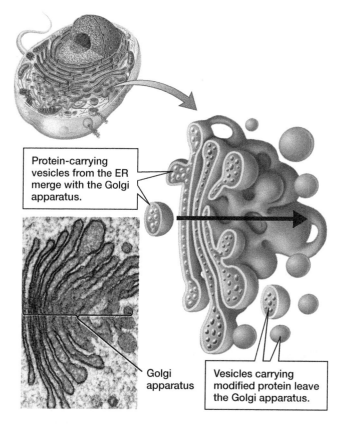

Protein-carrying vesicles from the ER merge with the Golgi apparatus.

Golgi apparatus

Vesicles carrying modified protein leave the Golgi apparatus.

▲ FIGURE 4-13 The Golgi apparatus The black arrow shows the direction of movement of materials through the Golgi as they are modified and sorted. Vesicles bud from the face of the Golgi opposite the ER.

act as "mailing labels" that specify the proteins' destination.

- The Golgi separates various proteins received from the ER according to their destinations. For example, the Golgi apparatus separates the digestive enzymes that are bound for lysosomes from the protein hormones that the cell will secrete.
- The Golgi packages the finished molecules into vesicles that are then transported to other parts of the cell or to the plasma membrane for export.

The Endomembrane System Synthesizes, Modifies, and Transports Proteins to Be Secreted

To understand how some of the components of the endomembrane system work together, let's look at the manufacture and export of antibodies (**FIG. 4-14**). Antibodies, produced by white blood cells, are glycoproteins that bind to foreign invaders (such as disease-causing bacteria) and help destroy them. Antibody proteins are synthesized on ribosomes of the rough ER and released into the ER channels ❶, where they are packaged into vesicles formed from ER membrane. These vesicles travel to the Golgi ❷, where their membranes fuse with the Golgi membranes and release the antibodies inside. Within the Golgi, carbohydrates are attached to the antibodies (transforming them into glycoproteins) ❸, which are then repackaged into vesicles formed from Golgi membrane ❹. The vesicle containing the completed antibodies travels to the plasma membrane and fuses with it, releasing the antibodies outside the cell by exocytosis ❺. From there, they will make their way into the bloodstream to help defend the body against infection.

Lysosomes Serve as the Cell's Digestive System

Lysosomes are membrane-bound sacs that digest food particles ranging from individual proteins to microorganisms such as bacteria (**FIG. 4-15**). Lysosomes contain dozens of different enzymes. These enzymes use hydrolysis to break down almost all large biological molecules including carbohydrates, lipids, proteins, and nucleic acids. The enzymes of lysosomes require an acidic environment (pH 5) to function effectively, so they are almost nonfunctional at the cytosolic pH of about 7.2 that exists in the ER compartment where they are manufactured ❶. Lysosomal enzymes are transported to the Golgi in vesicles that bud from the ER ❷. In the Golgi, a carbohydrate "mailing label" is added to the enzymes ❸; this tag directs them into specific Golgi vesicles that will travel to lysosomes ❹. Lysosomal membranes expend energy to pump hydrogen ions inside, creating an acidic environment (about pH 5) that allows the enzymes to perform optimally. The lysosomal membrane is chemically modified to resist the action of the enzymes it encloses.

Many cells of animals and protists "eat" by endocytosis—that is, by engulfing particles from just outside the cell ❺. The plasma membrane with its enclosed food then pinches off inside the cytosol and forms a large vesicle called a **food vacuole.** Lysosomes merge with these food vacuoles ❻, and the lysosomal enzymes digest the food into small molecules such as monosaccharides, fatty acids, and amino acids. Lysosomes also digest worn-out or defective organelles within the cell, breaking them down into their component molecules. All of these small molecules are released into the cytosol through the lysosomal membrane, where they are used in the cell's metabolic processes.

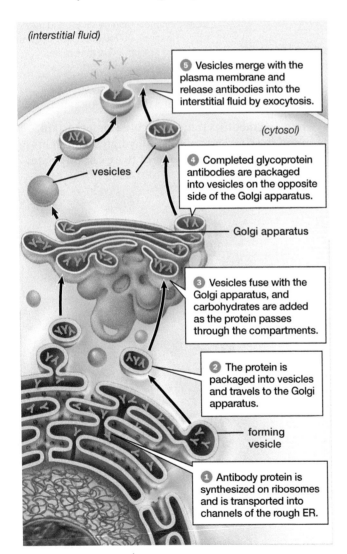

(interstitial fluid)

❺ Vesicles merge with the plasma membrane and release antibodies into the interstitial fluid by exocytosis.

(cytosol)

vesicles

❹ Completed glycoprotein antibodies are packaged into vesicles on the opposite side of the Golgi apparatus.

Golgi apparatus

❸ Vesicles fuse with the Golgi apparatus, and carbohydrates are added as the protein passes through the compartments.

❷ The protein is packaged into vesicles and travels to the Golgi apparatus.

forming vesicle

❶ Antibody protein is synthesized on ribosomes and is transported into channels of the rough ER.

▲ **FIGURE 4-14 A protein is manufactured and exported through the endomembrane system** The formation of an antibody is an example of the process of protein manufacture and export.

THINK CRITICALLY Why is it advantageous for all cellular membranes to have a fundamentally similar composition?

Vacuoles Serve Many Functions, Including Water Regulation, Storage, and Support

Some types of vacuoles, such as food vacuoles, are temporary structures. Other vacuoles, however, persist for the

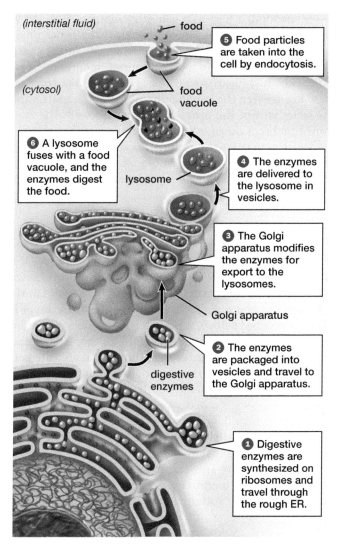

(interstitial fluid)

food

5 Food particles are taken into the cell by endocytosis.

(cytosol)

food vacuole

6 A lysosome fuses with a food vacuole, and the enzymes digest the food.

lysosome

4 The enzymes are delivered to the lysosome in vesicles.

3 The Golgi apparatus modifies the enzymes for export to the lysosomes.

Golgi apparatus

2 The enzymes are packaged into vesicles and travel to the Golgi apparatus.

digestive enzymes

1 Digestive enzymes are synthesized on ribosomes and travel through the rough ER.

▲ **FIGURE 4-15 Lysosomes and food vacuoles are formed by the endomembrane system**

THINK CRITICALLY Why is it important for lysosomal enzymes to be inactive at pH 7.2?

lifetime of a cell. In the following sections, we describe the permanent vacuoles found in some freshwater protists and in plant cells.

Freshwater Protists Have Contractile Vacuoles

Freshwater protists such as *Paramecium* possess **contractile vacuoles** composed of collecting ducts, a central reservoir, and a tube leading to a pore in the plasma membrane (**FIG. 4-16**). Fresh water constantly leaks into the cell through the plasma membrane and then into contractile vacuoles. This influx of water would soon burst the fragile organism if it did not use cellular energy to draw water from its cytosol into collecting ducts. The water then drains into the central reservoir. When the reservoir is full, the contractile vacuole contracts, squirting the water out through a pore in the plasma membrane.

Plant Cells Have Central Vacuoles

A large **central vacuole** occupies three-quarters or more of the volume of most mature plant cells (see Fig. 4-5) and serves several functions. Its membrane helps to regulate the ion content of the cytosol and secretes wastes and toxic substances into the water that fills the central vacuole. Some plants store substances in central vacuoles that deter animals from munching on their otherwise tasty leaves. Vacuoles may also store sugars and amino acids not immediately needed by the cell. Blue or purple pigments stored in central vacuoles are responsible for the colors of many flowers.

Central vacuoles also provide support for plant cells. Dissolved substances cause water to move by osmosis into the vacuole. The resulting water pressure, called *turgor pressure,* within the vacuole pushes the fluid portion of the cytoplasm up against the cell wall with considerable force. Cell walls are usually somewhat flexible, so both the overall shape and the rigidity of the cell depend on turgor pressure within the cell. Turgor pressure thus provides support for the non-woody parts of plants (see Fig. 5-7).

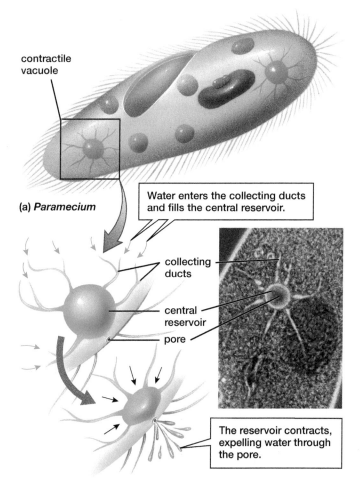

contractile vacuole

(a) *Paramecium*

Water enters the collecting ducts and fills the central reservoir.

collecting ducts

central reservoir

pore

The reservoir contracts, expelling water through the pore.

(b) Contractile vacuole

▲ **FIGURE 4-16 A contractile vacuole (a)** *Paramecium* lives in freshwater ponds and lakes. **(b)** (Left) The vacuole collects and expels water. (Right) The contractile vacuole seen under a light microscope using fluorescent dyes.

Mitochondria Extract Energy from Food Molecules and Chloroplasts Capture Solar Energy

Both mitochondria and chloroplasts are complex organelles with a unique origin. Nearly all biologists accept the **endosymbiont hypothesis** (see Chapter 18) that both mitochondria and chloroplasts evolved from prokaryotic bacteria. Roughly 1.7 billion years ago, these prokaryotes took up residence within other prokaryotic cells, a process called endosymbiosis (Gk. *symbiosis,* living together). Both mitochondria and chloroplasts are surrounded by a double membrane; the outer membrane may have come from the original host cell and the inner membrane from the guest cell. Mitochondria and chloroplasts resemble each other, and prokaryotic cells, in several ways. They are both the size of a typical prokaryotic cell (1 to 5 micrometers in diameter). Both are surrounded by double membranes. Both have assemblies of enzymes that synthesize ATP, as would have been needed by an independent cell. Finally, both possess their own DNA and ribosomes that more closely resemble prokaryotic than eukaryotic DNA and ribosomes.

Mitochondria Use Energy Stored in Food Molecules to Produce ATP

All eukaryotic cells contain **mitochondria** (singular, mitochondrion), organelles that are sometimes called the "powerhouses" of the cell because they extract energy from food molecules and store it in the high-energy bonds of ATP.

Mitochondria possess a pair of membranes (FIG. 4-17). The outer membrane is smooth, whereas the inner membrane forms deep folds called cristae (singular, crista; meaning "crest"). The mitochondrial membranes enclose two fluid-filled spaces: the intermembrane compartment lies between the two membranes, and the matrix fills the space within the inner membrane. Some of the reactions that break down high-energy molecules occur in the fluid of the matrix; the rest are conducted by a series of enzymes attached to the membranes of the cristae. (The role of mitochondria in energy production is described in Chapter 8.)

Chloroplasts Are the Sites of Photosynthesis

Photosynthesis, which captures sunlight and provides the energy to power life, occurs in the chloroplasts found in the cells of plants and some protists. **Chloroplasts** are a type of plastid (described below), surrounded by a double membrane (FIG. 4-18). The inner membrane of the chloroplast encloses a fluid called the *stroma*. Within the stroma are interconnected stacks of hollow, membranous sacs. An individual sac is called a *thylakoid*, and a stack of thylakoids is a *granum* (plural, grana).

The thylakoid membranes contain the pigment molecule **chlorophyll** (which gives plants their green color). During photosynthesis, chlorophyll captures the energy of sunlight and transfers it to other molecules in the thylakoid membranes. These molecules transfer the energy to ATP and other energy carriers. The energy

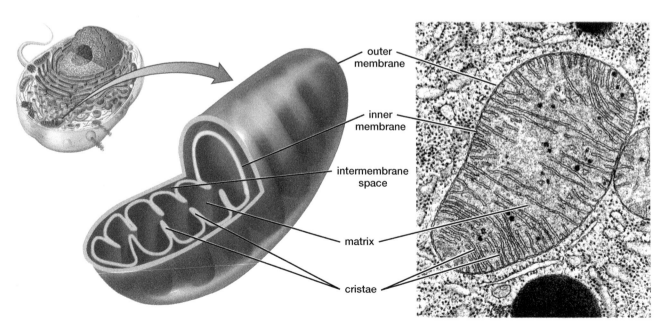

▲ **FIGURE 4-17 A mitochondrion** (Left) Mitochondrial membranes enclose two fluid compartments. The inner membrane forms deep folds called cristae. (Right) A TEM showing mitochondrial structures.

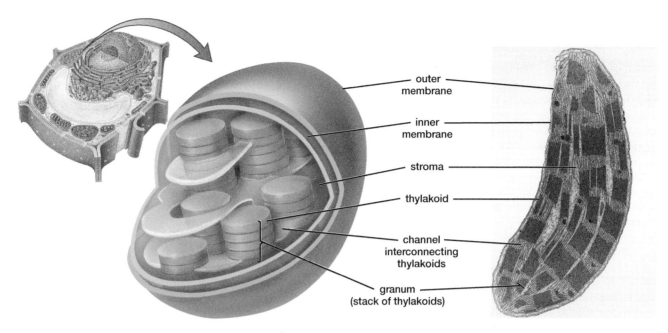

▲ **FIGURE 4-18 The chloroplast is a complex plastid** (Left) A chloroplast is surrounded by a double membrane that encloses the fluid stroma. Within the stroma are stacks of thylakoid sacs called grana. (Right) A TEM showing chloroplast structures.

carriers diffuse into the stroma, where their energy is used to drive the synthesis of sugar from carbon dioxide and water. The sugar stores energy that powers nearly all life on Earth.

Plants Use Some Plastids for Storage

Chloroplasts are highly specialized **plastids,** organelles surrounded by double membranes and used for the synthesis and/or storage of pigments or food molecules. Plastids are found only in plants and photosynthetic protists (FIG. 4-19); all are thought to have originated from prokaryotic cells. Some storage plastids are packed with pigments that give ripe fruits or flower petals their yellow, orange, or red colors. In plants that continue growing from one year to the next, plastids store food produced during the growing season, usually in the form of starch granules. For example, potato cells are stuffed with starch-filled plastids, food for the next spring's growth (see Fig. 4-19, upper right).

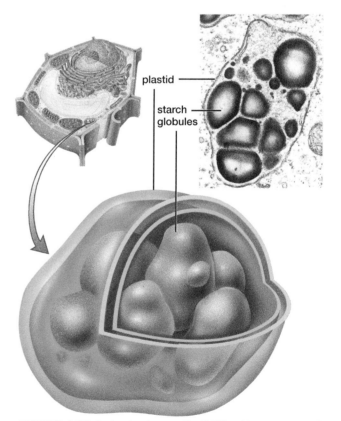

▲ **FIGURE 4-19 A simple storage plastid** Plastids are surrounded by a double outer membrane. This potato plastid stores starch, also seen in the upper right TEM.

CHECK YOUR LEARNING

Can you ...
- define organelles?
- list the structures found in animal but not plant cells, and vice versa?
- describe the structure and function of each major structure found in eukaryotic cells?

New Parts for Human Bodies

Rapid advances in bioengineered tissues and organs requires the coordinated efforts of biochemists, biomedical engineers, cell biologists, and physicians—experts who rarely communicated in the past. But now teams of scientists from various disciplines are working together to grow not only windpipes, but also bone, cartilage, heart valves, bladders, blood vessels, and even small, partially functioning organs.

Recent progress in understanding how cells function within the extracellular matrix they create has set the stage for constructing organs with no synthetic parts. Scientists now recognize that the ECM exists in a dynamic partnership with the cells that secrete it; different cell types secrete unique matrices that support their own specific needs. Even when isolated from their cells, these matrices retain molecular cues that attract appropriate stem cells and stimulate them to differentiate into functioning cells typical of the original organ. This knowledge has generated hope that entire organs from animals such as pigs can be stripped of cells, leaving the matrix intact. The ECM might then serve as both a physical and a biochemical scaffold upon which to recreate the organ, using stem cells taken from the person needing the transplant to avoid tissue rejection.

One challenge is to infuse cells throughout the entire three-dimensional scaffolding of a major organ, such as the heart or liver. Stem cells will need to infiltrate deeply into the ECM and produce not only cells unique to the organ, but also an extensive network of blood vessels to keep it alive and functioning. Scientists have made significant progress by perfusing detergent solution through the natural blood supply of animal—and recently—entire human livers. This procedure washes away all the liver and blood vessel cells, but leaves the three-dimensional channels of the blood vessel network intact within the ECM. Researchers injected suspensions of immature human liver and blood vessel cells into the entry vessel, which conducted the cells throughout the vessel network. After a week in a nutrient-filled bioreactor, the human blood vessel cells had formed a lining within the blood vessel channels, and the liver cells had multiplied within the rest of the scaffold. There is a long road to travel before these one-inch-diameter liver-like tissues are ready to help people whose livers have failed, but the rapidly expanding field of bioengineering raises the prospect that bioartificial body parts will help people live longer, healthier lives in the coming decades.

CONSIDER THIS   What advantages do bioengineered organs have over donor transplants? If you had a failing organ and an experimental bioengineered organ was just starting human trials, would you volunteer to be a recipient?

CHAPTER REVIEW

 Go to **MasteringBiology** for practice quizzes, activities, eText, videos, current events, and more.

Answers to Think Critically, Evaluate This, Multiple Choice, and Fill-in-the-Blank questions can be found in the Answers section at the back of the book.

Summary of Key Concepts

4.1 What Is the Cell Theory?

The cell theory states that every living organism consists of one or more cells, the smallest organisms are single cells, cells are the functional units of multicellular organisms, and all cells arise from preexisting cells.

4.2 What Are the Basic Attributes of Cells?

Cells are small because they must exchange materials with their surroundings by diffusion, a slow process that requires the interior of the cell to be close to the plasma membrane. All cells are surrounded by a plasma membrane that regulates the interchange of materials between the cell and its environment. All cells use DNA as a genetic blueprint and RNA to direct protein synthesis based on DNA. There are two fundamentally different types of cells. Prokaryotic cells lack membrane-enclosed organelles. Eukaryotic cells are generally larger than prokaryotic cells and have a variety of organelles, including a nucleus. See Table 4-1 for a comparison of prokaryotic and eukaryotic cells.

4.3 What Are the Major Features of Prokaryotic Cells?

All members of the domains Archaea and Bacteria consist of prokaryotic cells. Prokaryotic cells are generally smaller than eukaryotic cells and have a simpler internal structure that lacks membrane-enclosed organelles. Some prokaryotes have flagella. Most bacteria are surrounded by a cell wall made of peptidoglycan. Some bacteria, including many that cause disease, attach to surfaces using external capsules or slime layers and/or hair-like protein strands called attachment pili. Sex pili draw bacteria together to allow transfer of plasmids, small rings of DNA that confer special features such as antibiotic resistance. Most bacterial DNA is in a single chromosome in the nucleoid region. Bacterial cytoplasm includes ribosomes and a cytoskeleton. Photosynthetic bacteria may have internal membranes where the reactions of photosynthesis occur.

4.4 What Are the Major Features of Eukaryotic Cells?

Eukaryotic cells have a variety of membrane-enclosed structures called organelles, some of which differ between plant and animal cells (see Table 4-1). Both secrete an extracellular matrix. In animal cells, the ECM consists of proteins and polysaccharides that provide structural and biochemical support. In plants cells, the ECM is the supportive and porous cell wall composed primarily of cellulose.

Eukaryotic cells have an internal cytoskeleton of protein filaments that transports and anchors organelles, and that, in animal cells, shapes the cells, aids in cell division, and allows certain cells to move. Some eukaryotic cells have cilia or flagella, extensions of the plasma membrane that contain microtubules in a characteristic pattern. These structures move fluids past the cell or move the cell through a fluid.

Genetic material (DNA) is contained within the nucleus, surrounded by the double membrane of the nuclear envelope. Pores in the nuclear envelope regulate the movement of molecules between nucleus and cytoplasm. The genetic material is organized into strands called chromosomes, which consist of DNA and proteins. The nucleolus within the nucleus is the site of ribosome synthesis. Ribosomes, composed of rRNA and protein, are the sites of protein synthesis within the cytoplasm.

The endomembrane system within eukaryotic cells includes the nuclear envelope, endoplasmic reticulum (ER), Golgi apparatus, and lysosomes and other vesicles. The ER forms a series of interconnected membranous compartments and is a major site of new membrane production. Rough ER, continuous with the outer nuclear envelope, bears ribosomes where proteins are manufactured. These proteins are modified, folded, and transported within the ER channels. Smooth ER, which lacks ribosomes, manufactures lipids such as steroid hormones, detoxifies drugs and metabolic wastes, and stores calcium. The Golgi apparatus is a series of flattened membranous sacs. The Golgi processes and modifies materials that are synthesized in the rough ER. Substances modified in the Golgi are sorted and packaged into vesicles for transport elsewhere in the cell. Lysosomes are specialized sacs of membrane containing digestive enzymes. These merge with food vacuoles and break down food particles. Lysosomes also digest defective organelles.

Some freshwater protists have contractile vacuoles that collect and expel excess water. Plants use central vacuoles to support their cells and may also use these vacuoles to store nutrients, pigments, wastes, and toxic materials.

All eukaryotic cells contain mitochondria, which extract energy from food molecules and store it in the high-energy bonds of ATP. Cells of plants and photosynthetic protists contain plastids. Plastids include chloroplasts, in which photosynthesis captures solar energy and stores it in sugar molecules. Other plastids store pigments or starch. The endosymbiont hypothesis states that mitochondria and chloroplasts (as well as other plastids) originated from prokaryotic cells.

Key Terms

archaea *56*
bacteria *56*
basal body *63*
cell theory *53*
cell wall *58*
central vacuole *69*
centriole *63*
chlorophyll *70*
chloroplast *70*
chromatin *64*
chromosome *64*
cilium *62*
contractile vacuole *69*
cytoplasm *56*
cytoskeleton *56*
cytosol *56*
deoxyribonucleic acid (DNA) *56*
diffusion *53*
endomembrane system *66*
endoplasmic reticulum (ER) *66*
endosymbiont hypothesis *70*
eukaryotic *56*
extracellular matrix *60*
flagellum *58*
food vacuole *68*
Golgi apparatus *67*
intermediate filament *61*
lysosome *68*
microfilament *61*
microtubule *61*
mitochondrion *70*
nuclear envelope *63*
nuclear pore complex *63*
nucleoid *58*
nucleolus *64*
nucleus *63*
organelle *59*
pilus *58*
plasma membrane *56*
plasmid *58*
plastid *71*
prokaryotic *56*
ribonucleic acid (RNA) *56*
ribosome *56*
vesicle *66*

Thinking Through the Concepts

Multiple Choice

1. Which of the following is/are found only in prokaryotic cells?
   a. plasmids
   b. a cytoskeleton
   c. mitochondria
   d. ribosomes

2. Which of the following is *not* a function of the cytoskeleton?
   a. organelle movement
   b. extracellular support
   c. cell movement
   d. maintenance of cell shape

3. Which of the following statements is False?
   a. Cilia and flagella can move cells through fluids.
   b. Cilia and flagella are supported and moved by microfilaments.
   c. Cilia are shorter and more numerous than flagella.
   d. Flagella propel human sperm.

4. Which of the following is *not* a location of ribosomes?
   a. on the nuclear membrane
   b. free in the cytoplasm
   c. strung along messenger RNA
   d. inside the rough ER

5. Which of the following statements is False?
   a. Photosynthesis occurs in plastids.
   b. Chloroplasts extract energy from food storage molecules.
   c. Mitochondria likely originated from prokaryotic cells.
   d. Plant cell walls are a type of extracellular matrix.

Fill-in-the-Blank

1. The plasma membrane is composed of two major types of molecules, _____ and _____ .
   Which type of molecule is responsible for each of the following functions? Isolation from the surroundings: _____ ; interactions with other cells: _____ .

2. The three types of cytoskeleton fibers are _____, _____, and _____. Which of these supports cilia? _____. Moves organelles? _____. Allows muscle contraction? _____. Provides a supporting internal framework for the cell? _____.

3. After each description, fill in the appropriate term: "workbenches" of the cell: _____; comes in rough and smooth forms: _____; site of ribosome production: _____; a stack of flattened membranous sacs: _____; outermost layer of plant cells: _____; ferries blueprints for protein production from the nucleus to the cytoplasm: _____.

4. Antibody proteins are synthesized on ribosomes associated with the _____. The antibody proteins are packaged into membranous sacs called _____ and are then transported to the _____. There, what type of molecule is added to the protein? _____ After the antibody is completed, it is packaged into vesicles that fuse with the _____.

5. After each description, fill in the appropriate structure: "powerhouses" of the cell: _____; capture solar energy: _____; structure outside of animal cells: _____; region of prokaryotic cell containing DNA: _____; propel fluid past cells: _____; consists of the cytosol and the organelles within it: _____.

6. Two organelles that are believed to have evolved from prokaryotic cells are _____ and _____. Evidence for this hypothesis is that both have _____ membranes, both have groups of enzymes that synthesize _____, and their _____ is similar to that of prokaryotic cells.

7. What structure in bacterial cells is composed of peptidoglycan? _____ What structure in prokaryotic cells serves a similar function to the nucleus in eukaryotic cells? _____ Short segments of DNA that confer special features such as antibiotic resistance on bacteria are called _____. Bacterial structures called _____ pull bacterial cells together so they can transfer DNA.

Review Questions

1. What are the three principles of the cell theory?

2. Which cytoplasmic structures are common to both plant and animal cells, and which are found in one type but not the other?

3. Name the proteins of the eukaryotic cytoskeleton; describe their relative sizes and major functions.

4. Describe the nucleus and the function of each of its components, including the nuclear envelope, chromatin, chromosomes, DNA, and the nucleolus.

5. What are the functions of mitochondria and chloroplasts? Why do scientists believe that these organelles arose from prokaryotic cells? What is this hypothesis called?

6. What is the function of ribosomes? Where in the cell are they found? Are they limited to eukaryotic cells?

7. Describe the structure and function of the endoplasmic reticulum (smooth and rough) and the Golgi apparatus and how they work together.

8. How are lysosomes formed? What is their function?

9. Diagram the structure of eukaryotic cilia and flagella. Describe how each moves and what their movement accomplishes.

10. List the structures of bacterial cells that have the same name and function as some eukaryotic structures, but a different molecular composition.

Applying the Concepts

1. If samples of muscle tissue were taken from the legs of a world-class marathon runner and a sedentary individual, which would you expect to have a higher density of mitochondria? Why?

2. One of the functions of the cytoskeleton in animal cells is to give shape to the cell. Plant cells have a fairly rigid cell wall surrounding the plasma membrane. Does this mean that a cytoskeleton is unnecessary for a plant cell? Explain.

3. What problems would an enormous round cell encounter? What adaptations might help a very large cell survive?

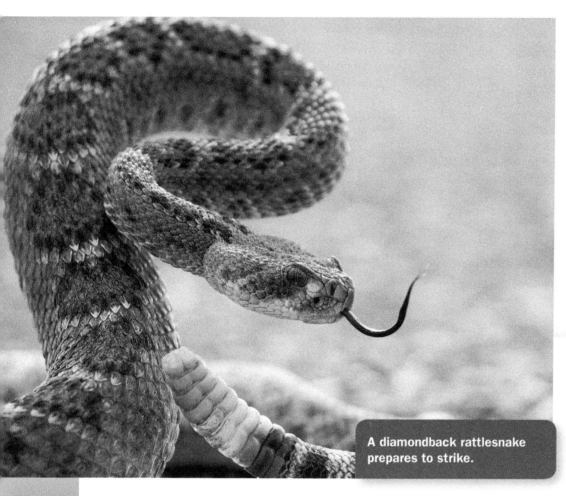

A diamondback rattlesnake prepares to strike.

Vicious Venoms

THIRTEEN-YEAR-OLD JUSTIN SCHWARTZ was enjoying his 3-week stay at a summer camp near Yosemite National Park. But that all changed when, after hiking 4.5 miles, Justin rested on some sunny rocks, hands hanging loosely at his sides. Suddenly, he felt a piercing pain in his left palm. A 5-foot rattlesnake—probably feeling threatened by Justin's dangling arm—had struck without warning.

His campmates stared in alarm as the snake slithered into the undergrowth, but Justin focused on his hand, where his palm was swelling and the pain was becoming agonizing. He suddenly felt weak and dizzy. As counselors and campmates spent the next 4 hours carrying him down the trail, pain and discoloration spread up Justin's arm, and his hand felt as if it were going to burst. A helicopter whisked him to a hospital, where he fell unconscious. A day later, he regained consciousness at the University of California Davis Medical Center. There, Justin spent more than a month undergoing 10 surgeries. These relieved the enormous pressure from swelling in his arm,

removed dead muscle tissue, and began the long process of repairing the extensive damage to his hand and arm.

Diane Kiehl's ordeal began as she dressed for an informal Memorial Day celebration with her family, pulling on blue jeans that she had tossed on the bathroom floor the previous night. Feeling a sting on her right thigh, she ripped off the jeans and watched with irritation as a long-legged spider crawled out. Living in an old house in the Kansas countryside, Diane had grown accustomed to spiders—which are often harmless—but this was an exception: a brown recluse. The two small puncture wounds seemed merely a minor annoyance until the next day, when an extensive, itchy rash appeared at the site. By the third day, intermittent pain pierced like a knife through her thigh. A physician gave her painkillers, steroids to reduce the swelling, and antibiotics to combat bacteria introduced by the spider's mouthparts. The next 10 days were a nightmare of pain from the growing sore, now covered with oozing blisters and underlain with clotting blood. It took 4 months for the lesion to heal. Even a year later, Diane sometimes felt pain in the large scar that remained.

How do rattlesnake and brown recluse spider venoms cause leaky blood vessels, disintegrating skin and tissue, and sometimes life-threatening symptoms throughout the body? What do venoms have to do with cell membranes?

AT A GLANCE

5.1 HOW IS THE STRUCTURE OF THE CELL MEMBRANE RELATED TO ITS FUNCTION?

All cells, as well as organelles within eukaryotic cells, are surrounded by membranes. All the membranes of a cell have a similar basic structure: proteins suspended in a double layer, or bilayer (Gk. *bi*, double), of phospholipids (FIG. 5-1). Beyond this basic structure, membranes differ from one tissue type to another. The structures of their proteins and phospholipids can change dynamically in response to the environment and the cell's changing needs.

Cell membranes perform several crucial functions:

- They isolate the contents of membrane-enclosed organelles from the surrounding cytosol and the contents of the cell from the surrounding interstitial fluid.

- They regulate the exchange of substances between the cell and the interstitial fluid or between membrane-enclosed organelles and the surrounding cytosol.
- They allow communication among the cells of multicellular organisms.
- They create attachments within and between cells.
- They regulate many biochemical reactions.

These are formidable tasks for a structure so thin that 10,000 membranes stacked atop one another would scarcely equal the thickness of a book's page.

Membranes Are "Fluid Mosaics" in Which Proteins Move Within Layers of Lipids

Before the 1970s, cell biologists knew that cell membranes consist primarily of proteins and a double layer of lipids, but they

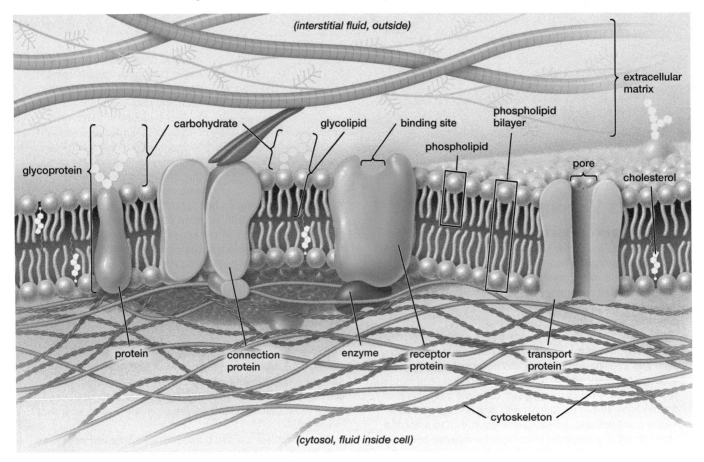

(interstitial fluid, outside)

extracellular matrix

glycoprotein
carbohydrate
glycolipid
binding site
phospholipid bilayer
phospholipid
pore
cholesterol

protein
connection protein
enzyme
receptor protein
transport protein
cytoskeleton

(cytosol, fluid inside cell)

▲ **FIGURE 5-1 The plasma membrane** The plasma membrane is a bilayer of phospholipids interspersed with cholesterol molecules and embedded with proteins (blue). Membrane proteins include recognition, connection, receptor, and transport proteins, as well as enzymes. There are also many glycoproteins and glycolipids with attached carbohydrates.

did not know how these molecules were arranged within the membrane. In 1972, S. J. Singer and G. L. Nicolson proposed the **fluid mosaic model** of cell membranes, which forms the basis for our understanding of membrane structure and function. A **fluid** is any substance whose molecules can flow past one another; fluids include gases, liquids, and cell membranes. According to the fluid mosaic model, the cell membrane consists of a fluid formed by the bilayer of phospholipids, with a variety of different embedded proteins forming a sort of "mosaic" patchwork within this fluid (see Fig. 5-1).

The Fluid Phospholipid Bilayer Helps to Isolate the Cell's Contents

A phospholipid consists of two very different parts: a "head" that is polar and hydrophilic (attracted to water) and a pair of fatty acid "tails" that are nonpolar and hydrophobic (not attracted to water). Cell membranes contain a variety of phospholipids with structures similar to those shown in FIGURE 5-2. Most phospholipids help isolate the cell from its surroundings, but some have other functions, such as identifying cells. For example, *glycolipids* (lipids with carbohydrates attached) on red blood cell membranes identify blood as type A, B, AB, or O. Other glycolipids help identify a cell as belonging to a specific individual.

Phospholipids in membranes arrange themselves in a particular way (see Fig. 5-1) due to the fact that all cells are immersed in watery solutions. Single-celled organisms may live in marine or freshwater environments, and water saturates the cellulose walls that surround plant cells. The outer surfaces of animal plasma membranes are bathed in watery **interstitial fluid,** a weakly salty liquid resembling blood, but without its cells or large proteins. Inside the plasma membrane, the *cytosol* (the fluid portion of the cytoplasm) is mostly water. In these watery surroundings, phospholipids spontaneously arrange themselves into a double layer called a **phospholipid bilayer.** Hydrogen bonds between water and the hydrophilic phospholipid heads cause the heads to face the water on either side. The hydrophobic phospholipid tails cluster together within the bilayer.

The components of cell membranes are in constant motion. To understand why, it is important to be aware that, at any temperature above absolute zero (−459.4°F or −273°C), atoms, molecules, and ions are in constant random motion. As the temperature increases, their rate of motion increases; at temperatures that support life, these particles move rapidly indeed. The phospholipid molecules in a membrane are not chemically bonded, so at body temperature their constant random motion causes them to shift about freely, although they rarely flip between the two layers of membrane.

The flexibility of the bilayer is crucial for membrane function. If plasma membranes were stiff, your cells would break open and die as you moved about. The fluid nature of membranes also allows membranes to merge with one another. For example, vesicles from the Golgi expel their contents to the outside of the cell by merging with the plasma membrane (see Chapter 4). To maintain flexibility, most membranes have a consistency similar to room-temperature olive oil. But olive oil becomes a solid if you refrigerate it, so what happens to membranes when an organism gets cold? To find out, see "Health Watch: Membrane Fluidity, Phospholipids, and Fumbling Fingers."

All animal cell membranes contain cholesterol (see Fig. 5-1), which is especially abundant in the plasma membrane. Interactions between cholesterol and phospholipids help to stabilize the membrane, making it less fluid at higher temperatures and less solid at lower temperatures. A high cholesterol content reduces the permeability of the membrane to hydrophilic substances and small molecules that would otherwise diffuse through it. Reducing permeability allows the cell to exert greater control over which substances enter and leave it.

Some biological molecules, including fat-soluble vitamins and steroid hormones such as estrogen and testosterone (see Chapter 3), are hydrophobic and can diffuse directly through the phospholipid bilayer. However, most molecules used by cells, including salts, amino acids, and sugars, are hydrophilic. Because these molecules are polar and water soluble, they cannot move through the nonpolar, hydrophobic fatty acid tails of the phospholipid bilayer. Movement of these substances in or out of the cell relies on the mosaic of proteins within the membrane, which we will discuss next.

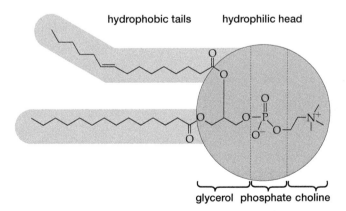

hydrophobic tails   hydrophilic head

glycerol   phosphate   choline

▲ FIGURE 5-2 **A phospholipid** Phosphatidylcholine (shown here) is abundant in cell membranes. The double bond in one of the fatty acid tails causes the tail to bend.

CASE STUDY   CONTINUED

Vicious Venoms

Some of the most devastating effects of certain snake and spider venoms occur because they contain *phospholipases*, enzymes that break down phospholipids. You now know that phospholipids are a major component of cell membranes, which isolate the cell's contents from its surroundings. As the phospholipids degrade, the membranes become leaky, causing the cells to die.

As if phospholipases aren't deadly enough, snake venoms also contain enzymes that break down proteins. What functions do membrane proteins serve?

Membrane Fluidity, Phospholipids, and Fumbling Fingers

Cell membranes need to maintain optimal fluidity to allow the many embedded proteins in the membrane to function. Temperature has a significant impact on membrane fluidity. As temperature increases, phospholipid molecules jiggle around more vigorously and maintain greater distance from one another, which makes the membrane more fluid. As temperatures cool, the molecules pack together more tightly, causing the membrane to stiffen.

Many organisms do not maintain constant body temperatures, so they must possess mechanisms for maintaining optimal membrane fluidity in the face of seasonal changes. Scientists studying plants, fish, frogs, snails, and mammals have found that these organisms can modify the composition of their cell membranes. As the temperature falls, they incorporate phospholipids containing more unsaturated fatty acids into their membranes. When the temperature rises, the organisms restore the saturated phospholipids. Why? How fluid a membrane is at a given temperature is strongly influenced by the relative amounts of saturated and unsaturated fatty acid tails in membrane phospholipids. Saturated fatty acids (with no double-bonded carbons) are straight and can pack tightly together, forming a relatively stiff membrane. Unsaturated fatty acids have one or more double-bonded carbons, each introducing a kink into the tail (see Fig. 5-2). This structure forces the phospholipids farther apart, making the membrane more fluid (FIG. E5-1). Adjusting the fatty acids in the phospholipids helps organisms maintain optimal membrane fluidity during seasonal temperature changes.

But when you get caught out in the cold, your membranes don't have time to adjust their phospholipids. If your core temperature suddenly begins to fall, your body will reduce blood flow to your hands and feet, conserving warmth for vital organs such as your heart and brain. As your hands get colder, it becomes harder to control your fingers, and your sense of touch will diminish (FIG. E5-2). What is happening?

Cooling causes the nerves that control muscles and carry sensations to conduct nerve impulses more slowly, which makes it difficult to coordinate delicate hand movements like zipping a coat or lighting a fire. Scientists do not yet know exactly why this happens, but there is evidence supporting the hypothesis that as membranes stiffen in the cold, the functioning of embedded proteins—including the ion channels responsible for transmitting nerve impulses—is hampered. If your hands get extremely cold (but your tissues have not frozen, which eliminates sensation), you are likely to feel excruciating "cold pain." The pain will persist even though you will be practically unable to move your hands and you will have lost your sense of touch.

◀ FIGURE E5-2 Hand thermograph taken with a temperature-sensitive camera

coolest

warmest

more saturated fatty acids
less fluidity

more unsaturated fatty acids
greater fluidity

▲ FIGURE E5-1 Tail kinks in phospholipids increase membrane fluidity

THINK CRITICALLY Researchers have recently discovered ion channels in pain-generating skin nerve cells whose ability to conduct ions is actually enhanced by cold, making the nerve cell more active. Form a hypothesis as to why these receptors evolved.

A Variety of Proteins Form a Mosaic Within the Membrane

Thousands of different membrane proteins are embedded within or attached to the surfaces of the phospholipid bilayer of cell membranes. Many membrane proteins bear carbohydrate groups that project from the outer membrane surface (see Fig. 5-1). These proteins are called **glycoproteins** (Gk. *glyco*, sweet; referring to the carbohydrate sugar subunits). Membrane proteins may be grouped into five major categories based on their function: enzymes, recognition proteins, receptor proteins, transport proteins, and connection proteins.

Enzymes

Proteins called **enzymes** promote chemical reactions that synthesize or break apart biological molecules (see Chapter 6). A variety of enzymes are associated with cell membranes, performing different functions in the plasma membrane and in various organelles. For example, enzymes involved in ATP synthesis are embedded in the inner mitochondrial membrane. Plasma membrane enzymes help synthesize the supportive extracellular matrix that fills spaces between animal cells. In cells lining the small intestine, plasma membrane enzymes complete the breakdown of carbohydrates and proteins as these nutrients are taken into the cells.

Recognition Proteins

Recognition proteins are glycoproteins that serve as identification tags. The cells of each individual organism bear distinctive glycoproteins that identify the cells as "self." Immune cells ignore self-cells and attack invading cells, such as bacteria, that have different recognition proteins on their membranes. For successful organ transplants, the most important recognition glycoproteins of the donor must match those of the recipient so the organ won't be attacked by the recipient's immune system.

Transport Proteins

Transport proteins span the phospholipid bilayer and regulate the movement of hydrophilic molecules across the membrane. Some transport proteins form pores (channels) that can be opened or closed to allow specific substances to pass across the membrane. Other transport proteins bind substances and conduct them through the membrane, sometimes using cellular energy. Transport proteins are described later in this chapter.

Receptor Proteins

Most cells bear dozens of types of **receptor proteins** (some of which are glycoproteins; see Fig. 5-1) that span their plasma membranes. Each has a binding site specific for a messenger molecule, such as a particular hormone or neurotransmitter (a nerve cell messenger). When the appropriate messenger molecule binds, it activates the receptor protein.

Some membrane proteins act as both receptors and ion channels. One of the ways they do this is through direct receptor action. When a messenger molecule binds the receptor, it immediately and directly causes an ion channel within the same protein to open (**FIG. 5-3a**). The best known example of such direct receptor action occurs in a protein in the membranes of skeletal muscle cells (which move the body). This protein binds the neurotransmitter acetylcholine, which opens an ion channel in the same protein and allows ions to flow that stimulate the muscle cell to contract. Other receptor proteins produce their effects through an indirect action. Upon binding a messenger molecule—which can be a neurotransmitter or a hormone—the receptor protein changes its shape and biochemical activity. This starts a series of reactions within the cell that produce effects (such as opening many ion channels) at different sites (**FIG. 5-3b**). Most neurotransmitters and hormones act in this manner.

Connection Proteins

A diverse group of **connection proteins** anchors cell membranes in various ways. Some connection proteins help maintain cell shape by linking the plasma membrane to the cell's cytoskeleton. Other connection proteins span the plasma membrane, linking the cytoskeleton inside the cell with the extracellular matrix outside, which helps anchor the cell in place within a tissue (see Fig. 5-1). Connection proteins also link adjacent cells, as described later.

(a) Direct receptor action

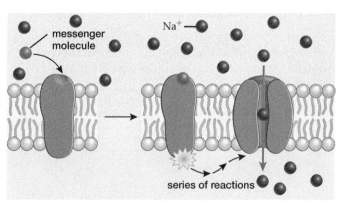

(b) Indirect receptor action

▲ FIGURE 5-3 **Receptor protein activation (a)** A neurotransmitter binds a receptor site on a membrane channel protein, causing the channel to open and allow a flow of ions. **(b)** A messenger molecule (such as a hormone or neurotransmitter) binds a membrane receptor, which stimulates a series of reactions inside the cell that cause channel proteins to open.

CHECK YOUR LEARNING

Can you ...

- describe the components, structure, and functions of cell membranes?
- diagram and describe the fluid mosaic model of cell membranes?
- explain how the different components of cell membranes contribute to their functions?

Vicious Venoms

Most snake venoms are nasty cocktails of toxins. In addition to breaking down phospholipids, some rattlesnake venoms contain toxins that bind to and inhibit the activity of receptor proteins for acetylcholine. Inhibiting the action of acetylcholine on heart muscle cells increases heart rate, which speeds the travel of venom through the body. Krait snakes, native to Asia, produce a venom protein that binds to the direct-acting membrane channel receptors for acetylcholine, including those on skeletal muscle cells. Once bound, the protein remains firmly attached, blocking acetylcholine from binding. This prevents muscles from contracting; an untreated krait bite victim often dies when the skeletal muscles that control breathing are paralyzed.

The ability of substances to move across membranes is crucial not only to controlling heart rate and breathing, but also to all other aspects of staying alive. How do proteins control the movement of substances across membranes?

5.2 HOW DO SUBSTANCES MOVE ACROSS MEMBRANES?

Some substances, especially individual molecules and ions, can move across membranes by diffusing through the phospholipid bilayer or traveling through specialized transport proteins. To provide some background on how membrane transport works, we begin our study with a few definitions:

- A **solute** is a substance that can be dissolved (dispersed into individual atoms, molecules, or ions) in a **solvent,** which is a fluid (usually a liquid) capable of dissolving the solute. Water, in which all of the cell's chemical processes occur, dissolves so many different solutes that it is sometimes called the "universal solvent."
- **Concentration** is the amount of solute in a given volume of solvent.
- A **gradient** is a difference in certain properties—such as temperature, pressure, electrical charge, or concentration—between two adjacent regions. Energy must be expended to create a gradient. Gradients decrease over time unless an impenetrable barrier separates the adjacent regions or energy is supplied to maintain them.

Molecules in Fluids Diffuse in Response to Gradients

Recall that atoms, molecules, and ions are in constant random motion. As a result of this motion, molecules and ions in solution are continuously bombarding one another and the structures surrounding them. Over time, random movements of solutes produce a net movement from regions of high concentration to regions of low concentration, a process called **diffusion.** The greater the concentration gradient, the more rapidly diffusion occurs. If nothing opposes this diffusion (such as electrical charge, pressure differences, or physical barriers), then the random movement of molecules will eventually cause the substance to become evenly dispersed throughout the fluid. In an analogy to gravity, molecules moving from regions of high concentration to regions of low concentration are described as moving "down" their concentration gradients.

To watch diffusion in action, place a drop of food coloring in a glass of water (FIG. 5-4 ❶). Random motion propels dye molecules both into and out of the dye droplet, but there is a net transfer of dye into the water and of water into the dye, down their respective concentration gradients ❷. The net movement of dye will continue until it is uniformly dispersed in the water ❸. If you compare the diffusion of a dye in hot water to that in cold water, you will see that heat increases the diffusion rate by causing molecules to move faster.

SUMMING UP: Principles of Diffusion

- Diffusion is the net movement of molecules down a gradient from high to low concentration.
- The greater the concentration gradient, the faster the rate of diffusion.
- The higher the temperature, the faster the rate of diffusion.
- If no other processes intervene, diffusion will continue until the concentrations become equal throughout the solution, that is, until the concentration gradient is eliminated.

❶ A drop of dye is placed in water.

❷ Dye molecules diffuse into the water; water molecules diffuse into the dye.

❸ Both dye molecules and water molecules are evenly dispersed.

dye molecules

water molecule

◀ FIGURE 5-4 **Diffusion of a dye in water**

TABLE 5-1	**Transport Across Membranes**
Passive Transport	Diffusion of substances across a membrane down a gradient of concentration, pressure, or electrical charge; does not require cellular energy
Simple diffusion	Diffusion of water, dissolved gases, or lipid-soluble molecules through the phospholipid bilayer of a membrane
Facilitated diffusion	Diffusion of water, ions, or water-soluble molecules through a membrane via a channel or carrier protein
Osmosis	Diffusion of water across a selectively permeable membrane from a region of higher free water concentration to a region of lower free water concentration
Energy-Requiring Transport	Movement of substances through membranes using cellular energy, usually supplied by ATP
Active transport	Movement of individual small molecules or ions against their concentration gradients through membrane-spanning proteins
Endocytosis	Movement of fluids, specific molecules, or particles into a cell; occurs as the plasma membrane engulfs the substance in a membranous sac that pinches off and enters the cytosol
Exocytosis	Movement of particles or large molecules out of a cell; occurs as a membrane within the cell encloses the material, moves to the cell surface, and fuses with the plasma membrane, allowing its contents to diffuse out

Movement Through Membranes Occurs by Passive Transport and Energy-Requiring Transport

To stay alive, cells must generate and maintain concentration gradients, or the differences in solute concentrations across their membranes. Plasma membranes are described as **selectively permeable** because their proteins allow only specific ions or molecules to pass through, or permeate. The selective permeability of the plasma membrane creates a barrier that helps maintain the cell's concentration gradients.

The plasma membrane permits substances to move through it in two different ways: passive transport and energy-requiring transport (**TABLE 5-1**). **Passive transport** involves diffusion of substances across cell membranes down their concentration gradients, whereas **energy-requiring transport** requires that the cell expend energy to move substances across membranes. Energy-requiring transport occurs when transporting substances against concentration gradients, or when moving particles or fluid droplets into or out of the cell.

Passive Transport Includes Simple Diffusion, Facilitated Diffusion, and Osmosis

Diffusion can occur within a fluid or across a membrane that is permeable to the diffusing substance. Many molecules cross plasma membranes by diffusion, driven by concentration differences between the cytosol and the surrounding interstitial fluid.

Some Molecules Move Across Membranes by Simple Diffusion

Some molecules diffuse directly through the phospholipid bilayer of cell membranes, a process called **simple diffusion** (**FIG. 5-5a**). Very small molecules with no net charge, such

(a) Simple diffusion through the phospholipid bilayer

(b) Facilitated diffusion through carrier proteins

(c) Facilitated diffusion through channel proteins

(d) Osmosis through aquaporins or the phospholipid bilayer

▲ **FIGURE 5-5 Types of diffusion through the plasma membrane (a)** Small, uncharged, or lipid-soluble molecules diffuse directly through the phospholipid bilayer. Here, oxygen molecules diffuse down their concentration gradient (red arrow). **(b)** Carrier proteins have binding sites for specific molecules, such as glucose. Binding causes the carrier to change shape and shuttle the molecule across the membrane down its concentration gradient. **(c)** Facilitated diffusion through specific channel proteins allows ions, such as chloride, to cross membranes. **(d)** Osmosis is the diffusion of water. Water molecules can pass through the phospholipid bilayer by simple diffusion, or they move far more rapidly by facilitated diffusion through aquaporins.

as water, oxygen, and carbon dioxide, can travel across cell membranes by simple diffusion, as can lipid-soluble molecules, including alcohol, certain vitamins, and steroid hormones. The rate of simple diffusion is increased by larger concentration gradients, higher temperatures, smaller molecular sizes, and greater solubility in lipids.

How can water—a polar molecule—diffuse directly through the hydrophobic (literally "water-fearing") phospholipid bilayer? Water molecules are so small, some stray into the thicket of phospholipid tails, and the random movement of these water molecules carries them through the membrane. Because simple diffusion of water through the phospholipid bilayer is relatively slow, many cell types have specific transport proteins for water, described later.

Some Molecules Cross Membranes by Facilitated Diffusion Using Membrane Transport Proteins

The phospholipid bilayers of cell membranes are quite impermeable to most polar molecules, for example, sugars, whose size and lack of lipid solubility keeps them out. Ions, such as K^+, Na^+, Cl^-, and Ca^{2+}, are also excluded even though they are small, because their charges cause polar water molecules to cluster around them, forming an aggregation that is too large to move directly through the phospholipid bilayer. Therefore, ions and polar molecules must use specific transport proteins to move through cell membranes, a process called **facilitated diffusion.** Two types of proteins allow facilitated diffusion: carrier proteins and channel proteins. The cell does not expend energy when using these transport proteins, which facilitate diffusion down a pre-existing concentration gradient either into or out of the cell.

Carrier proteins span the cell membrane and have regions that loosely bind certain ions or specific molecules such as sugars or small proteins. This binding of ions or molecules causes the carrier proteins to change shape and transfer the bound molecules across the membrane. For example, glucose carrier proteins in plasma membranes allow this sugar to diffuse down its concentration gradient from the interstitial fluid into cells, which continuously use up glucose to meet their energy needs (FIG. 5-5b).

Channel proteins form pores through the cell membrane. For example, the cell membranes of mitochondria and chloroplasts have pores that allow passage of many different water-soluble substances. In contrast, ion channel proteins (ion channels) are small and highly selective (FIG. 5-5c). Many ion channels help preserve concentration gradients by remaining closed unless they are opened by specific stimuli, such as a neurotransmitter binding to a receptor protein. Ion channel proteins are selective because their interior diameters limit the size of the ions that can pass through and because specific amino acids that line the pore have weak electrical charges that attract specific ions and repel others. For example, slight negative charges on some amino acids inside Na^+ channels attract Na^+ but repel Cl^-.

Many cells have specialized water channel proteins called **aquaporins** (literally, "water pores"; FIG. 5-5d). The narrow aquaporin channels are selective for water molecules, which are extremely small. Some amino acids lining the aquaporin channel protein have slight positive charges that attract the negative poles of water but repel positive ions. To learn more about aquaporins, see "How Do We Know That? The Discovery of Aquaporins."

Osmosis Is the Diffusion of Water Across Selectively Permeable Membranes

Osmosis is the diffusion of water across a membrane that is selectively permeable to water in response to gradients of concentration, pressure, or temperature. Here, we will focus on osmosis from a region of higher water concentration to a region of lower water concentration.

What do we mean by a "high water concentration" or a "low water concentration"? Water containing no solutes has the highest possible water concentration, causing more water molecules to collide with—and so move through—a water-permeable membrane. Any solute reduces the water concentration by replacing some of the water molecules in a given volume of the solution. In addition to displacing water molecules, polar solutes and ions also attract and weakly bind water molecules around them, so the water molecules aren't as free to move across a water-permeable membrane. For these reasons, the higher the concentration of solute, the lower the concentration of water. Osmosis (like other forms of diffusion) will cause a net movement of water molecules from the solution with a higher water concentration (a lower solute concentration) into the solution with a lower water concentration (a higher solute concentration). For example, water will move by osmosis from a solution with less dissolved sugar into a solution with more dissolved sugar.

Solutions with equal concentrations of solute—and thus equal concentrations of water—are described as being **isotonic** to one another (Gk. *iso*, same). When isotonic solutions are separated by a water-permeable membrane, water moves equally through the membrane in both directions, so there is no net movement of water. When comparing two solutions with different concentrations of a solute, the solution with the greater concentration of solute is described as being **hypertonic** (Gk. *hyper*, greater than) to the less concentrated solution. The more dilute solution is described as **hypotonic** (Gk. *hypo*, below). Water tends to move through water-permeable membranes from hypotonic solutions into hypertonic solutions. This movement will continue until the water concentrations (and thus the solute concentrations) on both sides of the membrane are equal.

SUMMING UP: **Principles of Osmosis**

- Osmosis is the movement of water through a selectively water-permeable membrane by simple diffusion or by facilitated diffusion through aquaporins.
- Water moves down its concentration gradient from a higher concentration of free water molecules to a lower concentration of free water molecules.

HOW DO WE KNOW THAT?

The Discovery of Aquaporins

Sometimes a chance observation leads to a scientific break-through. Scientists had long observed that osmosis directly through the phospholipid bilayer is much too slow to account for water movement across certain cell membranes, such as those of red blood cells (see Fig. 5-6). But attempts to identify selective transport proteins for water repeatedly failed. Then, in the mid-1980s, Peter Agre (FIG. E5-3), working at the Johns Hopkins School of Medicine in Maryland, was attempting to determine the structure of a glycoprotein on red blood cells. The glycoprotein he isolated was contaminated, however, with large quantities of an unknown protein. Instead of discarding the mystery protein, Agre and his coworkers collaborated with researchers at other universities to determine its structure and function.

To test their hypothesis that the protein was involved with water transport, they performed an experiment using frog egg cells, whose membranes are nearly impermeable to water. Agre's team predicted that if the proteins were water channels, insert-ing the mystery protein into the egg cells would cause them to swell when they were placed in a hypotonic solution. The researchers injected frog eggs with messenger RNA that coded for the unidentified protein, causing the eggs to synthesize the protein and insert it into their plasma membranes. Control eggs were injected with an equal quantity of water. Three days later, the eggs appeared identical—that is, until they were placed in a hypotonic solution. The control eggs swelled only slightly, whereas those with the inserted protein swelled rapidly and burst (FIG. E5-4). Further studies revealed that only water could move through this channel protein. Agre reached the conclusion that these were water channels and named them aquaporins. In 2000, Agre's group and other research teams reported the three-dimensional structure of aquaporin. Billions of water molecules can move through an aquaporin in single file every second, while larger molecules and small positively charged ions (such as hydrogen ions) are excluded.

Many subtypes of aquaporin proteins have now been identi-fied, and these water channels have been found in all forms of life that have been investigated. For example, the membrane of the central vacuole of plant cells is rich in aquaporins, allow-ing it to fill rapidly when water is available (see Fig. 5-7). Kidney cells insert aquaporins into their plasma membranes when the body becomes dehy-drated and water needs to be conserved. Aquaporins have also been implicated in many pathological conditions including brain swelling, glaucoma, and cancer; research-ers are working to design therapeutic drugs for these disorders that will block or facilitate water movement through these channels.

In 2003, Peter Agre shared the Nobel Prize in Chemistry for his discovery. In his Nobel lecture, he shared an insight that is fundamen-tal to scientific advances today: "In science, one should use all available resources to solve difficult problems. One of our most powerful resources

(a) Frog eggs

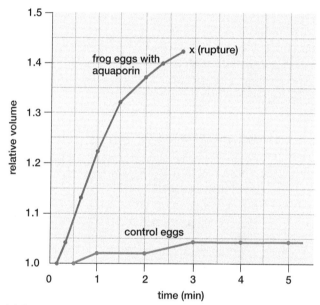

(b) Comparison of swelling in hypotonic medium

▲ FIGURE E5-4 **Investigating aquaporins (a)** The frog egg on the right with aquaporins inserted into its plasma membrane burst after immersion in a hypotonic solution. The normal frog egg on the left swelled only slightly. **(b)** When transferred from a normal to a hypotonic solution, the average volume of frog eggs increased rapidly until they burst, while control eggs swelled very slightly (the relative volume of 1 is the size of the egg just prior to transfer).

is the insight of our colleagues." As a result of collaboration, careful observation, persistence, and perhaps a bit of what he described modestly as the "scientific approach known as sheer blind luck," Agre and his team identified the elusive transport protein for water.

THINK CRITICALLY Based on Figure E5-4b, graph what likely would have happened if eggs with and without aquaporins had been immersed in a concentrated salt solution, extending the y-axis if needed. Explain your reasoning.

◀ FIGURE E5-3 **Peter Agre**

- Dissolved substances, called solutes, reduce the concentration of free water molecules in a solution.
- When comparing two solutions, the one with a higher solute concentration is hypertonic, and the solution with the lower solute concentration is hypotonic.

Osmosis Across the Plasma Membrane Plays an Important Role in the Lives of Cells

Osmosis across plasma membranes is crucial to many biological processes, including water uptake by the roots of plants, absorption of dietary water from the intestine, and the reabsorption of water into the bloodstream that occurs in kidneys.

In animals, the interstitial fluid that surrounds cells is isotonic to the cell cytosol. Although the concentrations of specific solutes are rarely the same both inside and outside of cells, the total concentrations of water and solutes inside and outside are equal. As a result, there is no overall tendency for water to enter or leave animal cells. To demonstrate the importance of maintaining isotonic conditions between fragile cells and their surrounding interstitial fluid, we can observe cells placed in solutions with different solute concentrations, illustrated in FIGURE 5-6.

Red blood cells have an abundance of aquaporins in their plasma membranes, making them very water permeable. Placed in an isotonic salt solution, they retain their normal size. But if the salt solution is hypertonic to the cytosol of the blood cells, water leaves by osmosis, causing the cells to shrivel. Immersion in a hypotonic salt solution, in contrast, causes the cells to swell (and eventually burst) as water diffuses in.

Freshwater organisms must continuously expend energy to counteract osmosis because their cells are hypertonic to the surrounding water. For example, protists such as *Paramecium* use cellular energy to pump salts from the cytosol into their contractile vacuoles. Water follows by osmosis and is squirted out through a pore in the plasma membrane (see Fig. 4-16).

Nearly every living plant cell is supported by water that enters through osmosis. Most plant cells have a large central vacuole enclosed by a membrane that is rich in aquaporins. Dissolved substances stored in the vacuole make its contents hypertonic to the surrounding cytosol, which in turn is usually hypertonic to the interstitial fluid that bathes the cells. Water therefore flows through the cell wall into the cytosol and then into the central vacuole by osmosis. This produces **turgor pressure,** which inflates

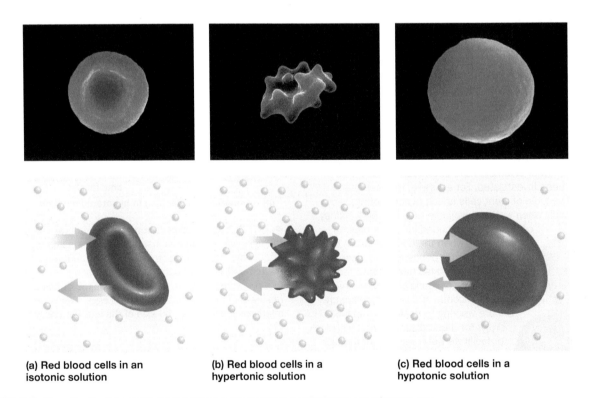

(a) Red blood cells in an isotonic solution

(b) Red blood cells in a hypertonic solution

(c) Red blood cells in a hypotonic solution

▲ FIGURE 5-6 **The effects of osmosis on red blood cells** Red blood cell plasma membranes are rich in aquaporins, so water flows readily in or out along its concentration gradient. **(a)** Cells immersed in an isotonic solution retain their normal dimpled shape. **(b)** Cells in a hypertonic solution shrivel as more water moves out than flows in. **(c)** Cells in a hypotonic solution expand.

THINK CRITICALLY A student pours some distilled water into a sample of blood. Later, she looks at the blood under a microscope and sees no blood cells at all. What happened?

the cell, forcing the cytosol within its plasma membrane against the cell wall (FIG. 5-7a). If you forget to water a houseplant, the cytosol and cell vacuole lose water, causing the cell to shrink away from its cell wall. Like a leaky balloon, the plant droops as its cells lose turgor pressure (FIG. 5-7b). Now you know why grocery stores are always spraying their leafy produce: to keep it looking perky and fresh with full central vacuoles.

Energy-Requiring Transport Includes Active Transport, Endocytosis, and Exocytosis

Many cellular activities rely on energy-requiring transport. Active transport, endocytosis, and exocytosis are crucial to maintaining concentration gradients, acquiring food, excreting wastes, and (in multicellular organisms) communicating with other cells.

Cells Maintain Concentration Gradients Using Active Transport

By building gradients and then allowing the gradients to run down under specific circumstances, cells generate ATP and respond to stimuli. For example, concentration gradients of various ions provide the energy to form ATP in mitochondria and chloroplasts (see Chapters 7 and 8), power the electrical signals of neurons, and trigger the contraction of muscles. But gradients cannot form spontaneously—they require active transport across a membrane.

During **active transport,** membrane proteins use cellular energy to move molecules or ions across a plasma membrane *against* their concentration gradients, which means that the substances are transported from areas of lower concentration to areas of higher concentration. For example, every cell must use active transport to acquire some nutrients that are less concentrated in the environment than in the cell's cytoplasm. In addition, substances such as sodium and calcium ions are actively transported to maintain them at much lower concentrations in the cytosol than in the interstitial fluid. Nerve cells maintain large ion concentration gradients because generating their electrical signals requires rapid, passive flow of ions when channels are opened. After these ions diffuse into or out of the cell, their concentration gradients must be restored by active transport.

Active transport proteins span the width of the membrane and have two binding regions (FIG. 5-8). One of these loosely binds with a specific molecule or ion, such as a calcium ion (Ca^{2+}); the second region, on the inside of the membrane,

When water is plentiful, it fills the central vacuole, pushes the cytoplasm against the cell wall, and helps maintain the cell's shape.

Water pressure supports the leaves of this impatiens plant.

(a) Turgor pressure provides support

When water is scarce, the central vacuole shrinks and the cell wall is unsupported.

Deprived of the support from water, the plant wilts.

(b) Loss of turgor pressure causes the plant to wilt

▲ **FIGURE 5-7 Turgor pressure in plant cells** Aquaporins allow water to move rapidly in and out of the central vacuoles of plant cells. **(a)** The cell and the plant are supported by turgor pressure. **(b)** The cell and the plant have lost turgor pressure and support due to dehydration.

THINK CRITICALLY If a plant cell is placed in water containing no solutes, will the cell eventually burst? Explain.

binds ATP ❶. The ATP donates energy to the protein, causing the protein to change shape and move the calcium ion across the membrane ❷. The energy for active transport comes from breaking the high-energy bond that links the last of the three phosphate groups in ATP. As it loses a phosphate group, releasing its stored energy, ATP becomes ADP (adenosine diphosphate) plus a free phosphate ❸. Active transport proteins are often called *pumps* because, like pumping water into an elevated storage tank, they use energy to move ions or molecules "uphill" against a concentration gradient.

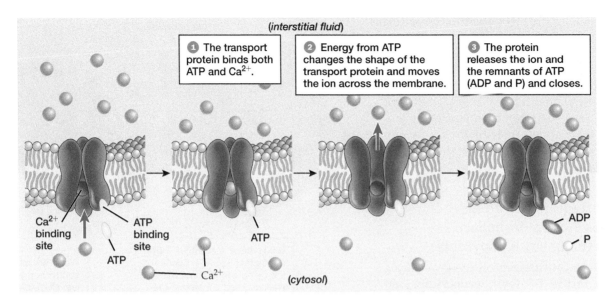

(interstitial fluid)

1 The transport protein binds both ATP and Ca^{2+}.

2 Energy from ATP changes the shape of the transport protein and moves the ion across the membrane.

3 The protein releases the ion and the remnants of ATP (ADP and P) and closes.

Ca^{2+} binding site

ATP binding site

ATP

ATP

Ca^{2+}

ADP

P

(cytosol)

▲ **FIGURE 5-8 Active transport** Cellular energy is used to move molecules across the plasma membrane against a concentration gradient. The active transport protein has an ATP binding site and a binding site for the transported substance, such as these calcium ions. When ATP donates its energy, it loses its third phosphate group and becomes ADP plus a free phosphate.

THINK CRITICALLY Would a cell ever use active transport to move water across its membrane? Explain.

HAVE YOU EVER

WONDERED...

Why Bacteria Die When You Take Antibiotics?

Penicillin and related antibiotics fight bacterial infections by interfering with cell wall synthesis in newly forming bacterial cells. Under normal conditions, a bacterium uses active transport to maintain an internal environment that is hypertonic to its surroundings. This allows the bacterial cytoplasm to maintain turgor pressure against its tough cell wall, much as in a plant cell. In the absence of this confining wall, osmosis into the hyperosmotic cytosol of the bacterium causes it to swell and rupture its fragile plasma membrane. We are fortunate to have medical antibiotics to help us fight bacterial infections, but unfortunately bacteria evolve rapidly, and antibiotics select for resistant strains. Resistance to antibiotics can occur as a result of several different adaptations. These include bacterial enzymes that break down the antibiotic, bacterial membranes that block entry of the antibiotic, and membrane pumps that expel the antibiotic. As a result, hospitals are now battling some bacterial strains that cause serious infections but resist nearly all antibiotics.

Endocytosis Allows Cells to Engulf Particles or Fluids

A cell may need to acquire materials from its extracellular environment that are too large to move directly through the membrane. These materials are engulfed by the plasma membrane and are transported within the cell inside vesicles. This energy-requiring process is called **endocytosis** (Gk. *endo,* inside). Here, we describe three forms of endocytosis based on the size and type of material acquired and the method of acquisition: pinocytosis, receptor-mediated endocytosis, and phagocytosis.

In **pinocytosis** (Gk. *pino,* drink; FIG. 5-9), a very small patch of plasma membrane dimples inward as it surrounds

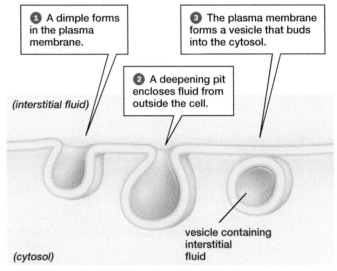

1 A dimple forms in the plasma membrane.

2 A deepening pit encloses fluid from outside the cell.

3 The plasma membrane forms a vesicle that buds into the cytosol.

(interstitial fluid)

(cytosol)

vesicle containing interstitial fluid

(a) Pinocytosis

(interstitial fluid)

(cytosol)

(b) TEM of pinocytosis

▲ **FIGURE 5-9 Pinocytosis**

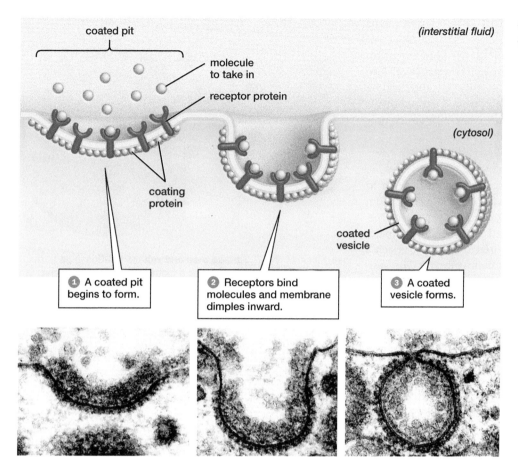

◀ **FIGURE 5-10** Receptor-mediated endocytosis

interstitial fluid, and then the membrane buds off into the cytosol as a tiny vesicle. Pinocytosis moves a droplet of interstitial fluid, contained within the dimpling patch of membrane, into the cell. Therefore, the cell acquires materials in the same concentration as in the interstitial fluid. Virus particles in interstitial fluid may be taken up into cells by pinocytosis, resulting in infection. Countering this, some immune system cells patrol for viruses by routinely taking in large quantities of interstitial fluid via pinocytosis. After ingesting viruses, they alert other immune cells to produce antibodies that will destroy the viruses.

Cells use **receptor-mediated endocytosis** to selectively take up specific molecules or complexes of molecules that cannot move through channels or diffuse through the plasma membrane (**FIG. 5-10**). Receptor-mediated endocytosis occurs in thickened depressions called *coated pits*. The coating material consists of proteins on the inside surface of the plasma membrane that assist in forming the pit. Receptor proteins for a specific substance project from the plasma membrane. These receptors bind the molecules to be transported. Then the depression deepens into a pocket that pinches off, forming a coated vesicle that carries the molecules into the cytosol. Molecules moved by receptor-mediated endocytosis include most protein hormones and packets of lipoprotein containing cholesterol.

Phagocytosis (Gk. *phago,* eat) moves large particles—sometimes whole microorganisms—into the cell (**FIG. 5-11a**). When the predatory protist *Amoeba,* for example, senses a

(a) Phagocytosis

(b) An *Amoeba* engulfs a *Paramecium*

(c) A white blood cell engulfs a disease-causing fungal cell

▲ **FIGURE 5-11 Phagocytosis (a)** The mechanism of phagocytosis. **(b)** Amoebas use phagocytosis to feed, and **(c)** white blood cells use phagocytosis to engulf disease-causing microorganisms.

Paramecium, the *Amoeba* extends parts of its plasma membrane, forming pseudopods (Gk. *pseudo,* false, and *pod,* foot; FIG. 5-11b). The pseudopods fuse around the prey, enclosing it inside a vesicle called a **food vacuole.** The vacuole will fuse with a lysosome (described in Chapter 4) where the food will be digested. White blood cells use phagocytosis, followed by digestion, to engulf and destroy invading bacteria, a drama that occurs continuously within your body (FIG. 5-11c).

Exocytosis Moves Material Out of the Cell

Cells also use energy to dispose of undigested particles or to secrete substances such as hormones into the interstitial fluid, a process called **exocytosis** (Gk. *exo,* outside; FIG. 5-12). During exocytosis, a membrane-enclosed vesicle carrying material to be expelled moves to the cell surface, where the vesicle's membrane fuses with the cell's plasma membrane. The vesicle's contents then diffuse into the fluid outside the cell.

Exchange of Materials Across Membranes Influences Cell Size and Shape

As you learned in Chapter 4, most cells are too small to be seen with the naked eye; they range from about 1 to 100 micrometers (millionths of a meter) in diameter. Why are cells so small? To acquire nutrients and eliminate wastes, all parts of a cell rely on the slow process of diffusion, so the cell must be small enough that no part of it is too far removed from the surrounding fluid.

Assuming that a cell is roughly spherical, the larger its diameter, the farther its innermost contents are from the plasma membrane. In a hypothetical giant cell 8.5 inches (20 centimeters) in diameter, oxygen molecules would take more than 200 days to diffuse to the center of the cell, but the cell would be long dead. In addition, all cellular wastes and nutrients must diffuse through the cell's plasma membrane. As a hypothetical spherical cell enlarges, its volume of cytoplasm

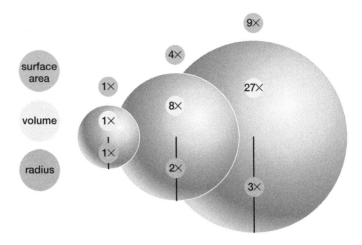

▲ **FIGURE 5-13 Surface area and volume relationships** If the radius of a sphere increases by a factor of 3, then the volume increases by a factor of 27 but the surface area only increases by a factor of 9.

(where all its metabolic reactions occur) increases more rapidly than does its surface area (through which it must exchange nutrients and wastes; FIG. 5-13).

These constraints limit the size of most cells. However, some cells, such as nerve and muscle cells, have an extremely elongated shape that increases their membrane surface area, keeping the ratio of surface area to volume relatively high.

CHECK YOUR LEARNING
Can you ...
- explain simple diffusion, facilitated diffusion, and osmosis?
- describe active transport, endocytosis, and exocytosis?
- explain how the need to exchange materials across membranes influences cell size and shape?

▲ **FIGURE 5-12 Exocytosis** Exocytosis is functionally the reverse of endocytosis. Material enclosed in a vesicle from inside the cell is transported to the cell surface. It then fuses with the plasma membrane, releasing its contents into the surrounding fluid.

THINK CRITICALLY How does exocytosis differ from diffusion of materials out of a cell?

5.3 HOW DO SPECIALIZED JUNCTIONS ALLOW CELLS TO CONNECT AND COMMUNICATE?

In multicellular organisms, some specialized structures on plasma membranes hold cells together, whereas others provide avenues through which cells communicate with neighboring cells. Here we discuss four major types of cell-to-cell connections: adhesive junctions, tight junctions, gap junctions, and plasmodesmata. The first three types of junctions are found only in animal cells; plasmodesmata are restricted to plant cells.

Adhesive Junctions Attach Cells Together

Adhesive junctions are specialized groups of proteins that link cells to one another within tissues. Adhesive junctions function by connecting the cytoskeleton to the inner plasma membrane and extending through the plasma membrane to extracellular linking proteins that join to the plasma membranes of adjacent cells. There are several types of adhesive junctions; here we focus on *desmosomes* (FIG. 5-14a). Desmosomes join cells in tissues that are repeatedly stretched, such as those found in skin, intestines, and the heart. These strong adhesive junctions prevent forces on the tissues from pulling them apart. In a desmosome, anchoring proteins lie on the inner side of the membranes of adjacent cells. The anchoring proteins are attached to intermediate filaments of the cytoskeleton that extend into the cytoplasm. Linking proteins join to the anchoring proteins and span the narrow space between the adjacent cells, linking them firmly together.

Tight Junctions Make Cell Attachments Leakproof

Tight junctions are formed by proteins that span the plasma membranes at corresponding sites on adjacent cells (FIG. 5-14b), joining the cells almost as if their adjacent membranes had been stitched together. Interlocking tight junction proteins create barriers that prevent nearly all substances from passing between the linked cells. For example,

▶ **FIGURE 5-14 Links between cells (a)** In desmosomes, anchoring proteins on adjacent plasma membranes are bound together by linking proteins. Intermediate filaments of the cytoskeleton inside each cell strengthen the connection. (Right) A transmission electron micrograph of a desmosome. **(b)** Tight junction proteins of adjacent cells fuse to one another, forming a stitch-like pattern. (Right) A scanning electron micrograph of a membrane whose bilayer has been split reveals the pattern of tight junction proteins. **(c)** Gap junctions consist of protein channels interconnecting the cytosol of adjacent cells to allow small molecules and ions to pass through. (Right) An atomic force micrograph looking down on connexons on one of the two membranes they connect. **(d)** Plasmodesmata connect the plasma membranes and cytosol of adjacent plant cells and allow large molecules to move between them. (Right) A transmission electron micrograph showing a cross-section of plasmodesmata connecting adjacent plant cells. SEM in part (b) from Claude, P., and Goodenough, D. 1973. "Fracture Faces of Zonulae Occludentes from 'Tight' and 'Leaky' Epithelia." *Journal of Cell Biology* 58:390–400.

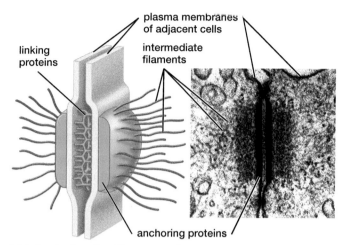

(a) Adhesive junction (desmosome)

linking proteins
plasma membranes of adjacent cells
intermediate filaments
anchoring proteins

(b) Tight junctions

plasma membranes of adjacent cells
tight junction proteins

(c) Gap junctions

plasma membranes of adjacent cells
connexons
pore

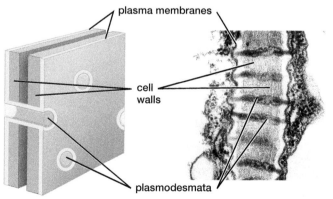

(d) Plasmodesmata

plasma membranes
cell walls
plasmodesmata

tight junctions in the bladder prevent cellular wastes in urine from leaking back into the blood. Tight junctions between cells lining the digestive tract protect the rest of the body from the acids, digestive enzymes, and bacteria found in its various compartments.

Gap Junctions and Plasmodesmata Allow Direct Communication Between Cells

The cells of many tissues in the animal body are interconnected by **gap junctions** (FIG. 5-14c), clusters of channels ranging in number from a few to thousands. The channels are formed by six-sided tubes of protein called *connexons* that span the plasma membrane. Connexons line up so that their central pores link the cytosol of adjacent cells. The small size of the pore allows small water-soluble molecules—including sugars, various ions, amino acids, and small messenger molecules such as cAMP—to pass between cells, but excludes organelles and large molecules such as proteins. Gap junctions coordinate the metabolic activities of many cells. They allow electrical signals to pass extremely rapidly among certain groups of nerve cells, and they synchronize contraction of heart muscle and of smooth muscles, such as in the walls of the digestive tract, bladder, and uterus.

Plasmodesmata are channels that link nearly all adjacent plant cells and allow movement of large molecules between them (FIG. 5-14d). These openings, which are lined with plasma membrane and filled with cytosol, make the membranes and the cytosol of adjacent cells continuous with one another. Many plant cells have thousands of plasmodesmata, allowing water, nutrients, and hormones to pass freely from one cell to another. These connections among plant cells serve a function somewhat similar to the gap junctions of animal cells in coordinating metabolic activities among groups of cells.

CHECK YOUR LEARNING

Can you ...
- describe the major types of junctions between cells?
- explain how these junctions function and provide an example of where each is found?

CASE STUDY REVISITED

Vicious Venoms

The "witches' brews" of rattlesnake and brown recluse spider venoms contain phospholipases that destroy the tissue around the bite (FIG. 5-15). When phospholipases attack the membranes of capillary cells, these tiny blood vessels rupture and release blood into the tissue surrounding the wound. In extreme cases, capillary damage can lead to internal bleeding. By attacking the membranes of red blood cells, rattlesnake venoms can cause anemia (an inadequate number of oxygen-carrying red blood cells). Rattlesnake phospholipases also attack muscle cell membranes; this attack caused extensive damage to muscles in Justin Schwartz's forearm. Justin required large quantities of antivenin, which contains specialized proteins that bind and neutralize the snake venom proteins. Unfortunately, no antivenin is available for brown recluse bites, and treatment generally consists of preventing infection, controlling pain and swelling, and waiting—sometimes for months—for the wound to heal.

Although both snake and spider bites can have serious consequences, very few of the spiders and snakes found in the Americas are dangerous to people. The best defense is to learn

(a) Justin's rattlesnake bite

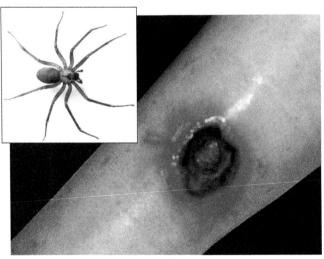

(b) Brown recluse spider bite

▲ **FIGURE 5-15 Phospholipases in venoms can destroy cells (a)** Justin Schwartz's hand 36 hours after the rattlesnake bite. **(b)** A brown recluse spider bite. (Inset) A brown recluse spider.

which venomous animals live in your area and where they prefer to hang out. If your activities bring you to such places, wear protective clothing—and always look before you reach! Knowledge can help us coexist with spiders and snakes, avoid their bites, and keep our cell membranes intact.

THINK CRITICALLY Phospholipases are found in animal digestive tracts as well as in venom. How does the role of phospholipase in a snake's venom differ from its role in the snake's digestive tract?

CHAPTER REVIEW

(MB) Go to **MasteringBiology** for practice quizzes, activities, eText, videos, current events, and more.

Answers to Think Critically, Evaluate This, Multiple Choice, and Fill-in-the-Blank questions can be found in the Answers section at the back of the book.

Summary of Key Concepts

5.1 How Is the Structure of the Cell Membrane Related to Its Function?

The cell membrane consists of a bilayer of phospholipids in which a variety of proteins are embedded, often described as a fluid mosaic. The plasma membrane isolates the cytoplasm from the external environment, regulates the flow of materials into and out of the cell, allows communication between cells, allows attachments within and between cells, and regulates many biochemical reactions. There are five major types of membrane proteins: (1) enzymes, which promote chemical reactions; (2) recognition proteins, which label the cell; (3) transport proteins, which regulate the movement of most water-soluble substances through the membrane; (4) receptor proteins, which bind molecules and trigger changes within the cell; and (5) connection proteins, which anchor the plasma membrane to the cytoskeleton and extracellular matrix or bind cells to one another.

5.2 How Do Substances Move Across Membranes?

Diffusion is the movement of particles from regions of higher concentration to regions of lower concentration. In simple diffusion, water, dissolved gases, and lipid-soluble molecules diffuse through the phospholipid bilayer. During facilitated diffusion, carrier proteins or channel proteins allow water and water-soluble molecules to cross the membrane down their concentration gradients without expending cellular energy. Osmosis is the diffusion of water across a selectively permeable membrane down its concentration gradient through the phospholipid bilayer or through aquaporins.

Energy-requiring transport includes active transport, in which carrier proteins use cellular energy (ATP) to drive the movement of molecules across the plasma membrane against concentration gradients. Interstitial fluid, large molecules, and food particles may be acquired by endocytosis, which includes pinocytosis, receptor-mediated endocytosis, and phagocytosis. The secretion of substances and the excretion of particulate cellular wastes are accomplished by exocytosis.

Cells exchange materials between the cytoplasm and the external environment principally by the slow process of diffusion through the plasma membrane. This requires that no part of the cell be too far from the plasma membrane, limiting the diameter of cells.

5.3 How Do Specialized Junctions Allow Cells to Connect and Communicate?

Animal cell junctions include (1) adhesive junctions, which attach adjacent cells within tissues and prevent tissues from tearing apart during ordinary movements; (2) tight junctions, which leak-proof the spaces between adjacent cells; (3) gap junctions, which connect the cytosol of adjacent animal cells; and (4) plasmodesmata, which connect adjacent plant cells.

Key Terms

active transport 85	interstitial fluid 77
adhesive junction 89	isotonic 82
aquaporin 82	osmosis 82
carrier protein 82	passive transport 81
channel protein 82	phagocytosis 87
concentration 80	phospholipid
connection protein 79	bilayer 77
diffusion 80	pinocytosis 86
endocytosis 86	plasmodesmata 90
energy-requiring transport 81	receptor protein 79
enzyme 79	receptor-mediated
exocytosis 88	endocytosis 87
facilitated diffusion 82	recognition protein 79
fluid 77	selectively
fluid mosaic model 77	permeable 81
food vacuole 88	simple diffusion 81
gap junction 90	solute 80
glycoprotein 78	solvent 80
gradient 80	tight junction 89
hypertonic 82	transport protein 79
hypotonic 82	turgor pressure 84

Thinking Through the Concepts

Multiple Choice

1. Animal cells are surrounded by _____ fluid. This fluid is _____ to the cytosol.
   a. phospholipid; isotonic
   b. plasma; hypertonic
   c. interstitial; isotonic
   d. interstitial; hypotonic

2. Which of the following *cannot* enter a cell by simple diffusion?
   a. water
   b. sugar
   c. estrogen
   d. oxygen

3. Glycoproteins are important for
   a. binding hormones.
   b. cell recognition by the immune system.
   c. forming ion channels.
   d. active transport through the membrane.

4. Diffusion
   a. is always facilitated.
   b. occurs by active transport.
   c. is increased when temperature increases.
   d. requires aquaporin proteins.

5. Which of the following is *not* true of endocytosis?
   a. It is a form of passive transport.
   b. It includes pinocytosis.
   c. It can occur in coated pits.
   d. It is used by *Amoeba* to feed on *Paramecium*.

Fill-in-the-Blank

1. Membranes consist of a bilayer of _____ . The five major categories of protein within the bilayer are _____ , _____ , _____ , _____ , and _____ proteins.

2. A membrane that is permeable to some substances but not to others is described as being _____ . The movement of a substance through a membrane down its concentration gradient is called _____ . When applied to water, this process is called _____ . Channels that are specific for water are called _____ . The process that moves substances through a membrane against their concentration gradient is called _____ .

3. Facilitated diffusion involves either _____ proteins or _____ proteins. Diffusion directly through the phospholipid bilayer is called _____ diffusion, and molecules that take this route must be soluble in _____ or be very small and have no net electrical charge.

4. The three types of cell attachment structures in animal cells are _____ , _____ , and _____ . The structures that interconnect plant cells are called _____ .

5. After each molecule, place the two-word term that most specifically describes the *process* by which it moves through a plasma membrane. Carbon dioxide: _____ ; ethyl alcohol: _____ ; a sodium ion: _____ ; glucose: _____ .

6. The general process by which fluids or particles are transported out of cells is called _____ . Does this process require energy? _____ The substances to be expelled are transported within the cell in membrane-enclosed sacs called _____ .

Review Questions

1. Describe and diagram the structure of a plasma membrane. What are the two principal types of molecules in plasma membranes, and what is the general function of each?

2. Sketch the configuration that 10 phospholipid molecules would assume if placed in water. Explain why they arrange themselves this way.

3. What are the five categories of proteins commonly found in plasma membranes, and what is the function of each one?

4. Define *diffusion* and *osmosis*. Explain how osmosis helps plant leaves remain firm. What is the term for water pressure inside plant cells?

5. Define *hypotonic*, *hypertonic*, and *isotonic*. What would be the fate of an animal cell immersed in each of these three types of solution?

6. Describe the following types of transport processes in cells: simple diffusion, facilitated diffusion, active transport, pinocytosis, receptor-mediated endocytosis, phagocytosis, and exocytosis.

7. Name the protein that allows facilitated diffusion of water. What experiment demonstrated the function of this protein?

8. Imagine a container of glucose solution, divided into two compartments (A and B) by a membrane that is permeable to both water and glucose. If some glucose is added to compartment A, how will the contents of compartment B change? Explain.

9. Name four types of cell-to-cell junctions, and describe the function of each. Which are found in plants and which in animals?

Applying the Concepts

1. Different cells have different plasma membranes. The plasma membrane of a *Paramecium,* for example, is only about 1% as permeable to water as the plasma membrane of a human red blood cell. Hypothesize why this is the case. Is *Paramecium* likely to have aquaporins in its plasma membrane? Explain your answer.

2. Predict and sketch the configuration that ten phopholipid molecules would assume if they were completely submerged in vegetable oil. Explain your prediction.

6

ENERGY FLOW IN THE LIFE OF A CELL

The bodies of these runners in the New York Marathon convert stored energy to the energy of movement and heat. Their pounding footsteps shake the Verrazano Narrows Bridge.

Energy Unleashed

PICTURE THE NEW YORK CITY MARATHON, where well over 50,000 people from countries throughout the world gather to run 26.2 miles. All participate in a personal odyssey and a testimony to persistence, endurance, and the ability of the human body to utilize energy. On average, each runner expends roughly 3,000 Calories before reaching the finish line. Once finished, they douse their overheated bodies with water and replenish their energy stores with celebratory meals. Finally, subways, trains, cars, buses, and airplanes—burning vast quantities

of fossil fuels and releasing enormous amounts of heat—transport the runners home.

Training for a marathon takes months, especially for someone unaccustomed to running long distances. During training, several important physiological changes occur that prepare the body to expend the tremendous amount of energy necessary for the race. Muscle mitochondria, with their glucose-metabolizing enzymes, increase in number. The cells of muscles that move the body increase their ability to store glycogen, a polymer of glucose. Capillaries around muscles proliferate to supply the extra oxygen needed to break down glucose in the mitochondria.

What exactly is energy? Do our bodies use energy according to the same principles that govern its use in the engines of cars and airplanes? Why do our bodies generate heat, and why do we give off more heat when exercising than when studying or watching TV?

AT A GLANCE

6.1 WHAT IS ENERGY?

Energy is the capacity to do work. **Work,** in turn, is the transfer of energy to an object that causes the object to move. It is obvious that marathoners are working; their chests heave, their arms pump, and their legs stride, moving their bodies relentlessly forward for 26.2 miles. This muscular work is powered by the energy available in the bonds of molecules. The molecules that provide this energy—including glucose, glycogen, and fat—are stored in the cells of the runners' bodies. Within each cell, specialized molecules such as ATP accept, briefly store, and transfer energy from the reactions that release energy to those that demand it, such as muscle contraction.

There are two fundamental types of energy: potential energy and kinetic energy, each of which takes several forms. **Potential energy** is stored energy, including the elastic energy stored in a compressed spring or a drawn bow and the gravitational energy stored in water behind a dam or a roller-coaster car about to begin its downward plunge (FIG. 6-1). Potential energy also includes **chemical energy,** which is energy stored in, for example, batteries, the biological molecules that power marathon runners, and the fossil fuels used by vehicles to transport the runners. **Kinetic energy** is the energy of movement. It includes radiant energy (such as waves of light, X-rays, and other forms of *electromagnetic radiation*), heat or thermal energy (the motion of molecules or atoms), electrical energy (electricity; the flow of charged particles), and any motion of larger objects, such as the plummeting roller-coaster car or running marathoners. Under the right conditions, kinetic energy can be transformed into potential energy, and vice versa. For example, the roller-coaster car converts the kinetic energy of its downward plunge into gravitational potential energy as it coasts to the top of the next rise. At a molecular level, during photosynthesis, the kinetic energy of light is captured and transformed into the potential energy of chemical bonds (see Chapter 7). To understand energy flow and change, we need to know more about its properties.

The Laws of Thermodynamics Describe the Basic Properties of Energy

The laws of thermodynamics describe some basic properties of energy. The **first law of thermodynamics** states that energy can be neither created nor destroyed by ordinary processes. (Nuclear reactions, in which matter is converted into

▲ FIGURE 6-1 **Converting potential energy to kinetic energy** Roller coasters convert gravitational potential energy to kinetic energy as they plummet downhill.

THINK CRITICALLY Could one design a roller coaster that didn't use any motors to pull the cars uphill after they were released from a high point?

energy, are the exception.) This means that within an **isolated system**—a space where neither mass nor energy can enter or leave—the total amount of energy before and after any process will be unchanged. For this reason, the first law of thermodynamics is often called the **law of conservation of energy.** An isolated system is a theoretical concept, but for practical purposes, you can visualize energy transformations occurring in an enormous, perfectly sealed and insulated chamber.

To illustrate the law of conservation of energy, consider a gasoline-powered car. Before you turn the ignition key, the energy in the car is all potential energy, stored in the chemical bonds of its fuel. As you drive, only about 20% of this potential energy is converted into the kinetic energy of motion. But if energy is neither created nor destroyed, what happens to the other 80% of the energy? The burning fuel also heats

▲ **FIGURE 6-2 All energy conversions result in a loss of useful energy**

100 units chemical energy → 80 units heat energy + 20 units kinetic energy

up the engine, the exhaust system, and the air around the car, while friction from the tires heats the road. So, as the first law dictates, the total amount of energy remains the same, although it has changed in form—about 20% of it converted to kinetic energy and 80% of it to heat (**FIG. 6-2**).

The **second law of thermodynamics** states that when energy is converted from one form to another, the amount of useful energy decreases. In other words, all ordinary (non-nuclear) processes cause energy to be converted from more useful into less useful forms, such as the heat in our combustion example, which increased the random movement of molecules in the car, the air, and the road. One way of reducing the chemical energy lost as heat while driving is discussed in "Earth Watch: Step on the Brakes and Recharge Your Battery."

Now consider the human body. Whether running or reading, your body "burns" food to release the chemical energy stored in its molecules. Your body warmth results from the heat given off, which is radiated to your surroundings. This heat is not available to power muscle contraction or to help brain cells interpret written words. Thus, the second law tells us that no energy conversion process, including those that occur in the body, is 100% efficient; some energy is lost to the environment—almost always in the form of heat—which cannot be used to power muscles or brain activity.

The second law of thermodynamics also tells us something about the organization of matter. Useful energy tends to be stored in highly ordered matter, such as in the bonds of complex molecules. As a result, whenever energy is used within an isolated system, there is an overall loss of organization as complex molecules are broken apart into simpler ones. The loss of organization also occurs as we perform activities of daily life: Dirty dishes accumulate, clothes collect in confusion, the bed gets rumpled, and books and papers pile up (**FIG. 6-3**). This randomness and disorder can only be reversed by adding energy to the system through energy-demanding cleaning and organizing efforts. You'll see a bit later where this energy comes from.

This tendency toward the loss of complexity, orderliness, and useful energy is called **entropy.** At the molecular level, we see the same principle at work. Let's look at what happens when we burn glucose sugar.

$$C_6H_{12}O_6 + 6\,O_2 \longrightarrow 6\,CO_2 + 6\,H_2O + \text{heat energy}$$

glucose   oxygen   carbon   water
                          dioxide

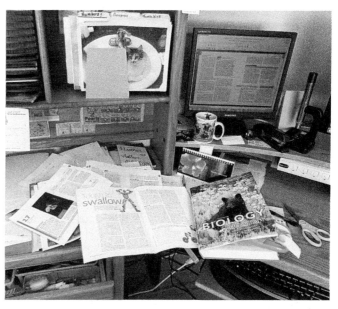

▲ **FIGURE 6-3 Entropy at work**

Although you'll find the same number and types of atoms on both sides of the equation, if you count the molecules, you will see that there is an overall increase in simple product molecules (carbon dioxide and water) as the single molecule of sugar is broken down and combined with oxygen. The heat energy that is released causes the product molecules to move about randomly and more rapidly. To counteract entropy—for example, to synthesize glucose from carbon dioxide and water—energy must be infused into the system from an outside source, ultimately the sun. When the eminent Yale scientist G. Evelyn Hutchinson stated, "Disorder spreads through the universe, and life alone battles against it," he was making an eloquent reference to entropy and the second law of thermodynamics.

CASE STUDY \ CONTINUED
Energy Unleashed

Much like a car's engine, the marathoner's muscles are only about 20% efficient in converting chemical energy into movement; much of the other 80% is lost as heat. Sweating helps to prevent overheating because the water in sweat absorbs large amounts of heat as it evaporates. But even while sitting at the computer and doing other non-sweaty activities, we still burn energy, just to stay alive. Where does this energy come from?

Living Things Use Solar Energy to Maintain Life

If you think about the second law of thermodynamics, you may wonder how life can exist at all. If chemical reactions, including those inside living cells, cause the amount

Earth
WATCH

Step on the Brakes and Recharge Your Battery

As carbon dioxide levels in the atmosphere continue to rise, fueling global climate change, it is increasingly urgent that we reduce our impact by improving auto fuel economy.

In a typical car powered only by an internal combustion engine, whenever you step on the brake, brake pads are forced against brake discs. The resulting friction that stops the car converts the kinetic energy of forward motion almost entirely into waste heat. Fortunately, engineers have devised a way to capture and use some of this squandered energy. Called regenerative braking, this technology is used in hybrid or all-electric cars, which are partly or entirely driven by battery-powered electric motors. As you drive, potential chemical energy stored in a large battery is converted to kinetic energy by the car's electric motor, which drives the wheels. Stepping on the brake flips a switch that reverses this process, forcing the turning wheels to drive the electric motor in the opposite direction. This reversal converts the electric motor into a generator of electricity (**FIG. E6-1**), and the resistance to reversing the electric motor helps slow the car. This electrical energy, derived from the kinetic energy of the car's forward motion, is transmitted back to the battery, where it is stored as chemical energy. This chemical energy can be used to propel the car forward when you start up again. Of course, the second law of thermodynamics tells us that each of these energy conversions will generate some heat, but regenerative braking wastes 30% to 50% less energy than conventional friction braking. Regenerative braking allows cars to travel much farther on less energy.

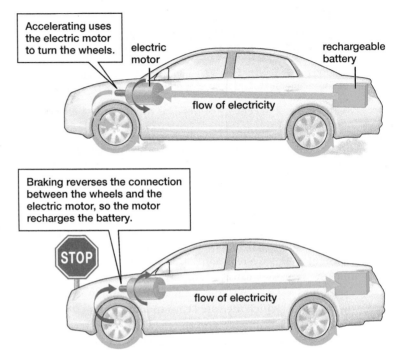

Accelerating uses the electric motor to turn the wheels.

electric motor

rechargeable battery

flow of electricity

Braking reverses the connection between the wheels and the electric motor, so the motor recharges the battery.

STOP

flow of electricity

▲ **FIGURE E6-1** **Regenerative braking**

CONSIDER THIS What other changes would help reduce fossil fuel use in transportation?

of usable energy to decrease, and if matter tends toward increasing randomness and disorder, how can organisms maintain the amazingly organized complexity of life? Where does useful energy originate, and where does all the waste heat go? The answer is that cells, the bodies of organisms, and Earth itself are not isolated systems; they receive useful solar energy released by nuclear reactions in the sun, 93 million miles away. As they generate light and other forms of electromagnetic energy, these nuclear reactions liberate an almost unimaginable amount of heat; the temperature of the sun's core is estimated to be 27 million °F (16 million °C).

Living things "battle against disorder" by using a continuous influx of sunlight to synthesize complex molecules and maintain their intricate bodies. All solar energy enters the biosphere through photosynthetic organisms such as plants and algae. The chemical equation for photosynthesis is:

$$6\,CO_2 + 6\,H_2O + \text{light energy} \longrightarrow C_6H_{12}O_6 + 6\,O_2$$

Notice that photosynthesis reverses the reaction that breaks down glucose; the energy of sunlight is captured and stored in the chemical bonds of glucose. Thus, the highly ordered (and therefore low-entropy) systems that characterize life do not violate the second law of thermodynamics.

Such systems are produced and maintained through a continuous influx of useful energy from the sun. So when you organize your desk or make your bed, your muscles are (indirectly) using solar energy that was originally trapped by photosynthesis.

What happens to the solar energy that is not trapped in living things? Most of it is converted to heat. Some heat remains in the atmosphere and maintains Earth within a temperature range that sustains life. But humans are also changing the composition of the atmosphere. Since the 1800s, we have increased atmospheric CO_2 levels by about 30% by burning fossil fuels to use their stored chemical energy. Because CO_2 traps heat in the atmosphere somewhat like the glass of a greenhouse or the closed windows of a car in the sun, we are changing Earth's climate.

CHECK YOUR LEARNING
Can you ...
- define energy and work?
- define potential energy and kinetic energy and provide three examples of each?
- state and explain the first and second laws of thermodynamics?

6.2 HOW IS ENERGY TRANSFORMED DURING CHEMICAL REACTIONS?

A **chemical reaction** is a process that breaks and forms chemical bonds. Chemical reactions convert one combination of molecules, the **reactants**, into different molecules, the **products**, that contain the same numbers and types of atoms. Since all chemical reactions transfer energy, all release some heat. A reaction is **exergonic** if there is an overall release of heat, that is, if the products contain less energy than the original reactants, as in burning sugar (**FIG. 6-4a**). A reaction is **endergonic** if it requires a net input of energy, that is, if the products contain more energy than the reactants. Endergonic reactions require an overall influx of energy from an outside source (**FIG. 6-4b**).

Exergonic Reactions Release Energy

Sugar can be ignited by heat, as any cook can tell you. As it burns, sugar undergoes the same overall reaction as it does in our bodies and in most other forms of life. Organisms combine sugar with oxygen, producing carbon dioxide and water, while generating both stored chemical energy (ATP) and releasing heat. The total energy in the reactant molecules (glucose and oxygen) is much higher than in the product molecules (carbon dioxide and water), so burning sugar is an exergonic reaction. It may be helpful to think of exergonic reactions as running "downhill," from a higher energy state to a lower energy state, like a rock rolling down a hill to rest at the bottom.

Endergonic Reactions Require a Net Input of Energy

Many reactions in living things are endergonic, requiring a net input of energy and yielding products that contain more energy than the reactants. The synthesis of large biological molecules is endergonic. For example, the proteins in a muscle cell contain more energy than the individual amino acids that were linked together to synthesize them. How do organisms power endergonic reactions? They use high-energy

(a) An exergonic reaction

(b) An endergonic reaction

▲ **FIGURE 6-4 Exergonic and endergonic reactions (a)** In an exergonic reaction, the products contain less energy than the reactants. **(b)** In an endergonic reaction, the products contain more energy than the reactants.

THINK CRITICALLY Is glucose breakdown endergonic or exergonic? What about photosynthesis?

molecules synthesized using solar energy that was captured during photosynthesis. We can think of endergonic reactions as "uphill" reactions because they require a net input of energy, just as pushing a rock up a hill requires effort.

All Chemical Reactions Require Activation Energy to Begin

All chemical reactions require **activation energy** to get started (**FIG. 6-5a**). Think of a rock sitting at the top of a hill; it will remain there indefinitely unless a push starts it rolling down. Like the rolling rock, many chemical reactions continue spontaneously if enough activation energy is supplied to start them. We see this in wood burning in a campfire or in a marshmallow ignited by the fire's flames (**FIG. 6-5b**). After the sugar in a marshmallow is ignited as it reacts with oxygen from the air, the

(a) An exergonic reaction

(b) A flame ignites the sugar in a marshmallow

◀ **FIGURE 6-5 Activation energy in an exergonic reaction (a)** After the activation hump is overcome, there will be a net release of energy. **(b)** Heat released by the burning sugar will allow the reaction to continue spontaneously.

reaction releases enough heat to sustain itself, and the marshmallow burns spontaneously.

Why is activation energy required for chemical reactions? Shells of negatively charged electrons surround all atoms (see Chapter 2). These negative charges repel one another and tend to keep the atoms separated. Activation energy is required to overcome this repulsion and force the atoms close enough together to react and form new chemical bonds.

Activation energy can be provided by the kinetic energy of moving molecules. Atoms and molecules are in constant motion. If they are moving fast enough, collisions between reactive molecules force their electron shells to mingle and react. Because molecules move faster as the temperature increases, most chemical reactions occur more readily at high temperatures; this is why a flame's heat can ignite a marshmallow.

CHECK YOUR LEARNING

Can you ...

- describe how energy is captured and released by chemical reactions?
- explain exergonic and endergonic reactions and provide examples of each?
- explain activation energy?

CASE STUDY \ **CONTINUED**

Energy Unleashed

Marathoners rely on glycogen stored in their muscles and liver for much of the energy to power their run. Glycogen consists of long, branched chains of glucose molecules. When energy is needed, glucose molecules are cleaved from the chain and then broken down into carbon dioxide and water. This exergonic reaction generates the chemical energy in ATP that will power muscle contraction. The carbon dioxide is exhaled as the runners breathe rapidly to supply their muscles with adequate oxygen. The water generated by glucose breakdown (and a lot more that the runners drink during the race) is lost as cooling sweat.

The glucose molecules in muscle and other cells do not need to be ignited and do not literally burn as they are broken down, so how do cells provide activation energy and control the release of chemical energy to allow it to do work?

6.3 HOW IS ENERGY TRANSPORTED WITHIN CELLS?

Most organisms are powered by the chemical energy supplied by the exergonic breakdown of glucose. But the chemical energy stored in glucose must first be transferred to energy-carrier molecules, such as ATP. **Energy-carrier molecules** are high-energy molecules that are synthesized at the site of an exergonic reaction, where they capture and temporarily store some of the released chemical energy. Just as rechargeable flashlight batteries can store electrical

energy that is later released as light, energy-carrier molecules are charged up by exergonic reactions and then release their energy to drive endergonic reactions. They can then be recharged, as described later. Energy-carrier molecules capture and transfer energy only within cells; they cannot ferry energy through cell membranes, nor are they used for long-term energy storage.

ATP and Electron Carriers Transport Energy Within Cells

Many exergonic reactions in cells, such as breaking down sugars and fats, produce ATP, the most common energy-carrier molecule in the body. ATP (adenosine triphosphate) is a nucleotide composed of the nitrogen-containing base adenine, the sugar ribose, and three phosphate groups. Because ATP provides energy to drive a wide variety of endergonic reactions, it is sometimes called the "energy currency" of cells. It is produced when energy from exergonic reactions is used to combine the lower-energy molecules of inorganic phosphate (HPO_4^{2-}, also designated P_i) with ADP (adenosine diphosphate) (**FIG. 6-6a**). Because it requires a net input of energy, ATP synthesis is endergonic.

ATP diffuses throughout the cell, carrying energy to sites where endergonic reactions occur. There its energy is liberated as it is broken down, regenerating ADP and P_i (**FIG. 6-6b**). The life span of an ATP molecule in a cell is very short; each molecule is recycled roughly 1,400 times every day. A marathon runner may use a pound (0.45 kilogram) of ATP molecules every minute, so if ATP were not almost instantly recycled, marathons would never happen. In contrast to ATP, far more stable molecules such as starch in plants and

(a) ATP synthesis: Energy is stored in ATP

(b) ATP breakdown: Energy is released

▲ **FIGURE 6-6 The interconversion of ADP and ATP (a)** Energy is captured when a phosphate group (P_i) is added to adenosine diphosphate (ADP) to make adenosine triphosphate (ATP). **(b)** Energy to power cellular work is released when ATP is broken down into ADP and P_i.

glycogen and fat in animals can store energy for hours, days, or—in the case of fat—years.

ATP is not the only energy-carrier molecule within cells. In some exergonic reactions, including both glucose breakdown and the light-capturing stage of photosynthesis, some energy is transferred to electrons. These energetic electrons, along with hydrogen ions (H^+; present in the cytosol of cells), are captured by molecules called **electron carriers.** The loaded electron carriers donate their high-energy electrons to other molecules, which are often involved in pathways that generate ATP. Common electron carriers include NADH (nucleotide nicotinamide adenine dinucleotide) and its relative, $FADH_2$ (flavin adenine dinucleotide). You will learn more about electron carriers in Chapters 7 and 8.

Coupled Reactions Link Exergonic with Endergonic Reactions

In a **coupled reaction,** an exergonic reaction provides the energy needed to drive an endergonic reaction (**FIG. 6-7**), using ATP or electron carriers as intermediaries. During photosynthesis, for example, plants use sunlight (from exergonic reactions in the sun's core) to drive the endergonic synthesis of high-energy glucose molecules from lower-energy reactants. Nearly all organisms use the energy released by exergonic reactions (such as the breakdown of glucose) to drive endergonic reactions (such as the synthesis of proteins from amino acids). Because some energy is lost every time it is transformed, in coupled reactions the energy released by exergonic reactions always exceeds the energy needed to drive the endergonic reactions. Thus, the coupled reaction overall is exergonic.

The exergonic and endergonic portions of coupled reactions often occur in different places within a cell, so energy is transferred by energy-carrier molecules such as ATP. In its role as an intermediary in coupled reactions, ATP is constantly being synthesized to capture the energy released during exergonic reactions and then broken down to power endergonic reactions.

CHECK YOUR LEARNING
Can you ...
- name and describe two important energy-carrier molecules in cells?
- explain coupled reactions?

6.4 HOW DO ENZYMES PROMOTE BIOCHEMICAL REACTIONS?

Ignite sugar and it will go up in flames as it combines rapidly with oxygen, releasing carbon dioxide and water. The same overall reaction occurs in our cells, although not with uncontrolled blasts of heat. To capture energy in ATP, cells channel the release of energy produced by the breakdown of sugar in controlled steps. These steps are important because a single sugar molecule contains sufficient energy to produce dozens of ATP molecules.

Catalysts Reduce the Energy Required to Start a Reaction

In general, how likely a reaction is to occur is determined by its activation energy, that is, by how much energy is required to overcome the barrier created by repelling forces between atoms (see Fig. 6-5a). Some reactions, such as sugar dissolving in water, have low activation energies and occur rapidly at human body temperature (approximately 98.6°F, or 37°C). In contrast, you could store sugar at body temperature in the presence of oxygen for decades and it would remain virtually unchanged. Why? Although the reaction of sugar with oxygen to yield carbon dioxide and water is exergonic, this reaction has a high activation energy. The heat of a flame can overcome this activation energy barrier by increasing the rate of movement of sugar molecules and nearby oxygen

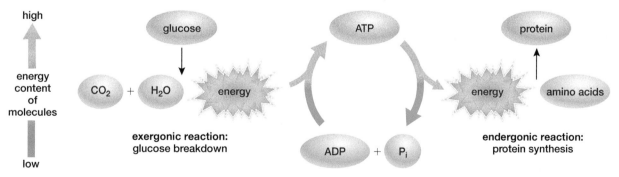

▲ **FIGURE 6-7 Coupled reactions within cells** Exergonic reactions, such as glucose breakdown, drive the endergonic reaction that synthesizes ATP from ADP and P_i. The ATP molecule carries its chemical energy to a part of the cell where energy is needed to drive an endergonic reaction, such as protein synthesis.

THINK CRITICALLY Why is the overall coupled reaction exergonic?

molecules, causing them to collide with sufficient force to react; the sugar burns as it releases energy. But, obviously, ignition doesn't start biological reactions in the body. Instead, life takes a different approach, lowering activation energy with catalysts.

Catalysts speed up the rate of a reaction by reducing its activation energy (**FIG. 6-8**); in the process catalysts themselves are neither used up nor permanently altered. Consider the catalytic converters on automobile exhaust systems. Incomplete combustion of gasoline generates poisonous carbon monoxide gas, which could reach dangerous levels in heavy traffic. Catalytic converters consist of a metallic catalyst that provides a surface upon which the carbon monoxide combines rapidly with atmospheric oxygen to produce carbon dioxide.

Enzymes Are Biological Catalysts

Inorganic catalysts speed up a number of different chemical reactions. But in cells, indiscriminately speeding up dozens of reactions would almost certainly be deadly. Instead, cells employ highly specific biological catalysts called **enzymes,** nearly all of which are proteins. Most enzymes catalyze one or a few types of chemical reactions involving specific molecules, leaving very similar molecules unchanged.

Both exergonic and endergonic reactions are catalyzed by enzymes. The synthesis of ATP from ADP and P_i, for example, is catalyzed by the enzyme ATP synthase. When energy is required to drive an endergonic reaction, ATP is broken down by an ATPase. As you read about enzymes, be aware that enzyme names are not consistent. In some cases, the suffix "ase" is added to what the enzyme does (ATP synthase), in other cases, "ase" is added to the molecule upon which the enzyme acts (e.g. ATPase), while some enzymes have their own unique names (e.g. pepsin).

The Structure of Enzymes Allows Them to Catalyze Specific Reactions

The function of an enzyme, like the function of any protein, is determined by its structure (see Chapter 3). Each enzyme's distinctive shape is determined by its amino acid sequence and the precise way in which the amino acid chain is twisted and folded. The three-dimensional structure of enzymes allows them to orient, distort, and reconfigure other molecules, causing these molecules to react, while the enzyme emerges unchanged.

Each enzyme has a pocket, called the **active site,** into which reactant molecules, called **substrates,** can enter. The shape of the active site, as well as the charges on the amino acids that form the active site, determine which molecules can enter. Consider the enzyme amylase, for example. Amylase breaks down starch molecules by hydrolysis, but leaves cellulose molecules intact, even though both starch and cellulose consist of chains of glucose molecules. Why? Because the bonding pattern between glucose molecules in starch allows the glucose chain to fit into the active

▲ **FIGURE 6-8 Catalysts lower activation energy** At any given temperature, a reaction is much more likely to proceed in the presence of a catalyst.

THINK CRITICALLY Can an enzyme catalyst make an endergonic reaction occur spontaneously at body temperature?

HAVE YOU EVER
WONDERED...

If Plants Can Glow in the Dark?

You may have seen the almost magical glow of fireflies, but did you know that plants can be bioengineered to glow in the dark, too? The firefly's natural glow comes from specialized cells in their abdomens that are bioluminescent, meaning that they produce light from biological reactions. These cells are rich in both ATP and the fluorescent chemical luciferin (L. *lucifer*, light-bringer). Luciferin and ATP serve as substrates for the enzyme luciferase. In the presence of oxygen, luciferase catalyzes a reaction that modifies luciferin, using the energy from ATP to boost electrons briefly into a higher-energy electron shell. As they fall back into their original shell, the electrons emit their excess energy as light.

Plants don't naturally glow, but bioluminescence has been bioengineered into glowing *Arabidopsis* plants by the Glowing Plant team. First, the team ordered commercial luciferin and luciferase DNA synthesized from its computerized gene sequence. Then they implanted these genes into a special form of bacterial DNA that incorporates itself into plant cells. They used a "gene gun" to shoot microscopic particles coated with the modified bacterial DNA into masses of plant stem cells, which developed into plants. Choosing the brightest-glowing plants, the team harvested their seeds to grow new generations, whose seeds are now sold online to buyers who wish to brighten their abodes.

site of amylase, but the bonding pattern in cellulose does not. In the stomach, the enzyme pepsin breaks down proteins, attacking them at certain sites along their amino acid chains. Certain other protein-digesting enzymes (trypsin, for example) will break bonds only between specific amino acids. Therefore, digestive systems must manufacture several different enzymes that work together to completely break down dietary protein into its individual amino acids.

How does an enzyme catalyze a reaction? You can follow the events in **FIGURE 6-9**, which illustrates two substrate molecules combining into a single product. The shape and charge of the active site allow substrates to enter the enzyme only in specific orientations ❶. When appropriate substrates enter the active site, both the substrates and active site change shape slightly as weak chemical bonds form between specific amino acids in the active site and specific parts of the substrate ❷. This shape change distorts the original bonds within the substrate, making these bonds easier to break. The combination of substrate selectivity, substrate orientation, temporary bonds, and the distortion of existing bonds promotes the specific chemical reaction catalyzed by a particular enzyme. This holds true whether the enzyme is causing two molecules to react with one another or causing a single molecule to split into smaller products. When the reaction is complete, the product no longer fits properly into the active site and diffuses away ❸. The enzyme reverts to its original configuration, and it is then ready to accept another set of the same substrates. When substrate molecules are abundant, some fast-acting enzymes can catalyze tens of thousands of reactions per second, while others act far more slowly.

Enzymes, Like All Catalysts, Lower Activation Energy

The breakdown or synthesis of a molecule within a cell usually occurs in many small, discrete steps, each catalyzed by a different enzyme. Each of these enzymes lowers the activation energy for its particular reaction, allowing the reaction to occur readily at body temperature. Imagine how much easier it is to walk up a flight of stairs compared to scaling a cliff of the same height. In a similar manner, a series of reaction "stair steps"—each requiring a small amount of activation energy and each catalyzed by an enzyme that lowers activation energy—allows the overall reaction to surmount its high activation energy barrier and to proceed at body temperature.

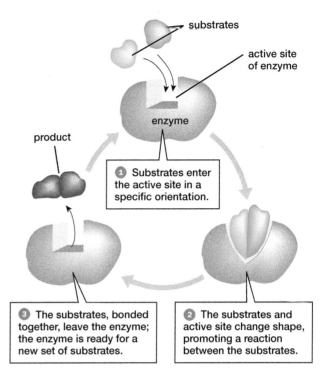

❶ Substrates enter the active site in a specific orientation.

❷ The substrates and active site change shape, promoting a reaction between the substrates.

❸ The substrates, bonded together, leave the enzyme; the enzyme is ready for a new set of substrates.

▲ **FIGURE 6-9 The cycle of enzyme–substrate interactions** This diagram shows two reactant substrate molecules combining to form a single product. Enzymes can also catalyze the breakdown of a single substrate into two product molecules.

CHECK YOUR LEARNING
Can you …
- explain how catalysts reduce activation energy?
- explain how enzymes function as biological catalysts?

6.5 HOW ARE ENZYMES REGULATED?

The **metabolism** of a cell is the sum of all its chemical reactions. Many of these reactions, such as those that break down glucose into carbon dioxide and water, are linked in sequences called **metabolic pathways** (**FIG. 6-10**). In a metabolic pathway, a starting reactant molecule is converted, with the help of an enzyme, into a slightly different intermediate molecule, which is modified by yet another enzyme to form a second intermediate, and so on, until an end product is produced. Photosynthesis (see Chapter 7), for example, is a metabolic pathway, as is the breakdown of glucose (Chapter 8). Different

◀ **FIGURE 6-10 Simplified metabolic pathways** The initial reactant molecule (A) undergoes a series of reactions, each catalyzed by a specific enzyme. The product of each reaction serves as the reactant for the next reaction in the pathway. Metabolic pathways are commonly interconnected, so the product of a step in one pathway (C in pathway 1) often serves as a substrate for an enzyme in a different pathway (enzyme 5 in pathway 2).

metabolic pathways often use some of the same molecules; as a result, all the thousands of metabolic pathways within a cell are directly or indirectly interconnected.

Cells Regulate Metabolic Pathways by Controlling Enzyme Synthesis and Activity

In a test tube under constant, ideal conditions, the rate of a particular reaction will depend on how many substrate molecules diffuse into the active sites of enzyme molecules in a given time period. This, in turn, will be determined by the concentrations of the enzyme and substrate molecules. Generally, increasing the concentrations of either the enzyme or the substrate (or both) will increase the reaction rate, because it will boost the chances that the two types of molecules will meet. But living cells must precisely control the rate of reactions in their metabolic pathways, requiring a system far more complex than that in a test tube. Cells must keep the amounts of end products within narrow limits, even when the amounts of reactants (enzyme substrates) fluctuate considerably. For example, when glucose molecules flood into the bloodstream after a meal, it would not be desirable to metabolize them all at once, producing far more ATP than the cell needs. Instead, some of the glucose molecules should be stored as glycogen or fat for later use. To be effective, then, metabolic reactions within cells must be precisely regulated;

they must occur at the proper times and proceed at the proper rates. Cells regulate their metabolic pathways by controlling the type, quantity, and activity levels of the enzymes they produce.

Genes That Code for Enzymes May Be Turned On or Off

A very effective way for cells to regulate enzymes is to turn the genes that code for specific enzymes on or off depending on the cell's changing needs. Gene regulation may cause enzymes to be synthesized in larger quantities when more of their substrate is available. Larger concentrations of an enzyme make it more likely that substrate molecules will encounter the enzyme, speeding up the rate at which the reaction occurs. For example, glucose entering the bloodstream after a starchy meal triggers an elaborate series of metabolic adjustments. One of these causes the pancreas to release the hormone insulin. Insulin activates the gene that codes for the first enzyme in the metabolic pathway that breaks down glucose. Insulin also activates a gene that codes for fatty acid synthase, an enzyme that helps convert molecules liberated by glucose breakdown into fats that store energy for later use.

Some enzymes are synthesized only during specific stages in an organism's life. For example, the enzyme that allows organisms to digest lactose (milk sugar) is typically lost after the animal is weaned. A mutation can alter this type

---

Health WATCH   Lack of an Enzyme Leads to Lactose Intolerance

If you enjoy ice cream and pizza, it might be hard for you to imagine life without these treats. However, such dairy-containing treats cannot be enjoyed by much of the world's population. Although all young children normally produce lactase (the enzyme that breaks down lactose, or "milk sugar"), about 65% of people worldwide, including 30 to 50 million people in the United States, produce less of this enzyme as they progress through childhood, a condition called *lactose intolerance*. In the worst cases, people may experience abdominal pain, flatulence, nausea, and diarrhea after consuming milk products (FIG. E6-2).

Why do people stop synthesizing the enzyme for this nutritious food? From an evolutionary perspective, it makes sense not to continue expending energy to produce an enzyme that has no function. In our early ancestors (who had not yet domesticated livestock), lactase lost its function in very early childhood because, after weaning, these people no longer had access to milk—the main source of lactose. As a result, many modern adults cannot digest lactose because the gene that encodes lactase is regulated by being turned off after weaning.

Lactose intolerance is particularly prevalent in people of East Asian, West African, and Native American descent. Genetic studies have revealed that between 10,000 and 6,000 years ago, some people in northern Europe and the Middle East acquired mutations that allowed them to digest lactose throughout their lives. These mutations were advantageous and gradually spread because they provided better nutrition for members of agricultural societies, who could obtain milk as well as meat from their livestock. Their descendants today continue to enjoy milk, ice cream, and extra-cheese pizzas.

▲ **FIGURE E6-2** **Risky behavior?** For the majority of the world's adults, drinking milk invites unpleasant consequences.

EVALUATE THIS A family brings their 8-year-old adopted child to a pediatric clinic because she has begun to suffer from diarrhea and stomach cramps after drinking milk. What would the pediatrician suspect was the cause? If tests confirm his suspicions, what approaches would he recommend to deal with the issue? Are there dairy products that would not cause the reaction? How might they work?

of regulation, as described in "Health Watch: Lack of an Enzyme Leads to Lactose Intolerance."

Some Enzymes Are Synthesized in Inactive Forms

Some enzymes are synthesized in an inactive form that is activated under the conditions found where the enzyme is needed. Examples include the protein-digesting enzymes pepsin and trypsin, which cells produce with the active site covered, preventing the enzyme from digesting and killing the cell that manufactures it. Acid conditions in the stomach cause a transformation of the inactive pepsin that exposes its active site and allows it to begin breaking down proteins from a meal. Trypsin (which helps to finish protein digestion) is released into the small intestine in an inactive form that is activated by a different enzyme secreted by intestinal cells.

Enzyme Activity May Be Controlled by Competitive or Noncompetitive Inhibition

After an enzyme has been synthesized and is in its active state, there are two additional ways in which the enzyme can be inhibited to control metabolic pathways: competitive inhibition and noncompetitive inhibition. In both cases, an inhibitor molecule binds temporarily to the enzyme. The higher the concentration of inhibitor molecules, the more likely they are to bind to enzymes.

We know that for an enzyme to catalyze a reaction, its substrate must bind to the enzyme's active site (**FIG. 6-11a**). In **competitive inhibition,** a substance that is not the enzyme's normal substrate can also bind to the active site of the enzyme, competing directly with the substrate for the active site (**FIG. 6-11b**). Usually, a competitive inhibitor molecule has structural similarities to the usual substrate that allow it to occupy the active site.

In **noncompetitive inhibition,** a molecule binds to a site on the enzyme that is distinct from the active site. This causes the active site to change shape and become unavailable, making the enzyme unable to catalyze the reaction (**FIG. 6-11c**).

Allosteric Regulation of Enzymes Is Important in Controlling Reaction Rates

The most important mechanism for adjusting the rate at which metabolic reactions occur to meet the needs of the cell is through **allosteric regulation** (Gk. *allosteric*, other shape). During allosteric regulation, the same enzyme is either activated or inhibited by molecules binding to an allosteric site on the enzyme; these sites are always distinct from the active site. Enzymes regulated in this manner are called *allosteric enzymes*. Allosteric enzymes switch easily and spontaneously between an active and an inactive configuration but can be stabilized in either form. *Allosteric inhibition* is a form of noncompetitive inhibition in which an allosteric inhibitor molecule binds an allosteric inhibiting site and stabilizes the enzyme in its inactive form (a process similar to that shown in Fig. 6-11c).

Allosteric activation occurs when an allosteric activator molecule binds to an allosteric activating site, stabilizing the

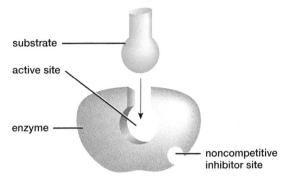

(a) A substrate binding to an enzyme

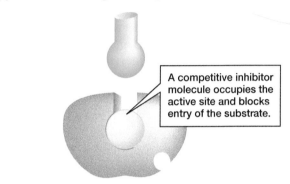

A competitive inhibitor molecule occupies the active site and blocks entry of the substrate.

(b) Competitive inhibition

The active site changes shape so the substrate no longer fits when a noncompetitive inhibitor molecule binds the enzyme.

(c) Noncompetitive inhibition

▲ **FIGURE 6-11 Competitive and noncompetitive enzyme inhibition (a)** The normal substrate fits into the enzyme's active site. **(b)** In competitive inhibition, a competitive inhibitor molecule that resembles the substrate enters and blocks the active site. **(c)** In noncompetitive inhibition, a molecule binds to a different site on the enzyme, distorting the active site so that the enzyme's substrate no longer fits.

enzyme in its active form. Allosteric activators and inhibitors bind briefly and reversibly to allosteric sites. As a result of this temporary binding, the number of enzyme molecules being activated (or inhibited) is proportional to the numbers of activator (or inhibitor) molecules that are present at any given time.

To see an example of allosteric regulation, let's look at ATP synthesis from its substrate molecule ADP. ADP is an allosteric activator and ATP an allosteric inhibitor of PFK (phosphofructokinase), an enzyme near the beginning of the metabolic pathway that breaks down glucose. ADP builds up in cells when a lot of ATP has been broken down. At high concentrations, ADP molecules are very likely to encounter the allosteric activator site on PFK, stabilizing PFK in its active ate. The activated enzyme will cause an increase in ATP production, using up ADP. Then, as ADP levels fall and ATP levels increase, ATP will become much more likely to bind the allosteric inhibitor site on PFK, stabilizing PFK in its inactive state and causing ATP levels to fall and ADP to build up. This balancing act by allosteric regulation very precisely controls cellular ATP levels.

The inhibition of the enzyme PFK by ATP is an example of an important form of allosteric regulation called feedback inhibition. In **feedback inhibition,** the activity of an enzyme near the beginning of a metabolic pathway is inhibited by the end product, which acts as an allosteric inhibitor (FIG. 6-12). Feedback inhibition causes a metabolic pathway to stop producing its end product when the product concentration reaches an optimal level, much as a thermostat turns off a heater when a room becomes warm enough.

Poisons, Drugs, and Environmental Conditions Influence Enzyme Activity

Poisons and drugs that act on enzymes usually inhibit them, either competitively or noncompetitively. In addition, environmental conditions can denature enzymes, distorting the three-dimensional structure that is required for their function.

Some Poisons and Drugs Are Competitive or Noncompetitive Inhibitors of Enzymes

Competitive inhibitors of enzymes, including nerve gases such as sarin and certain insecticides such as malathion, permanently block the active site of the enzyme acetylcholinesterase, which breaks down acetylcholine (a substance that nerve cells release to activate muscles). This allows acetylcholine to build up and overstimulate muscles, causing paralysis. Death may ensue because victims become unable to breathe. Other poisons are noncompetitive inhibitors of enzymes; these include the heavy metals arsenic, mercury, and lead. The poison potassium cyanide causes rapid death by noncompetitively inhibiting an enzyme that is crucial for the production of ATP.

Many drugs act as competitive inhibitors of enzymes. For example, the antibiotic penicillin destroys bacteria by competitively inhibiting an enzyme that is needed to synthesize bacterial cell walls. Both aspirin and ibuprofen (Advil) act as competitive inhibitors of an enzyme that catalyzes the synthesis of molecules that contribute to swelling, pain, and fever. Statin drugs (such as Lipitor) competitively inhibit an enzyme in the pathway that synthesizes cholesterol, thus reducing blood cholesterol levels. Many anticancer drugs block cancer cell proliferation by interfering with one or more of the numerous enzymes required to copy DNA, because each cell division requires the synthesis of new DNA. Unfortunately, these anticancer drugs also interfere with the growth of other rapidly dividing cells, such as those in hair follicles and the lining of the digestive tract. This explains why cancer chemotherapy may cause hair loss and nausea.

The Activity of Enzymes Is Influenced by Their Environment

The complex three-dimensional structures of enzymes are sensitive to environmental conditions. Recall that hydrogen bonds between polar amino acids are important in determining the three-dimensional structure of proteins (see Chapter 3). These bonds only occur within a narrow range of chemical and physical conditions, including the proper pH, temperature, and salt concentration. Thus, most enzymes have a very narrow range of conditions in which they function optimally. When conditions fall outside this range, the enzyme becomes **denatured,** meaning that it loses the exact three-dimensional structure required for it to function properly.

In humans, cellular enzymes generally work best at a pH around 7.4, the level maintained in and around our cells (FIG. 6-13a). For these enzymes, an acid pH alters

(a) Allosteric regulation by feedback inhibition

(b) Feedback inhibition by ATP on the enzyme PFK

◀ **FIGURE 6-12 Allosteric regulation by feedback inhibition (a)** In the general process of feedback inhibition, the end product of a metabolic pathway acts as an allosteric inhibitor, thus reducing the rate at which that end product is produced. **(b)** PFK inhibition is an example of feedback inhibition.

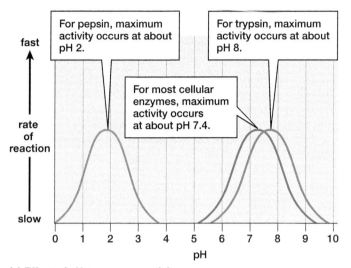

(a) Effect of pH on enzyme activity

(b) Effect of temperature on enzyme activity

▲ **FIGURE 6-13 Human enzymes function best within narrow ranges of pH and temperature (a)** The digestive enzyme pepsin, released into the stomach, works best at an acidic pH. Trypsin, released into the small intestine, works best at a basic pH. Most enzymes within cells work best at the pH found in the blood, interstitial fluid, and cytosol (about 7.4). **(b)** The maximum activity of most human enzymes occurs at human body temperature.

the charges on amino acids by adding hydrogen ions to them, which in turn will change the enzyme's shape and compromise its ability to function. Enzymes that operate in the human digestive tract, however, may function outside of the pH range maintained within cells. The protein-digesting enzyme pepsin, for example, requires the acidic conditions of the stomach (pH around 2). In contrast, the protein-digesting enzyme trypsin, found in the small intestine where alkaline conditions prevail, works best at a pH close to 8.

Temperature affects the rate of enzyme-catalyzed reactions, which are slowed by lower temperatures and accelerated by moderately higher temperatures (FIG. 6-13b). Why?

Recall that molecular motion increases as temperature increases and decreases as the temperature falls. The rate of movement of molecules, in turn, influences how likely they are to encounter the active site of an enzyme. Cooling the body can drastically slow human metabolic reactions. Consider the real-life example of a young boy who fell through the ice on a lake, where he remained submerged for about 20 minutes before being rescued. At normal body temperature, the brain dies from lack of ATP after about 4 minutes without oxygen. But, fortunately, this child recovered because the icy water drastically reduced his need for oxygen by lowering his body temperature and thus slowing his metabolic rate.

In contrast, when temperatures rise too high, the hydrogen bonds that regulate protein shape may be broken apart by the excessive molecular motion, denaturing the protein. Think of the protein in egg white and how its appearance and texture are completely altered by cooking. Far lower temperatures than those required to fry an egg can still be too hot to allow enzymes to function properly. Excessive heat may be fatal; every summer, children in the United States die when left unattended in overheated cars.

Food remains fresh longer in the refrigerator or freezer because cooling slows the enzyme-catalyzed reactions that allow bacteria and fungi (which can spoil food) to grow and reproduce. Before the advent of refrigeration, meat was commonly preserved by using concentrated salt solutions, which kill most bacteria; think of bacon or salt pork. Salts dissociate into ions, which form bonds with amino acids in enzyme proteins. Too much salt interferes with the three-dimensional structure of enzymes, destroying their activity. Dill pickles are very well preserved in a vinegar-salt solution, which combines both highly salty and acidic conditions (FIG. 6-14). The enzymes of organisms that live in salty environments, as you might predict, have configurations that depend on a relatively high concentration of salt ions.

▶ **FIGURE 6-14 Preservation** Only the pickled cucumbers will be edible months from now.

CHECK YOUR LEARNING

Can you ...

- describe how cells regulate the rate at which metabolic reactions proceed?
- explain how poisons, drugs, and environmental conditions influence enzyme activity, and provide examples?

Energy Unleashed

During the course of a 26.2-mile race, a marathoner burns a great deal of glucose to provide enough ATP to power muscles through roughly 34,000 running steps. People store glucose molecules linked together in long branched chains of glycogen, primarily in the muscles and liver. Adults typically store about 3.5 ounces (100 grams) of glycogen in the liver and about 10 ounces (280 grams) in muscles. Highly trained distance athletes may store over 50% more glycogen than average in their livers, and the ability of their muscles to store glycogen may be more than double that of non-athletes.

Glycogen storage is crucial for marathon runners. During a marathon, a runner depletes essentially all of his or her body's stored glycogen, often about 90 minutes into the race. The body then begins converting fat into glucose. This is a much slower process, which can leave the muscles and brain starved for

glucose. Low blood glucose levels can cause extreme muscle fatigue, loss of motivation, and occasionally even hallucinations. Runners describe this sensation as "hitting the wall" or "bonking." To store the greatest possible amount of glycogen, endurance athletes practice carbo-loading by consuming large quantities of starches and sugars during the 3 days preceding the race. By packing their livers and muscles with glycogen before the race, and also by consuming energy drinks during the race, some runners manage to cross the finish line before they hit the wall.

THINK CRITICALLY When a runner's body temperature begins to rise, the body activates several mechanisms, including sweating and circulating more blood to the skin. How does this response both resemble and differ from feedback inhibition in enzymes?

CHAPTER REVIEW

 Go to **MasteringBiology** for practice quizzes, activities, eText, videos, current events, and more.

Answers to Think Critically, Evaluate This, Multiple Choice, and Fill-in-the-Blank questions can be found in the Answers section at the back of the book.

Summary of Key Concepts

6.1 What Is Energy?

Energy is the capacity to do work. Potential energy is stored energy, and kinetic energy is the energy of movement. Potential energy and kinetic energy can be interconverted. The first law of thermodynamics states that in an isolated system, the total amount of energy remains constant, although the energy may change form. The second law of thermodynamics states that any use of energy causes a decrease in the quantity of useful energy and an increase in entropy (disorder or less useful forms of energy such as heat). The highly organized, low-entropy systems that characterize life do not violate the second law of thermodynamics because they are achieved through a continuous influx of usable energy from the sun, accompanied by an enormous increase in solar entropy.

6.2 How Is Energy Transformed During Chemical Reactions?

All chemical reactions involve making and breaking bonds, and all release some heat. In exergonic reactions, the reactant molecules have more energy than do the product molecules, so the overall reaction releases energy. In endergonic reactions, the reactants have less energy than do the products, so the reaction requires a net input of energy. Exergonic reactions can occur spontaneously, but all reactions, including exergonic ones, require an initial input of activation energy to overcome electrical repulsions between reactant molecules. Exergonic and endergonic reactions may be coupled such that the energy liberated by an exergonic reaction is stored in ATP, which can then drive an endergonic reaction.

6.3 How Is Energy Transported Within Cells?

Energy released by chemical reactions within a cell is captured and transported within the cell by unstable energy-carrier molecules, such as ATP and the electron carriers NADH and $FADH_2$. These molecules are the major means by which cells couple exergonic and endergonic reactions occurring at different places in the cell.

6.4 How Do Enzymes Promote Biochemical Reactions?

Enzymes are proteins that act as biological catalysts by lowering activation energy and allowing biochemical reactions to occur without a permanent change of the enzyme. Enzymes usually promote one or a few specific reactions. The reactants temporarily bind to the active site of the enzyme, causing less activation energy to be needed to produce the product. Cells control their metabolic reactions by regulating the synthesis and use of enzymes. Enzymes allow the breakdown of energy-rich molecules such as glucose in a series of small steps so that energy is released gradually and can be captured in ATP for use in endergonic reactions.

6.5 How Are Enzymes Regulated?

Cellular metabolism involves complex, interconnected sequences of reactions called metabolic pathways. Each reaction is catalyzed by an enzyme. Cells precisely control the amounts and activities of these enzymes. Enzyme action can be regulated by altering the rate of enzyme synthesis, activating previously inactive enzymes, competitive and noncompetitive inhibition, and allosteric regulation, which includes feedback inhibition. Many poisons and drugs act as enzyme inhibitors. Environmental conditions—including pH, salt concentration, and temperature—can promote or inhibit enzyme function by altering or preserving the enzyme's three-dimensional structure.

Key Terms

activation energy *97*
active site *100*
allosteric regulation *103*
catalyst *100*
chemical energy *94*
chemical reaction *97*
competitive inhibition *103*
coupled reaction *99*
denatured *104*
electron carrier *99*
endergonic *97*
energy *94*
energy-carrier molecule *98*
entropy *95*
enzyme *100*
exergonic *97*
feedback inhibition *104*

first law of
   thermodynamics *94*
isolated system *94*
kinetic energy *94*
law of conservation of
   energy *94*
metabolic pathway *101*
metabolism *101*
noncompetitive
   inhibition *103*
potential energy *94*
product *97*
reactant *97*
second law of
   thermodynamics *95*
substrate *100*
work *94*

Thinking Through the Concepts

Multiple Choice

1. Which of the following is True?
 a. Enzymes increase activation energy requirements.
 b. Activation energy is required to initiate exergonic reactions.
 c. Heat *cannot* supply activation energy.
 d. Stomach acid inactivates pepsin.

2. Which is *not* an example of an exergonic reaction?
 a. photosynthesis
 b. a nuclear reaction in the sun
 c. $ATP \rightarrow ADP + P_i$
 d. glucose breakdown

3. Which of the following is True?
 a. ATP is a long-term energy storage molecule.
 b. ATP can carry energy from one cell to another.
 c. ADP inhibits glucose breakdown in cells.
 d. ATP can act as an allosteric regulator molecule.

4. Coupled reactions
 a. are endergonic overall.
 b. both synthesize and break down ATP.
 c. are catalyzed by the same enzyme.
 d. end with reactants that contain more energy than their products.

5. Which of the following is False?
 a. Allosteric inhibition is noncompetitive.
 b. Allosteric regulation can either stimulate or inhibit enzyme activity.
 c. Feedback inhibition is a form of allosteric regulation.
 d. Competitive inhibition is a form of allosteric enzyme regulation.

Fill-in-the-Blank

1. According to the first law of thermodynamics, energy can be neither _____ nor _____. Energy occurs in two major forms: _____, the energy of movement, and _____, or stored energy.

2. According to the second law of thermodynamics, when energy changes forms, some is always converted into _____ useful forms. This tendency is called _____.

3. Once started, some reactions release energy and are called _____ reactions. Others require a net input of energy and are called _____ reactions. Which type of reaction will continue spontaneously once it starts? _____. Which type of reaction allows the formation of complex biological molecules from simpler molecules? _____.

4. The abbreviation ATP stands for _____. The molecule is synthesized by cells from _____ and _____. This synthesis requires an input of _____, which is temporarily stored in ATP.

5. Enzymes are what type of biological molecule? _____ Enzymes promote reactions in cells by acting as biological _____ that lower the _____. Each enzyme possesses a region called a(n) _____ that binds specific biological molecules.

6. Some poisons and drugs act by _____ enzymes. When a drug is similar to the enzyme's substrate, it acts as a(n) _____ inhibitor.

Review Questions

1. Explain why organisms do not violate the second law of thermodynamics. What is the ultimate energy source for most forms of life on Earth?

2. Define *potential energy* and *kinetic energy* and provide two specific examples of each. Explain how one form of energy can be converted into another. Will some energy be lost during this conversion? If so, what form will it take?

3. Define *metabolism,* and explain how reactions can be coupled to one another.

4. What is activation energy? How do catalysts affect activation energy? How do catalysts affect the reaction rate?

5. Compare breaking down glucose in a cell to setting it on fire with a match. What is the source of activation energy in each case?

6. Compare the mechanisms of competitive and noncompetitive inhibition of enzymes.

7. Describe the structure and function of enzymes. How is enzyme activity regulated?

Applying the Concepts

1. While vacuuming, you show off by telling a friend that you are using electrical energy to create a lower-entropy state. She replies that you are taking advantage of increasing solar entropy. Explain this conversation.

2. Refute the following: "According to evolutionary theory, organisms have increased in complexity through time. However, an increase in complexity contradicts the second law of thermodynamics. Therefore, evolution is impossible."

3. Can a bear use all the energy contained in the body of the fish it eats? Explain, and based on your explanation, predict and further explain whether a forest would likely have more predators or more prey animals (by weight)?

7

CAPTURING SOLAR ENERGY: PHOTOSYNTHESIS

Did the Dinosaurs Die from Lack of Sunlight?

ABOUT 66 MILLION YEARS AGO, the Cretaceous-Tertiary (K-T) extinction event brought the Cretaceous period to a violent end, and life on Earth suffered a catastrophic blow. The fossil record indicates that a devastating mass extinction eliminated at least 80% of all forms of life—both marine and terrestrial—that are known to have existed at that time. The 160-million-year reign of the dinosaurs, including the massive *Triceratops* and its predator *Tyrannosaurus rex*, ended abruptly. It would be many millions of years before Earth became repopulated with a diversity of species even approaching that of the late Cretaceous.

In 1980, Luis Alvarez, a Nobel Prize–winning physicist, his geologist son Walter Alvarez, and nuclear chemists Helen Michel and Frank Asaro published what was then a very controversial hypothesis. They proposed that an invader from outer space—a massive asteroid—had brought the Cretaceous period to an abrupt and violent end. Their evidence consisted of a thin layer of clay deposited at the end of the Cretaceous period and found at sites throughout the world. Known as the "K-T boundary layer," this clay deposit contains from 30 to 160 times the iridium level typically found in Earth's crust. Iridium is a silvery-white metal that, although extremely rare on Earth, is abundant in certain types of asteroids. How large must an iridium-rich asteroid have been to create the K-T boundary layer encircling Earth? The Alvarez team calculated that this iridium-enriched space rock must have been at least 6 miles (10 kilometers) in diameter. As it crashed into Earth, its impact released the energy equivalent to 8 billion of the atomic bombs that destroyed Hiroshima and Nagasaki. The asteroid's impact blasted out a plume of pulverized rock, some of which reached the moon and beyond. Most of the asteroid's fragments and pellets of debris grew incandescent as they re-entered the atmosphere,

The end of the reign of the dinosaurs?

plummeting down in a fiery shower that ignited wildfires, possibly over most of Earth's surface. A shroud of dust and soot blocked the sun's rays, and the broiling heat gave way to a cooling darkness that enveloped Earth.

How could an asteroid impact have eliminated most known forms of life? In the months following the firestorms, one of the most damaging effects would have been darkness that disrupted photosynthesis, the most important biochemical pathway on Earth. What occurs during photosynthesis? What makes this process so important that interrupting it would wipe out much of Earth's biodiversity?

AT A GLANCE

7.1 WHAT IS PHOTOSYNTHESIS?

Roughly 3.5 billion years ago, chance mutations allowed a prokaryotic (bacterial) cell to harness the energy of sunlight. Exploiting abundant water and sunshine, early photosynthetic cells proliferated and filled the shallow seas. The evolution of photosynthesis made life as we know it possible. This amazing process provides not only fuel for life but also the oxygen required to burn this fuel efficiently. **Photosynthesis** is the process by which light energy is captured and then stored as chemical energy in the bonds of organic molecules such as sugar (**FIG. 7-1**). In lakes and oceans, photosynthesis is performed primarily by photosynthetic protists and certain bacteria, and on land, mostly by plants. Collectively, these organisms incorporate close to 100 billion tons of carbon into their bodies annually. The carbon- and energy-rich molecules of photosynthetic organisms eventually become available to feed all other forms of life. Fundamentally similar reactions occur in all photosynthetic organisms; here we will concentrate on the most familiar of these: land plants.

Leaves and Chloroplasts Are Adaptations for Photosynthesis

The leaves of plants are beautifully adapted to the demands of photosynthesis. A leaf's flattened shape exposes a large surface area to the sun, and its thinness ensures that sunlight can penetrate to reach the light-trapping chloroplasts inside. Both the upper and lower surfaces of a leaf consist of a layer of transparent cells that form the **epidermis,** which protects

▲ **FIGURE 7-1 An overview of photosynthesis**

the inner parts of the leaf while allowing light to penetrate. The outer surface of the epidermis is covered by the **cuticle,** a transparent, waxy, waterproof covering that reduces the evaporation of water from the leaf.

A leaf obtains the carbon dioxide (CO_2) necessary for photosynthesis from the air, through adjustable pores in the epidermis called **stomata** (singular, stoma; **FIG. 7-2**). Inside the leaf are layers of cells collectively called **mesophyll** (Gk. *meso,* middle; **FIG. 7-3**) where most chloroplasts are located. Mesophyll cells in the leaf's center are loosely packed, allowing air to circulate around them and CO_2 and O_2 to be exchanged through their moist membranes. *Vascular bundles,* which form veins in the leaf (see Fig. 7-3b), supply water and minerals to the leaf's cells and carry the sugar molecules produced during photosynthesis to other parts of the plant. Surrounding the vascular bundles are **bundle sheath cells,** which lack chloroplasts in most plants.

(a) Stomata open

(b) Stomata closed

◀ **FIGURE 7-2 Stomata (a)** Open stomata allow CO_2 to diffuse in and O_2 to diffuse out. **(b)** Closed stomata reduce water loss by evaporation but prevent CO_2 from entering and O_2 from leaving.

(a) Leaves

(b) Internal leaf structure

vascular bundle (vein)
cuticle
upper epidermis
mesophyll cells
lower epidermis
stoma
chloroplasts
bundle sheath cells
stoma

(e) Chloroplast

inner membrane
outer membrane
grana (stacks of thylakoids)
stroma
thylakoids

(d) Electron micrograph of a chloroplast

(c) Mesophyll cell containing chloroplasts

▲ FIGURE 7-3 **Photosynthetic structures (a)** Photosynthesis occurs primarily in the leaves. **(b)** A section of a leaf. **(c)** A light micrograph of a single mesophyll cell, packed with chloroplasts. **(d)** A TEM of a single chloroplast, showing the stroma and thylakoids where photosynthesis occurs. **(e)** An illustrated chloroplast.

Photosynthesis in plants takes place within **chloroplasts,** most of which are contained within mesophyll cells. A single mesophyll cell often contains 40 to 50 chloroplasts (see Fig. 7-3c), and up to 500,000 of them may be packed into a 1 mm^2 area of leaf. Chloroplasts are organelles that consist of a double outer membrane enclosing a semifluid substance, the **stroma.** Embedded in the stroma are interconnected membrane-enclosed compartments called **thylakoids.** Thylakoids often form disk-shaped structures, which are arranged into stacks called **grana** (see Figs. 7-3d, e). Each of these sacs encloses a fluid-filled region called the thylakoid space.

Photosynthesis Consists of the Light Reactions and the Calvin Cycle

Starting with the simple molecules of carbon dioxide and water, photosynthesis converts the energy of sunlight into

chemical energy stored in the bonds of glucose and releases oxygen as a by-product. The overall chemical reaction for photosynthesis is:

$$6\,CO_2 + 6\,H_2O + \text{light energy} \rightarrow C_6H_{12}O_6 \text{ (sugar)} + 6\,O_2$$

This straightforward equation obscures the fact that photosynthesis actually involves dozens of individual reactions, each catalyzed by a separate enzyme. These reactions occur in two distinct stages: the light reactions and the Calvin cycle. Each stage takes place in a different region of the chloroplast, but the two are connected by an important link: energy-carrier molecules.

In the **light reactions** (the "photo" part of photosynthesis), **chlorophyll** and other molecules embedded in the thylakoid membranes of the chloroplast capture sunlight energy and convert it into chemical energy. This chemical

▼ **FIGURE 7-4 The relationship between the light reactions and the Calvin cycle** Notice that H_2O and CO_2, the raw materials for photosynthesis, enter at different stages and are used in different parts of the chloroplast. The O_2 liberated by photosynthesis is derived from H_2O, while the carbon used in the synthesis of sugar is obtained from CO_2.

CASE STUDY CONTINUED

Did The Dinosaurs Die from Lack of Sunlight?

Over 2 billion years before the K-T extinction event, the first photosynthetic cells filled the seas and released what was then a deadly gas: oxygen. Oxygen accumulated in what had originally been an oxygen-free atmosphere, radically altering Earth's environment. This "Great Oxygenation Event" triggered a massive extinction. But unlike the K-T extinction, most of the casualties left no trace, because life had not evolved beyond single cells, which are rarely preserved in the fossil record. Fortunately, these simple life-forms reproduce rapidly, allowing their DNA to accumulate mutations over a relatively short time span. A serendipitous combination of random mutations allowed some early cells to not only survive exposure to oxygen, but also use it to their advantage. These organisms became the ancestors of nearly all modern forms of life. Eventually, plants invaded the land, and by the Cretaceous period, plants growing in luxuriant profusion provided sustenance for herbivorous giants such as the 12-ton *Triceratops*.

What chemical reactions allow plants to capture solar energy and store it in chemical bonds, releasing oxygen in the process?

energy is stored in the energy-carrier molecules ATP (adenosine triphosphate) and **NADPH (NADP+; nicotinamide adenine dinucleotide phosphate).** Water is split apart, and oxygen gas is released as a by-product.

The reactions of the **Calvin cycle** (the "synthesis" part of photosynthesis) can occur in either light or darkness. During these reactions, enzymes in the stroma surrounding the thylakoids combine CO_2 from the atmosphere and chemical energy from ATP and NADH. The end product is a three-carbon sugar that will be used to make glucose.

FIGURE 7-4 shows the locations at which the light reactions and the Calvin cycle occur and illustrates the interdependence of the two processes. In the following sections, we examine each stage of photosynthesis.

CHECK YOUR LEARNING

Can you ...

• explain why photosynthesis is important?
• diagram the structure of leaves and chloroplasts and explain how these structures function in photosynthesis?
• write out and explain the basic equation for photosynthesis?
• summarize the main events of the light reactions and the Calvin cycle and explain the relationship between these two processes?

7.2 THE LIGHT REACTIONS: HOW IS LIGHT ENERGY CONVERTED TO CHEMICAL ENERGY?

Recall that the light reactions capture the energy of sunlight, storing it as chemical energy in ATP and NADPH. The molecules that make these reactions possible, including light-capturing pigments and enzymes, are anchored in a precise array within the membranes of the thylakoids. As you read this section, notice how the thylakoid membranes and the spaces they enclose support the light reactions.

Light Is Captured by Pigments in Chloroplasts

The sun emits energy that spans a broad spectrum of electromagnetic radiation. The **electromagnetic spectrum** ranges from short-wavelength gamma rays, through ultraviolet, visible, and infrared light, to very long-wavelength radio waves (**FIG. 7-5**). Light and all other electromagnetic waves are composed of individual packets of energy called **photons.** The energy of a photon corresponds to its wavelength: Short-wavelength photons, such as gamma and X-rays, are very energetic, whereas long-wavelength photons, such as microwaves and radio waves, carry lower energies. Visible light consists of wavelengths with energies that are high enough to alter biological pigment molecules (light-absorbing molecules) such as chlorophyll, but not high enough to break the bonds of crucial molecules such as DNA.

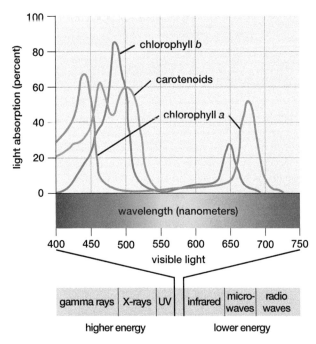

Biologist Nancy Kiang and her colleagues at NASA have developed hypotheses about alien plant colors. M-type stars, the most abundant type in our galaxy, emit light that is redder and dimmer than that of our sun. If photosynthetic organisms happened to evolve on an Earth-like planet circling an M-type star, to capture enough energy, the plants very possibly would require pigments that would absorb all visible wavelengths of light. Such pigments would reflect almost no light back to our eyes, so these alien photosynthesizers would probably be black, creating a truly eerie landscape to human eyes.

What Color Plants Might Be on Other Planets?

▲ **FIGURE 7-5 Light and chloroplast pigments** The rainbow colors that we perceive are a small part of the electromagnetic spectrum. Chlorophyll *a* and *b* (green and blue curves, respectively) strongly absorb violet, blue, and red light, reflecting a green or yellowish-green color to our eyes. Carotenoids (orange curve) absorb blue and green wavelengths.

THINK CRITICALLY You continuously monitor the photosynthetic oxygen production from the leaf of a plant illuminated by white light. How and why would oxygen production change if you placed filters in front of the light source that transmit (a) only red, (b) only infrared, and (c) only green light onto the leaf?

(It is no coincidence that these wavelengths, with just the right amount of energy, also stimulate the pigments in our eyes, allowing us to see.)

When a specific wavelength of light strikes an object such as a leaf, one of three events occurs: The light may be reflected (bounced back), transmitted (passed through), or absorbed (captured). Wavelengths of light that are reflected or transmitted can reach the eyes of an observer; these wavelengths are seen as the color of the object. Light energy that is absorbed can drive biological processes such as photosynthesis.

Chloroplasts contain a variety of pigment molecules that absorb different wavelengths of light. **Chlorophyll *a*,** the key light-capturing pigment molecule in chloroplasts, strongly absorbs violet, blue, and red light, but reflects green, thus giving green leaves their color (see Fig. 7-5). Chloroplasts also contain other molecules, collectively called **accessory pigments,** which absorb additional wavelengths of light energy and transfer their energy to chlorophyll *a*. Accessory pigments include chlorophyll *b*, a slightly different form of chlorophyll *a* that reflects yellow-green light and absorbs some of the blue and red-orange wavelengths of light that are missed by chlorophyll *a*. **Carotenoids** are

accessory pigments found in all chloroplasts. They absorb blue and green light and therefore appear mostly yellow or orange (see Fig. 7-5). Carotenoid accessory pigments include beta-carotene, which gives many vegetables and fruits (including carrots, squash, oranges, and cantaloupes) their orange colors. Interestingly, animals convert beta-carotene into vitamin A, which is used to synthesize the light-capturing pigment in our eyes. Thus, in a beautiful symmetry, the beta-carotene that captures light energy in plants is converted into a substance that captures light in animals as well.

Although carotenoids are present in leaves, their color is usually masked by the more abundant green chlorophyll. In temperate regions, as leaves begin to die in autumn, chlorophyll breaks down before carotenoids do, revealing these bright yellow and orange pigments as fall colors (**FIG. 7-6**).

The Light Reactions Occur in Association with the Thylakoid Membranes

The light reactions occur in and on the thylakoid membranes. These membranes contain many **photosystems,** each consisting of a cluster of chlorophyll and accessory

▲ **FIGURE 7-6 Loss of chlorophyll reveals carotenoid pigments** As winter approaches, chlorophyll in these aspen leaves breaks down, revealing yellow and orange carotenoid pigments.

pigment molecules surrounded by various proteins. There are two types of photosystems—photosystem II and photosystem I—that work together during the light reactions. The photosystems are named according to the order in which they were discovered, but the light reactions start with photosystem II and then proceed to photosystem I.

Adjacent to each photosystem is an **electron transport chain (ETC)** consisting of a series of electron-carrier molecules embedded in the thylakoid membrane. Electrons flow through the following pathway in the light reactions: photosystem II → electron transport chain → photosystem I → electron transport chain → NADPH.

You can think of the light reactions as a sort of arcade pinball game: Energy (sunlight) is introduced when a player

pulls back and releases a knob. The energy is transferred from spring-driven pistons (chlorophyll molecules) to a ball (an electron), propelling it upward (into a higher-energy level). As the ball bounces back downhill, the energy it releases can be used to turn a wheel (generate ATP) and ring a bell (generate NADPH). With this overall scheme in mind, let's look more closely at the sequence of events in the light reactions.

Photosystem II and Its Electron Transport Chain Capture Light Energy, Create a Hydrogen Ion Gradient, and Split Water

As you read the following descriptions, refer to the numbered steps in **FIGURE 7-7**. The light reactions begin when photons of light are absorbed by pigment molecules clustered in photosystem II ❶. The energy hops from one pigment molecule to the next until it is funneled into the photosystem II reaction center ❷. The **reaction center** of each photosystem consists of a pair of specialized chlorophyll *a* molecules and a *primary electron acceptor* molecule embedded in a complex of proteins. When the energy from light reaches the reaction center, it boosts an electron from one of the reaction center

◀ **FIGURE 7-7 Energy transfer and the light reactions of photosynthesis** Light reactions occur in and immediately adjacent to the thylakoid membrane. The vertical axis indicates the relative energy levels of the molecules involved.

chlorophylls to the primary electron acceptor, which captures the energized electron ❸.

For photosynthesis to continue, the electrons that were boosted out of the reaction center of photosystem II must be replaced. The replacement electrons come from water (see ❷). Water molecules are split by an enzyme associated with photosystem II, liberating electrons that will replace those lost by the reaction center chlorophyll molecules. Splitting water also releases two hydrogen ions, and for every two water molecules split, one molecule of O_2 is produced.

Once the primary electron acceptor in photosystem II captures the electron, it passes the electron to the first molecule of the adjacent ETC in the thylakoid membrane ❹. The electron then travels from one electron carrier molecule to the next, releasing energy as it goes. Some of this energy is harnessed to pump H^+ across the thylakoid membrane and into the thylakoid space, where it contributes to the H^+ gradient that generates ATP (❺; to be discussed shortly). Finally, the energy-depleted electron leaves the ETC and enters the reaction center of photosystem I, where it replaces the electron ejected when light strikes photosystem I ❻.

Photosystem I and Its Electron Transport Chain Generate NADPH

Meanwhile, light has also been striking the pigment molecules of photosystem I. This light energy is passed to a chlorophyll *a* molecule in the reaction center ❻. Here, it energizes an electron that is absorbed by the primary electron acceptor of photosystem I ❼. (This energized electron is immediately replaced by an energy-depleted electron from the first electron transport chain.) From the primary electron acceptor of photosystem I, the energized electron is passed to a second ETC adjacent to photosystem I in the thylakoid membrane ❽. Here, the final electron carrier is an enzyme that catalyzes the synthesis of NADPH. To form NADPH, the enzyme combines $NADP^+$ and H^+ (both dissolved in the stroma) with two energetic electrons from the ETC ❾.

The Hydrogen Ion Gradient Generates ATP by Chemiosmosis

FIGURE 7-8 shows how electrons move through the thylakoid membrane and how their energy is used to create an H^+ gradient that drives ATP synthesis through a process called **chemiosmosis.** As an energized electron travels along the ETC associated with photosystem II, it releases energy in steps. Some of this energy is harnessed to pump H^+ across the thylakoid membrane and into the thylakoid space ❶. This creates a high concentration of H^+ inside the space ❷

◀ **FIGURE 7-8** **Events of the light reactions occur in and near the thylakoid membrane**

and a low concentration in the surrounding stroma. During chemiosmosis, H^+ flows back down its concentration gradient through a special type of channel called **ATP synthase** that spans the thylakoid membrane. ATP synthase produces ATP using ADP and phosphate dissolved in the stroma ❸. It takes the energy from about three H^+ passing through ATP synthase to synthesize one ATP molecule.

The H^+ gradient serves the same function as water stored behind a dam at a hydroelectric plant. When the stored water is released at the hydroelectric plant, it is channeled downward through turbines. Similarly, the hydrogen ions in the thylakoid space are funneled through ATP synthase channels. In the hydroelectric plant, turbines convert the energy of moving water into electrical energy. In an analogous way, ATP synthase converts the energy liberated by the flow of H^+ into chemical energy stored in the bonds of ATP.

SUMMING UP: Light Reactions

- Chlorophyll and carotenoid pigments of photosystem II absorb light that energizes and ejects an electron from a reaction center chlorophyll *a* molecule. The energized electron is captured by the primary electron acceptor molecule.
- The electron is passed from the primary electron acceptor to the adjacent ETC, where it moves from molecule to molecule, releasing energy with each transfer. Some of the energy is used to create a hydrogen ion gradient across the thylakoid membrane. This gradient is used to drive ATP synthesis by chemiosmosis.
- Enzymes associated with photosystem II split water. This releases electrons that replace those ejected from the reaction center chlorophylls, supplies H^+ that enhances the H^+ gradient for ATP production, and liberates O_2.
- Chlorophyll and carotenoid pigments in photosystem I absorb light that energizes and ejects an electron from a reaction center chlorophyll *a* molecule into the primary electron acceptor molecule. This electron is replaced by an energy-depleted electron from the ETC associated with photosystem II.
- The energized electron passes from the primary electron acceptor into the adjacent ETC, where it moves from molecule to molecule, releasing energy.
- The final molecule in this second ETC is an enzyme that synthesizes the energy-carrier NADPH from $NADP^+$ and H^+ for every two energized electrons that reach it.
- The overall products of the light reactions are the energy carriers NADPH and ATP; O_2 is released as a by-product.

CHECK YOUR LEARNING
Can you ...

- list the light-capturing molecules in chloroplasts and describe their functions?
- diagram and describe the molecules within the thylakoid membranes and explain how they capture and transfer light energy?
- explain how NADPH and ATP are generated?

CASE STUDY \ **CONTINUED**

Did the Dinosaurs Die from Lack of Sunlight?

Air bubbles trapped in amber from the Cretaceous period have revealed that oxygen made up nearly 35% of the atmosphere at that time, compared to 21% today. Abundant oxygen would have intensified the conflagrations caused by the flaming re-entry of debris from the asteroid impact. Marine ecosystems, which relied on photosynthesizing microorganisms, would have collapsed rapidly in the twilight conditions.

A large portion of Earth's terrestrial vegetation was likely consumed by fire, and many of those land plants that survived the fires would have succumbed during the cold, dark "global winter" that began as the planet was encompassed by soot and dust. Most plant-eating animals that survived the initial blast would have soon starved, especially enormous ones like the 12-ton *Triceratops,* which needed to consume hundreds of pounds of vegetation daily. Predators such as *Tyrannosaurus,* which relied on plant-eaters for food, would have died soon afterward.

What reactions allow plants to store the high-energy molecules that they and most other forms of life still rely on today?

7.3 THE CALVIN CYCLE: HOW IS CHEMICAL ENERGY STORED IN SUGAR MOLECULES?

Our cells produce carbon dioxide as we burn sugar for energy (described in Chapter 8), but they can't form organic molecules by capturing (or *fixing*) the carbon atoms in CO_2. Although this feat can be accomplished by a few types of *chemosynthetic* bacteria that fix carbon using energy gained by breaking down inorganic molecules, nearly all carbon fixation is performed by photosynthetic organisms. The carbon is captured from atmospheric CO_2 during the Calvin cycle using energy from sunlight harnessed during the light reactions. The details of the Calvin cycle were discovered in the 1950s by chemists Melvin Calvin, Andrew Benson, and James Bassham. Using radioactive isotopes of carbon (see Chapter 2), they were able to follow carbon atoms as they moved from CO_2 through the various compounds of the cycle and, finally, into sugar molecules.

The Calvin Cycle Captures Carbon Dioxide

The ATP and NADPH synthesized during the light reactions are dissolved in the fluid stroma that surrounds the thylakoids. There, these energy carriers power the synthesis of the three-carbon sugar *glyceraldehyde-3-phosphate (G3P)* from CO_2 in the Calvin cycle. This metabolic pathway is described as a "cycle" because it begins and ends with the same five-carbon molecule, *ribulose bisphosphate (RuBP).*

For simplicity, we illustrate the cycle starting and ending with three molecules of RuBP. Each "turn" of the cycle captures three molecules of CO_2 and produces one molecule of

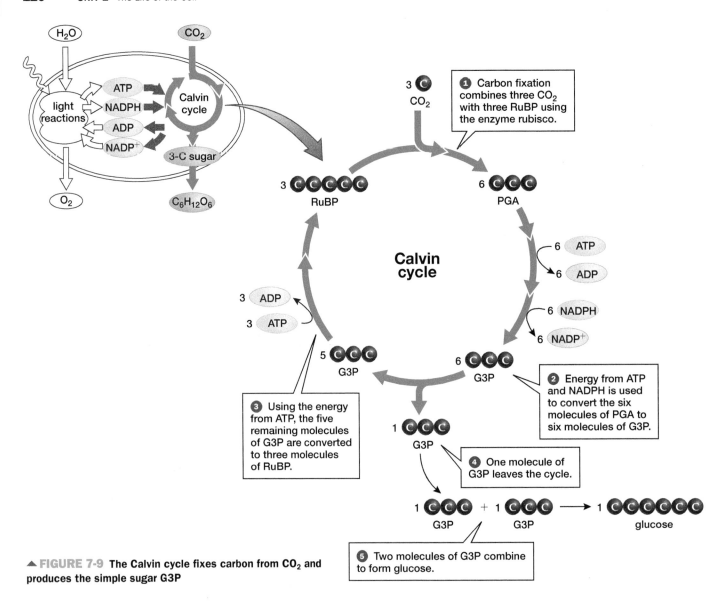

▲ **FIGURE 7-9 The Calvin cycle fixes carbon from CO$_2$ and produces the simple sugar G3P**

the simple sugar end product: G3P. The Calvin cycle is best understood if we divide it into three parts: (1) carbon fixation, (2) the synthesis of G3P, and (3) the regeneration of RuBP that allows the cycle to continue (**FIG. 7-9**).

During **carbon fixation,** carbon from CO$_2$ is incorporated into organic molecules. The enzyme **rubisco** combines three CO$_2$ molecules with three RuBP molecules to produce three unstable six-carbon molecules that immediately split in half, forming six molecules of *phosphoglyceric acid (PGA, a three-carbon molecule)* ❶. Because carbon fixation generates this three-carbon PGA molecule, the Calvin cycle is often referred to as the **C$_3$ pathway.**

The synthesis of the simple three-carbon sugar G3P occurs *via* a series of reactions using energy donated by ATP and NADPH. During these reactions, six three-carbon PGA molecules are rearranged to form six three-carbon G3P molecules ❷. Five of the six G3P molecules are used to regenerate three five-carbon RuBP molecules, using ATP generated during the light reactions ❸. The single remaining G3P molecule exits the Calvin cycle ❹.

Carbon fixation, the first step in the Calvin cycle, can be disrupted by O$_2$. The enzyme rubisco that fixes carbon is not completely selective, and it will allow O$_2$ instead of CO$_2$ to combine with RuBP. When O$_2$ replaces CO$_2$, the result is a wasteful process called **photorespiration,** which reduces the rate of carbon fixation by roughly 33%. If photorespiration could be avoided, plants could capture solar energy much more efficiently. Many researchers are working to genetically modify the enzyme rubisco to make it more selective for CO$_2$, with the hope of increasing the yields of crops such as wheat. Other researchers have already taken genes for a faster-acting version of rubisco from photosynthetic bacteria and inserted it into plants.

A small percentage of Earth's terrestrial plants have evolved biochemical pathways that consume a bit more energy but increase the efficiency of carbon fixation in hot, dry environments. These pathways—the **C$_4$ pathway** and the **crassulacean acid metabolism (CAM)** pathway—are explored in "In Greater Depth: Alternate Pathways Increase Carbon Fixation."

IN GREATER DEPTH | Alternate Pathways Increase Carbon Fixation

In hot, dry conditions, stomata remain closed much of the time to prevent water from evaporating. But this also prevents the exchange of gases, so as photosynthesis occurs, the concentration of CO_2 drops and the concentration of O_2 rises. The O_2 can bind to the active site of the enzyme rubisco and prevent CO_2 from binding, an example of competitive inhibition. The O_2 then combines with RuBP, causing photorespiration, which greatly reduces the rate of carbon fixation. Plants, particularly fragile seedlings, may die under these circumstances because they are unable to capture enough energy to meet their metabolic needs.

Rubisco is the most abundant protein on Earth and arguably one of the most important. It catalyzes the reaction by which carbon enters the biosphere, and all life is based on carbon. Why, then, is rubisco so unselective? When rubisco first evolved, Earth's atmosphere was high in CO_2 but contained little O_2, so there was no threat of competitive inhibition. As atmospheric O_2 increased, the chance mutations that would have prevented competitive inhibition never occurred. Instead, certain flowering plants evolved two different but closely related mechanisms that circumvent photorespiration: the C_4 pathway and crassulacean acid metabolism (CAM). Each uses the Calvin cycle, but each also involves several additional reactions and consumes more ATP than does the Calvin cycle alone. But in compensation for the loss of ATP, these plants conserve more water under hot, dry conditions.

C_4 Plants Capture Carbon and Synthesize Sugar in Different Cells

In typical plants, known as C_3 *plants* (because they use only the C_3 cycle, another name for the Calvin cycle), the chloroplasts in which the Calvin cycle occurs are located primarily in mesophyll cells. No chloroplasts are found in bundle sheath cells that surround the leaf's veins (see Fig. 7-3). In contrast, C_4 *plants* have chloroplasts in both mesophyll and bundle sheath cells. Such plants use an initial series of reactions, called the C_4 pathway, to selectively capture carbon in their mesophyll chloroplasts. The mesophyll chloroplasts lack Calvin cycle enzymes and use the enzyme *PEP carboxylase* to fix CO_2. Unlike rubisco, PEP carboxylase is highly selective for CO_2 over O_2. PEP carboxylase causes CO_2 to react with a three-carbon molecule called phosphoenolpyruvate (PEP). So in C_4 plants, carbon fixation produces the four-carbon molecule oxaloacetate, from which the C_4 pathway gets its name. Oxaloacetate is rapidly converted into another four-carbon molecule, malate, which diffuses from the mesophyll cells into bundle sheath cells. The malate acts as a shuttle for CO_2.

In C_4 plants, Calvin cycle enzymes (including rubisco) are present only in the chloroplasts of the bundle sheath cells. In the bundle sheath cells, malate is broken down, forming the three-carbon molecule pyruvate and releasing CO_2. This generates a high CO_2 concentration in the bundle sheath cells (up to 10 times higher than atmospheric CO_2). The resulting high CO_2 concentration allows rubisco to fix carbon with little competition from O_2, minimizing photorespiration. The pyruvate is then actively transported back into the mesophyll cells. Here, more ATP energy is used to convert pyruvate back into PEP, allowing the cycle to continue (**FIG. E7-1**). Plants using C_4 photosynthesis include crabgrass, corn, daisies, and some thistles.

CAM Plants Capture Carbon and Synthesize Sugar at Different Times

CAM plants also use the C_4 pathway, but in contrast to C_4 plants, CAM plants do not use different cell types

▲ **FIGURE E7-1 The C_4 pathway** Both the C_4 and CAM pathways form the same molecules, fixing carbon into oxaloacetate using the selective enzyme PEP carboxylase, and then storing it in malate. In C_4 plants, atmospheric CO_2 is trapped in mesophyll cells and enters the Calvin cycle in bundle sheath cells.

THINK CRITICALLY Why do C_3 plants have an advantage over C_4 plants under cool, moist conditions?

...pture carbon and to synthesize ...ar. Instead, they perform both activi...es in the same mesophyll cells, but at different times: Carbon fixation occurs at night, and sugar synthesis occurs during the day (FIG. E7-2).

The stomata of CAM plants open at night, when less water will evaporate because temperatures are cooler and humidity is higher. Carbon dioxide diffuses into the leaf and is captured in mesophyll cells using the C_4 pathway. The malate produced by the C_4 pathway is then shuttled into the central vacuole, where it is stored as malic acid until daytime. During the day, when stomata are closed to conserve water, the malic acid leaves the vacuole and re-enters the cytoplasm as malate. The malate is broken down, forming pyruvate (which will be converted to PEP) and releasing CO_2, which enters the Calvin cycle (via rubisco) to produce sugar. CAM plants include pineapples, succulents, and cacti.

C_4 plants and CAM Pathways Are Specialized Adaptations

Because C_4 and CAM plants greatly reduce competitive inhibition of rubisco by O_2, why don't all plants use these pathways? The trade-off is that both the C_4 and the CAM pathways consume more energy than does the Calvin cycle by itself; hence, these plants waste some of the solar energy that they capture. As a result, they only

have an advantage in warm, sunny, dry environments. This explains why a lush spring lawn of Kentucky bluegrass (a C_3 plant) may be taken over by spiky crabgrass (a C_4 plant) during a hot, dry summer.

▲ FIGURE E7-2 **The CAM pathway** As with the C_4 pathway, the CAM pathway fixes carbon into oxaloacetate using PEP carboxylase and stores it in malate. In CAM plants, both processes occur in mesophyll cell, but CO_2 capture occurs at night and CO_2 enters the Calvin cycle during the day.

Carbon Fixed During the Calvin Cycle Is Used to Synthesize Glucose

In reactions that occur outside of the Calvin cycle, two three-carbon G3P sugar molecules can be combined to form one six-carbon glucose molecule (see Fig. 7-9 ❺). Glucose can then be used to synthesize sucrose (table sugar), a disaccharide storage molecule consisting of a glucose linked to a fructose. Glucose molecules can also be linked together in long chains to form starch (another storage molecule) or cellulose (a major component of plant cell walls). Some plants convert glucose into lipids for storage. Glucose is also broken down during cellular respiration to provide energy for the plant's cells.

The storage products of photosynthesis are being eyed by Earth's growing and energy-hungry human population as a substitute for fossil fuels. These "biofuels" have the potential advantage of not adding additional CO_2 (a "greenhouse gas" that contributes to global climate change) to the atmosphere, but do they live up to their promise? We explore this question in "Earth Watch: Biofuels—Are Their Benefits Bogus?"

SUMMING UP: The Calvin Cycle

The Calvin cycle can be divided into three stages:

1. Carbon fixation: Three RuBP capture three CO_2, forming six PGA.
2. G3P synthesis: A series of reactions, driven by energy from ATP and NADPH (from the light reactions), produces six G3P. One G3P leaves the cycle and is available to form glucose.
3. RuBP regeneration: Three RuBP molecules are regenerated from the remaining five G3P using ATP energy, allowing the cycle to continue.

In a separate process outside the chloroplast, two G3P molecules produced by the Calvin cycle combine to form glucose.

CHECK YOUR LEARNING
Can you ...
- describe the function of the Calvin cycle and where it occurs?
- list the three stages of the Calvin cycle, including the molecules that enter the cycle and those that are formed at each stage?
- describe the fate of the simple sugar G3P generated by the Calvin cycle?

Biofuels—Are Their Benefits Bogus?

When you drive your car, turn up the thermostat, or flick on your desk lamp, you are actually unleashing the energy of prehistoric sunlight trapped by prehistoric photosynthetic organisms. This is because over hundreds of millions of years, heat and pressure converted the bodies of these organisms—with their stored solar energy and carbon captured from ancient atmospheric CO_2—into coal, oil, and natural gas. Without human intervention, these fossil fuels would have remained trapped deep underground.

A major contributor to global climate change is increased burning of fossil fuels by a growing human population. This combustion releases CO_2 into the atmosphere; the added carbon dioxide traps heat in the atmosphere that would otherwise radiate into space. Since we began using fossil fuels during the industrial revolution in the mid-1800s, humans have increased the CO_2 content of the atmosphere by about 38%. As a result, Earth is growing warmer, and many experts fear that a hotter future climate will place extraordinary stresses on Earth's inhabitants, ourselves included (see Chapter 29).

To reduce CO_2 emissions and reliance on imported oil, many governments are subsidizing and promoting the use of biofuels, especially ethanol and biodiesel. Ethanol is produced by fermenting plants rich in sugars, such as sugarcane and corn, to produce alcohol (fermentation is described in Chapter 8). Biodiesel fuel is made primarily from oil derived from plants such as soybeans, canola, or palms. Because the carbon stored in biofuels was removed from the modern atmosphere by photosynthesis, burning them seems to simply restore CO_2 that was recently present in the atmosphere. Is this a solution to global climate change?

The environmental and social benefits of burning fuels derived from food crops in our gas tanks are hotly debated. Over 35% of the U.S. corn crop is now feeding vehicles rather than animals and people; this transition has driven up corn prices worldwide (**FIG. E7-3**). Higher corn prices translate into increased food prices as cars compete with animal and human consumers. Another concern is that growing corn and

▲ **FIGURE E7-4 Cleared tropical forest** This aerial view shows the aftermath of clearing lush tropical forest, the former home of rare Sumatran tigers, elephants, leopards, orangutans, and a wealth of bird species. The cleared area will become a palm oil plantation for biofuels. Endangered orangutans (such as the ones pictured) are increasingly rendered homeless by deforestation and are often killed as they are forced closer to human settlements.

converting it into ethanol uses large quantities of fossil fuel, negating corn ethanol's advantages over burning gasoline. The environmental costs of using food crops as an alternative fuel source are also enormous. For example, Indonesia's luxurious tropical rain forests—home to orangutans, Sumatran tigers, and clouded leopards—are being destroyed to make room for oil palm plantations for biofuels, with at least 15 million acres (an area the size of West Virginia) cleared between 2000 and 2012, and over 2 million acres annually in more recent years (**FIG. E7-4**). In Brazil, soybean plantations for biofuels have replaced large expanses of rain forest. Ironically, clearing these forests for agriculture increases atmospheric CO_2 because rain forests trap far more carbon than the crops that replace them.

Biofuels would have far less environmental and social impact if they were not produced from food crops or by destroying Earth's dwindling rain forests. Algae show great promise as an alternative. Some algae produce starch that can be fermented into ethanol; others produce oil that can become biodiesel. Some of these microscopic photosynthesizers can potentially produce 60 times as much oil per acre as soybeans and 5 times as much as oil palm. Researchers are also attempting to cleave cellulose into its component sugars, which would allow ethanol to be generated from corn stalks, wood chips, or grasses. Commercial scale cellulosic biorefineries have recently opened in the United States; their long-term success remains uncertain. Although the benefits of most biofuels in wide use today may not justify their environmental costs, there is hope that this will change as we develop better technologies to harness the energy captured by photosynthesis.

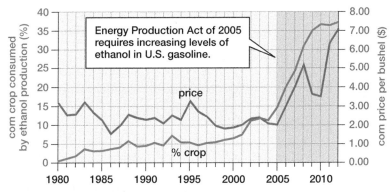

▲ **FIGURE E7-3 Corn prices have increased dramatically since corn ethanol has been added to gasoline**

THINK CRITICALLY The percentage of ethanol in gasoline has reached 10% and is not likely to increase in the near future. Sketch a possible scenario for corn prices and the percentage of corn used for ethanol by continuing the graph in Figure E7-3 to 2030, and provide a rationale to support your projection. Your scenario should assume a constant-sized corn harvest.

Did the Dinosaurs Die from Lack of Sunlight?

Did an asteroid end the reign of dinosaurs? The Alvarez hypothesis was initially met with skepticism. If such a cataclysmic event had occurred, where was the crater? In 1991, scientists finally located it near the coastal town of Chicxulub on Mexico's Yucatán Peninsula. The crater, estimated at over 110 miles in diameter and 10 miles deep, was filled with debris and sedimentary rock laid down during the 66 million years since the impact. Ocean and dense vegetation hid most remaining traces from satellite images. The final identification of the Chicxulub crater was based on rock core samples, unusual gravitational patterns, and faint surface features.

Some paleontologists argue that the asteroid's impact may have exacerbated more gradual changes in climate, to which the dinosaurs (with the exception of those ancestral to modern-day birds) could not adapt. Such changes might have been caused by prolonged intense volcanic activity, such as occurred at a site in India at about the time of the K-T extinction. Volcanoes spew out soot and ash, and iridium is found in higher levels in lava from Earth's molten mantle than in its crust. So furious volcanism could significantly reduce the amount of sunlight for plant growth, spew climate-changing gases into the air, and also contribute to the iridium-rich K-T boundary layer.

In 2010, alternative hypotheses to the asteroid impact were dealt a blow when an expert group of 41 researchers published a review article in the journal *Science*. This publication analyzed the previous 20 years of research by paleontologists, geochemists, geophysicists, climatologists, and sedimentation experts dealing with the K-T extinction event. The conclusion: Land and ocean ecosystems were destroyed extremely rapidly, and evidence overwhelmingly supports the asteroid impact hypothesis first proposed by the Alvarez group 30 years earlier.

Recently, researchers applied high-precision radioactive dating techniques to the K-T boundary layer and to debris kicked up by the Chicxulub asteroid. These findings dramatically narrow the time frame for both occurrences, revealing with as much accuracy as is currently possible that the two coincided. The authors of this study stress that the asteroid impact may have been the "final straw," culminating a series of ecological perturbations that had already stressed existing ecosystems. The hothouse conditions of the late Cretaceous period had previously been interrupted by several rapid drops in temperature and sea level. Pulses of volcanic activity may have caused these cold snaps, leaving the biosphere particularly vulnerable to the devastating climate change associated with the asteroid impact.

CONSIDER THIS The K-T extinction event was the most recent of five major extinctions documented in the fossil record. The ultimate cause of any such event is a massive environmental change occurring on a timescale too rapid to allow species to adapt. In 1968, biologist Paul Ehrlich published the controversial book *The Population Bomb* to describe the impact of overpopulation on Earth's ecosystems. Since Ehrlich's publication, human numbers have more than doubled. Many scientists are now recognizing a sixth mass extinction caused entirely by people; current extinction rates are estimated to be from 100 to 1,000 times the extinction rate that would occur in the absence of human activity. We have modified roughly half of all Earth's land area, co-opting a significant percentage of all terrestrial photosynthesis to feed ourselves. We are changing Earth's climate at a rate at least 10 times that of previous natural cycles between warming and ice ages. The impact of humanity is collective, but the human population consists of individuals. What global policy changes and what individual choices can help us sustain the planet that sustains us?

CHAPTER REVIEW

Go to **MasteringBiology** for practice quizzes, activities, eText, videos, current events, and more.

Answers to Think Critically, Evaluate This, Multiple Choice, and Fill-in-the-Blank questions can be found in the Answers section at the back of the book.

Summary of Key Concepts

7.1 What Is Photosynthesis?

Photosynthesis is the process that captures the energy of sunlight and uses it to convert inorganic molecules of carbon dioxide and water into a high-energy sugar molecule, releasing oxygen as a by-product. In plants, photosynthesis takes place in the chloroplasts, using two major reaction sequences: the light reactions and the Calvin cycle.

7.2 The Light Reactions: How Is Light Energy Converted to Chemical Energy?

The light reactions occur in the thylakoids of chloroplasts. Light energizes electrons in chlorophyll molecules located in photosystems II and I. Energetic electrons jump to a primary electron acceptor and then move into adjacent electron transport chains. Energy lost as the electrons travel through the first ETC is used to pump hydrogen ions into the thylakoid space, creating an H$^+$ gradient across the thylakoid membrane. Hydrogen ions flow down this concentration gradient through ATP synthase channels in the membrane, driving ATP synthesis by chemiosmosis. For every two energized electrons that pass through the second ETC, one molecule of the energy-carrier NADPH is formed from NADP⁺ and H⁺. Electrons lost from photosystem II are replaced by electrons liberated by splitting water, which also generates H⁺ and O_2. Energized electrons lost from photosystem I are replaced by energy-depleted enzymes from photosystem II.

7.3 The Calvin Cycle: How Is Chemical Energy Stored in Sugar Molecules?

The Calvin cycle, which occurs in the stroma of chloroplasts, uses energy from the ATP and NADPH generated during the light reactions to drive the synthesis of G3P. Two molecules of G3P may then be combined to form glucose. The Calvin cycle has three parts: (1) *Carbon fixation*: Carbon dioxide combines with ribulose bisphosphate (RuBP) to form phosphoglyceric acid (PGA). (2) *Synthesis of G3P*: PGA is converted to glyceraldehyde-3-phosphate (G3P), using energy from ATP and NADPH. (3) *Regeneration of RuBP*: Five molecules of G3P are used to regenerate three molecules of RuBP, using ATP energy. One molecule of G3P exits the cycle; this G3P may be used to synthesize glucose and other molecules.

Key Terms

accessory pigment   *112*
ATP synthase   *115*
bundle sheath cells   *109*
C_3 pathway   *116*
C_4 pathway   *116*
Calvin cycle   *111*
carbon fixation   *116*
carotenoid   *112*
chemiosmosis   *114*
chlorophyll   *110*
chlorophyll *a*   *112*
chloroplast   *110*
crassulacean acid
   metabolism
   (CAM)   *116*
cuticle   *109*
electromagnetic
   spectrum   *111*

electron transport
   chain (ETC)   *113*
epidermis   *109*
grana   *110*
light reactions   *110*
mesophyll   *109*
NADPH (NADP+; nicotinamide
   adenine dinucleotide
   phosphate)   *111*
photon   *111*
photorespiration   *116*
photosynthesis   *109*
photosystem   *112*
reaction center   *113*
rubisco   *116*
stoma (plural, stomata)   *109*
stroma   *110*
thylakoid   *110*

Thinking Through the Concepts

Multiple Choice

1. Which of the following is True?
   a. Photosynthesis evolved in an atmosphere with little or no oxygen.
   b. Photosynthesis occurs only in plants.
   c. Oxygen is necessary for photosynthesis.
   d. Carbon dioxide is necessary for photorespiration.

2. The Calvin cycle
   a. can only occur when light is present.
   b. is the part of photosynthesis where carbon is captured.

   c. produces ATP and NADPH.
   d. occurs in the thylakoids.

3. Which of the following is True?
   a. Chloroplasts are found primarily in leaf mesophyll cells.
   b. The space between the outer and inner membranes of chloroplasts is called the thylakoid space.
   c. Mesophyll cells in the leaf's center are packed tightly together.
   d. Vascular bundles of the leaf circulate CO_2 and O_2.

4. Carotenoids
   a. include chlorophylls *a* and *b*.
   b. serve as accessory pigments.
   c. are produced in the fall in temperate climates.
   d. absorb mostly yellow and orange light.

5. Which of the following is False?
   a. Photosystem II splits water.
   b. Photosystem II captures energy directly from light.
   c. Reaction centers contain chlorophyll *a* molecules.
   d. Photosystem I generates O_2.

Fill-in-the-Blank

1. Plant leaves contain pores called _____ that allow the plant to release _____ and take in _____. In hot dry weather, these pores are closed to prevent _____. Photosynthesis occurs in organelles called _____ that are concentrated within the _____ cells of most plant leaves.

2. Chlorophyll *a* captures wavelengths of light that correspond to the three colors _____, _____, and _____. What color does chlorophyll reflect? _____ Accessory pigments that reflect yellow and orange are called _____. These pigments are located in clusters called _____ in the _____ membrane of the chloroplast.

3. During the first stage of photosynthesis, light is captured and funneled into _____ chlorophyll *a* molecules. The energized electron is then passed into a(n) _____. From here, it is transferred through a series of molecules called the _____. Energy lost during these transfers is used to create a gradient of _____. The process that uses this gradient to generate ATP is called _____.

4. The oxygen produced as a by-product of photosynthesis is derived from _____, and the carbons used to make glucose are derived from _____. The biochemical pathway that captures atmospheric carbon is called the _____. The process of capturing carbon is called _____.

5. In plants, the enzyme that catalyzes carbon capture is _____, which binds _____ as well as CO_2. When it binds the "wrong" molecule, this enzyme causes _____ to occur. Two pathways that reduce this process are called the _____ and the_____.

6. Light reactions generate the energy-carrier molecules _____ and _____, which are then used in the _____ cycle. Carbon fixation combines carbon dioxide with the five-carbon molecule _____. Two molecules of _____ can be combined to produce the six-carbon sugar _____.

Review Questions

1. Explain what would happen to life if photosynthesis ceased. Why would this occur?

2. Write and then explain the equation for photosynthesis.

3. Draw a simplified diagram of a leaf cross-section and label it. Explain how a leaf's structure supports photosynthesis.

4. Draw a simplified diagram of a chloroplast and label it. Explain how the individual parts of the chloroplast support photosynthesis.

5. Explain photorespiration and why it occurs. Describe the two mechanisms that some groups of plants have evolved to reduce photorespiration.

6. Trace the flow of energy in chloroplasts from sunlight to ATP, including an explanation of chemiosmosis.

7. Summarize the events of the Calvin cycle. Where does it occur? What molecule is fixed? What is the product of the cycle? Where does the energy come from to drive the cycle? What molecule is regenerated?

Applying the Concepts

1. Suppose an experiment is performed in which plant I is supplied with normal carbon dioxide but with water that contains radioactive oxygen atoms. Plant II is supplied with normal water but with carbon dioxide that contains radioactive oxygen atoms. Each plant is allowed to perform photosynthesis, and the oxygen gas and sugars produced are tested for radioactivity. Which plant would you expect to produce radioactive sugars, and which plant would you expect to produce radioactive oxygen gas? Explain why.

2. If you were to measure the pH in the space surrounded by the thylakoid membrane in an actively photosynthesizing plant, would you expect it to be acidic, basic, or neutral? Explain your answer.

3. Assume you want to add an accessory pigment to the photosystems of a plant chloroplast to help it photosynthesize more efficiently. What wavelengths of light would the new pigment absorb? Describe the color of your new pigment. Would this be a useful project for genetic engineers? Explain.

8 HARVESTING ENERGY: GLYCOLYSIS AND CELLULAR RESPIRATION

The skeleton of King Richard III (inset) is revealed.

Wounds on his ribs and pelvis suggest that the defeated king's body was further mutilated after death. Franciscan friars apparently buried him hastily in the Greyfriars Church—naked, without a coffin, and in a shallow grave that was too short for his body.

Prior to the excavation in 2012, the Franciscan church and its associated monastery had not been seen since 1538, when they were leveled and newer buildings were erected on the site. The location of the church and monastery was subsequently forgotten, but a historian and archaeologists (aided by ground-penetrating radar) did some detective work that led to the hypothesis that the ruins were likely to be found beneath a Leicester parking lot. Despite this compelling hypothesis, experts still believed there was only a very remote possibility that Richard III's body was buried there, so the discovery of a skeleton disfigured by battle wounds and severe spinal curvature (consistent with historical records; see arrow in photo) was met with astonishment.

Painstaking investigations led by geneticist Turi King of the University of Leicester identified the king's body with near-certainty. King analyzed mitochondrial DNA from a tooth of the 529-year-old skeleton. A mitochondrion has several copies of a tiny circular loop of DNA, with each loop containing about 1/200,000 as much DNA as is found in the nucleus.

Mitochondria provide energy for every cell in the bodies of eukaryotic organisms. These complex organelles powered the muscles of the soldiers and their horses at the Battle of Bosworth, while simultaneously performing the mundane task of keeping their teeth alive. How do mitochondria work? Why do we begin dying in seconds if their function is blocked? And why do mitochondria have their own DNA?

Raising a King

"A HORSE! A HORSE! MY KINGDOM FOR A HORSE!" shouts King Richard III in Shakespeare's *King Richard III*, moments after his horse is slain at the Battle of Bosworth Field in Leicester, England in 1485. The 32-year-old monarch had ruled for only 2 years before this final battle of the 30-year War of the Roses, and his short life was riddled with political intrigue and conspiracy. Now, thanks to the DNA in mitochondria, his skeleton has been identified, providing details of his final moments in battle, as well as a broad sketch of his appearance. For example, although he did not have the hunched back portrayed by Shakespeare, his skeleton does reveal a severe spinal deformity (see the chapter-opening photo).

No one knows what King Richard III was really shouting as he died, but we do know that his wounds were horrendous. His eight head injuries included a sword wound that pierced his skull, penetrating entirely through his brain, and mutilation from an axe-like weapon that hacked out a large chunk of his skull.

AT A GLANCE

8.1 HOW DO CELLS OBTAIN ENERGY?

Cells require a continuous supply of energy to power the multitude of metabolic reactions that are essential just to stay alive. In this chapter, we describe the cellular reactions that transfer energy from energy-storage molecules, particularly glucose, to energy-carrier molecules, such as ATP.

The second law of thermodynamics tells us that every time a spontaneous reaction occurs, the amount of useful energy in a system decreases and heat is produced (see Chapter 6). Cells are relatively efficient at capturing chemical energy during glucose breakdown when oxygen is available, storing about 40% of the chemical energy from glucose in ATP molecules, and releasing the rest as heat. (If 60% waste heat sounds high, compare this to the 80% of chemical energy released as heat by conventional engines burning gasoline.)

Photosynthesis Is the Ultimate Source of Cellular Energy

The energy utilized by life on Earth comes almost entirely from sunlight, captured during photosynthesis by plants and other photosynthetic organisms and stored in the chemical bonds of sugars and other organic molecules (see Chapter 7). Almost all organisms, including those that photosynthesize, use glycolysis and cellular respiration to break down these sugars and other organic molecules and capture some of the energy as ATP. FIGURE 8-1 illustrates the interrelationship between photosynthesis and the breakdown of glucose. Glucose ($C_6H_{12}O_6$) breakdown begins with glycolysis in the cell cytosol, liberating small quantities of ATP. Then the end product of glycolysis is further broken down during cellular respiration in mitochondria, supplying far greater amounts of energy in ATP. In forming ATP during cellular respiration, cells use oxygen (originally released by photosynthetic organisms) and liberate both water and carbon dioxide—the raw materials for photosynthesis.

Photosynthesis

$$6\,CO_2 + 6\,H_2O + \text{light energy} \rightarrow C_6H_{12}O_6 + 6\,O_2$$

The chemical equation describing complete glucose breakdown is the reverse of glucose formation by photosynthesis.

Complete Glucose Breakdown

$$C_6H_{12}O_6 + 6\,O_2 \rightarrow 6\,CO_2 + 6\,H_2O + \text{ATP energy}$$

energy from sunlight

chloroplast

photosynthesis

$6\;CO_2$ $6\;H_2O$ $6\;O_2$ $C_6H_{12}O_6$

cellular respiration

glycolysis

ATP

mitochondrion

▲ **FIGURE 8-1 The interrelationship between photosynthesis and glucose breakdown** The products of each process are used by the other. The ultimate source of energy is sunlight, captured during photosynthesis and liberated during glycolysis and cellular respiration.

The only difference is in the forms of energy involved. The light energy stored in glucose during photosynthesis is released during glucose breakdown and used to generate ATP, with some lost as heat during each conversion.

All Cells Can Use Glucose As a Source of Energy

Few organisms store glucose in its simple form. Plants convert glucose to sucrose or starch for storage. Humans and many other animals store energy in molecules such as glycogen (a long chain of glucose molecules) and fat (see Chapter 3). Although most cells can use a variety of organic molecules to produce ATP, in this chapter, we focus on the breakdown of glucose, which all cells can use as an energy source. Glucose breakdown occurs via two major processes: It starts with *glycolysis* and proceeds to *cellular respiration* if oxygen is available. Some energy is captured in ATP during glycolysis and far more is captured during cellular respiration (see FIG. 8-2).

▲ **FIGURE 8-2 A summary of glucose breakdown**

8.2 HOW DOES GLYCOLYSIS BEGIN BREAKING DOWN GLUCOSE?

Glycolysis (Gk. *glyco,* sweet, and *lysis,* to split apart) splits a six-carbon glucose molecule into two molecules of pyruvate. Glycolysis has an *energy investment stage* and an *energy harvesting stage,* each with several steps (FIG. 8-3). Extracting energy from glucose first requires an investment of energy from ATP. During a series of reactions that constitutes the energy investment stage, each of two ATP molecules donates a phosphate group and energy to glucose, forming an "energized" molecule of *fructose bisphosphate.* Fructose is a monosaccharide sugar similar to glucose; "bisphosphate" (L. *bis,* two) refers to the two phosphate groups acquired from the ATP molecules. Fructose bisphosphate is much more easily broken down than glucose because of the extra energy it has acquired from ATP.

Next, during the energy harvesting stage, fructose bisphosphate is converted into two three-carbon molecules of *glyceraldehyde-3-phosphate,* or *G3P.* Each G3P molecule, which retains one phosphate and some energy from ATP, then undergoes a series of reactions that convert the G3P to pyruvate. During these reactions, energy is stored when two high-energy electrons and a hydrogen ion (H^+) are added to the electron carrier **nicotinamide adenine dinucleotide (NAD$^+$)** to produce **NADH.** Two molecules of NADH are produced for every glucose molecule broken down. Additional energy is captured in two ATP from each G3P, for a total of four ATP per glucose molecule. But because two ATP were used up to form fructose bisphosphate, there is a net gain of only two ATP per glucose molecule during glycolysis. For the details of glycolysis, see "In Greater Depth: Glycolysis" on page 126.

CHECK YOUR LEARNING

Can you ...

- explain how photosynthesis and glucose breakdown are related to one another using their overall chemical equations?
- summarize glucose breakdown in the presence and absence of oxygen?

CHECK YOUR LEARNING

Can you ...

- explain the energy investment and energy-harvesting phases of glycolysis?
- describe the two types of high-energy molecule produced by glucose breakdown?

▲ FIGURE 8-3 **The essentials of glycolysis** In the energy investment stage, the energy of two ATP molecules is used to convert glucose into the fructose bisphosphate, which then breaks down into two molecules of G3P. In the energy harvesting stage, the two G3P molecules undergo a series of reactions that capture energy in four ATP and two NADH molecules. (Only carbon skeletons are shown.)

THINK CRITICALLY What is the net energy yield in ATP and NADH produced?

IN GREATER DEPTH | Glycolysis

Glycolysis is a series of enzyme-catalyzed reactions that break down a single molecule of glucose into two molecules of pyruvate. In FIGURE E8-1, we show only the carbon skeletons of molecules. Blue arrows represent enzyme-catalyzed reactions.

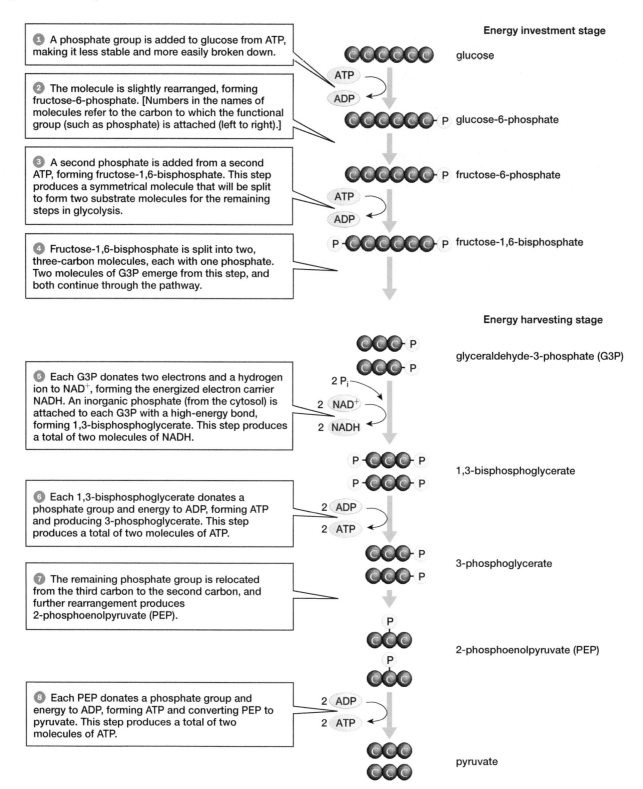

Energy investment stage

① A phosphate group is added to glucose from ATP, making it less stable and more easily broken down.

② The molecule is slightly rearranged, forming fructose-6-phosphate. [Numbers in the names of molecules refer to the carbon to which the functional group (such as phosphate) is attached (left to right).]

③ A second phosphate is added from a second ATP, forming fructose-1,6-bisphosphate. This step produces a symmetrical molecule that will be split to form two substrate molecules for the remaining steps in glycolysis.

④ Fructose-1,6-bisphosphate is split into two, three-carbon molecules, each with one phosphate. Two molecules of G3P emerge from this step, and both continue through the pathway.

glucose

glucose-6-phosphate

fructose-6-phosphate

fructose-1,6-bisphosphate

Energy harvesting stage

⑤ Each G3P donates two electrons and a hydrogen ion to NAD⁺, forming the energized electron carrier NADH. An inorganic phosphate (from the cytosol) is attached to each G3P with a high-energy bond, forming 1,3-bisphosphoglycerate. This step produces a total of two molecules of NADH.

glyceraldehyde-3-phosphate (G3P)

1,3-bisphosphoglycerate

⑥ Each 1,3-bisphosphoglycerate donates a phosphate group and energy to ADP, forming ATP and producing 3-phosphoglycerate. This step produces a total of two molecules of ATP.

3-phosphoglycerate

⑦ The remaining phosphate group is relocated from the third carbon to the second carbon, and further rearrangement produces 2-phosphoenolpyruvate (PEP).

2-phosphoenolpyruvate (PEP)

⑧ Each PEP donates a phosphate group and energy to ADP, forming ATP and converting PEP to pyruvate. This step produces a total of two molecules of ATP.

pyruvate

▲ **FIGURE E8-1 Glycolysis**

8.3 HOW DOES CELLULAR RESPIRATION EXTRACT ENERGY FROM GLUCOSE?

In most organisms, if oxygen is available, the second process in glucose breakdown, called **cellular respiration,** occurs. Cellular respiration breaks down the two pyruvate molecules produced by glycolysis into six carbon dioxide molecules and six water molecules. During this process, the chemical energy from the two pyruvate molecules is used to produce 34 ATP.

In eukaryotic cells, cellular respiration occurs within **mitochondria,** organelles that are sometimes called the "powerhouses of the cell." A mitochondrion has two membranes. The inner membrane encloses a central compartment containing the fluid **matrix,** and the outer membrane surrounds the organelle, producing an **intermembrane space** between the two membranes. Each structure is crucial to the process of cellular respiration (**FIG. 8-4**).

In the following sections, we discuss the two major stages of cellular respiration: first, the formation of acetyl CoA and its breakdown via the Krebs cycle, and second, the transfer of electrons along the electron transport chain and the generation of ATP by chemiosmosis.

Cellular Respiration Stage 1: Acetyl CoA Is Formed and Travels Through the Krebs Cycle

Pyruvate, the end product of glycolysis, is synthesized in the cytosol. Before cellular respiration can occur, the pyruvate diffuses from the cytosol through the porous outer mitochondrial membrane. It is then actively transported through the inner mitochondrial membrane and into the matrix, where cellular respiration begins.

Two sets of reactions occur within the mitochondrial matrix during stage 1 of cellular respiration: the formation of acetyl CoA and the Krebs cycle (**FIG. 8-5**). Acetyl CoA consists of a two-carbon functional (acetyl) group attached to a molecule called *coenzyme A (CoA)*. To generate acetyl CoA, pyruvate is split, releasing CO_2 and leaving behind an acetyl group. The acetyl group reacts with CoA, forming acetyl CoA. This reaction liberates and stores energy by transferring two high-energy electrons and a hydrogen ion to NAD^+, forming NADH.

The next set of reactions is known as the **Krebs cycle,** named after its discoverer, Hans Krebs, who won a Nobel Prize for this work in 1953. The Krebs cycle is also called the *citric acid cycle* because citrate (the dissolved, ionized form of citric acid) is the first molecule produced in the cycle. This metabolic pathway is called a cycle because it continuously regenerates the same substrate molecule with which it begins: oxaloacetate (see Fig. E8-2 on page 130).

With each pass around the Krebs cycle, the two carbon atoms that enter in the form of acetate are released as carbon dioxide, liberating energy. Some of this energy is captured

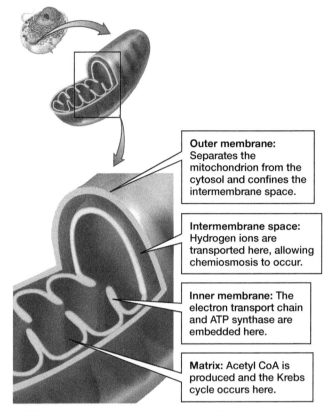

Outer membrane: Separates the mitochondrion from the cytosol and confines the intermembrane space.

Intermembrane space: Hydrogen ions are transported here, allowing chemiosmosis to occur.

Inner membrane: The electron transport chain and ATP synthase are embedded here.

Matrix: Acetyl CoA is produced and the Krebs cycle occurs here.

(a) Mitochondrial structures and their functions

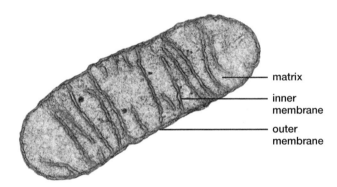

matrix

inner membrane

outer membrane

(b) TEM of a mitochondrion

▲ **FIGURE 8-4 The mitochondrion**

during the Krebs cycle in high-energy electron carriers (described later) and some in ATP.

The breakdown of acetate begins when acetyl CoA is combined with the four-carbon molecule oxaloacetate, forming a six-carbon citrate molecule and releasing the catalyst CoA. CoA is not permanently altered during these reactions and is reused many times. As the Krebs cycle proceeds, enzymes within the mitochondrial matrix break down the acetyl group, releasing two CO_2 and regenerating the oxaloacetate molecule to continue the cycle. In your body, the CO_2 generated in cells during the stage 1 reactions diffuses into your blood, which carries the CO_2 to your lungs. This is why the air you breathe out contains more CO_2 than the air you breathe in.

(in mitochondrial matrix)

formation of acetyl CoA

coenzyme A

CO₂ coenzyme A

pyruvate

NAD⁺ NADH

CoA
acetyl CoA

3 NADH

3 NAD⁺

Krebs cycle

FAD

FADH₂

2 CO₂

ADP

ATP

◀ **FIGURE 8-5 Reactions in the mitochondrial matrix: acetyl CoA formation and the Krebs cycle**

As the Krebs cycle continues, chemical energy is captured in energy-carrier molecules. The breakdown of each acetyl group from acetyl CoA produces one ATP and three NADH. It also produces one **flavin adenine dinucleotide (FADH₂),** a high-energy electron carrier similar to NADH. During the Krebs cycle, FAD picks up two energetic electrons along with two H⁺, forming FADH₂. Remember that for each glucose molecule, two pyruvate molecules are formed during glycolysis, so the energy generated per glucose molecule is twice that generated for one pyruvate (for details, see "In Greater Depth: Acetyl CoA Production and the Krebs Cycle" on page 130.)

Cellular Respiration Stage 2: High-Energy Electrons Traverse the Electron Transport Chain and Chemiosmosis Generates ATP

By the end of stage 1, the cell has gained only four ATP from the original glucose molecule (a net of two during glycolysis and two during the Krebs cycle). However, the cell has also captured many high-energy electrons in a total of 10 NADH and two FADH₂ molecules for each glucose molecule.

In the second stage of cellular respiration, the high-energy electron carriers each release two high-energy electrons into an **electron transport chain (ETC),** a series of electron-transporting molecules, many copies of which are embedded in the inner mitochondrial membrane (FIG. 8-6). The depleted carriers are then available for recharging by glycolysis and the Krebs cycle.

The Electron Transport Chain Releases Energy in Steps

The ETCs in the mitochondrial membrane serve the same function as those embedded in the thylakoid membrane of chloroplasts (see Chapter 7). High-energy electrons jump from molecule to molecule along the ETC, releasing small amounts of energy at each step. The energy liberated in these stages is just the right amount to pump H⁺ across the inner membrane, from the matrix into the intermembrane space (although some is always lost as heat). This ion pumping produces a concentration gradient of H⁺, high in the intermembrane space and low in the matrix (see Fig. 8-6). Expending energy to create an H⁺ gradient is similar to charging a battery. This H⁺ battery will be discharged as ATP is generated by chemiosmosis, discussed later.

Finally, at the end of the electron transport chain, the energy-depleted electrons are transferred to oxygen, which acts as an electron acceptor. The energy-depleted electrons, oxygen, and hydrogen ions combine, forming water. One water molecule is produced for every two electrons that traverse the ETC (see Fig. 8-6).

Without oxygen to accept electrons, the ETC would become saturated with electrons and could not acquire more from NADH and FADH₂. With electrons unable to move through the ETC, H⁺ could not be pumped across the inner membrane. The H⁺ gradient would rapidly dissipate, and ATP synthesis by chemiosmosis would stop. Because of their high demand for energy from ATP, most eukaryotic cells die within minutes without a steady supply of oxygen to accept electrons.

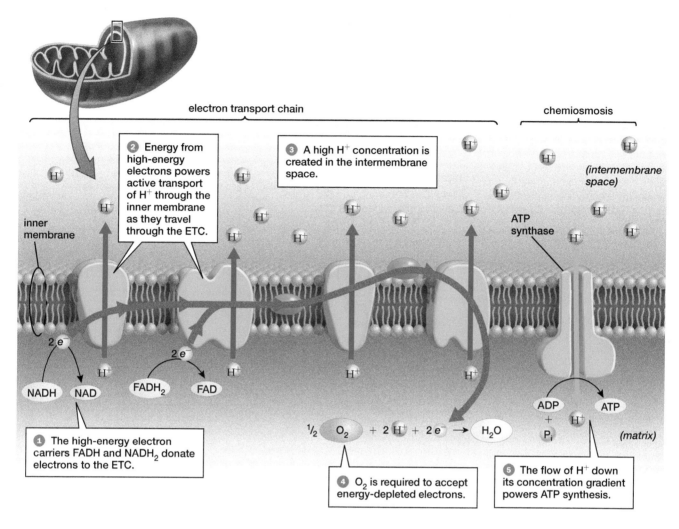

▲ **FIGURE 8-6** **The electron transport chain and chemiosmosis** Many copies of the electron transport chain and ATP synthase are embedded in the inner mitochondrial membrane.

THINK CRITICALLY How would the rate of ATP production be affected by the absence of oxygen?

Your body obtains oxygen through the air you breathe, which enters your lungs and is transported in the bloodstream to every cell. Because of cellular respiration, the air you breathe out contains less oxygen than the air you breathe in.

HAVE YOU EVER
WONDERED...

Cyanide is a favorite poison in old murder mysteries, causing the hapless victim to die almost instantly. Cyanide exerts its lethal effects by blocking the last protein in the ETC: an enzyme that combines energy-depleted electrons with oxygen. If these electrons are not carried away by oxygen, they act like a plug in a pipeline. Additional high-energy electrons cannot travel through the ETC, so no more hydrogen can be pumped across the membrane, and ATP production by chemiosmosis stops abruptly. Because the energy demands of our cells are so great, blocking cellular respiration with cyanide can kill a person within a few minutes.

Why Cyanide Is So Deadly?

Chemiosmosis Captures Energy in ATP

Chemiosmosis is the process by which some of the energy stored in the concentration gradient of H+ is captured in ATP as H+ flows down its gradient. How is the energy captured? The inner membranes of mitochondria are permeable to H+ only at channels that are part of an ATP synthase enzyme. As hydrogen ions flow from the intermembrane space into the matrix through these ATP-synthesizing enzymes, ATP is formed from ADP and inorganic phosphate ions dissolved in the matrix.

ATP Is Transported out of the Mitochondrion

How does ATP escape from the mitochondrion to power reactions throughout the cell? Movement through the inner mitochondrial membrane is highly regulated, so a specialized carrier protein in the inner membrane selectively exchanges ATP for ADP. The protein does this by simultaneously exporting ATP from the matrix into the intermembrane space while

IN GREATER DEPTH | Acetyl CoA Production and the Krebs Cycle

Two sets of reactions occur in the mitochondrial matrix: (1) the formation of acetyl CoA from pyruvate and (2) the Krebs cycle (**FIG. E8-2**).

Formation of Acetyl CoA

Pyruvate is split to form an acetyl group and CO_2. The formation of CO_2 releases energy that is captured in 2 high-energy electrons and an H^+, converting NAD^+ to NADH. The acetyl

group attaches to CoA, forming acetyl CoA, which enters the Krebs cycle.

The Krebs Cycle

Each acetyl CoA entering the Krebs cycle is broken down into 2 CO_2, releasing energy that is captured in 1 ATP, 3 NADH, and 1 $FADH_2$.

Total Energy Capture

Acetyl CoA formation and the Krebs cycle together produce 3 CO_2, 1 ATP,

4 NADH, and 1 $FADH_2$ from each pyruvate. Each glucose molecule produces 2 pyruvates, doubling the number of product molecules. The electron-carrier molecules NADH and $FADH_2$ will deliver their high-energy electrons to the electron transport chain (ETC). The ETC will store energy in an H^+ gradient that will be used to synthesize ATP by chemiosmosis.

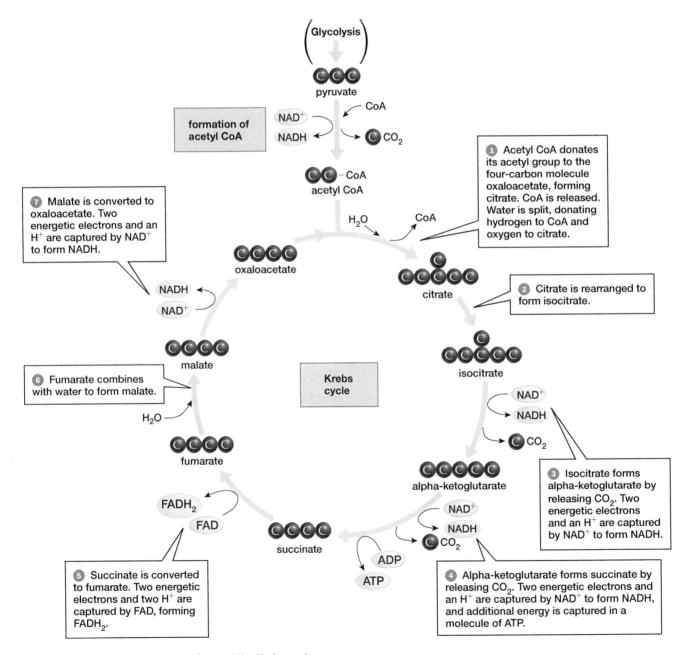

▲ **FIGURE E8-2 Acetyl CoA production and the Krebs cycle**

▶ **FIGURE 8-7 A summary of the ATP harvest from glycolysis and cellular respiration** Cellular respiration provides the biggest ATP payoff. Nearly all of the ATP comes from high-energy electrons donated by NADH and FADH$_2$. As the electrons flow through the electron transport chain, they generate the H$^+$ gradient, which allows chemiosmosis to occur.

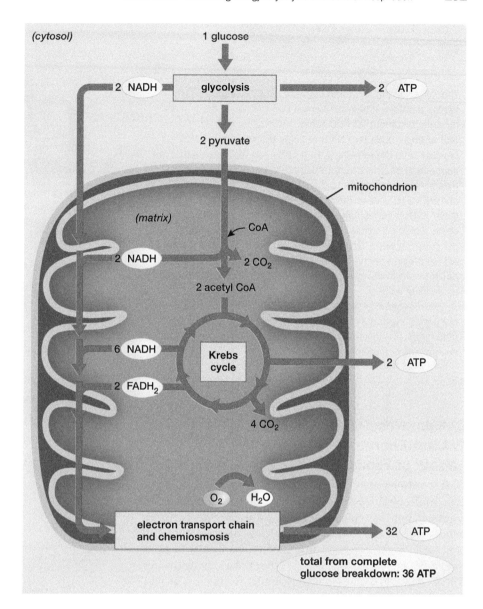

importing ADP from the intermembrane space into the matrix. The outer mitochondrial membrane, in contrast to the inner membrane, is perforated by large pores, through which ATP and ADP can diffuse freely along their concentration gradients. Thus, from the intermembrane space, ATP diffuses through the outer membrane to power reactions throughout the cell, while energy-depleted ADP diffuses into the intermembrane space. Without this continuous recycling, life would cease. Each day, a person produces, uses, and then regenerates the equivalent of roughly his or her body weight of ATP.

You now know why glycolysis followed by cellular respiration generates far more ATP than glycolysis alone. FIGURE 8-7 and TABLE 8-1 summarize the breakdown of one glucose molecule in a eukaryotic cell with oxygen present, showing the energy produced during each stage and the general locations where the pathways occur. In summary, the two ATPs formed during glycolysis are supplemented by two more formed during the Krebs cycle and an additional 32 via chemiosmosis, for a total of 36 ATP per glucose molecule.

TABLE 8-1	A Summary of Glucose Breakdown		
Stage of glucose breakdown	**Electron carriers**	**Net ATP produced**	**Location**
Glycolysis	Energy captured in 2 NADH	2 ATP	Cytosol
Cellular respiration stage 1: Acetyl CoA formation and the Krebs cycle	Energy captured in 8 NADH and 2 FADH$_2$	2 ATP	Mitochondrial matrix
Cellular respiration stage 2: Electron transport chain and chemiosmosis	Energy released from 10 NADH and 2 FADH$_2$	32 ATP	Inner mitochondrial membrane and intermembrane space
Fermentation	2 NAD regenerated	0 ATP	Cytosol
Total	0 NADH and 0 FADH$_2$	36 ATP	Cytosol and mitochondrion

CASE STUDY   CONTINUED
Raising a King

The mitochondrial DNA (mtDNA) that identified Richard III serves a unique role in the human body. Although the human nucleus has about 20,000 genes, mtDNA has only 37. Twenty-four of these code for RNA that helps translate genes into proteins, and the remaining 13 genes code for proteins that are subunits of enzymes that participate in the ETC and chemiosmosis. Some contribute to the ETC enzymes that cause NADH and $FADH_2$ to release their high-energy electrons into the chain. Other mtDNA genes help to produce the final enzyme in the chain, which combines the energy-depleted electrons with oxygen, forming water. Some genes in mtDNA code for parts of the ATP synthase enzyme on the inner mitochondrial membrane. If mtDNA were to disappear, cellular respiration would come to a screeching halt!

We've seen how NADH and $FADH_2$ can gain high-energy electrons that originated in glucose. Can these electron carriers also obtain high-energy electrons from other molecules in our diets, such as fat or protein?

Cellular Respiration Can Extract Energy from a Variety of Foods

Glucose often enters the body as starch (a long chain of glucose molecules) or sucrose (table sugar; glucose linked to fructose), but the typical human diet also provides considerable energy in the form of fat and some from protein. This is possible because various intermediate molecules of cellular respiration can be formed by other metabolic pathways. These intermediates then enter cellular respiration at various stages and are broken down to produce ATP (FIG. 8-8). For example, some of the 20 amino acids from protein can be directly converted into pyruvate, and the others can be transformed through complex pathways into molecules of the Krebs cycle. To release the energy stored in fats, the long fatty acid tails (which comprise most of each fat molecule; see Chapter 3) are broken into two-carbon fragments and combined with CoA, producing acetyl CoA, which enters the Krebs cycle.

An excess of intermediate molecules from glucose breakdown can be converted to fat. So if you overeat, not only are the fats from your meal stored in your body, but excess sugar and starch are also used to synthesize body fat, as described in "Health Watch: How Can You Get Fat by Eating Sugar?"

CHECK YOUR LEARNING
Can you ...
- summarize the two major stages of cellular respiration?
- explain how ATP is generated by chemiosmosis?
- describe the role of oxygen in cellular respiration?

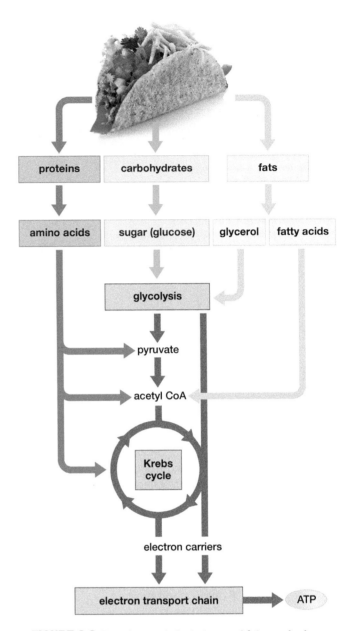

▲ **FIGURE 8-8** Proteins, carbohydrates, and fats are broken down and release ATP

8.4 HOW DOES FERMENTATION ALLOW GLYCOLYSIS TO CONTINUE WHEN OXYGEN IS LACKING?

Glycolysis is employed by virtually every organism on Earth, providing evidence that this is one of the most ancient of all biochemical pathways. Under **aerobic** conditions—that is, when oxygen is available—cellular respiration usually follows. But scientists have concluded that the earliest forms of life appeared under the **anaerobic** (no oxygen) conditions that existed before photosynthesis evolved and enriched the air with oxygen. These pioneering life-forms relied entirely on glycolysis for energy production. Many

Health WATCH

How Can You Get Fat by Eating Sugar?

From an evolutionary perspective, feeling hungry even if you are overweight and overeating when rich food is abundant are highly adaptive behaviors. During the famines common during early human history, heavier people were more likely to survive. It is only recently (from an evolutionary vantage point) that many people have had continuous access to high-calorie food. As a result, obesity is an expanding health problem. Why do we accumulate fat? Fats (triglycerides) are more difficult to break down and also store twice as much energy for their weight as do carbohydrates. Stockpiling energy with minimum weight was important to our prehistoric ancestors who needed to move quickly to catch prey or to avoid becoming prey themselves.

Acquiring fat by eating sugar and other carbohydrates is common among animals. How is fat made from sugar? As glucose is broken down during the Krebs cycle, acetyl CoA is formed. Excess acetyl CoA molecules are used as raw materials to synthesize the fatty acids that will be linked together to form a fat molecule (**FIG. E8-3**). Starches, such as those in bread, potatoes, or pasta, are actually long chains of glucose molecules, so you can see how eating excess starch can also make you fat.

To understand why storing fat rather than sugar can be advantageous, let's look at the ruby-throated hummingbird, which begins the summer weighing

▲ **FIGURE E8-3 How sugar is converted to fat**

3 to 4 grams (in comparison, a nickel weighs 5 grams). In late summer, hummingbirds feed voraciously on the sugary nectar of flowers and nearly double their weight in stored fat. The energy from fat powers their migration from the eastern United States across the Gulf of Mexico and into Mexico or Central America for the winter. If hummingbirds stored sugar instead of fat, they would be too heavy to fly.

EVALUATE THIS Colin, a 45-year-old obese man, comes to you, his physician, complaining that he has been on a fat-free diet for months without losing weight. What do you hypothesize about Colin's weight issue? What questions would you ask him to develop your hypothesis? If the answers support your hypothesis, what dietary recommendations would you make?

---

microorganisms still thrive in places where oxygen is rare or absent, such as in the stomach and intestines of animals (including humans), deep in soil, or in bogs and marshes. Most of these rely on glycolysis, whose end product is pyruvate. In the absence of oxygen, this metabolic pathway continues through **fermentation,** the process by which pyruvate is converted either into lactate or into ethanol and CO_2, depending on the organism. Some microorganisms lack the enzymes for cellular respiration and are completely dependent on fermentation. Others, such as yeasts, are opportunists, using fermentation when oxygen is absent, but switching to more efficient cellular respiration when oxygen is available.

Fermentation is not limited to microorganisms. **Lactate fermentation,** which converts pyruvate to *lactic acid,* is a temporary recourse in most vertebrates, especially during intense muscular activity. If you feel your muscles "burning" during vigorous exercise, they are probably fermenting pyruvate into lactic acid.

Compared to cellular respiration, fermentation is an extremely inefficient way to metabolize pyruvate; it produces no additional ATP. So what good is it? Glycolysis generates two ATP and two NADH for each molecule of glucose metabolized; without oxygen, there is no final acceptor for the electrons accumulated by NAD^+ to form NADH. Fermentation is required to convert the NADH produced during glycolysis back to NAD^+. If the supply of NAD^+ were to be exhausted—which would happen quickly without fermentation—glycolysis would stop, energy production would cease, and the organism would rapidly die.

Fermentation Produces Either Lactate or Alcohol and Carbon Dioxide

Muscles contracting so vigorously that blood cannot supply adequate oxygen for cellular respiration briefly use glycolysis to generate ATP. The pathway then regenerates NAD$^+$ by using the electrons and hydrogen ions from NADH to convert pyruvate into lactate (the dissolved form of lactic acid; FIG. 8-9). Glycolysis uses a great deal of glucose relative to the meager 2 ATPs per glucose molecule it produces, but this far simpler pathway also generates ATP much faster than does cellular respiration. The ATPs can provide the energy needed for a final, brief burst to the finish line (FIG. 8-10) or for fighting, fleeing, or pursuing prey, when the ability to persist just a bit longer can make the difference between life and death. Most of the lactate generated by muscle cells during fermentation diffuses into the bloodstream and is carried to cells of the liver, which convert the lactate back to pyruvate and then back to glucose. Many microorganisms also utilize lactate fermentation, as described later.

Certain microorganisms, including some bacteria and all forms of yeast (single-celled fungi), engage in **alcoholic fermentation** under anaerobic conditions. During alcoholic

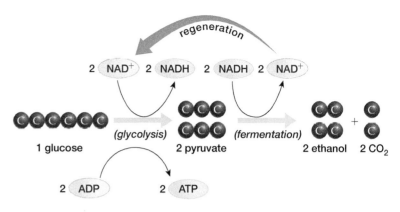

▲ FIGURE 8-11 **Glycolysis followed by alcoholic fermentation**

THINK CRITICALLY What would happen if cells were prevented from producing lactic acid or alcohol after glycolysis?

fermentation, pyruvate is converted into ethanol and CO_2. This process converts NADH into NAD$^+$, which is then available to accept more high-energy electrons during glycolysis (FIG. 8-11).

▲ FIGURE 8-9 **Glycolysis followed by lactic acid fermentation**

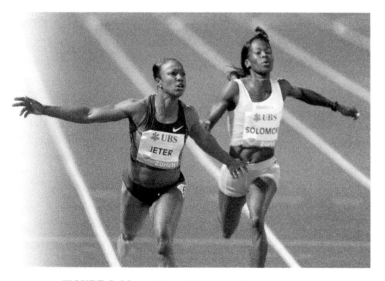

▲ FIGURE 8-10 **Lactic acid fermentation in action**

CASE STUDY **CONTINUED**
Raising a King

Richard III included plenty of fermented products in his diet. How do we know? The ratio of isotopes of certain minerals and oxygen derived from food and stored in teeth and bones provides evidence of both the types of food consumed and where these foods originated. Researchers have been analyzing these isotopes to glean information about Richard III's life history and lifestyle. Based on oxygen isotope ratios in his bones, investigators hypothesize that during the last few years of his life, starting about when he became king, roughly one-quarter of his fluid intake consisted of imported wine. This beverage—fit for a king—was produced, of course, by alcoholic fermentation.

What other ancient and modern staples result from fermentation?

Fermentation Has Played a Long and Important Role in the Human Diet

The poet Omar Khayyam (1048–1122) described his vision of paradise on Earth as "A Jug of Wine, a Loaf of Bread—and Thou Beside Me" (FIG. 8-12). Historical evidence suggests that wine and beer, whose alcohol is produced by yeast, were being made roughly 7,000 years ago. Yeasts are opportunists; they engage in efficient cellular respiration if oxygen is available, but switch to alcoholic fermentation (producing alcohol and CO_2) if they run out of oxygen. To make beer or wine, sugars from mashed grain (beer) or grapes (wine) are fermented by specialized strains of yeast. Fermentation is carried out in

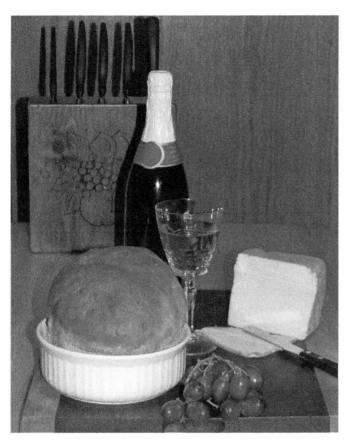

▲ FIGURE 8-12 **Some products of fermentation**

casks with valves that prevent air from entering (so cellular respiration can't occur) but that allow the CO_2 to escape (so the cask doesn't explode). To put the characteristic fizz in beer and champagne, fermentation is allowed to continue after the bottle is sealed, trapping CO_2 under pressure.

Fermentation also gives bread its airy texture. Enzymes in yeast cells break the starch in flour into its component glucose molecules. As the yeast cells rapidly grow and divide, they release CO_2, first during cellular respiration and later during alcoholic fermentation after the O_2 dissolved in the water used to make the dough is used up. The dough, made stretchy and resilient by kneading, traps the CO_2 gas, which expands in the heat of the oven. The alcohol evaporates as the bread is baked.

A variety of microorganisms rely primarily on glycolysis followed by lactate fermentation for energy. These include the lactic acid bacteria that assist in transforming milk into yogurt, sour cream, and cheese. These bacteria first split lactose (milk sugar, a disaccharide) into glucose and galactose; then these simple sugars enter glycolysis followed by fermentation that produces lactic acid. Lactic acid denatures milk protein, altering its three-dimensional structure and giving sour cream and yogurt their semisolid textures. Like all acids, lactic acid tastes sour and contributes to the distinctive tastes of these foods. Lactic acid bacteria are also used to begin the coagulation of milk during cheese production. In addition, lactate fermentation by salt-tolerant bacteria convert sugars in vegetables such as cucumbers and cabbage into lactic acid. The result: dill pickles and sauerkraut.

CHECK YOUR LEARNING

Can you ...

- explain the function of fermentation and the conditions under which it occurs?
- describe the two types of fermentation?
- list some examples of human uses of each type of fermentation?

CASE STUDY \ REVISITED

Raising a King

Richard III's skeleton yielded a wealth of information about his life, and ultimately it confirmed his identity because mtDNA is uniquely valuable for tracing the hereditary relationships of ancient remains. MtDNA originates from the mitochondria in the cytoplasm of the mother's egg cell; sperm mitochondria do not enter the egg when it is fertilized. As a result, mtDNA is passed directly from mother to child in an unbroken chain that can extend through thousands of generations on the mother's side of the family.

Over millennia, harmless mutations have accumulated in specific regions of the mtDNA that do not code for functional proteins. The original, ancient mutations persist while new mutations are gradually added to the noncoding regions. Scientists can sequence these regions and define distinct subgroups by their newer (and therefore less common and less

widespread) mutations. Each of these subgroups originated from the mutated mtDNA in an egg of one woman, whose female descendants formed a population that was originally localized to a specific geographic area; the unique mtDNA signature will remain common in that area even today. As a result, modern people with specific mutations can be traced to ancestors with the same genetic signature in their mtDNA and also to the specific areas of the world where the mutations first emerged.

Because there are many identical copies of mtDNA in each cell, modern techniques can reconstruct crucial mtDNA nucleotide sequences even from severely decomposed remains, such as the skeleton under the Leicester parking lot. Because even a trace of contaminating DNA would render the results useless, Turi King performed the analyses in two separate specially designed ultra-clean laboratories. In each lab, she extracted and sequenced mtDNA from inside a tooth of the skeleton, where it remained relatively well-preserved. The results from the two labs matched, independently verifying one another. The skeleton's mtDNA sequence is relatively rare, shared by only 1% to 2% of the population of the United Kingdom.

Meanwhile, genealogists had identified two living descendants of an unbroken maternal line from Cecily Neville, mother of Richard III. One remains anonymous; the other is Michael Ibsen, a Canadian-born carpenter living in London (**FIG. 8-13**). The five centuries and 18 generations that separate the descendants from Cecily Neville to Michael Ibsen have not altered their mitochondrial DNA, which matches that of the skeleton. The location of the skeleton in Greyfriars Church, its deformity and battle wounds, and, most importantly, the remarkable match of its mtDNA to the only known descendants, led Leicester University's lead archaeologist to state: ". . . beyond reasonable doubt, the individual exhumed at Greyfriars in September 2012 is indeed Richard III, the last Plantagenet king."

▲ **FIGURE 8-13 Michael Ibsen provides cheek cells to Turi King, who used them to sequence his mitochondrial DNA**

EVALUATE THIS Jeremy has always had difficulty walking rapidly and for long distances. Shortly before Jeremy's wedding, genetic testing revealed that his problem was caused by a mtDNA mutation. Should Jeremy be concerned about a future daughter inheriting the faulty gene? What about a son?

CHAPTER REVIEW

Go to **MasteringBiology** for practice quizzes, activities, eText, videos, current events, and more.

Answers to Think Critically, Evaluate This, Multiple Choice, and Fill-in-the-Blank questions can be found in the Answers section at the back of the book.

Summary of Key Concepts

8.1 How Do Cells Obtain Energy?

The ultimate source of energy for nearly all life is sunlight, captured during photosynthesis and stored in molecules such as glucose. Cells produce chemical energy by breaking down glucose and capturing some of the released energy as ATP. During glycolysis, glucose is broken down in the cytosol, forming pyruvate and generating two ATP and two NADH molecules, which are high-energy electron carriers. If oxygen is available, the NADH from glycolysis is captured in ATP, and pyruvate is broken down through cellular respiration in the mitochondria, generating a total of 34 additional molecules of ATP.

8.2 How Does Glycolysis Begin Breaking Down Glucose?

Figures 8-3 and E8-1 and Table 8-1 summarize glycolysis. During the energy investment stage of glycolysis, glucose is energized by adding energy-carrying phosphate groups from two ATP molecules, forming fructose bisphosphate. Then, during the energy-harvesting stage, a series of reactions breaks down the fructose bisphosphate into two molecules of pyruvate. This produces a net energy yield of two ATP molecules and two NADH molecules.

8.3 How Does Cellular Respiration Extract Energy from Glucose?

Cellular respiration, which requires O_2 and generates 17 times as much ATP as does glycolysis, is summarized in Figures 8-5, 8-6, and E8-2 and Table 8.1. Before cellular respiration begins, pyruvate is transported into the mitochondrial matrix. During stage 1 of cellular respiration, acetyl CoA is formed from pyruvate, releasing CO_2 and generating NADH. The acetyl CoA then enters the Krebs cycle, which releases the CoA for reuse and releases the remaining two carbons as CO_2. One ATP, three NADH, and one $FADH_2$ are also formed for each acetyl group that goes through the cycle. In the mitochondrial matrix, each molecule of glucose that originally entered glycolysis produces a total of two ATP, eight NADH, and two $FADH_2$ (see Fig. 8-7).

During stage 2 of cellular respiration, the NADH and $FADH_2$ deliver their high-energy electrons to the electron transport chain (ETC) within the inner mitochondrial membrane. As the electrons pass along the ETC, energy is released and used to pump hydrogen ions across the inner membrane from the matrix into the intermembrane space, creating a hydrogen ion gradient. At the end of the ETC, the depleted electrons combine with hydrogen ions and oxygen to form water. During chemiosmosis, the energy stored in the hydrogen ion gradient is used to produce ATP as the hydrogen ions diffuse down their concentration gradient across the inner membrane through ATP synthase channels. Chemiosmosis yields 32 ATP from the complete breakdown of a glucose molecule; all are generated by energy carried in $FADH_2$ and NADH (including two NADH from glycolysis). Two additional ATPs are formed directly during glycolysis, and two more during the Krebs cycle. So altogether, a single molecule of glucose provides a net yield of 36 ATP when it is broken down by glycolysis followed by cellular respiration.

8.4 How Does Fermentation Allow Glycolysis to Continue When Oxygen Is Lacking?

Glycolysis uses NAD^+ to produce NADH as glucose is broken down into pyruvate. For these reactions to continue, NAD^+ must be continuously recycled. Under anaerobic conditions, NADH cannot release its high-energy electrons to the electron transport chain because there is no oxygen to accept them. Fermentation regenerates NAD^+ from NADH by converting pyruvate to lactate (via lactic acid fermentation) or to ethanol and CO_2 (via alcoholic fermentation), allowing glycolysis to continue.

Key Terms

aerobic *132*	glycolysis *125*
alcoholic fermentation *134*	intermembrane space *127*
anaerobic *132*	Krebs cycle *127*
cellular respiration *127*	lactate fermentation *133*
chemiosmosis *129*	matrix *127*
electron transport chain	mitochondrion (plural,
(ETC) *128*	mitochondria) *127*
fermentation *133*	nicotinamide adenine
flavin adenine dinucleotide	dinucleotide (NAD^+ or
(FAD or $FADH_2$) *128*	NADH) *125*

Thinking Through the Concepts

Multiple Choice

1. Which of the following is True for one glucose molecule?
  a. Fermentation produces 2 ATP.
  b. Glycolysis followed by fermentation nets 4 ATP.
  c. Ethanol is one end product of glycolysis.
  d. The overall equation for photosynthesis is the reverse of that for aerobic glucose breakdown.

2. The portion of glucose breakdown that produces the most ATP is
  a. chemiosmosis.
  b. glycolysis.
  c. the Krebs cycle.
  d. fermentation.

3. ATP synthase enzymes are located in the
  a. cytosol.
  b. inner mitochondrial membrane.
  c. intermembrane space.
  d. mitochondrial matrix.

4. Fermentation
  a. regenerates NADH.
  b. follows cellular respiration when oxygen is lacking.
  c. generates additional ATP after glycolysis.
  d. uses pyruvate as its substrate.

5. Which of the following is produced in the intermembrane space of mitochondria?
  a. ATP
  b. a high concentration of H^+
  c. NADH and $FADH_2$
  d. acetyl CoA

Fill-in-the-Blank

1. The complete breakdown of glucose in the presence of oxygen occurs in two major stages: _____ and _____. The first of these stages occurs in the _____ of the cell, and the second stage occurs in organelles called _____. Conditions in which oxygen is present are described as _____.

2. Conditions in which oxygen is absent are described as _____. Some microorganisms break down glucose in the absence of oxygen using _____, which generates only _____ molecules of ATP. This process is followed by _____, in which no more ATP is produced, but the electron-carrier molecule _____ is regenerated so it can be used in further glucose breakdown.

3. Yeasts in bread dough and alcoholic beverages use a type of fermentation that generates _____ and _____. Muscles pushed to their limit use _____ fermentation. Which form of fermentation is used by microorganisms that produce yogurt, sour cream, and sauerkraut? _____

4. During cellular respiration, the electron transport chain pumps H^+ out of the mitochondrial _____ into the _____, producing a _____ of H^+. The ATP produced by cellular respiration is generated by a process called _____. ATP is generated as H^+ travels through membrane channels within _____.

5. The cyclic portion of cellular respiration is called the _____ cycle. The molecule that enters this cycle is _____. How many ATP molecules are generated by this cycle per molecule of glucose? _____ What types of high-energy electron-carrier molecules are generated during the cycle? _____ and _____

Review Questions

1. Starting with glucose ($C_6H_{12}O_6$), write the overall equation for glucose breakdown in the presence of oxygen, compare this to the overall equation for photosynthesis, and explain how the energy components of the equations differ.

2. Draw and label a mitochondrion, and explain how each structure relates to its function.

3. What role do the following play in breaking down and harvesting energy from glucose: glycolysis, cellular respiration, chemiosmosis, fermentation, and the electron carriers NAD^+ and FAD?

4. Outline the two major stages of glycolysis. How many ATP molecules (overall) are generated per glucose molecule during glycolysis? Where in the cell does glycolysis occur?

5. What molecule is the end product of glycolysis? How are the carbons of this molecule used in stage 1 of cellular respiration? In what form is most of the energy from the Krebs cycle captured?

6. Describe the electron transport chain and the process of chemiosmosis.

7. Why is oxygen necessary for cellular respiration to occur?

8. Compare the structure of chloroplasts (described in Chapter 7) to that of mitochondria, and describe how the similarities in structure relate to similarities in function.

Applying the Concepts

1. Some species of bacteria use aerobic respiration, and other species use fermentation. In an oxygen-rich environment, would either type be at a competitive advantage? What about in an oxygen-poor environment?

2. Many microorganisms in lakes use cellular respiration to generate energy. Dumping large amounts of raw sewage into rivers or lakes typically leads to massive fish kills, even if the sewage itself is not toxic to fish. What kills the fish? How might you reduce fish mortality after raw sewage is accidentally released into a small pond?

3. Imagine a hypothetical situation in which a starving cell reaches the stage where every bit of its ATP has been depleted and converted to ADP plus phosphate. If at this point you place the cell in a solution containing glucose, will it recover and survive? Explain your answer based on what you know about glucose breakdown.

4. Some species of bacteria that live at the surface of sediment on the bottom of lakes are capable of using either glycolysis plus fermentation or cellular respiration to generate ATP. There is very little circulation of water in lakes during the summer. Predict and explain what will happen to the bottommost water of a deep lake as the summer progresses, and describe how this situation will affect the amount of energy production by bacteria.

UNIT 4
Behavior and Ecology

Human observers are captivated by the bright colors and ethereal beauty of coral reefs, which are among the most diverse, productive, and fragile of Earth's ecosystems.

"When we try to pick out anything by itself, we find it hitched to everything else in the universe." —JOHN MUIR, *in My First Summer in the Sierra (1911)*

26
ANIMAL BEHAVIOR

Sex and Symmetry

WHAT MAKES A MAN SEXY? According to a growing body of research, it's his symmetry. Female sexual preference for symmetrical males was first documented in insects. For example, biologist Randy Thornhill found that symmetry accurately predicts the mating success of male Japanese scorpionflies (see the inset photo). In Thornhill's experiments and observations, the most successful males were those whose left and right wings were equal or nearly equal in length. Males with one wing longer than the other were less likely to copulate; the greater the difference between the two wings, the lower the likelihood of mating success.

Thornhill's work with scorpionflies led him to wonder if the effects of male symmetry also extend to humans. To test the hypothesis that female humans find symmetrical males more attractive, Thornhill and colleagues began by measuring symmetry in some young adult males. Each man's degree of symmetry was assessed by measurements of his ear length and the width of his foot, ankle, hand, wrist, elbow, and ear. From these measurements, the researchers derived an index that

Both this male scorpionfly and this male human are exceptionally attractive to females of their species. The secret to their sex appeal may be that both have highly symmetrical bodies.

summarized the degree to which the size of these features differed between the right and left sides of the body.

The researchers next gathered a panel of heterosexual female observers who were unaware of the nature of the study and showed them photos of the faces of the measured males. As predicted by the researchers' hypothesis, men judged by the panel to be most attractive were also the most symmetrical. Apparently, a man's attractiveness to women is correlated with his body symmetry.

Why might females prefer symmetrical males? Consider this question as you read about animal behavior.

AT A GLANCE

26.1 HOW DOES BEHAVIOR ARISE?

Behavior is any observable activity of a living animal. For example, a moth flies toward a bright light, a honeybee flies toward a cup of sugar water, and a housefly flies toward a piece of rotting meat. Bluebirds sing, wolves howl, and frogs croak. Mountain sheep butt heads in ritual combat, chimpanzees groom one another, ants attack a termite that approaches an anthill. Humans dance, play sports, and wage wars. Even the most casual observer encounters many fascinating examples of animal behavior each day.

An animal's behavior is influenced by its genes and by its environment. All behavior develops out of an interaction between the two.

Genes Influence Behavior

Several lines of evidence indicate that variation in behavior is influenced by variation in genes. The evidence includes observation of innate behaviors, behavioral experiments, and genetic analysis.

Innate Behaviors Can Be Performed Without Prior Experience

One indication that genes influence the development of behavior comes from behaviors that are performed by newborn animals and that therefore appear to be inherited. Such **innate** behaviors occur in reasonably complete form the first time an animal encounters a particular stimulus. For instance, a gull chick pecks at its parent's bill very soon after hatching, which stimulates the parent to feed it. Innate behavior also occurs in the common cuckoo, a bird species in which females lay eggs in the nests of other bird species, to be raised by the unwitting adoptive parents. Soon after a cuckoo egg hatches, the cuckoo chick performs the innate behavior of shoving the nest owner's eggs (or baby birds) out of the nest (**FIG. 26-1**).

(a) A cuckoo chick ejects an egg

(b) A foster parent feeds a cuckoo

▲ **FIGURE 26-1 Innate behavior (a)** The cuckoo chick, just hours after it hatches and before its eyes have opened, evicts the eggs of its foster parents from the nest. **(b)** The parents, responding to the stimulus of the cuckoo chick's wide-gaping mouth, feed the chick, unaware that it is not related to them.

THINK CRITICALLY The cuckoo chick benefits from its innate behavior, but the foster parent harms itself with its innate response to the cuckoo chick's begging. Why hasn't natural selection eliminated the foster parent's disadvantageous innate behavior?

The gull and the cuckoo benefit from their behaviors. The young gull acquires nutrition, and the young cuckoo eliminates its competitors for food. These examples illustrate a more general point about behavior: Much of it is adaptive and therefore may have evolved by natural selection.

Experiments Show That Behavior Can Be Inherited

Although the widespread occurrence of innate behaviors provides circumstantial evidence that behaviors can be inherited and are therefore influenced by genes, stronger evidence comes from experiments. One such experiment began when researchers noticed that fruit fly larvae exhibit two phenotypes with respect to feeding behavior. Some larvae are "rovers" and move about continually to search for food. Others are "sitters" and remain in more or less one place and eat whatever is there. When the researchers crossed adult rovers and sitters, all the offspring were rovers. When these first generation rovers bred with one another, however, the resulting generation contained both rovers and sitters in a ratio of roughly 3:1. As you may recall from your study of inheritance in Chapter 11, the pattern observed in this experiment is the one expected for a trait controlled by a single gene with two alleles, one of which is dominant.

Another cross-breeding experiment, this time with blackcap warblers, showed that these birds have a genetically influenced tendency to migrate in a particular direction. Blackcap warblers breed in Europe and migrate to Africa, but populations from different areas travel by different routes. Blackcaps from western Europe travel in a southwesterly direction to reach Africa, whereas birds from eastern Europe travel to the southeast. If birds from the two populations are crossbred in captivity, however, the hybrid offspring try to migrate due south, which is intermediate between the directions of the two parents. This result suggests that genes influence migratory direction.

Geneticists Can Identify Particular Genes That Influence Behavior

Sometimes researchers can pinpoint the particular genes that influence behavior. To determine which genes affect a behavior, an investigator may select a candidate gene and then examine the effects of mutations that inactivate the gene. In some species, researchers may be able to engineer "knockout" animals in which the candidate gene is disabled. For example, mice in which the *V1aR* gene has been knocked out exhibit increased levels of risky behaviors, such as lingering in brightly lit, open areas (which normal mice avoid, presumably because risk of predation is higher in such places). *V1aR* codes for a protein that is a receptor for the hormone arginine vasopressin (AVP). When AVP binds to receptors in the brain, it influences behavior, and mice lacking the receptor fail to respond appropriately to dangerous circumstances.

Before researchers can knock out candidate genes, they must have some idea of which genes are likely to affect the behavior of interest. To identify likely candidates, researchers often use techniques that identify chromosomal locations at which genetic variation is correlated with variation in a behavior. They also use techniques that reveal which genes are expressed in particular tissues (especially the brain) when a particular behavior occurs. These methods often reveal that complex behaviors are influenced by many genes. For example, researchers have identified more than 800 different genes whose expression in a zebra finch brain changes each time the bird sings.

The Environment Influences Behavior

The development and expression of behavior can be influenced by variation in an animal's environment, including both the animal's physical environment and its experiences.

Behaviors Are Influenced by the Physical Environment

The environment in which an animal develops can affect its adult behavior. Consider, for example, the zebrafish. This species is found in diverse habitats, including fast-flowing streams in which the water contains ample oxygen and stagnant ponds in which oxygen levels are very low. In an experiment, genetically similar zebrafish were reared from eggs in two different conditions: oxygen-rich or oxygen-poor water. When the fish grew up, the experimenters measured their response to **aggression,** or antagonistic behavior, from another fish in both an oxygen-rich and an oxygen-poor environment. In the high-oxygen environment, the behavior of fish that were reared in a high-oxygen environment was much more aggressive. In the low-oxygen environment, however, the most aggressive fish were those reared in a low-oxygen environment. It appears that the environment in which a fish develops causes the fish to develop the ability to behave appropriately in the environment that it is most likely to encounter as an adult.

An animal's behavior can also be influenced by the living part of its environment, especially its interactions with other animals. For example, in prairie voles (a small rodent), pups raised by a single mother receive less licking and grooming than do pups raised by a mother and father together. In adulthood, the mating and parental behavior of voles varies, depending on their experience as pups. Those cared for by two parents mate sooner and provide more attentive parental care than do voles raised by a single parent.

Behaviors Are Influenced by the Experiential Environment

The capacity to make relatively permanent changes in behavior on the basis of experience is called **learning.** This deceptively simple definition encompasses a vast array of phenomena. A toad learns to avoid distasteful insects; a baby shrew learns which adult is its mother; a human learns to speak a language; a sparrow learns to use the stars for

(a) Prairie dog alarm call

(b) Habituated prairie dogs

▲ FIGURE 26-2 **Habituation (a)** When a prairie dog detects the approach of a potential predator, it may produce a loud alarm call. However, if harmless intruders approach repeatedly, as when **(b)** human hikers routinely pass by, prairie dogs learn to stop responding with an alarm call.

navigation. Each of the many examples of animal learning represents the outcome of a unique evolutionary history, so learning is as diverse as animals themselves. Nonetheless, it can be useful to categorize types of learning, keeping in mind that the categories are only rough guides and that many examples of learning will not fit neatly into any category.

Habituation Is a Decline in Response to a Repeated Stimulus A common form of simple learning is **habituation,** defined as a decline in response to a repeated stimulus. The ability to habituate prevents an animal from wasting its energy and attention on irrelevant stimuli. For example, a sea anemone will retract its tentacles when first touched, but gradually stops retracting if touched repeatedly. Prairie dogs, which are ground-dwelling rodents, utter loud alarm calls and race to their burrows when potential predators approach their colony (**FIG. 26-2**). But prairie dogs habituate to repeated approaches by animals that prove to be nonthreatening, such as people on a well-used hiking path that passes near the colony, and stop responding with alarm calls.

The ability to habituate is generally adaptive. If a prairie dog ran to its burrow every time a harmless human passed by, the animal would waste a great deal of time and energy that could otherwise be spent on beneficial activities such as acquiring food. Habituation can also fine-tune an organism's innate responses to environmental stimuli. For example, newborn chicks instinctively crouch when any object moves over their heads, but birds that are a few weeks old crouch down when a hawk flies over but ignore harmless birds such as geese. The birds have habituated to things that soar by harmlessly and frequently, such as leaves, songbirds, and geese. Predators are much less common, and the novel shape of a hawk continues to elicit instinctive crouching. Thus, learning modified the innate response, making it more advantageous.

Researchers may intentionally induce habituation in animal subjects so they can be studied. For example, most of

what we know about the social behavior of primates such as chimpanzees, gorillas, and baboons comes from studies of wild populations in which animals have been laboriously habituated to human presence. Only then can researchers approach closely enough to observe behavior (**FIG. 26-3**).

Imprinting Is Rapid Learning by Young Animals Learning often occurs within limits that help increase the chances that only the appropriate behavior is acquired. Such constraints on learning are perhaps most strikingly illustrated by **imprinting,** a form of learning in which an animal's nervous system is rigidly programmed to learn a certain thing only during a certain period of development. The information learned during this *sensitive period* is incorporated into behaviors that are not easily altered by later experience.

Imprinting is best known in birds such as geese, ducks, and chickens. These birds learn to follow the animal or object that they most frequently encounter during an early sensitive period. In nature, a mother bird is likely to be nearby during

▲ FIGURE 26-3 **Chimpanzees habituate to researchers** Scientific investigation of animal behavior often relies on animals that have habituated to human presence.

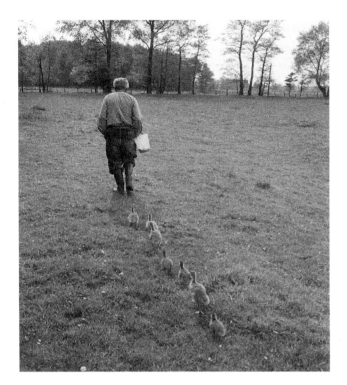

▲ FIGURE 26-4 **Konrad Lorenz and imprinting** Konrad Lorenz, a pioneer in the scientific study of animal behavior, is followed by goslings that imprinted on him shortly after they hatched. They follow him as they would their mother.

the sensitive period, so her offspring imprint on her. In the laboratory, however, these birds may imprint on a toy train or other moving object (FIG. 26-4).

Imprinting is a concern for conservationists who aim to preserve endangered species by rearing animals in captivity for release into the wild. Such programs often go to great pains to ensure that captive-reared animals do not imprint on their human caretakers (FIG. 26-5a), so that released animals will be attracted to others of their species and not to people. However, conservationists can also take advantage of imprinting to help ensure that captive-reared animals develop behaviors necessary for survival (FIG. 26-5b).

Conditioning Is a Learned Association Between a Stimulus and a Response Behaviors generally occur in response to a particular stimulus, and many animals can learn to associate a behavior with a different stimulus. For example, in a classic experiment conducted by Ivan Pavlov, dogs that normally salivated in response to the sight of food were trained to salivate in response to hearing a ringing bell. This kind of learning, in which an animal learns a new association between a stimulus and an innate response, is known as **classical conditioning.** For example, lemon damselfish perform innate predator avoidance behavior—hiding and scanning their surroundings—in response to a chemical alarm signal released by other damselfish. After experimenters repeatedly exposed young damselfish to the alarm signal mixed with the scents of several unfamiliar fish species, the damselfish performed the alarm response when exposed only to

the scent of any of the previously unfamiliar species. As the damselfish experiment suggests, learning by classical conditioning can result in adaptive behavior, such as avoiding novel predators.

A more complex form of learning is **trial-and-error learning,** in which animals learn through experience to associate a behavior with a positive or negative outcome. Many animals are faced with naturally occurring rewards and punishments and learn to modify their behavior in response to them. For example, a hungry toad that captures a bee quickly learns to avoid future encounters with bees (FIG. 26-6). After only one experience with a stung tongue, a toad ignores bees and even other insects that resemble them.

Trial-and-error learning is sometimes known as **operant conditioning,** especially when the learning results from training in a laboratory setting. For example, an animal may learn to perform a behavior (such as pushing a lever or

(a) Feeding a condor chick

(b) Leading a flock of cranes

▲ FIGURE 26-5 **Imprinting and endangered species (a)** To prevent young California condors from imprinting on humans, caretakers use a condor puppet to feed them. When the captive-reared birds are released to the wild, they will be drawn to other condors rather than to people. **(b)** Early in life, captive-reared whooping cranes are exposed to and imprint on ultralight aircraft. The young cranes later follow an ultralight to learn the route for their southward migration.

① A naive toad is presented with a bee.

② While trying to eat the bee, the toad is stung painfully on the tongue.

③ Presented with a harmless robber fly, which resembles a bee, the toad cringes.

④ The toad is presented with a dragonfly.

⑤ The toad immediately eats the dragonfly, demonstrating that the learned aversion is specific to bees.

▲ FIGURE 26-6 **Trial-and-error learning in a toad**

pecking a button) to receive a reward or to avoid punishment. This technique is most closely associated with the psychologist B. F. Skinner, who designed the "Skinner box," in which an animal is isolated and allowed to train itself. The box might contain a lever that, when pressed, ejects a food pellet. If the animal accidentally bumps the lever, a food reward appears. After a few such occurrences, the animal learns the connection between pressing the lever and receiving food and begins to press the lever repeatedly.

Operant conditioning has been used to train animals to perform tasks far more complex than pressing a lever. For example, Gambian giant pouched rats have been trained to sniff out buried land mines and, in return for a banana or peanut reward, scratch the ground vigorously when they find a mine (**FIG. 26-7**). Unexploded land mines pose a major threat to the safety of millions of people in countries around the world; more than 100 million mines remain buried where they were planted during past wars and forgotten. The rats are very good at detecting mines and are too light to detonate the ones they find. Gambian giant pouched rats can also detect the scent of the bacteria that cause tuberculosis (TB) and have been trained to distinguish TB-infected mucus from uninfected mucus. This ability may soon become the basis of a cheap and effective diagnostic test for TB.

In Social Learning, Animals Learn from Other Animals In **social learning**, animals learn behaviors by watching or listening to others of their species. By observing and copying the behavior of others, animals may learn which foods to eat, where to find food or breeding sites, or how to avoid predators. Songbirds of many species acquire their songs by copying the songs of other birds. In animals that use tools, information about how to use them is usually gained by watching other animals use them. For example, some dolphins in Shark Bay, Australia, use sponges to help protect their snouts as they

▲ FIGURE 26-7 **A Gambian giant pouched rat at work, detecting land mines**

dig for prey in the stony seabed (FIG. 26-8a). Young dolphins learn this behavior by watching their mother perform it. Similarly, chimpanzees may use stones to crack open nuts or sticks to fish termites out of their mounds (FIG. 26-8b). These skills are transmitted from one chimpanzee to another by social learning.

Insight Is Problem Solving Without Trial and Error In certain situations, animals seem able to solve problems suddenly, without the benefit of prior experience. This kind of sudden problem solving is sometimes called **insight learning,** because it seems at least superficially similar to the process by which humans mentally manipulate concepts to arrive at a solution. We cannot, of course, know for sure if non-human animals experience similar mental states when they solve problems.

One species that seems to be good at solving problems is the New Caledonian crow. These birds not only use tools, but also manufacture them, shaping twigs and leaves into

▲ FIGURE 26-9 **Insight learning** New Caledonian crows learn to solve fairly complex problems without prior training. Here, a crow obtains a reward by selecting the object that is most effective for raising the water level in a tube.

(a) Dolphin wearing a sponge tool

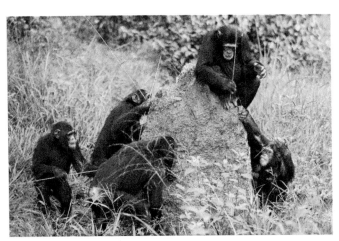

(b) Chimpanzees probing for termites

▲ FIGURE 26-8 **Social learning** Animals may learn helpful behaviors from other animals. By observing others, **(a)** bottlenose dolphins learn to use a sponge plucked from the seafloor as a snout protector, and **(b)** chimpanzees learn to use a twig to extract termites from a mound.

hooks that the birds use to extract insects from their hiding places. In a lab experiment, a New Caledonian crow was presented with a straight piece of wire and a bucket of meat that had been placed down a well, so the bird could not reach it. The crow quickly used its beak to bend the wire into a hook, which the bird used to lift the bucket up so it could eat the meat. New Caledonian crows also readily solved, on the first try, a multistep puzzle that required them to use a short stick to reach a long stick that was in turn used to reach a food reward. In experiments that tested crows' ability to gain access to food rewards floating on water at the bottom of a clear, vertical tube, researchers found that crows quickly reacted by dropping objects into the tube so that the water level rose, bringing the food to within the birds' reach (FIG. 26-9). What's more, the crows dropped solid objects that would sink rather than hollow objects that would float.

CHECK YOUR LEARNING

Can you ...

- describe evidence that genes influence behavior?
- describe evidence that the physical and experiential environments influence behavior?
- explain habituation, imprinting, classical conditioning, trial-and-error learning, social learning, and insight learning?

26.2 HOW DO ANIMALS COMPETE FOR RESOURCES?

Resources such as food, space, and mates are scarce relative to the reproductive potential of populations, leading to a contest to survive and reproduce. The resulting competition underlies many of the most frequent types of interactions between animals.

▲ FIGURE 26-10 **Combat** Fighting can be dangerous for combatants, such as these male elephants.

Aggressive Behavior Helps Secure Resources

One of the most obvious manifestations of competition for resources is aggression between members of the same species. Aggressive behavior includes physical combat between rivals (FIG. 26-10). A fight, however, can injure its participants; even the victorious animal might not survive to pass on its genes. As a result, natural selection has favored the evolution of displays or rituals for resolving conflicts. Aggressive displays allow competitors to assess each other and determine a winner on the basis of size, strength, and motivation, rather than on the basis of wounds inflicted. Thanks to these displays, most aggressive encounters end without physical damage to the participants. We discuss signals of aggression in more detail in Section 26.5.

Dominance Hierarchies Help Manage Aggressive Interactions

Even when they do not cause injuries, aggressive interactions use a lot of energy and can disrupt other important tasks, such as finding food, watching for predators, or raising young. Thus, there are advantages to resolving conflicts with minimal aggression. When animals live in social groups in which individuals interact repeatedly, they may form a **dominance hierarchy,** in which each animal establishes a rank that determines its access to resources. Although aggressive encounters occur frequently while the dominance hierarchy is being established, once each animal learns its place in the hierarchy, disputes are infrequent, and the dominant individuals obtain the most access to the resources needed for reproduction, including food, space, and mates. For example, domestic chickens, after some initial squabbling, sort themselves into a reasonably stable "pecking order." Thereafter, all birds in the group defer to the dominant bird, all but the dominant bird give way to the second most dominant, and so on. In wolf packs, one member of each sex is the dominant, or "alpha," individual to whom all others of that sex are subordinate.

Animals May Defend Territories That Contain Resources

In many animal species, competition for resources takes the form of **territoriality,** the defense of an area where important resources are located. As with dominance hierarchies, territoriality tends to reduce aggression, because once a territory is established through aggressive interactions, relative peace prevails as boundaries are recognized and respected. One reason for this stability is that an animal is highly motivated to defend its territory and will often repel even larger, stronger animals that attempt to invade it.

Territories are most commonly defended by individual males, but may be defended by individual females, mated pairs, families, or larger social groups The defended area may include places to mate, raise young, feed, or store food. Territories are as diverse as the animals defending them. For example, a territory can be a tree where a woodpecker stores acorns (FIG. 26-11), a small depression in a lake floor used as a nesting site by a cichlid fish, a hole in the sand that is home to a crab, or a mouse carcass defended by a pair of burying beetles whose offspring are developing inside it.

Territoriality Occurs When Benefits Outweigh Costs

Acquiring and defending a territory require a costly investment of time and energy, but making the investment can increase an animal's reproductive success enough to offset the cost. For example, American redstarts are migratory songbirds that defend territories both on their breeding grounds in northern forests and in their wintering areas in the tropics. Birds that defend winter territories in lush, moist forests have a larger number of offspring than do birds whose winter territories are in less productive habitats. Thus, in redstarts, resources acquired via territorial behavior in the nonbreeding season have an important effect on breeding success months

▲ FIGURE 26-11 **A feeding territory** Acorn woodpeckers live in communal groups that excavate acorn-sized holes in dead trees and stuff the holes with green acorns for dining during the lean winter months. The group defends the trees vigorously against other groups of acorn woodpeckers and against acorn-eating birds of other species, such as jays.

later, probably because the birds with good winter territories are in better condition and can migrate north more quickly to acquire the best breeding territories and get an earlier start on reproduction.

The costs and benefits of defending a territory may change as conditions change, so many animals are territorial only at certain times or only under certain conditions. For example, nonbreeding pied wagtail birds defend feeding territories on days when the invertebrates they feed on are relatively scarce, but abandon territoriality on days when prey animals are especially abundant. When the breeding season arrives, male wagtails defend territories continuously, regardless of the abundance of food. If all goes well for a male, a female will join him on the territory. Many animal species defend territories only while breeding, when it is critical to monopolize the resources required to produce offspring.

CHECK YOUR LEARNING

Can you ...

- describe the function of aggressive behavior?
- explain why natural selection has favored the evolution of aggressive signals and displays, dominance hierarchies, and territoriality?

26.3 HOW DO ANIMALS BEHAVE WHEN THEY MATE?

Sexual selection (see Chapter 16) has fostered the evolution of behaviors that help animals compete for access to mates and that help them choose suitable mates. In most cases, males experience strong selection for traits that help them compete, and females experience selection for traits that help them make advantageous choices.

Males May Fight to Mate

The aggressive behaviors that we described in Section 26.2 often occur in the context of competition among males for opportunities to mate. For example, in the wasp *Sycoscapter australis*, males often must fight in order to mate. In this species, eggs develop within a fig, and newly hatched wasps emerge in the hollow space inside the fruit. Males hatch first and move about looking for emerging females to mate with. But when males encounter one another, they battle fiercely. The fights are intense; up to a quarter of combatants suffer fatal wounds. Winners earn the chance to mate.

In many species, males compete not for direct access to females, but for control of a territory that will attract females. In such species, males who successfully defend territories have the greatest chance of mating. Females usually prefer high-quality territories, which might have features such as large size, abundant food, and secure nesting areas. For example, male side-blotched lizards that defend territories containing many rocks are more successful in attracting mates than are males that defend territories with few rocks. Rockier territories provide more vantage points for detecting

▲ **FIGURE 26-12 Nuptial gifts** A male dance fly copulates with a female that has accepted his gift of a dead insect.

predators and a greater range of microclimates, which is important for "cold-blooded" animals like lizards that regulate body temperature by moving between warmer and cooler spots. Females that select males with the best territories increase their own reproductive success. When experimenters moved rocks from one male's territory to another, females strongly preferred to settle on the improved territories, showing that their preference was based on the territory rather than on the male defending it.

Males May Provide Gifts to Mates

In some species, females are induced to mate by males that provide resources more directly, in the form of a meal. For example, female dance flies mate only with males that bring them a dead insect to eat (**FIG. 26-12**). Copulation occurs while the female eats the insect. If the insect is too small, copulation does not last long enough for sperm to be transferred, so males that present larger insects have greater reproductive success. Similar *nuptial gifts* are presented by males of a number of spider and insect species and may consist of nutritious secretions rather than prey items. Perhaps the ultimate in nutritious gifts is presented by the male red-backed spider. Following copulation, a male throws his own body into the much larger female's jaws, and she usually obliges by eating him. The reproductive cost of this sacrifice is probably small, as even the males that are not eaten after mating are very unlikely to survive long enough to mate with a second female. The tiny males are preyed upon by many predators, and among those that do not sacrifice themselves during mating, almost all are killed and eaten before they can reach a second female's web.

Competition Between Males Continues After Copulation

Among animal species, it is common for both males and females to copulate with multiple partners. When females have multiple partners, males may evolve behaviors that increase

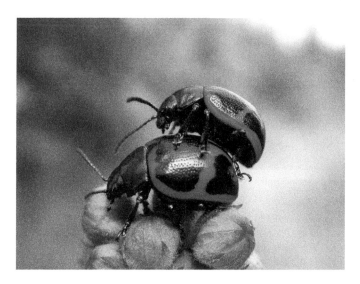

▲ **FIGURE 26-13 Mate guarding** After mating, a male may continue to guard his mate to prevent her from mating with other males. A male swamp milkweed beetle guards his mate by riding around on her back.

the odds that a male's sperm, and not those of a competitor, fertilize the female's eggs. For example, a male may continue to guard a female after copulation to prevent her from mating with other males. In many species of birds, lizards, fish, and insects, males spend days or weeks closely following previous sexual partners, fighting off the advances of other males. In some cases, the male even rides around on the female (FIG. 26-13).

If a male copulates with a female and does not subsequently guard her, his reproductive success may be usurped by competitors. For example, in the dunnock, a small songbird in which a female may copulate with multiple males, a male ready to copulate first pecks the female's genital opening. In response, the female ejects any sperm from recent prior copulations, increasing the odds that the current male's sperm will be the ones that fertilize her eggs. Other males take an even more direct approach. Before a male blackwinged damselfly copulates with a female that has landed

in his territory, he uses the tip of his penis to scoop out any sperm that a previous sexual partner may have left in the female's sperm storage organ (FIG. 26-14).

Reproductive competition among males may continue even after conception. Lions live in social groups called *prides* that contain a few males that maintain exclusive reproductive access to a larger number of females. As ruling a pride is the only way for a male to reproduce, there is intense competition for the role; roaming males without a pride may attempt to overthrow a pride's current males and oust them from the group. If a takeover attempt is successful, the new males are likely to kill any cubs present in the pride. By eliminating the offspring of other males, the new males ensure that the females will reproduce again soon, this time investing their reproductive effort in the offspring of the new males. This kind of *infanticide* is widespread among animals.

Multiple Mating Behaviors May Coexist

In some species, a relatively small number of males can monopolize a large proportion of the opportunities for reproduction. For example, a few males in a population may be especially proficient at producing signals that females find attractive, or scarcity of resources may allow only a few males to secure a territory.

When some males are excluded from the optimal way of reproducing, alternative mating behaviors may arise. For example, in bluegill fish, two types of males, dubbed "parentals" and "cuckolders," coexist and exhibit distinctively different mating behavior (FIG. 26-15). Parental males are large, colorful, and territorial; they build and defend nests scooped out of the streambed. Females visit the nests and choose a territorial male to spawn with, laying eggs that mix with the male's sperm. Cuckolder males are very small "sneakers" that hide in vegetation near a nest and wait for an opportunity to deposit some sperm in the nest of a spawning pair without being noticed by the territory holder. When cuckolder males grow a bit larger, they may become female mimics, sporting drab colors that resemble those of females and behaving as a spawning female might. This subterfuge may allow a female-mimic male to slip between a spawning pair and add his sperm to the mix.

(a) Damselflies mating

(b) Damselfly penis

◀ **FIGURE 26-14 Sperm competition (a)** During copulation, a male damselfly (the upper fly in the photo) grasps the female behind her head with claspers on his rearmost segment. The male's penis is located on his underside just below his wings and transfers sperm to the genital opening on the female's rearmost segment, which she swings forward and upward toward the male's body. Before copulating, however, the male uses his **(b)** spiny penis to scrape out any sperm that a competing male may have deposited in the female's sperm storage organ.

(a) Territorial male

(b) Sneaker males lurk near a mating pair

(c) A female-mimic male approaches a mating pair

▲ FIGURE 26-15 **Alternative mating strategies** Different male mating behaviors coexist in populations of bluegills. **(a)** Some males are territorial, defending nests that attract females. **(b)** Other males are sneakers that do not defend territories but may be able to opportunistically fertilize eggs. **(c)** Female-mimic males look and act like females and may not be recognized as competitors by territorial males.

CHECK YOUR LEARNING

Can you ...

- describe some types of behavior that have evolved as a result of competition for mates?
- give specific examples of these types of behavior?
- explain why multiple mating behaviors may coexist in a population?

26.4 HOW DO ANIMALS COMMUNICATE?

Animals frequently broadcast information. If this information evokes a response from other individuals, and if that response tends to benefit the sender and the receiver, then a communication channel can form. **Communication** is the production of a signal by one organism that causes another organism to change its behavior. These changes in behavior, on average, benefit both the signaler and receiver. However, the overall benefit may be reduced if the communication channel is exploited by other animals that harm the communicators.

Although animals of different species may communicate, as when a cat hisses at a dog, most animals communicate primarily with members of their own species. The ways in which animals communicate are astonishingly diverse and use all of the senses. In the following sections, we will look at communication by visual displays, sound, chemicals, and touch.

Visual Communication Is Most Effective over Short Distances

Animals with well-developed eyes use visual signals to communicate. Visual communication may involve passive signals in which the size, shape, or color of the signal conveys important information. For example, when female mandrills become sexually receptive, they develop a large, brightly colored swelling on their buttocks (FIG. 26-16). Alternatively, visual signals can be active, consisting of specific movements or postures that convey a message. For example, a wolf signals aggression by lowering its head, raising its hackles (fur on its neck and back), and exposing its fangs (FIG. 26-17a).

Like all forms of communication, visual signals have both advantages and disadvantages. On the positive side, visual signals communicate instantaneously, and active visual signals can be rapidly changed to convey a variety of messages in a short period. For example, an initially aggressive wolf that encounters a more dominant individual can quickly shift to a submissive display, crouching with its rump lowered and its tail tucked (FIG. 26-17b). Visual communication is quiet and unlikely to alert distant predators, although the signaler does make itself conspicuous to those nearby. On the negative side, visual signals are generally ineffective in dense vegetation or in darkness and are limited to close-range communication.

Communication by Sound Is Effective over Longer Distances

Acoustic signals (messages broadcast by sound) overcome many of the shortcomings of visual displays. Like visual

▲ FIGURE 26-16 **A passive visual signal** The female mandrill's colorfully swollen buttocks serve as a passive visual signal that she is fertile and ready to mate.

(a) Aggressive display

(b) Submissive display

▲ **FIGURE 26-17 Active visual signals (a)** A wolf communicates aggressive intent by facing its opponent, lowering its head, erecting the fur along its backbone, and exposing its fangs. These signals can vary in intensity, communicating different levels of aggression. **(b)** A wolf communicates submission by lowering its rump and tucking its tail.

displays, acoustic signals reach receivers almost instantaneously. But unlike visual signals, acoustic signals can be transmitted through darkness, dense forests, and murky water. Acoustic signals can also be effective over longer distances than visual signals. For example, the low, rumbling calls of an African elephant can be heard by elephants several miles away, and the songs of humpback whales are audible for hundreds of miles. Even the small kangaroo rat produces a sound (by striking the desert floor with its hind feet) that is audible 150 feet (45 meters) away. The advantages of long-distance transmission, however, are offset by an important disadvantage: Predators and other unwanted receivers can also detect an acoustic signal from a distance and can use that signal to locate the signaler.

Like visual displays, acoustic signals can be varied to convey rapidly changing messages. An individual can convey different messages by varying the pattern, volume, or pitch of a sound. A wolf's vocal repertoire, for example, includes a variety of barks, howls, whimpers, and growls.

Some animals communicate with vibrations akin to the stimuli that humans perceive as sounds. For example, male water striders vibrate their legs, sending species-specific patterns of vibrations through the water to be detected by other water striders (FIG. 26-18). Caterpillars of some moth species communicate with other caterpillars by scraping or drumming on a leaf with a specialized structure, thereby sending vibrations through the surrounding vegetation.

Chemical Messages Persist Longer but Are Hard to Vary

Chemical substances that are produced by animals and that influence the behavior of other members of the species are called **pheromones.** Unlike visual or sound signals that may attract predators, pheromones are typically not detectable by other species. In addition, a pheromone can act as a kind of signpost, persisting over time and conveying a message long after the signaling animal has departed.

Pheromones can travel fairly far in air or water and so are effective for long-range communication. However, chemical communication requires animals to synthesize a different substance for each message. As a result, chemical signaling systems communicate fewer and simpler messages than do sight- or sound-based systems. In addition, pheromone signals cannot easily convey rapidly changing messages.

Humans have harnessed the power of pheromones to combat insect pests. The sex attractant pheromones of some agricultural pests, such as the Japanese beetle and the gypsy moth, have been successfully synthesized. These synthetic pheromones can be used to disrupt mating or to lure these insects into traps. Controlling pests with pheromones has major environmental advantages over conventional pesticides, which kill beneficial as well as harmful insects and foster the evolution of pesticide-resistant insects. In contrast,

▲ **FIGURE 26-18 Communication by vibration** The light-footed water strider relies on the surface tension of water to support its weight. By vibrating its legs, the water strider sends signals that radiate out over the surface of the water. These vibrations advertise the strider's species and sex to others nearby.

each pheromone is specific to a single species and does not promote the spread of resistance because insects resistant to the attraction of their own pheromones do not reproduce successfully.

CASE STUDY CONTINUED
Sex and Symmetry

Does symmetry have a scent? In one study, researchers measured the body symmetry of 80 men and then issued a clean T-shirt to each one. Each subject wore his shirt to bed for two consecutive nights. A panel of 82 women sniffed the shirts and rated their scents for "pleasantness" and "sexiness." Which shirts had the sexiest, most pleasant scents? The ones worn by the most symmetrical men. The researchers concluded that women can identify symmetrical men by their scent.

What other kinds of messages do animals send with pheromones and other signals? Find out just ahead, in Section 26.5.

Communication by Touch Requires Close Proximity

Communication by physical contact is, for obvious reasons, limited to signaling between animals that are very close together. As a result, it is most common in species that spend a great deal of time in social groups. However, even members of nonsocial species may come into close contact with other individuals during courtship or combat. So communication by touch may also occur in those contexts (FIG. 26-19).

Communication Channels May Be Exploited

Even though sending or receiving a signal is in general beneficial, communicators are sometimes harmed by organisms that exploit a communication channel. The exploiter may be an illegitimate receiver that intercepts a signal. For example,

▲ FIGURE 26-19 **Communication by touch** Touch is important in sexual communication. These land snails engage in courtship behavior that will culminate in mating.

▲ FIGURE 26-20 **Illegitimate receivers** A tungara frog's loud calls may be intercepted by a predatory fringe-lipped bat.

parasitic flies that lay their eggs in the bodies of field crickets find their hosts by moving toward the chirps that male crickets produce. Similarly, predatory fringe-lipped bats find tungara frogs to eat by homing in on the loud calls of male frogs (FIG. 26-20).

The exploiter of a communication channel may also be an illegitimate signaler. For example, as male fireflies in the genus *Photinus* fly about, they emit flashes in a distinctive pattern that identifies them as members of their species. If a receptive female on the ground sees the flashes, she may respond with flashes of her own, and the male flies down to mate with her. However, fireflies of the genus *Photuris* have evolved the ability to imitate the female *Photinus* flashing pattern. If a male *Photinus* approaches the deceptive signal, the larger *Photuris* firefly kills and eats him.

CHECK YOUR LEARNING
Can you ...
- compare the advantages and disadvantages of visual, acoustic, and chemical signals?
- describe examples of visual, acoustic, chemical, and tactile (touch) signals?

26.5 WHAT DO ANIMALS COMMUNICATE ABOUT?

The information shared by communicating helps animals manage a range of interactions with other animals. Animals may communicate to help resolve conflicts. They may communicate about sex, about food, or about predators. Members of a social group may communicate to help coordinate activities.

(a) A male baboon

(b) Sarcastic fringeheads

▲ FIGURE 26-21 **Aggressive displays (a)** Threat display of the male baboon. Despite the potentially lethal fangs so prominently displayed, aggressive encounters between baboons rarely cause injury. **(b)** The aggressive display of many male fish, such as these sarcastic fringeheads, includes elevating the fins and flaring the gill covers, thus making the body appear larger.

Animals Communicate to Manage Aggression

As you learned in our earlier discussion of aggression, the costliness of direct combat has fostered the evolution of signals that communicate aggression. During aggressive displays, animals may exhibit weapons, such as claws and fangs (FIG. 26-21a), and often make themselves appear larger (FIG. 26-21b). Competitors often stand upright and erect their fur, feathers, ears, or fins. These visual signals are typically accompanied by vocal signals such as growls, croaks, roars, or chirps. Fighting tends to be a last resort when displays fail to resolve a dispute.

In addition to aggressive visual and vocal displays, many animal species engage in ritualized combat. Deadly weapons may clash harmlessly (FIG. 26-22) or may be displayed without contacting the opponent. The ritual thus allows contestants to assess the strength and the motivation of their rivals, and the loser retreats. Ritual contests often involve communication by touch, as when two male sandperch fish lock mouths in ritualized wrestling, or two male zebras begin a contest over access to mates by placing their heads on one another's shoulders.

Aggressive visual and vocal displays are commonly deployed in territorial defense. For example, a male roe deer warns intruders away from its territory by displaying its antlers and a male anole lizard does so by displaying the colorful dewlap that extends from his throat. A male sea lion defends a strip of beach by swimming up and down in front of it, calling continuously. A male cricket uses a special structure on its wings to produce chirps that advertise its ownership of its burrow. The often beautiful and elaborate vocalizations

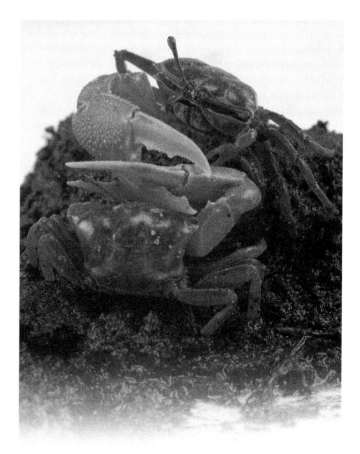

▲ FIGURE 26-22 **Displays of strength** The oversized claws of fiddler crabs, which could severely injure another animal, grasp harmlessly. Eventually one crab, sensing greater vigor in his opponent, retreats unharmed.

of songbirds are also used in territory defense. For example, the husky trill of a male seaside sparrow warns other males to steer clear of his territory.

An animal that has a territory but cannot always be present may use pheromones to scent-mark the boundaries. For example, male sac-winged bats use secretions from their chin glands to mark the perimeter of the small territory that each male defends within a communal roost site that is occupied only during daytime. Scent-marking is also useful for territories that are too large for continuous monitoring of boundaries. A solitary tiger, for example, uses pheromones to mark its presence in a territory that may be as large as 385 square miles (1000 square kilometers).

Mating Signals Encode Sex, Species, and Individual Quality

Before animals can successfully mate, they must identify one another as members of the same species, as members of the opposite sex, and as being sexually receptive. In many species, finding an appropriate potential partner is only the first step. Often the male must demonstrate his quality before the female will accept him as a mate. The need to fulfill all of these requirements has resulted in the evolution of a diverse and fascinating array of courtship signals.

Animals often use sounds to advertise their sex and species. Male grasshoppers and crickets advertise their sex and species with chirps, and a male fruit fly does so with a buzz he produces by vibrating one wing. Acoustic signals may also be used by potential mates to compare rival suitors. During mating season, male hammer-headed bats gather together and produce a chorus of loud, honking calls. The males have a very large head that helps the vocalizations resonate (**FIG. 26-23**). Females fly among the gathered males, listening to their calls before choosing a male to mate with.

Many species use visual displays for courting. Male fence lizards, for example, bob their heads in a species-specific

▲ **FIGURE 26-23 Sexual vocalizations** The huge head of a male hammer-headed bat acts as a resonator that amplifies that male's loud courtship calls.

rhythm, and females prefer the rhythm of their own species. The elaborate construction projects of the male gardener bowerbird and the scarlet throat of the male frigatebird serve as flashy advertisements of sex, species, and male quality (**FIG. 26-24**).

Pheromones can also play an important role in reproductive behavior. A sexually receptive female silk moth, for example, sits quietly and releases a chemical message that can be detected by males up to 3 miles (5 kilometers) away. The exquisitely sensitive and selective receptors on the antennae of the male silk moth respond to just a few molecules of the substance, allowing him to travel upwind along a concentration gradient to find the female (**FIG. 26-25a**). Water is an excellent medium for dispersing chemical signals, and fish commonly use a combination of pheromones and elaborate courtship movements to ensure the synchronous release of gametes. Mammals, with their highly developed sense of smell, often rely on pheromones released by the female during her fertile periods to attract males (**FIG. 26-25b**).

(a) A bowerbird bower

(b) A male frigatebird

◀ **FIGURE 26-24 Sexual displays** **(a)** During courtship, a male gardener bowerbird builds a bower out of twigs and decorates it with colorful items that he gathers. **(b)** A male frigatebird inflates his scarlet throat pouch to attract passing females.

THINK CRITICALLY The male bowerbird provides no protection, food, or other resources to his mate or offspring. Why, then, do females carefully compare the bowers of different males before choosing a mate?

(a) Antennae detect pheromones

(b) Noses detect pheromones

▲ FIGURE 26-25 **Sexual pheromones (a)** Male moths find females not by sight but by following airborne pheromones released by females. These odors are sensed by receptors on the male's huge antennae, whose enormous surface area maximizes the chances of detecting the female scent. **(b)** When dogs meet, they typically sniff each other near the base of the tail. Scent glands there broadcast information about the bearer's sex and interest in mating.

THINK CRITICALLY Female dogs use a pheromone to signal readiness to mate, but female mandrills (see Fig. 26-16) signal mating readiness with a visual signal. What differences would you predict between the two species' methods of searching for food?

CASE STUDY \ **CONTINUED**

Sex and Symmetry

If females are attracted to symmetrical males, we might expect females to assess the symmetry of male visual signals that function in mate attraction. For example, a male house finch has a patch of bright red feathers on the crown of his head, and researchers have shown that males whose crown patches are brightly colored are more likely to attract a mate than are males with dull patches. But males with patches that are both colorful *and* highly symmetrical have the highest mating success of all.

Animals Warn One Another About Predators

Animals may communicate about threats, especially threats from predators. When aphids are attacked by predators, they secrete an alarm pheromone that causes receivers to stop feeding and move away from the signal. If a Belding's ground squirrel spots an approaching predator, it produces an alarm call that sends nearby squirrels scrambling for safety. In some cases, varying alarm signals can convey different messages. For example, vervet monkeys produce different calls in response to threats from each of their major predators: snakes, leopards, and eagles. The response of listening monkeys to each of these calls is appropriate to the particular predator. The "bark" that warns of a leopard or other four-legged carnivore causes monkeys on the ground to take to trees and those in trees to climb higher. The "rraup" call, which advertises the presence of an eagle or other hunting bird, causes monkeys on the ground to look upward and take cover, whereas monkeys already in trees drop to the shelter of lower, denser branches. The "chutter" call that indicates the presence of a snake causes the monkeys to stand up and search the ground for the predator.

Animals Share Information About Food

Animals that live in groups may share information about food. For example, foraging termites that discover food lay a trail of pheromones from the food to the nest, and other termites follow the trail (**FIG. 26-26**). Honeybees share

▲ FIGURE 26-26 **Communication about food** A trail of pheromones, secreted by termites from their own colony, orients foraging termites toward a source of food.

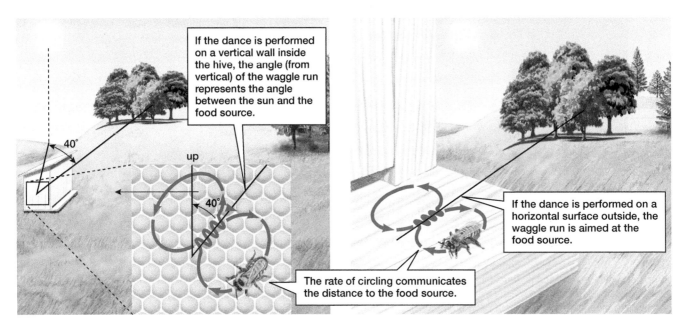

If the dance is performed on a vertical wall inside the hive, the angle (from vertical) of the waggle run represents the angle between the sun and the food source.

up

40°

40°

If the dance is performed on a horizontal surface outside, the waggle run is aimed at the food source.

The rate of circling communicates the distance to the food source.

▲ **FIGURE 26-27 Bee language: the waggle dance** A forager, returning from a rich source of nectar, performs a waggle dance that communicates the distance and direction of the food source as other foragers crowd around her, touching her with their antennae. The bee moves in a straight line while shaking her abdomen back and forth ("waggling") and buzzing her wings. She repeats this dance over and over in the same location, circling back in alternating directions.

information about the location of food by means of a **waggle dance** (FIG. 26-27) that is usually performed in the darkness inside a hive. Other bees crowd around the dancer, and a message is transmitted by vibrations from the dancer's moving wings and body.

Communication Aids Social Bonding

Social bonds between animals may be established or reinforced through communication by touch. For example, the return of a familiar individual to its group is facilitated by touch, as when an elephant puts its trunk in a new arrival's

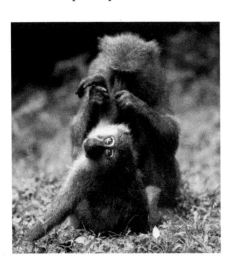

▲ **FIGURE 26-28 Grooming** An adult olive baboon grooms a juvenile. Grooming both reinforces social relationships and removes debris and parasites from the fur.

mouth, two reunited coyotes touch noses, or an ant touches a returning colony member with its antennae. Social signaling through touch is especially apparent in primates, which have many gestures—including kissing, nuzzling, patting, petting, and grooming—that facilitate social cohesion (FIG. 26-28).

CHECK YOUR LEARNING

Can you ...

- describe how signals function in aggression, courtship, and mating?
- describe how animals share information about predators and food?

26.6 WHY DO ANIMALS PLAY?

Many animals play. Pygmy hippopotamuses push one another, shake and toss their heads, splash in the water, and pirouette on their hind legs. Otters delight in elaborate acrobatics. Bottlenose dolphins balance fish on their snouts, throw objects, and carry them in their mouths while swimming. Baby vampire bats chase, wrestle, and slap each other with their wings. Even octopuses have been seen playing a game: pushing objects away from themselves and into a current, then waiting for the objects to drift back, only to push them back into the current to start the cycle over again.

Although play behavior seems easy to recognize, it is challenging to formulate a precise definition of play. A widely used definition describes **play** as behavior that seems to lack any immediate function, and that often includes modified versions of behaviors used in other contexts.

(a) Chimpanzees

(b) Polar bears

(c) Red foxes

◀ **FIGURE 26-29 Young animals at play**

Animals Play Alone or with Other Animals

Play can be solitary, as when a single animal manipulates an object, such as a cat with a ball of yarn, or when a macaque monkey makes and plays with a snowball. Play can also be social. Often, young animals of the same species play together, but parents may join them. Social play typically includes chasing, fleeing, wrestling, kicking, and gentle biting (**FIG. 26-29**).

Young animals play more frequently than do adults. Play typically borrows movements from other behaviors (attacking, fleeing, stalking, and so on) and uses considerable energy. Also, play is potentially dangerous. Many young humans and other animals are injured, and some are killed, during play. In addition, play can distract an animal from the presence of danger while making it conspicuous to predators. So why do animals play?

Play Aids Behavioral Development

It is likely that play has survival value and that natural selection has favored those individuals who engage in playful activities. One of the best explanations for the survival value of play is the *practice hypothesis*. It suggests that play allows young animals to gain experience in behaviors that they will use as adults. By performing these acts repeatedly in play, an animal practices skills that will later be important in hunting, fleeing, and social interactions.

Play is most intense early in life when the brain develops and crucial neural connections form. Species with large brains tend to be more playful than species with small brains. Because larger brains are generally linked to greater learning ability, this relationship supports the hypothesis that adult skills are learned during juvenile play. Watch children roughhousing or playing tag, and you will see how play might foster strength and coordination and develop skills that might have helped our hunting ancestors survive.

CHECK YOUR LEARNING

Can you ...

- describe the characteristics of animal play and some examples of it?
- describe a hypothesis about the function of play?

26.7 WHAT KINDS OF SOCIETIES DO ANIMALS FORM?

Sociality, the tendency to associate with others and form groups, is a widespread feature of animal life. Most animals interact at least a little with other members of their species. Many spend the bulk of their lives in the company of others, and a few species have developed complex, highly structured societies.

Group Living Has Advantages and Disadvantages

Living in a group has both costs and benefits, and a species will not evolve social behavior unless the benefits of doing so outweigh the costs. Benefits to social animals include the following:

- Increased abilities to detect, repel, and confuse predators.
- Increased hunting efficiency or increased ability to spot localized food resources.
- Advantages resulting from the potential for division of labor within the group.
- Increased likelihood of finding mates.

On the negative side, social animals may encounter:

- Increased competition for limited resources.
- Increased risk of infection from contagious diseases.
- Increased risk that offspring will be killed by other members of the group.
- Increased risk of being spotted by predators.

Sociality Varies Among Species

The degree to which animals of the same species cooperate varies from one species to the next. Some types of animals, such as the mountain lion, are basically solitary; interactions between adults consist of brief aggressive encounters and mating. Other animals form loose social groups, such as schools of fish, flocks of birds, and herds of musk oxen (FIG. 26-30). Still others form more structured social groups that may include more complex relationships among members. For example, members of a baboon troop often form alliances; if a baboon is threatened by another in the troop, the other members of its alliance may come to its defense. Similarly, male bottlenose dolphins often form alliances of two or three animals that cooperate to monopolize and

▲ FIGURE 26-30 **Cooperation in loosely organized social groups** A herd of musk oxen functions as a unit when threatened by predators such as wolves. Males form a circle, horns pointed outward, around the females and young.

▲ FIGURE 26-31 **Cooperation in a complex society** Naked mole rats are highly social rodents. The individuals in a colony belong to different castes.

defend reproductive females. Different dolphin alliances may band together to form super-alliances that engage in contests with other super-alliances to "steal" females.

In some species, social behavior includes division of labor. Consider the spider *Anelosimus studiosus*. These spiders live in groups of up to 50 that build large communal webs that capture larger prey than a solitary spider could trap on its own. Group members cooperate to rear all of the group's offspring. In this spider society, different members perform different roles. Some watch over eggs and regurgitate food to feed young spiders. Others maintain the web, capture prey, and defend the colony.

Division of labor is more extreme in the rigidly structured societies of many bees, ants, and termites, and of naked mole rats (FIG. 26-31). In these societies, individuals are born into one of several castes. For example, in naked mole rats, which live in large underground colonies in southern Africa, the colony is dominated by the *queen*, the only reproducing female, to whom all other members are subordinate *workers*. Some workers clean the tunnels and gather food. Others dig new tunnels or defend the colony against predators and members of other colonies.

A honeybee hive also contains a single queen. Her main function is to produce eggs (up to 1,000 per day). Male bees, called *drones*, serve merely as mates for the queen and die as soon as their mating duties are complete. The hive is run by sterile female workers. The workers' tasks include carrying food to the queen and to developing larvae, producing hexagonal cells of wax in which the queen deposits her eggs, cleaning the hive and removing the dead, protecting the hive against intruders, and foraging for food by gathering pollen and nectar for the hive.

Reciprocity or Relatedness May Foster the Evolution of Cooperation

In the animal societies we have described, individuals sometimes behave in ways that help others but seem to place the helper at an immediate disadvantage. A baboon helps defend another, putting itself at risk of injury. A social spider spends time and energy capturing insects for other spiders to eat. Worker bees spend their lives doing hard labor but do not reproduce. There are many other examples: Vampire bats may regurgitate part of a blood meal to feed another bat that did not find food; ground squirrels may risk their own safety to warn the rest of their group about an approaching predator; young, mature Florida scrub jays, instead of breeding, may remain at their parents' nest and help them raise subsequent broods.

At first glance, such cooperative behavior appears to be **altruism**—behavior that decreases the reproductive success of one individual to benefit another. But true altruism presents an evolutionary puzzle. If individuals perform self-sacrificing deeds that reduce their survival and reproduction, why aren't the alleles that contribute to this behavior eliminated from the gene pool?

One possibility is that cooperative behaviors that reduce an individual's fitness over the short term actually increase it over the longer term. For example, helping another individual now may pay benefits later when the favor is returned. Such *reciprocity* is most likely to be the basis of cooperation in groups that remain together for an extended period of time and in which individuals recognize and remember one another. Cooperation may also be favored when other members of the group are close relatives of the cooperating individual. Because close relatives share alleles, the altruistic individual may promote the survival of its own alleles through behaviors that maximize the survival of its close relatives. This concept is called **kin selection.** Kin selection is believed to underlie cooperation in many animal societies, perhaps including those of social insects like honeybees, whose distinctive system of sex determination produces female workers that are very genetically similar to one another.

CHECK YOUR LEARNING

Can you ...

- list the advantages and disadvantages of living in a group and describe the different degrees of sociality that occur among mammals?
- describe some hypotheses for the evolution of cooperation in animal societies?

26.8 CAN BIOLOGY EXPLAIN HUMAN BEHAVIOR?

The behaviors of humans, like those of all other animals, have an evolutionary history. Thus, the methods and concepts that help us understand and explain the behavior of other animals can help us understand and explain human behavior as well.

The Behavior of Newborn Infants Has a Large Innate Component

Because newborn infants have not had time to learn, we can assume that much of their behavior is innate. The rhythmic

▲ **FIGURE 26-32 A human instinct** Thumb sucking is a difficult habit to discourage in young children because sucking on appropriately sized objects is an instinctive, food-seeking behavior. This fetus sucks its thumb at about 4 months of development.

movement of an infant's head in search of its mother's breast is an innate behavior that is expressed in the first days after birth. Sucking, which can be observed even in a human fetus, is also innate (**FIG. 26-32**). Other behaviors seen in newborns include grasping with the hands and feet and making walking movements when the body is held upright and supported.

Another example is smiling, which can occur soon after birth. Initially, smiling can be induced by almost any object looming over the newborn. This initial innate response, however, is soon modified by experience. Infants up to 2 months old will smile in response to a stimulus consisting of two eye-sized spots, which at that stage of development is a more potent stimulus for smiling than is an accurate representation of a human face. But as the child's development continues, learning and further development of the nervous system interact to limit the response to more correct representations of a face.

Newborns prefer their mothers' voices to other female voices. Even in their first 3 days of life, infants can be conditioned to produce certain rhythms of sucking when their mother's voice is used as reinforcement (**FIG. 26-33**). The infant's ability to learn his or her mother's voice and respond positively to it within days of birth has strong parallels to imprinting and may help initiate bonding with the mother.

Young Humans Acquire Language Easily

One of the most important insights from studies of animal learning is that animals tend to have an inborn tendency for specific types of learning that are important to their species' mode of life. In humans, one such inborn tendency is for the acquisition of language. Young children are able to acquire language rapidly and nearly effortlessly; they typically acquire a vocabulary of 28,000 words before the age of 8. Research suggests that we are born with a brain that is already primed for this early facility with language. For example, a human fetus

▲ FIGURE 26-33 **Newborns prefer their mother's voice** Using a nipple connected to a computer that plays audio tapes, researcher William Fifer demonstrated that newborns can be conditioned to suck at specific rates in order to listen to their own mothers' voices through headphones. For example, if the infant sucks faster than normal, her mother's voice is played; if she sucks more slowly, another woman's voice is played. Researchers found that infants easily learned and were willing to work hard at this task just to listen to their own mothers' voices, presumably because they had become used to her voice in the womb.

begins responding to sounds during the third trimester of pregnancy, and researchers have demonstrated that infants are able to distinguish among consonant sounds by 6 weeks after birth. In one experiment, infants sucked on a pacifier that contained a force transducer to record the sucking rate. The infants were conditioned to suck at a higher rate in response to playback of adult voices making various consonant sounds. When one sound (such as "ba") was presented repeatedly, the infants became habituated and decreased their sucking rate. But when a new sound (such as "pa") was presented, sucking rate increased, revealing that the infants perceived the new sound as different.

Behaviors Shared by Diverse Cultures May Be Innate

Another way to study the innate bases of human behavior is to compare simple acts performed by people from diverse cultures. This comparative approach has revealed several gestures that seem to form a universal, and therefore probably innate, human signaling system. Such gestures include facial expressions for pleasure, rage, and disdain, and greeting movements such as an upraised hand or the "eye flash" (in which the eyes are widely opened and the eyebrows rapidly elevated). The evolution of the neural pathways underlying these gestures presumably depended on the advantages that

accrued to both senders and receivers from sharing information about the emotional state and intentions of the sender. A species-wide method of communication was perhaps especially important before the advent of language and later remained useful during encounters between people who shared no common language.

Certain complex social behaviors are widespread among diverse cultures. For example, the incest taboo (avoidance of mating with close relatives) seems to be universal across human cultures (and even across many species of non-human primates). It seems unlikely, however, that a shared belief could be encoded in our genes. Some biologists have suggested that the taboo is instead a cultural expression of an evolved, adaptive behavior. According to this hypothesis, close contact among family members early in life suppresses sexual desire, and this response arose because of the negative consequences of inbreeding (such as a higher incidence of genetic diseases). The hypothesis does not require us to assume an innate social belief, but rather proposes that we inherit a learning program that causes us to undergo a kind of imprinting early in life.

Humans May Respond to Pheromones

Although the main channels of human communication are through the eyes and ears, humans also seem to respond to chemical messages. In one experiment, for example, researchers asked nine female volunteers to wear cotton gauze in their armpits for 8 hours each day during their menstrual cycles. The gauze was then disinfected with alcohol and swabbed above the upper lips of another set of 20 female subjects (who reported that they could detect no odors other than alcohol on the gauze). The subjects were exposed to the gauze in this way each day for 2 months, with half the group sniffing armpit secretions from women in the early (preovulation) part of the menstrual cycle, while the other half was exposed to armpit secretions from later in the cycle (postovulation). Women exposed to early-cycle secretions had shorter-than-usual menstrual cycles, and women exposed to late-cycle secretions

HAVE YOU EVER WONDERED ...

Which Is the World's Loudest Animal?

Sounds louder than about 120 decibels are painful to human ears, but some animals make sounds that are far louder than that. The songs of blue whales, for example, can reach 188 decibels, louder than the noise you would hear if you stood next to a jet airplane at takeoff. But the loudest known sound from an animal is produced by a much smaller organism, the pistol shrimp. The pistol shrimp doesn't sing, but it does use a specially modified claw to shoot a high-speed jet of water that stuns its prey. An air bubble forms behind the jet, and when the bubble collapses under the surrounding water pressure, the implosion produces a sound that can reach 200 decibels, much louder than a gun firing right beside your ear.

had delayed menstruation. It appears that women release different pheromones, with different effects on receivers, at different points in the menstrual cycle.

Other research suggests that people may also be able to detect chemical indicators of fear or stress. For example, researchers performed an experiment in which they collected sweat samples from 144 people. Half the people were sampled during a first-time skydive with a 1-minute freefall; the other half (the controls) were sampled during a bout of exercise. Test subjects then smelled one of the two types of samples while undergoing brain imaging. A brain region called the amygdala, which is associated with strong emotions such as fear and rage, was active in subjects who smelled the "stress sweat" from the skydivers, but not in the subjects who smelled the exercise sweat. A chemical present in the sweat of emotionally stressed people apparently triggered a similar emotion, or at least a similar brain response, in people exposed to the chemical.

Although the experiments described above offer strong evidence for the existence of human pheromones, little else is known about chemical communication in humans. The actual molecules that caused the effects documented by these and other experiments remain unknown. Receptors for chemical messages have not yet been found in humans, and we don't know if "menstrual pheromones" and "stress pheromones" are examples of an important communication system or merely isolated cases of a vestigial ability. Despite the hopeful advertisements for "sex attraction pheromones" on late-night television, chemical communication in humans is a scientific mystery awaiting a solution.

Biological Investigation of Human Behavior Is Controversial

The study of evolved, inherited human behavior is controversial, especially among nonscientists, because it challenges the long-held belief that environment is the most important determinant of human behavior. As discussed earlier in this chapter, we now recognize that all behavior has some genetic basis and that complex behavior in non-human animals typically combines elements of both innate and learned behaviors. Thus, it seems certain that our own behavior is influenced by both our evolutionary history and our cultural heritage. The debate over the relative importance of heredity and environment in determining human behavior continues and is unlikely ever to be fully resolved. The scientific study of human behavior will always be hampered because we can neither view ourselves with detached objectivity nor experiment with people as if they were laboratory rats. Despite these limitations, there is much to be learned about the interaction of learning and innate tendencies in humans.

CHECK YOUR LEARNING

Can you ...

- describe evidence that some human behaviors and learning predispositions are innate?
- describe evidence that human behavior is influenced by pheromones?
- explain why biological investigation of human behavior is controversial?

CASE STUDY \ REVISITED
Sex and Symmetry

In the experiment described at the beginning of this chapter, women found males with the most symmetrical bodies to have the most attractive faces. But how did the women know which males were most symmetrical? After all, the researchers' measurement

▲ **FIGURE 26-34 Faces of varying symmetry** Researchers used sophisticated software to modify facial symmetry. The face at left is unaltered; the one on the right has been modified to be more symmetrical.

of male symmetry was based on small differences in the sizes of body parts that the female judges did not even see during the test.

Perhaps male body symmetry is reflected in facial symmetry, and females prefer symmetrical faces. To test this hypothesis, a group of researchers used computers to alter photos of male faces, either increasing or decreasing their symmetry (**FIG. 26-34**). Then heterosexual female observers rated each face for attractiveness. The observers had a strong preference for more symmetrical faces.

Why would females prefer to mate with symmetrical males? The most likely explanation is that symmetry indicates good physical condition. Disruptions of normal embryological development can cause bodies to be asymmetrical, so a highly symmetrical body indicates healthy, normal development. Females that mate with individuals whose health and vitality are announced by their symmetrical bodies are likely to have offspring that are similarly healthy and vital.

CONSIDER THIS Is our perception of human beauty determined by cultural standards, or is it part of our biological makeup, the product of our evolutionary heritage? What evidence would persuade you that beauty is a biological phenomenon? That it is a cultural one?

CHAPTER REVIEW

 Go to **MasteringBiology** for practice quizzes, activities, eText, videos, current events, and more.

Answers to Think Critically, Evaluate This, Multiple Choice, and Fill-in-the-Blank questions can be found in the Answers section at the back of the book.

Summary of Key Concepts

26.1 How Does Behavior Arise?

All animal behavior is influenced by both genetic and environmental factors. Biologists distinguish between innate behaviors, whose development is not highly dependent on external factors, and learned behaviors, which require more extensive experiences with environmental stimuli in order to develop. Innate behaviors can be performed properly the first time an animal encounters the appropriate stimulus, whereas learned behavior changes in response to the animal's social and physical environment.

26.2 How Do Animals Compete for Resources?

Although many competitive interactions are resolved through aggression, serious injuries are rare. Most aggressive encounters are settled by displays that communicate the motivation, size, and strength of the combatants. Some species establish dominance hierarchies that minimize aggression and determine access to resources. On the basis of initial aggressive encounters, each animal acquires a status in which it defers to more dominant individuals and, in turn, dominates subordinates. Territoriality, a behavior in which animals defend areas where important resources are located, also minimizes aggressive encounters.

26.3 How Do Animals Behave When They Mate?

Sexual selection has favored traits that help males gain access to mates and traits that help females choose beneficial mates. Males may fight to obtain mates, offer food gifts to females to induce them to mate, or defend territories that attract females. Females prefer to mate with males that win contests, offer high-quality gifts, or defend high-quality territories. Males may also compete by guarding their mates or by killing the offspring of other males. Multiple alternative mating behaviors may coexist in a species.

26.4 How Do Animals Communicate?

Communication allows animals of the same species to interact effectively in their quest for mates, food, shelter, and other resources. Animals communicate through visual signals, sound, chemicals (pheromones), and touch. Visual communication is quiet and can convey rapidly changing information. Visual signals are active (body movements) or passive (body shape and color). Sound communication can also convey rapidly changing information, and it is effective when vision is impossible. Pheromones can be detected after the sender has departed, conveying simple messages over time. Animals that associate in close proximity may communicate by touch. On average, signalers and receivers benefit from communication, but communication channels are sometimes exploited by animals that harm the communicators.

26.5 What Do Animals Communicate About?

Animals communicate to manage aggressive interactions and reduce the occurrence of potentially dangerous fighting.

Mating signals help animals recognize the species, sex, sexual receptivity, and quality of potential mates. Alarm signals warn other animals of predators. Members of a social group may use signals to share information about the location of food. Physical contact reinforces social bonds and is a part of many premating rituals.

26.6 Why Do Animals Play?

Animals of many species engage in seemingly wasteful (and sometimes dangerous) play behavior. Play behavior in young animals has been favored by natural selection, probably because it provides opportunities to practice and perfect behaviors that will later be crucial for survival and reproduction.

26.7 What Kinds of Societies Do Animals Form?

Social living has both advantages and disadvantages, and species vary in the degree to which their members cooperate. Some species form cooperative societies. The most rigid and highly organized are those of the social insects such as the honeybee, in which the members fill rigidly defined roles throughout life.

26.8 Can Biology Explain Human Behavior?

Researchers are increasingly investigating the extent to which human behavior is influenced by evolved, genetically inherited factors. This emerging field is controversial. Because we cannot freely experiment on humans, and because learning plays a major role in nearly all human behavior, investigators must rely on studies of newborn infants and comparative cultural studies. Evidence is mounting that our genetic heritage plays a role in personality, intelligence, simple universal gestures, our responses to certain stimuli, and our tendency to learn specific things such as language at particular stages of development.

Key Terms

aggression *468*	kin selection *485*
altruism *485*	learning *468*
behavior *467*	operant conditioning *470*
classical conditioning *470*	pheromone *477*
communication *476*	play *482*
dominance hierarchy *473*	social learning *471*
habituation *469*	territoriality *473*
imprinting *469*	trial-and-error
innate *467*	learning *470*
insight learning *472*	waggle dance *482*

Thinking Through the Concepts

Multiple Choice

1. When a male lizard defends a certain area, he is exhibiting
   a. insight learning.
   b. kin selection.
   c. territoriality.
   d. altruism.

2. The benefits to an individual of living in a social group include
   a. increased protection against predators.
   b. decreased competition for food.
   c. less competition for mates.
   d. lower incidence of infectious disease.

3. Very early in their lives, young chicks crouch in fear when a leaf flutters overhead. Later they learn to disregard it. This kind of learning is called
   a. imprinting.
   b. habituation.
   c. operant conditioning.
   d. insight learning.

4. Young sea turtles head for the ocean immediately after they hatch. This behavior is most likely
   a. innate.
   b. learned through trial and error.
   c. classically conditioned.
   d. the result of habituation.

5. When animals engage in _____, they often perform displays that make them look as large and dangerous as possible.
   a. courtship
   b. altruism
   c. kin selection
   d. aggression

Fill-in-the-Blank

1. In general, animal behaviors arise from an interaction between the animal's _____ and its _____. Some behaviors are performed correctly the first time an animal encounters the proper _____. Such behaviors are described as _____.

2. Play is almost certainly an adaptive behavior because it uses considerable _____, and it can distract the animal from watching for _____. The most likely explanation for why animals play is the "_____ hypothesis," which states that play teaches the young animal _____ that will be useful as a(n) _____. This hypothesis is supported by the observation that animals that have larger _____ are more likely to play.

3. One of the simplest forms of learning is _____, defined as a decline in response to a(n) _____, harmless stimulus. A different type of learning in which an animal's nervous system is rigidly programmed to learn a certain behavior during a certain period in its life is called _____. The time frame during which such learning occurs is called the _____.

4. Animals often deal with competition for resources through _____ behavior. Such conflicts are often resolved through _____, which allow the competing animals to assess each other without _____

each other. Animals that resolve conflicts this way often display their _____ and make their bodies appear _____.

5. The defense of an area where important resources are located is called _____. Examples of important resources that may be defended include places to _____, _____, _____, and _____. Such resources are most commonly defended by which sex? _____ Are these spaces usually defended against members of the same species or against members of different species? _____

6. After each form of communication, list a major advantage in the first blank and a major disadvantage in the second blank. Pheromones: _____; _____. Visual displays: _____; _____.

Review Questions

1. Explain why animals play. Include the features of play in your answer.

2. List four senses through which animals communicate, and give one example of each form of communication. For each sense listed, present both advantages and disadvantages of that form of communication.

3. A bird will ignore a squirrel in its territory, but will act aggressively toward a member of its own species. Explain why.

4. Why are most aggressive encounters among members of the same species relatively harmless?

5. Discuss the advantages and disadvantages of group living.

6. What kinds of evidence might indicate that a particular human behavior is innate?

Applying the Concepts

1. Male mosquitoes orient toward the high-pitched whine of the female, and female mosquitoes, the only sex that sucks blood, are attracted to the warmth, humidity, and carbon dioxide exuded by their prey. Using this information, design a mosquito trap or killer that exploits a mosquito's innate behaviors. Then design one for moths.

2. Describe and give an example of a dominance hierarchy. What role does it play in social behavior? Give a human parallel, and describe its role in human society. Are the two roles similar? Why or why not? Repeat this exercise for territorial behavior in humans and in another animal.

3. You are the manager of an airport. Planes are being endangered by large numbers of flying birds, which can be sucked into and disable the engines. Without harming the birds, what might you do to discourage them from nesting and flying near the airport and its planes?

POPULATION GROWTH AND REGULATION

Northern elephant seals were hunted almost to extinction in the 1800s. Today, they are a tourist attraction on the central California coast.

The Return of the Elephant Seals

In the eighteenth and early nineteenth centuries, oil for lamps and for lubricating machine parts was often harvested from whales. In the mid-1800s, as hunting depleted whale populations in the eastern Pacific near California and Mexico, whalers turned to northern elephant seals as an alternative source of oil. A large bull, which might be 15 feet long and weigh over 5,000 pounds, could produce more than 100 gallons of oil.

Although no one knows for certain, there were probably a couple of hundred thousand elephant seals in the mid-1800s. Each year, in the early winter, thousands of bulls emerged from the Pacific onto the beaches of islands off the coast of southern California and Baja California, Mexico. A month or two later, smaller but much more abundant females would haul out on the same beaches. Some beaches were so packed with seals that hunters had to wait for the seals to get out of the way before they could land their boats.

Being such easy targets, elephant seals were slaughtered by the tens of thousands. Within about 20 years, elephant seals had all but disappeared. Between 1884 and 1892, not a single elephant seal was sighted anywhere. Because elephant seals had become so rare, museum expeditions searched year after year, looking for specimens for their collections. In 1892, a Smithsonian expedition found 9 seals on Isla de Guadalupe, about 150 miles off the coast of Baja California (and killed 7 as specimens). Modern molecular research suggests that as few as 10 to 20 seals remained alive in the late 1800s. These few seals bred on isolated beaches, and the population slowly increased. Still, an intensive search of Isla de Guadalupe in 1922 found only 264 seals. The Mexican government then banned killing or capturing elephant seals and even put soldiers on Isla de Guadalupe to enforce the ban. The United States banned elephant seal hunting soon thereafter.

Today, there are about 200,000 elephant seals, breeding on both islands and mainland beaches, including popular viewing locations such as Año Nuevo and San Simeon in central California. In this chapter, we will study the growth of populations, from bacteria to seals to people. How fast can populations grow? How long can populations keep increasing? Since Earth is not blanketed with elephant seals or any other species of plant or animal, there must be natural conditions that slow down and stop population growth; what are some of those limiting factors?

AT A GLANCE

27.1 WHAT IS A POPULATION AND HOW DOES POPULATION SIZE CHANGE?

A **population** consists of all the members of a particular species that live in a specific area and can potentially breed with one another (see Fig. 1-10). Each population forms part of a **community,** defined as a group of interacting populations of multiple species living in the same area. A community and the nonliving components of the area (for example, soil, air, and water) form an **ecosystem** (from the Greek word *oikos*, a place to live). A natural ecosystem can be as small as a pond or as large as an ocean; it can be a field, a forest, or an island. All of the ecosystems in the entire habitable surface of Earth comprise the **biosphere. Ecology** is the study of the interrelationships of organisms with one another and with their nonliving environment. We begin our exploration of ecology with an overview of populations.

Changes in Population Size Result from Natural Increase and Net Migration

In natural ecosystems, some populations remain fairly stable in size over time, some undergo yearly cycles, and still others change, often dramatically, in response to complex environmental variables. For example, if members of a species invade new territory, such as an island, their population may grow rapidly for a while, but then the population usually either stabilizes or plummets.

Population size changes through births, deaths, and net migration. The **natural increase** of a population is the difference between births and deaths. Although it may sound strange, natural increase can be negative (a decrease) if deaths exceed births. The net migration of a population is the difference between **immigration** (migration into the population) and **emigration** (migration out). A population grows when the sum of natural increase and net migration is positive and declines when this sum is negative. The equation for the change in population size within a given time span is:

$$\begin{array}{ccc} \text{change in} & = & \text{natural increase} & + & \text{net migration} \\ \text{population size} & & \text{(births − deaths)} & & \text{(immigration − emigration)} \end{array}$$

In the wild, most migration is emigration of young animals out of a population. For example, the term "lone wolf" comes from young wolves that emigrate from their home packs and immigrate into new areas where they may join an existing pack or (if they find a mate) start a pack of their own. As the members of a population reproduce, emigration may help to keep the original population at a size that is relatively stable and consistent with the resources available to support it. Although migration is significant in some natural populations, for simplicity, we will ignore migration and use only birth and death rates in our calculations of population growth.

CASE STUDY CONTINUED
The Return of the Elephant Seals

In 1960, about 14,000 elephant seals used the beaches of Isla de Guadalupe, over 90% of the total population at that time. As Guadalupe became crowded, the seals looked for new beaches. Because many seals migrated to new territory in California, immigration was an important factor in elephant seal population growth on California beaches and islands during the mid and late 1900s. But why did the Mexican beaches become crowded? And why are California beaches becoming crowded with elephant seals today?

Birth Rate, Death Rate, and the Initial Population Size Affect the Growth of Populations

Growing populations add individuals in proportion to the population's size, much like a bank account accumulates compound interest: Large bank accounts earn more money from interest than small ones do, even if the interest rate is the same. The **growth rate (r)** of a population is the change in population size per individual per unit time (we will use 1 year in our examples). A population's growth rate equals its **birth rate (b),** the births per individual per unit time, minus its **death rate (d),** the deaths per individual per unit time:

$$\begin{array}{ccccc} b & - & d & = & r \\ \text{(birth rate)} & & \text{(death rate)} & & \text{(growth rate)} \end{array}$$

If the birth rate exceeds the death rate, the population growth rate will be positive and population size will increase. If the death rate exceeds the birth rate, the growth rate will be negative and population size will decrease. Birth and death rates are expressed as percentages or decimal fractions; for example, if half the population dies each year, then the death rate is 50%, or 0.5.

Let's calculate the growth rate of a herd of 100 adult white-tail deer, with 50 males and 50 females. Adult female white-tails typically give birth to twins each year, so the population produces 100 fawns (50 does × 2 fawns per doe = 100 fawns). The birth rate, therefore, is 1.0 births per individual per year.

We'll simplify the biology of white-tail deer and assume that female fawns mature and produce their own fawns the very next year. Predators and hunting kill many fawns and some adults, perhaps 70 each year, for a death rate of 0.7. The annual growth rate per individual, therefore, is 0.3:

$$\underset{\text{(birth rate)}}{1.0} \quad - \quad \underset{\text{(death rate)}}{0.7} \quad = \quad \underset{\text{(growth rate)}}{0.3}$$

To calculate population growth per unit time (G), we multiply the growth rate (r) by the population size (N) at the beginning of the time interval:

$$\underset{\substack{\text{(population growth} \\ \text{per unit time)}}}{G} \quad = \quad \underset{\text{(growth rate)}}{r} \quad \times \quad \underset{\text{(population size)}}{N}$$

The growth of the deer herd during the first year (G) is 0.3 × 100 = 30. At a constant growth rate (r), G and N both increase with each successive time interval. In our example, the herd begins its second year with 130 deer (the new value of N). If r remains the same, then the herd adds 39 deer (the new value of G) during this second year (0.3 × 130 = 39), for a total population of 169. In the third year, the herd adds 51 deer (0.3 × 169 = 51), and so on.

Real populations, of course, never follow this equation exactly. Rather, the equation only provides estimates of population sizes over time. Further, environmental conditions never remain the same for very long, so the birth and death rates of real populations fluctuate from year to year.

A Constant Positive Growth Rate Results in Exponential Growth

As this example shows, a constant positive growth rate adds ever-increasing numbers to a population during each succeeding time period; this is called **exponential growth.** If the size of an exponentially growing population is graphed against time, a characteristic shape called a **J-curve** will be produced (**FIG. 27-1**). Note that exponential growth does not require high growth rates. As you can see in Figure 27-1, exponential growth occurs at any constant positive rate of growth.

Differences in growth rates between populations or during changing environmental conditions can occur because of differences in birth rates, death rates, or both. Our deer herd, for example, might change from a growth rate of 0.3 to a growth rate of 0.1 either by a decreased birth rate (say from 1.0 to 0.8 per individual per year, perhaps because the does don't get enough food in a drought year) or by an increased death rate (from 0.7 to 0.9, if the number of predators increases). Of course, many different combinations of changes in birth and death rates could also reduce the growth rate to 0.1 per individual per year.

The Biotic Potential Is the Maximum Rate at Which a Population Can Grow

How many offspring an organism can produce is an inherited trait. Although the average number of offspring an individual produces each year varies from millions (for an oyster) to one or fewer (for people, porcupines, or elephants), a healthy organism of any species has the potential to replace itself many times during its reproductive lifetime. The **biotic potential** is the maximum rate at which a particular population can increase. Estimations of biotic potential for each species assume ideal conditions (unlimited resources, no predators, no diseases) that allow a maximum birth rate and a minimum death rate.

Factors that influence biotic potential include the following:

- The age of first reproduction
- The frequency of reproduction
- The average number of offspring produced each time the organism reproduces
- The organism's reproductive life span
- The death rate under ideal conditions

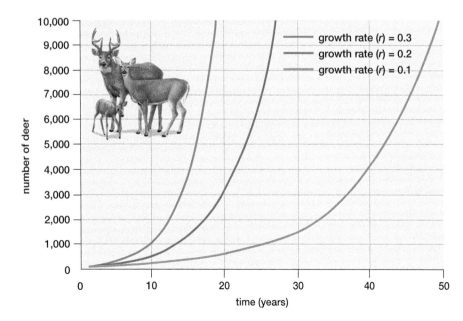

◀ **FIGURE 27-1 Exponential growth** The graph shows the growth of three hypothetical populations of deer, each starting with 100 adults with the same birth rate (1.0 per individual per year), but differing in death rate (0.7 to 0.9 per individual per year), producing three different growth rates: 0.3, 0.2, and 0.1 per individual per year. Any positive rate of growth produces an exponential (J-shaped) growth curve, but higher growth rates lead to higher populations much more quickly.

In modern times, Michelle Duggar of Arkansas probably comes close to demonstrating the realistic biotic potential of humans. Between 1988 and 2009, she gave birth to 19 children (including two sets of twins), all of whom remained healthy as of 2015. Duggar also had two miscarriages. Had all of her pregnancies resulted in live births, she would have borne about one child a year, for a little over 20 years. To see the population growth that this biotic potential can produce, let's start with one woman bearing one child each year from age 20 to age 40. Let's assume that half her children are female and that they all continue to bear children at this same reproductive rate, and then factor in reasonable estimates for death rates at various ages. In 100 years, this one woman could have 2.5 million descendants, and in 200 years, she could have almost 3 trillion!

How Many Children One Woman Can Bear?

A species with a low biotic potential, such as elephants (females may reproduce only once every 5 years), may take many years to reach the same population size that a species with a very high biotic potential, such as houseflies (which reproduce every few weeks), could reach in just a few months. Regardless of a species' biotic potential, however, unchecked exponential growth, even at very low rates, would eventually result in a staggering population size.

CHECK YOUR LEARNING

Can you ...

- explain how migration and natural increase cause population sizes to change?
- describe how population growth is calculated and how the growth rate interacts with population size to determine how populations grow per unit time?
- define *biotic potential* and list the factors that influence it?

CASE STUDY \ **CONTINUED**
The Return of the Elephant Seals

Female elephant seals reach sexual maturity at 3 to 4 years of age and produce one pup each year. Elephant seals breed harem-style, with a single large bull typically monopolizing and inseminating 30 to 100 females. Although males reach sexual maturity at 5 to 7 years of age, few are powerful enough to acquire a harem until 7 to 10 years of age; some are never able to compete. Further, although the maximum life span is about 20 years for females and 15 for males, only about 1 in 5 survives beyond 5 years of age. These factors combine to produce a biotic potential of about 12% per year. But elephant seal populations virtually never reproduce at their biotic potential. Why not?

27.2 HOW IS POPULATION GROWTH REGULATED?

In 1859, Charles Darwin wrote, "There is no exception to the rule that every organic being naturally increases at so high a rate that, if not destroyed, the Earth would soon be covered by the progeny of a single pair." In other words, a population cannot continue to grow indefinitely. In the following sections we discuss how population size results from the interaction between biotic potential and **environmental resistance,** which consists of all the factors that limit population growth, imposed by both the living and nonliving parts of the environment. Environmental resistance includes interactions among organisms, such as predation and competition for limited resources, and events such as freezing weather, storms, fires, floods, and droughts.

Exponential Growth in Natural Populations Is Always Temporary

Environmental resistance ensures that no natural population experiences exponential growth for very long.

Exponential Growth Occurs in Populations with Boom-and-Bust Cycles

Exponential growth occurs in populations that undergo regular cycles in which rapid population growth is followed by a sudden, massive die-off. These **boom-and-bust cycles** occur in a variety of organisms. Many short-lived, rapidly reproducing species—from photosynthetic microorganisms to insects—have seasonal population cycles that are linked to changes in rainfall, temperature, or nutrient availability, as is shown for a population of photosynthetic bacteria in FIGURE 27-2. Boom-and-bust cycles in these and other aquatic microorganisms can impact human health, as described in "Earth Watch: Boom-and-Bust Cycles Can Be Bad News" on page 494.

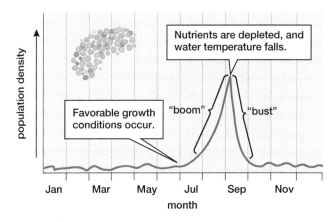

▲ **FIGURE 27-2 A boom-and-bust population cycle in photosynthetic bacteria** The density of a hypothetical population of photosynthetic bacteria in a lake. These microorganisms persist at a low level until early July. Then conditions become favorable for growth, and exponential growth occurs until early September, when the population plummets.

Earth WATCH — Boom-and-Bust Cycles Can Be Bad News

Although documented since Biblical times, during the past few decades, population explosions of sometimes toxic, single-celled photosynthetic protists and bacteria have occurred with increasing frequency throughout the world. Collectively called *harmful algal blooms (HABs)*, these population booms of toxic microorganisms kill fish and sicken people. They also cause major economic losses to the shellfish industry because clams, mussels, and scallops feed on these organisms and concentrate the poisons in their bodies, posing a hazard to human consumers. Some of the most damaging poisons are neurotoxins produced by dinoflagellates (protists), such as *Karenia brevis* (**FIG. E27-1**), which can reach densities of 20 million per liter of water. This and other protist species can cause red tides (see Fig. 21-9) that result in massive fish kills, usually in late summer.

Many of the bacteria and protists that produce harmful algal blooms are common residents of lakes and coastal waters. What causes these species to "bloom and boom"? Although the reasons are complex and vary with the species, warm water temperatures and adequate nutrients, such as phosphorus and nitrogen, are always required. Runoff of these nutrients from human agricultural activities has increased the frequency and intensity of HABs throughout the world. Global climate change may also contribute to the problem, because warmer waters foster more rapid growth of

◀ **FIGURE E27-1 One cause of harmful algal blooms** The dinoflagellate *Karenia brevis* (seen in this artificially colored SEM) causes harmful algal blooms in coastal waters of Florida and in the Gulf of Mexico. These blooms are sometimes called red tides, although the actual colors vary.

these protists and extend their growing season. The booming populations "bust" when the enormous populations of cells deplete the local water of nutrients and falling water temperatures in the autumn and winter further decrease their reproductive rate.

THINK CRITICALLY There are three major ways to minimize the effects of HABs: prevent their occurrence, disrupt or destroy ongoing blooms, and (to reduce human impacts) educate people about actions to take in case of a bloom. Find out more about each of these remedies. Which would be most preferable in the long run? Which are applicable right now? What are their costs and likely benefits?

In temperate climates, insect populations grow rapidly during the spring and summer, then crash with the freezing weather of winter. Female houseflies, for example, lay about 120 eggs at a time. The eggs hatch, and the resulting flies mature within 2 weeks. Thus, in many climates, seven generations can occur during spring and summer. If there were no environmental resistance, the seventh generation would "boom" to about 6 trillion flies—all descended from a single pregnant female. The actual population, of course, would be less than this, because many would be eaten by birds and bats or die from bacterial infections or other causes, but the fly population in early fall can still be very large. The "bust" part of the cycle occurs because hard frosts in autumn kill virtually all of the adults. However, a relatively small number of eggs survive the winter to start the cycle over again the following spring.

More complex factors can produce roughly 3- to 4-year boom-and-bust cycles for small rodents such as voles and lemmings (**FIG. 27-3**) and longer population cycles for hares, muskrats, and grouse. Lemming populations, for example, may grow until they overgraze their fragile arctic tundra ecosystem. Lack of food, increasing populations of predators, and social stress caused by crowding contribute to a sudden high mortality. Many more deaths occur as waves of lemmings emigrate from regions of high population density. During these mass migrations, lemmings are easy targets for predators. Many others drown as they encounter bodies of water and attempt to swim across. The reduced lemming

population eventually contributes to a decline in predator numbers, as well as a recovery of the plants on which the lemmings feed. These responses, in turn, set the stage for the next round of explosive growth in the lemming population.

Exponential Growth May Occur Temporarily if Environmental Resistance Is Reduced

In populations that do not experience boom-and-bust cycles, exponential growth may nevertheless occur under

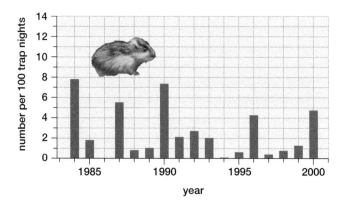

▲ **FIGURE 27-3 Boom-and-bust population cycles in a lemming population in the Canadian Arctic** This population follows a roughly 3- to 4-year cycle of boom and bust. The data are based on live trapping.

THINK CRITICALLY What factors might make these population data somewhat erratic?

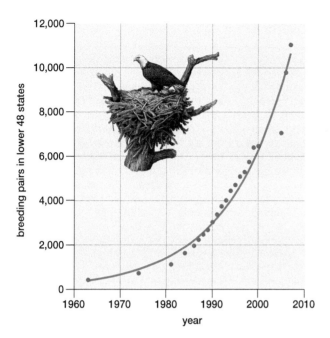

▲ **FIGURE 27-4 Exponential growth of the bald eagle population in the lower 48 United States** Hunting and the pesticide DDT reduced the bald eagle population in the lower 48 states to fewer than 500 nesting pairs in the early 1960s. Protection from hunting and banning DDT allowed the eagle population to grow exponentially for several decades, to more than 11,000 pairs by 2007. The smooth line is an exponential J-curve fit to the data points. Data from the U.S. Fish and Wildlife Service and the Center for Biological Diversity.

special circumstances—for example, if food supply or habitat is increased, if predation is reduced, or if other environmental conditions improve. For example, before 1940, bald eagles in the United States were hunted, as were some of their favored prey species. Hunting, disturbing nests, or harassing eagles was prohibited in 1940, but shortly after World War II, the insecticide DDT became widely used. An unintended side effect of DDT was to cause eagles to lay eggs with thin shells; the parents often crushed them during incubation (see "Health Watch: Biological Magnification of Toxic Substances" in Chapter 29 for more information). By the early 1960s there were only a few hundred nesting pairs of bald eagles in the lower 48 states. DDT was banned in the United States in 1972.

Protection from hunting and reduced DDT in the environment allowed bald eagle populations to grow exponentially between the early 1960s and 2007, to about 11,000 nesting pairs (**FIG. 27-4**).

Exponential growth may also occur when individuals invade a new habitat with favorable conditions and little competition. **Invasive species** (see Chapter 28) are organisms with a high biotic potential that have been introduced (deliberately or accidentally) into ecosystems where they did not evolve and where they encounter little environmental resistance. Invasive species often show explosive population growth. For example, people introduced a few thousand cane toads into Australia in the 1930s to control beetles that were destroying sugar cane crops. In their new environment, cane toads, with their poisonous skin, suffered very little predation. Cane toads also have a high biotic potential; females lay 7,000 to 35,000 eggs at a time. Spreading outward from their release point, cane toads now inhabit nearly 400,000 square miles in Australia and are migrating rapidly into new habitats, currently at a rate of about 30 miles a year. The cane toad population is now estimated at well over 200 million and growing. But even cane toads cannot increase their population forever. Why not?

Environmental Resistance Limits Population Growth Through Density-Dependent and Density-Independent Mechanisms

In all populations, environmental resistance eventually stops exponential growth.

Logistic Growth Occurs When New Populations Stabilize as a Result of Environmental Resistance

The maximum population size that can be sustained indefinitely without damage to an ecosystem is called the ecosystem's **carrying capacity (K).** Nutrients, energy, and space are the primary determinants of carrying capacity in many species. **Logistic population growth** is characteristic of populations that increase up to their environment's carrying capacity and then stabilize (**FIG. 27-5**). The curve that results when logistic growth is graphed is called an **S-curve,** after

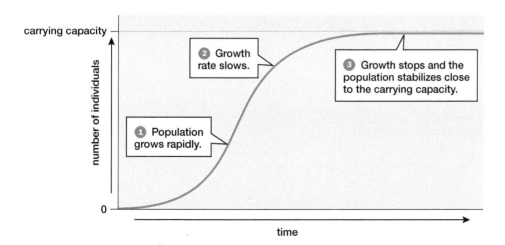

◀ **FIGURE 27-5 Logistic population growth** During logistic growth, a population begins growing exponentially, but the growth rate slows as the population encounters increasing density-dependent environmental resistance. Population growth finally ceases at or near carrying capacity (*K*). The result is a curve shaped like a "lazy S."

IN GREATER DEPTH | Logistic Population Growth

The equation for logistic population growth is:

$$G = rN\frac{(K - N)}{K}$$

This equation starts with the formula for exponential growth, $G = r \times N$, and multiplies the right-hand side by a factor, $(K - N)/K$, that models density-dependent environmental resistance. This new factor increasingly limits growth as the population size approaches the carrying capacity of its environment.

To see why, let's start with the value $(K - N)$. When we subtract the current population (N) from the carrying capacity (K), we get the number of individuals that can be added to the current

population before it reaches carrying capacity. Now, if we divide this number by K, we get a fraction that expresses how far the population is from carrying capacity. If the fraction is close to 1.0, then the population is very small relative to the carrying capacity; as the fraction approaches 0, the population is getting closer and closer to its carrying capacity.

For example, consider a population of 10 foxes introduced onto an island with a carrying capacity of 1,000 foxes. The initial population ($N = 10$) is small, and the factor $(K - N)/K = (1,000 - 10)/1,000 = 990/1000$, or 0.99. The logistic growth equation therefore becomes $G = r \times N \times 0.99$, which is virtually identical to the expo-

nential growth equation, $G = r \times N$. However, as N increases over time, $K - N$ becomes smaller and smaller, and the population growth curve begins to level off. When there are 900 foxes, $(1,000 - 900)/1,000 = 0.1$, so the logistic growth equation becomes $G = r \times N \times 0.1$, and the population growth rate is now only one-tenth as fast as the exponential growth equation would predict. When N equals K, then $(K - N) = 0$, and population growth will cease: $G = r \times N \times 0 = 0$, as illustrated by the final horizontal portion of the logistic curve (see Fig. 27-5). Therefore, when our fox population reaches the island's carrying capacity of 1,000, it stabilizes at about this number.

---

its general shape. "In Greater Depth: Logistic Population Growth" explains why logistic growth results in a population that stabilizes at carrying capacity.

An increase in population size above carrying capacity may be sustained for a short time. However, a population above its carrying capacity is living at the expense of resources that cannot regenerate as fast as they are being used up. A small overshoot above K is likely to be followed by a decrease in population, to a level below the original carrying capacity, until the resources recover and the original carrying capacity is restored. Repeated episodes of small overshoots and undershoots result in a population size that fluctuates around the carrying capacity (the green line in FIG. 27-6).

If a population far exceeds the carrying capacity of its environment, the consequences are more severe, because in this situation, the excess demands placed on the ecosystem are likely to destroy essential resources that may be unable to recover. This can permanently and severely reduce K, causing the population to decline to a fraction of its former size and then stabilize (the blue line in Fig. 27-6) or to disappear entirely (the red line in Fig. 27-6). For example, when reindeer were introduced onto St. Paul, an island off the coast of Alaska that lacks large predators, the reindeer population increased rapidly, seriously overgrazing the lichens that were their principal food source. Starvation then caused the reindeer population to plummet, as shown in FIGURE 27-7.

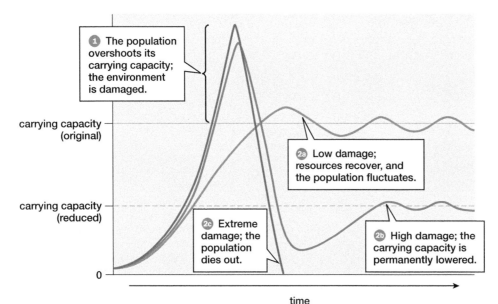

◀ **FIGURE 27-6 Consequences of exceeding carrying capacity** Populations can overshoot carrying capacity (K), but only for a limited time. Three possible results are illustrated.

① The population overshoots its carrying capacity; the environment is damaged.

2a Low damage; resources recover, and the population fluctuates.

2c Extreme damage; the population dies out.

2b High damage; the carrying capacity is permanently lowered.

carrying capacity (original)

carrying capacity (reduced)

0

time

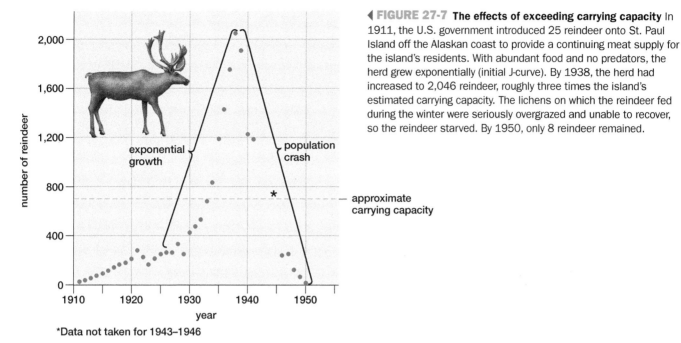

◀ FIGURE 27-7 **The effects of exceeding carrying capacity** In 1911, the U.S. government introduced 25 reindeer onto St. Paul Island off the Alaskan coast to provide a continuing meat supply for the island's residents. With abundant food and no predators, the herd grew exponentially (initial J-curve). By 1938, the herd had increased to 2,046 reindeer, roughly three times the island's estimated carrying capacity. The lichens on which the reindeer fed during the winter were seriously overgrazed and unable to recover, so the reindeer starved. By 1950, only 8 reindeer remained.

Logistic population growth can occur in nature when a species moves into a new habitat, as ecologist Joseph Connell demonstrated for barnacle populations colonizing bare rock along a rocky ocean shoreline (FIG. 27-8). Initially, new settlers may find ideal conditions that allow their population to grow exponentially. As population density increases, however, individuals increasingly compete with one another, particularly for space, energy, and nutrients. Laboratory experiments using fruit flies have shown that competition for resources can control population size by reducing both the birth rate and the average life span. During logistic population growth, as environmental resistance increases, population growth slows and eventually stops at approximately the carrying capacity of the environment. In nature,

conditions are never completely stable, so carrying capacity and population size usually fluctuate somewhat from year to year (the green and blue lines in Fig. 27-6).

Two forms of environmental resistance restrict population growth. **Density-independent** factors limit population size regardless of the population density (the number of individuals per unit area). **Density-dependent** factors, in contrast, increase in effectiveness as the population density increases.

Density-Independent Factors Limit Populations Regardless of Density

The most important natural density-independent factors are weather (short-term atmospheric conditions such as temperature, rainfall, and wind) and climate (long-term weather patterns), which are responsible for most boom-and-bust population cycles. For example, in temperate climates, populations of many insects and annual plants are limited in size by the number of individuals that can be produced before the first hard freeze. Such populations are controlled by the climate because they typically do not reach carrying capacity before winter sets in. Hurricanes, floods, droughts, and fire can also have profound effects on local populations, regardless of density.

Density-Dependent Factors Become More Effective As Population Density Increases

For long-lived species, the most important elements of environmental resistance are density-dependent factors, such as consumer-prey interactions (including predation and parasitism) and competition, which limit population growth more strongly as population density increases.

Predators Exert Density-Dependent Controls on Populations
Predators are organisms that eat other organisms, called their **prey.** We will use a broad definition of predators, to

▲ **FIGURE 27-8 A logistic curve in nature** Barnacles are crustaceans whose larvae are carried in ocean currents to rocky seashores where they settle, attach permanently to rock, and grow into the shelled adult form. On a bare rock, the number of settling larvae and newly metamorphosed juveniles produces a logistic growth curve as competition for space limits their population density.

(a) Predators often kill weakened prey

(b) Predator populations often increase when prey are abundant

▲ **FIGURE 27-9** **Predators help control prey populations (a)** A pack of grey wolves has brought down an elk that may have been weakened by age or parasites. **(b)** The snowy owl produces more chicks when prey (such as lemmings) are abundant.

include both *carnivores* (animals that eat other animals) and *herbivores* (animals that eat plants). Often, prey are killed directly and eaten (FIG. 27-9a), but not always. When deer browse on the buds of bushes and young trees, for example, or when gypsy moth larvae feed on the leaves of oaks, the plants are harmed but usually not killed.

Predators often eat a variety of prey, depending on which is most abundant and easiest to find. Coyotes might eat more field mice when the mouse population is high, but switch to eating more ground squirrels as the mouse population declines. In this way, predators often exert density-dependent population control over more than one prey population.

Predator populations often grow as their prey becomes more abundant, which make them even more effective as control agents. For predators such as the arctic fox and snowy owl, which rely heavily on lemmings for food, the number of offspring they can produce is determined by the abundance of prey. Snowy owls (FIG. 27-9b) hatch up to 12 chicks when lemmings are abundant, but may not reproduce at all in years when the lemming population has crashed.

In some cases, an increase in predators might cause a dramatic decline in the prey population, which in turn may result in an eventual decline in the predator population. This pattern can result in out-of-phase **population cycles** of predators and prey. In natural ecosystems, both predators and prey are subjected to a variety of other influences, so clear-cut examples of such cycles in nature are rare. However, out-of-phase population cycles of predators and their prey have been demonstrated under controlled laboratory conditions (FIG. 27-10).

Predators may contribute to the overall health of prey populations by culling those individuals that are poorly adapted, weakened by age or disease, or unable to find adequate food and shelter. In this way, predation may maintain healthy prey populations near a density that can be sustained by the resources of the ecosystem.

Parasites Spread More Rapidly in Dense Populations A **parasite** is an organism that lives in or on a larger organism, called its **host,** feeding on the host and harming it. Although some kill their hosts, many parasites benefit by having their host remain alive. Parasites include tapeworms that live in the intestines of mammals, lice that cling to a host's skin or hair, and disease-causing microorganisms. Parasites are density-dependent factors: Because most parasites cannot easily travel long distances, they spread more readily among hosts with dense populations. For example, plant diseases often spread rapidly through densely planted crops, and childhood diseases spread swiftly through schools and day-care centers. Even when parasites do not kill their hosts directly, they influence population size by weakening their hosts and making them more susceptible to death from other causes, such as harsh weather or predators. Organisms weakened by parasites are also less likely to reproduce. Parasites, like predators, often contribute to the death of less-fit individuals, producing a balance in which the host population is regulated but not eliminated.

This balance can be destroyed if parasites or predators are introduced into regions where local prey species have had no opportunity to evolve defenses against them. For example, the smallpox virus, inadvertently carried by traveling Europeans during colonial times, caused heavy loss of life among native inhabitants of North America, Hawaii, South America, and Australia. The chestnut blight fungus, introduced from Asia, has almost eliminated chestnut trees from U.S. forests. Introduced predators, such as rats and mongooses, have exterminated several of Hawaii's native birds.

Competition for Resources Helps Control Populations The resources that usually determine carrying capacity—space, energy, and nutrients—may be inadequate to support all the organisms that need them. **Competition,** interactions among individuals attempting to use the same finite resources, limits population size in a density-dependent manner. There are two major forms of competition:

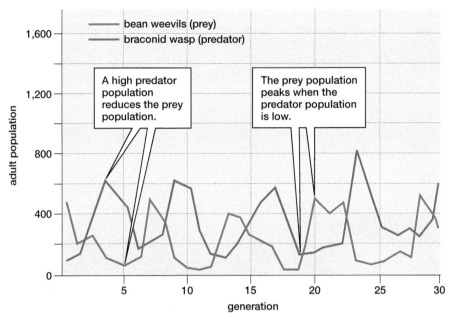

◀ **FIGURE 27-10 Experimental predator–prey cycles** Tiny braconid wasps lay their eggs on bean weevil larvae, which provide food for the newly hatched wasp larvae. A large weevil population ensures a high survival rate for wasp offspring, increasing the predator population. Then, under intense predation, the weevil population plummets, reducing the food available to the next generation of wasps, whose population declines as a result. Reduced predation then allows the weevil population to increase rapidly, and so on.

interspecific competition (competition among individuals of different species) and **intraspecific competition** (competition among individuals of the same species). Because the needs of members of the same species for water and nutrients, shelter, breeding sites, and other resources are almost identical, intraspecific competition is an extremely important density-dependent mechanism of population control.

When population densities increase and competition becomes intense, some types of animals, for example, lemmings and locusts, react by emigrating. Emigrating swarms of locusts periodically plague parts of Africa, consuming all vegetation in their path (**FIG. 27-11**).

Density-Independent and Density-Dependent Factors Interact

The size of a population at any given time is the result of complex interactions between density-independent and density-dependent forms of environmental resistance. For example, a stand of pines weakened by drought (a density-independent factor) may more readily fall victim to the pine bark beetle (density-dependent). Likewise, a caribou weakened by hunger (density-dependent) and attacked by parasites (density-dependent) is more likely to be killed by an exceptionally cold winter (density-independent). Human activities increasingly impose both density-independent and density-dependent limitations on natural populations. Examples include bulldozing grasslands and their prairie dog towns to build shopping malls and housing tracts or felling rain forests to replace them with croplands: A high percentage of the prairie dogs or rain-forest animals will be exterminated, regardless of the population density before the land was cleared, so the initial effect of these human actions is density-independent. However, some of the animals may be able to move to nearby undisturbed habitat, increasing the population density in these areas. The resulting increased competition for food, nesting places, and other essentials will exert density-dependent controls on these now-larger populations. In some cases, the increased population density could result in overexploitation of crucial resources such as prey animals or nutritious plants, causing population crashes (see Figs. 27-6 and 27-7).

▶ **FIGURE 27-11 Emigration** In response to overcrowding and lack of food, locusts emigrate in swarms, devouring nearly all vegetation (and even feeding on each other) as they go.

THINK CRITICALLY What benefits does mass emigration give to animals such as locusts or lemmings? Are there parallels to human emigrations?

CHECK YOUR LEARNING

Can you ...

- describe exponential growth, the conditions under which it occurs, and what shape of curve it produces?
- explain the stages of the logistic growth curve and describe the possible outcomes when populations overshoot carrying capacity?
- describe the two major forms of environmental resistance and provide examples of each?

CASE STUDY \ **CONTINUED**

The Return of the Elephant Seals

Elephant seal populations experience both density-dependent and density-independent environmental resistance. Density-dependent factors include predation by great white sharks and orcas (probably a minor factor), potential food scarcity (unknown impact), and deaths during reproduction, which is probably the major density-dependent factor. The dominant males chase challengers away from their harems, stressing the females and sometimes crushing pups beneath tons of charging bull; the denser the seal population on the beach, the more pups are lost. El Niño weather years often bring strong storms to California, causing density-independent environmental resistance. Storms erode the beaches; high tides and waves sometimes submerge beaches and wash away pups. In severe El Niño years, as many as half the pups in a colony may be lost. Overall, however, elephant seals have secure breeding sites, abundant food, and few predators, and their populations are stable or increasing. Does this mean that their future is secure? Find out in "Case Study Revisited" at the end of the chapter.

27.3 HOW DO LIFE HISTORY STRATEGIES DIFFER AMONG SPECIES?

As you learned in Chapter 15, natural selection favors traits that promote the production of offspring that, in turn, survive and reproduce. All organisms have limited resources to invest in their offspring and in their own survival; no organism can produce endless numbers of offspring and provide extensive parental care for all of them. The resulting **life history** strategies—when to reproduce, how many offspring to produce at a time, and how much energy and resources to devote to each offspring—vary tremendously among species.

Many factors influence life history strategies. Important considerations are the stability of a species' environment, the mortality rate and the accompanying likelihood of multiple opportunities to reproduce before dying, and the likelihood that a population can reach, and remain at, the carrying capacity of its environment. Species occupying the two extremes of life history strategies are often called *r*-selected species and *K*-selected species, named after the *r* (rate of growth)

and *K* (carrying capacity) terms, respectively, in the logistic growth equation (see "In Greater Depth: Logistic Population Growth").

At one extreme, ***r*-selected species** typically live in a rapidly changing, unpredictable environment and are unlikely to reach carrying capacity before catastrophe intervenes: a hard freeze in temperate climates, months of drought in a desert, or (for parasites) the death of a host. These species have typically evolved characteristics that favor rapid reproduction (hence the term *r*-selected). They mature rapidly, have a short life span, produce a large number of small offspring, and provide little parental care (**FIG. 27-12a**). It is common for *r*-selected species to reproduce just a few times,

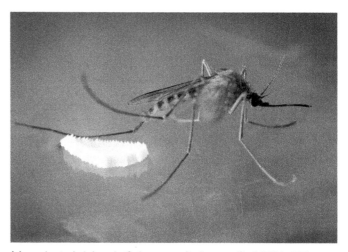

(a) *r*-selected: A female *Culex* mosquito lays a raft of 100 to 300 eggs every few days.

(b) *K*-selected: An African bush elephant and its calf.

▲ **FIGURE 27-12 Typical *r*-selected and *K*-selected species** **(a)** Most mosquitoes of the genus *Culex* have short life spans, produce numerous small eggs, and provide no parental care. Most offspring are eaten by predators in the larval stage. **(b)** African bush elephants have long life spans, produce single offspring after a 21-month-long pregnancy, and nurse their young for several years. Although a few infants fall prey to lions, elephants have no significant natural predators. Unless they fall victim to human poachers, elephants have a very high chance of surviving until old age.

sometimes only once, in their lives. The vast majority of the offspring die young. You will recognize these traits as typical of boom-and-bust species.

At the other extreme, **K-selected species** typically live in stable environments and often develop populations that persist near the carrying capacity of their environment for long periods of time (hence the term *K*-selected). *K*-selected species usually mature slowly, have a long life span, produce small numbers of fairly large offspring, and either provide significant parental care (as large mammals do) or package significant nutrients along with the embryo (as in acorns, walnuts, and other large-seeded trees). This parental investment allows a fairly high percentage of their offspring to live to maturity (FIG. 27-12b). Many *K*-selected species produce offspring one or more times a year for several, sometimes many, years.

Most species do not fit neatly into these two extreme categories, but have a combination of traits from the two extremes. For example, giant clams live mostly in stable tropical ocean environments, are slow to mature (5 to 10 years), and spawn many times in a typical life span of scores of years. However, they produce hundreds of millions of eggs at a time, have very few nutrients packaged in their eggs, and provide no parental care. As a result, perhaps only 1 egg in a billion successfully matures into an adult clam. Similarly, redwood trees live in a mild coastal climate, typically mature at 5 to 15 years of age, and may reproduce every year for 500 to 1,000 years, but the vast majority of their hundreds of thousands of tiny seeds never sprout. Both species frequently have populations that persist near the carrying capacity of their

environments for centuries, or even millennia. On the other hand, mice, which are considered to be strongly *r*-selected, invest significant parental care in their offspring, including about 3 weeks of pregnancy and another 3 weeks of nursing before the pups are weaned. This is not much compared to a human or an elephant, but much more than clams, insects, or dandelions. As these examples illustrate, there are many interacting factors that contribute to a species' life history. Many evolutionary ecologists suggest that a simple "*r*-selected" versus "*K*-selected" dichotomy does not do justice to crucial aspects of a species' evolution and interactions with living and nonliving components of its ecosystem.

A Species' Life History Predicts Survival Rates over Time

Species differ tremendously in their chances of dying at any given phase of their life cycle. **Survivorship tables** track groups of organisms (born at the same time) throughout their lives, recording how many survive in each succeeding year or other unit of time (FIG. 27-13a). When the proportion of the population that survives is plotted against the species' life span, the resulting **survivorship curves** are characteristic of the species in the environment where the data were collected (populations of the same species may show somewhat different survivorship curves if they live in different environments). Male and female survivorship may also differ. The three principal types of survivorship curves are shown in FIGURE 27-13b: late-loss, constant-loss, and early-loss, according to the part of the life span during which

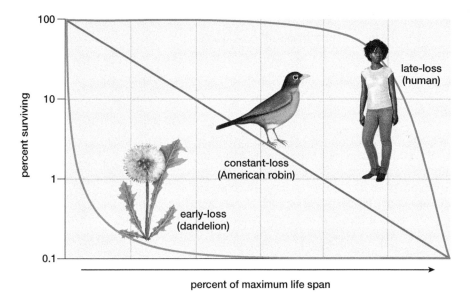

Age	Number of survivors
0	100,000
10	99,224
20	98,910
30	98,011
40	96,798
50	94,295
60	88,770
70	78,069
80	57,188
90	23,619
100	1,968
110	0

(a) A survivorship table

(b) Survivorship curves

▲ FIGURE 27-13 **Survivorship (a)** A survivorship table for the U.S. population in 2010, showing how many people are expected to remain alive at increasing ages, for each 100,000 people born. Plotting these data produce a curve similar to the blue curve in part (b). **(b)** Three types of survivorship curve are shown; note the logarithmic *y*-axis. Data in part (a) from Arias, E. 2014. "United States Life Tables, 2010." *National Vital Statistics Reports* 63(7): 1–63.

most deaths occur. The *y*-axis uses a logarithmic scale to compare the *proportion of the population* that survives at different times in the life span.

Late-loss populations have relatively low juvenile death rates, and most individuals survive to old age. The resulting survivorship curve is convex. Late-loss survivorship curves are characteristic of humans and other large and long-lived animals such as elephants and mountain sheep. These species produce relatively few offspring, which are protected and nourished by their parents during early life.

Constant-loss populations consist of individuals that have an equal chance of dying at any time during their life span, producing a straight line survivorship curve. This pattern is seen in some birds such as gulls and the American robin, in some species of turtles, and in laboratory populations of organisms that reproduce asexually, such as hydra and bacteria. *K*-selected species usually have late-loss or constant-loss survivorship curves.

Early-loss populations have a high death rate early in life, so the survivorship curve is concave. Although the death rate is very high among the young, those individuals that reach adulthood have a reasonable chance of surviving to old age. Early-loss survivorship curves are characteristic of organisms that produce large numbers of offspring but give them little or no care after they hatch or germinate. Most invertebrates (including giant clams), many fish and amphibians, and most plants (including redwoods) exhibit early-loss survivorship curves. Most *r*-selected species have early-loss survivorship curves.

CHECK YOUR LEARNING

Can you ...

- explain the important factors that determine a species' life history?
- describe and graph the three principal types of survivorship curves?

27.4 HOW ARE ORGANISMS DISTRIBUTED IN POPULATIONS?

Populations of different species show characteristic spacing of their members, determined by both behavior and environment. Spatial distributions may vary with time, changing with the breeding season, for example. Ecologists recognize three major types of spatial distribution: clumped, uniform, and random (FIG. 27-14).

Populations whose members live in clusters have a **clumped distribution.** Examples include family or social groupings, such as elephant herds, wolf packs, flocks of birds, and schools of fish (FIG. 27-14a). What are the advantages of clumping? Birds in flocks benefit from many eyes to spot food, such as a tree full of fruit. Schooling fish and flocks of birds may confuse predators with their sheer numbers. Predators, in turn, sometimes hunt in groups, cooperating to bring down large prey (see Fig. 27-9a). Some species, such as elephant seals, form temporary groups to mate and care for

(a) Clumped distribution

(b) Uniform distribution

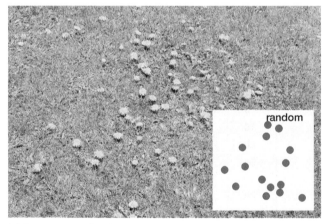

(c) Random distribution

▲ FIGURE 27-14 **Spatial distribution in populations (a)** A school of fish may confuse predators with their numbers. **(b)** Colonies of gannets consist of a remarkably uniform pattern of nests, each just out of pecking range of its neighbors. **(c)** Dandelions and other plants with wind-borne seeds often have random population distributions because the seeds germinate wherever the wind deposits them.

their young. Other plant or animal populations cluster because resources are localized. In North American prairies, for example, stands of cottonwood trees cluster along the banks of streams, because streambanks are typically the only places with enough moisture in the soil for cottonwoods to grow.

Organisms with a **uniform distribution** maintain a relatively constant distance between individuals. Among plants, mature desert creosote bushes are often spaced very evenly. This spacing results from competition among their root systems, which occupy a roughly circular area around each plant. The roots efficiently absorb water and other nutrients from the desert soil, reducing the survival of nearby plants. A uniform distribution may also occur among animals, such as songbirds, that defend territories during their breeding seasons, thereby spacing themselves fairly evenly throughout suitable habitat. Sometimes a uniform distribution is simply a way to avoid constant harassment by neighbors. Some birds, including penguins, gulls, and gannets, nest in colonies; their nests are often evenly spaced, just out of pecking reach of one another (FIG. 27-14b).

Organisms with a **random distribution** are rare. Individuals of species with random distributions neither attract nor repel each other and do not form social groupings. The resources they need must be more or less equally available throughout the area they inhabit, and those resources must be fairly abundant, minimizing competition. The dandelions in your lawn are often randomly distributed, as they sprout from windblown seeds that land in random locations in well-fertilized soil (FIG. 27-14c). There are probably no vertebrate animal species that maintain a random distribution

throughout the year; most interact socially, at least during the breeding season.

CHECK YOUR LEARNING

Can you ...

- describe the three types of spatial distribution and describe the typical characteristics of populations with each type of distribution?

27.5 HOW IS THE HUMAN POPULATION CHANGING?

Humans possess enormous brainpower and dexterous hands that can shape the environment to our demands. As our species was evolving, natural selection favored those with the ability and the drive to bear and nurture many offspring, which helped ensure that a few would survive. Ironically, this characteristic may now threaten us and the biosphere on which we depend.

The Human Population Has Grown Exponentially

Compare the graph of human population growth in FIG. 27-15a with the exponential growth curves in Figures 27-1 and 27-2:

Year	Billions	Time to add each billion (years)
1804	1	All of human history
1927	2	123
1960	3	33
1974	4	14
1987	5	13
1999	6	12
2011	7	12
2025*	8	13–14
2041*	9	16–18
2062*	10	18–24
*projected		

(b) Estimated human population from 1900 projected to 2100

(a) Estimated human population over the last 12,000 years

technical advances   agricultural advances   industrial and medical advances

▲ **FIGURE 27-15 Human population growth (a)** The human population from the Stone Age to the present has shown continued exponential growth as various advances overcame environmental resistance. Note the time intervals over which additional billions were added. **(b)** An expanded *x*-axis for the years 1900 to 2100 indicates that human population growth is slowing down. Note, however, that the population data after 2015 are projections. Actual population growth may not match these projections.
Photo courtesy of NASA.

Each has the J-curve characteristic of exponential growth. Initially, the human population grew slowly. The population was probably about 1 million people in 10,000 B.C. (no one knows for sure, of course), and reached about 1 billion in the early 1800s—almost 12,000 years later. But the second billion was added in about 125 years, and less than 100 years after that, our population reached 7 billion (see the table in Fig. 27-15a). The human population has increased so fast that about 6% of all the people who have *ever* lived on Earth are alive today.

However, although the human population continues to grow rapidly, it may no longer be growing exponentially (FIG. 27-15b). According to the U.S. Census Bureau, the world's annual growth rate (rate of natural increase) declined from 2.2% in 1963 to 1.1% in 2015. Our numbers now grow by about 78 million each year, down from a peak of about 88 million in 1990. Are humans starting to enter the final bend of an S-shaped logistic growth curve (see Fig. 27-5) that will eventually lead to a stable population? Only time will tell. Nevertheless, by 2050, the human population is expected to exceed 9 billion, and still be growing, although more slowly than at present. How has humanity managed to sustain such prolonged, rapid population growth? Are human populations exempt from the effects of environmental resistance?

No, humans aren't exempt, but we have responded to environmental resistance by devising ways to overcome it. To accommodate our growing numbers, we have altered the face of the globe. Is there an ultimate limit to Earth's carrying capacity? Have we already reached or possibly even exceeded it? We explore these questions in "Earth Watch: Have We Exceeded Earth's Carrying Capacity?" on page 508.

People Have Increased Earth's Capacity to Support Our Population

Human population growth has been made possible by advances that circumvented various types of environmental resistance, thereby increasing Earth's carrying capacity for people. *Technical advances* by early humans included controlling fire, inventing tools and weapons, building shelters, and designing protective clothing. Tools and weapons allowed people to hunt more effectively and obtain additional high-quality food, while shelter and clothing expanded the habitable areas of the globe.

Domesticated crops and animals supplanted hunting and gathering in many parts of the world about 8,000 to 10,000 years ago. These *agricultural advances* provided people with a larger, more dependable food supply. An increased food supply resulted in a longer life span and more childbearing years. However, a high death rate from disease restrained population growth for thousands of years until major *industrial and medical advances* permitted a population explosion, beginning in the mid-eighteenth century. Improved sanitation and medical progress, including the discovery of antibiotics and vaccines, combined to dramatically decrease the death rate from infectious diseases.

World Population Growth Is Unevenly Distributed

As is true of any population, the population of an individual country is a function of natural increase and migration. In some countries, such as the United States, immigration is a significant cause of population growth. In most countries, however, natural increase is the principal cause of population changes. In the long run, natural increase depends on a population's *fertility rate:* the average number of children that each woman bears. If immigration and emigration are equal, a population will eventually stabilize if parents, on average, have just the number of children required to replace themselves; this is called **replacement level fertility (RLF).** Replacement level fertility is 2.1 children per woman (rather than exactly 2) because not all children survive to maturity. As we will see below, even at replacement level fertility, a population with a high proportion of children will continue to grow for many years, a phenomenon often called *momentum,* as this large number of children mature and have families of their own.

Today, countries are usually described as more or less developed. People in **more developed countries**—including Australia, New Zealand, Japan, and countries in North America and Europe—benefit from a relatively high standard of living, with access to modern technology and medical care, including readily available contraception. Average income is high, education and employment opportunities are available to both sexes, and death rates from infectious diseases are low. Populations are usually stable or declining. However, fewer than 20% of the world's people live in more developed countries. In the **less developed countries** of Central and South America, Africa, and much of Asia—home to more than 80% of humanity—the average person lacks these advantages. In addition, the populations of less developed countries are usually expanding, sometimes rapidly. How does development affect population growth?

Countries Progress from Less Developed to More Developed Through the Demographic Transition

The historical rate of population growth in more developed countries has changed over time in reasonably predictable stages, producing a pattern called the **demographic transition** (FIG. 27-16). Before major industrial and medical advances occurred, today's more developed countries were in the *pre-industrial stage*, with relatively small, stable, or slowly growing populations in which high birth rates were balanced by high death rates. This was followed by the *transitional stage*, in which food production increased and health care improved. These advances caused death rates to fall, while birth rates remained high, leading to an explosive rate of natural increase. During the *industrial stage*, birth rates fell as more people moved from small farms to cities (where children were less important as a source of labor), contraceptives became more readily available, and opportunities for women increased. More developed countries are now in the *post-industrial stage* of the demographic transition, and, in most cases, their populations are stable, or even decreasing, with low rates of both births and deaths.

In less developed countries, such as most countries in Central and South America, Asia (excluding China and Japan), and Africa, medical advances have decreased death rates and increased life span, but birth rates remain relatively high. Although China is also considered a less developed country, years ago, as its population approached 1 billion, the Chinese government recognized the negative impacts of continued population growth and instituted policies (some of them punitive and unpopular) that brought China's fertility rate below replacement level. As a result, China's population has almost stopped growing, and India is expected to become the world's most populous country by about 2025. China has since somewhat relaxed its "one-child" policies; it remains to be seen whether its birth rate will increase.

Most less developed countries are in the late-transitional or the industrial stage of the demographic transition. In many of these nations, adult children provide financial security for aging parents. Young children may also contribute significantly to family income by working on farms or in factories. Social factors drive population growth in countries where children confer prestige and where religious beliefs promote large families. Also, in less developed countries, many people who would like to limit their family size lack access to contraceptives. For example, in the West African nation of Nigeria, less than 20% of couples use modern contraceptive methods, and the average woman bears 5.2 children. Nigeria is suffering from soil erosion, water pollution, and the loss of forests and wildlife, suggesting that its carrying capacity is already compromised. With 43% of its 182 million people under the age of 15, continued population growth there is inevitable.

As in Nigeria, population growth is highest in the countries that can least afford it, as a result of positive feedback, in which past and current population growth tends to promote future population increases. As more people compete for the same limited resources, poverty continues. Poverty diverts children away from schools and into activities that help support their families. A lack of education and lack of access to contraceptives then contributes to continued high birth rates. As a result, the population increases, which tends to keep the people poor, so the cycle continues. Of the 7.2 billion people on Earth in 2015, about 6 billion resided in less developed countries. Although fertility rates in some less developed countries, such as Brazil, have declined because of social changes and increased access to contraceptives, most are still above RLF. Therefore, the human population will continue to grow, in less developed countries and the world as a whole, for many years.

The Age Structure of a Population Predicts Its Future Growth

Age structure diagrams show age groups on the vertical axis and the numbers or percentages of individuals in each age group on the horizontal axis, with males and females shown on opposite sides. These diagrams not only illustrate current age distributions, but also predict future population growth. Age structure diagrams all rise to a peak that reflects the maximum human life span, but the shape of the rest of the diagram reveals whether the population is expanding, stable, or shrinking. If adults in the reproductive age group (15 to 44 years) are having more children (the 0- to 14-year age group) than are needed to replace themselves, the population is above RLF and is expanding. Its age structure will be

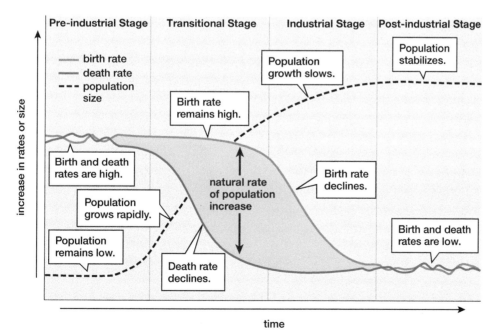

◀ **FIGURE 27-16 The demographic transition** A demographic transition typically begins with a relatively stable and small population with high birth and death rates. Death rates decline first, causing the population to increase. Then birth rates decline, causing the population to stabilize at a larger size with relatively low birth and death rates.

roughly triangular (**FIG. 27-17a**). If the adults of reproductive age have just the number of children needed to replace themselves, the population is at RLF. A population that has been at RLF for many years will have an age structure diagram with relatively straight sides (**FIG. 27-17b**). In shrinking populations, the reproducing adults have fewer children than are required to replace themselves, causing the age structure diagram to narrow at the base (**FIG. 27-17c**).

FIGURE 27-18 shows age structures for the populations of developed and developing countries for 2015, with projections for 2050. Even if rapidly growing countries were to achieve RLF immediately, their populations would continue to increase for decades. Why? When the number of children exceeds the number of reproducing adults, this creates momentum for future growth, as these children mature and enter their reproductive years. For example, when China reached RLF in the early 1990s, about 28% of its population was under age 15; in a stable human population, fewer than 20% are children. Because of this momentum, China has since grown by almost 200 million people. China will probably have a stable population soon, however, because now only 17% of its people are younger than 15. In contrast, children make up about 40% of the population of Africa, so its population will continue to increase rapidly.

Fertility in Some Nations Is Below Replacement Level

Although a reduced population will ultimately offer tremendous benefits for both the world's people and the biosphere that sustains them, current economic structures in many countries are based on growing populations. The difficult adjustments necessitated as populations decline—or even merely stabilize—motivate governments to adopt policies that encourage more childbearing and continued growth.

TABLE 27-1 provides growth rates for various world regions. In Europe, the population is shrinking slightly, by 0.1% per year, and the average fertility rate is 1.6—substantially below RLF—as many women delay or forgo having children. This situation raises concerns about the availability of future workers and taxpayers to support the resulting increase in the percentage of elderly people. As a result, several European countries are offering or considering incentives (such as large tax breaks) for couples to have children.

▶ **FIGURE 27-17** **Age structure diagrams (a)** The age structure for Africa illustrates a rapidly growing population that is projected to almost double by 2050. **(b)** North America represents a more slowly growing population that is still projected to add more than 100 million people by 2050 (about a 24% increase). **(c)** Europe's age structure is of a slowly shrinking population, projected to decline by more than 35 million (about 5%) by 2050. Background colors from bottom to top indicate age groups: prereproductive children (0 to 14 years), reproductive age adults (15 to 44 years), and postreproductive adults (45 to 100 years). Data from the U.S. Census Bureau, International Data Base.

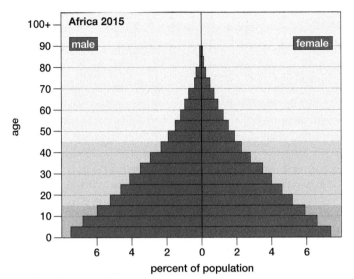

(a) **Africa: A rapidly growing population**

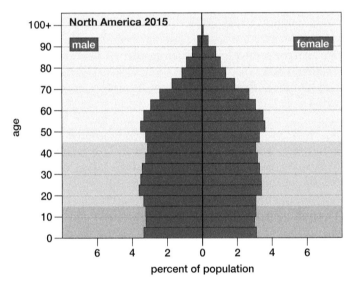

(b) **North America: A slowly growing population**

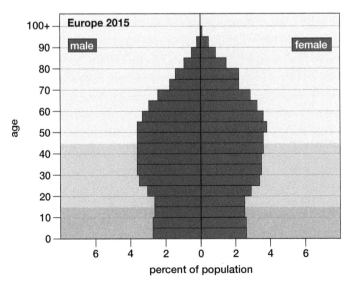

(c) **Europe: A slowly declining population**

(a) More developed countries

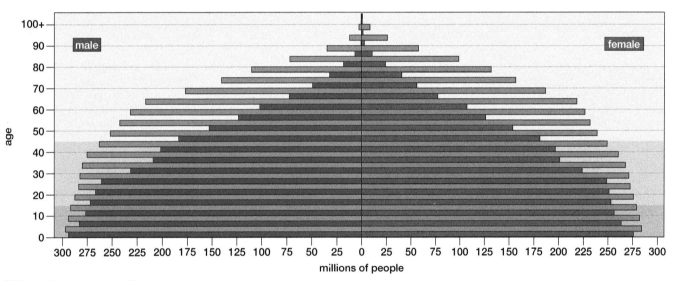

(b) Less developed countries

▲ **FIGURE 27-18 Age structure diagrams of more and less developed countries** Note that the predicted difference in the proportion of children compared to the proportion of adults in less developed countries is smaller in 2050 than in 2015, as these populations approach RLF. However, the large numbers of young people in less developed countries who will be entering their child-bearing years will cause continued population growth. Data from the U.S. Census Bureau, International Data Base.

THINK CRITICALLY How does a fertility rate above RLF produce positive feedback (in which a change creates a situation that amplifies itself) for population growth?

TABLE 27-1	Average Population Statistics by World Region: 2015	
Region	**Fertility Rate**	**Rate of Natural Increase (%)**
World	**2.4**	**1.1**
Less developed countries	**2.5**	**1.1**
Africa	4.3	2.3
Latin America/Caribbean	2.1	1.1
Asia*	2.5	1.4
China	1.6	0.4
More developed countries	**1.7**	**0.1**
Europe	1.6	−0.1
North America	2.0	0.5

*Excluding China.

Data from the U.S. Census Bureau International Data Base.

Earth WATCH

Have We Exceeded Earth's Carrying Capacity?

In Côte d'Ivoire, a country in western Africa, the government is waging a battle to protect some of its rapidly dwindling tropical rain forest from illegal hunters, farmers, and loggers. Officials destroy the shelters of the squatters, who immediately return and rebuild. One such squatter, Sep Djekoule, explained, "I have ten children and we must eat. The forest is where I can provide for my family, and everybody has that right." His words exemplify the conflict between population growth and wise management of Earth's finite resources.

How many people can Earth sustain? The Global Footprint Network, consisting of an international group of scientists and professionals from many fields, is attempting to assess humanity's *ecological footprint* (see Chapter 31). This project compares human demand for resources to Earth's capacity to supply these resources in a sustainable manner. "Sustainable" means that the resources can be renewed indefinitely and that the ability of the biosphere to supply them is not diminished over time. Is humanity living on the "interest" produced by our global endowment, or are we eating into the "principal"? The Global Footprint Network concluded that, in 2010 (the most recent year for which complete data are available), humanity consumed more than 150% of the resources that were sustainably available. In other words, to avoid damaging Earth's resources (thus reducing Earth's carrying capacity), our population in 2010 would require more than 1½ Earths. But by 2015, we had added about 400 million more people. Because people have used their technological prowess to overcome environmental resistance, our collective ecological footprint now dwarfs Earth's sustainable resource base, reducing Earth's future capacity to support us.

For example, the human population now uses almost 40% of Earth's productive land for crops and livestock. Despite this, the United Nations estimates that more than 800 million people are undernourished, including an estimated 25% of the population of sub-Saharan Africa. Erosion reduces the ability of land to support both crops and grazing livestock (FIG. E27-2). The quest for farmland drives people to clear-cut forests in places where the soil is poorly suited for agriculture. The demand for wood also causes large areas to be deforested annually, causing the runoff of much-needed fresh water, the erosion of topsoil, the pollution of rivers and oceans, and an overall reduction in the ability of the land and water to support not only future crops and livestock, but also the fish and other wild animals that people harvest for food. Human consumption of food, wood, and, more recently, biofuels (crops that provide fuel) drives the destruction of tens of millions of acres of rain forest annually (see Chapter 31).

The United Nations estimates that about 60% of commercial ocean fish populations are being harvested at their maximum sustainable yield, and another 30% are being overfished. In parts of India, China, Africa, and the United States, underground water stores are being depleted to irrigate cropland far faster than they are being refilled by rain and snow. Because irrigated land supplies about 40% of human food crops, water shortages can rapidly lead to food shortages.

▲ **FIGURE E27-2 Overgrazing can lead to the loss of productive land** Human activities, including overgrazing, deforestation, and poor agricultural practices, reduce the productivity of the land.

Our present population, at its present level of technology, is clearly "overgrazing" the biosphere. As the 6 billion people in less developed countries strive to raise their standard of living, and the billion people in more developed countries continue to increase theirs, the damage to Earth's ecosystems accelerates. We all want to enjoy luxuries far beyond bare survival, but unfortunately, the resources currently demanded to support the high standard of living in developed countries are unattainable for most of Earth's inhabitants. For example, supporting the world population sustainably at the average standard of living in the United States would require about 4½ Earths. Technology can help us improve agricultural efficiency, conserve energy and water, reduce pollutants, and recycle far more of what we use. In the long run, however, it is extremely unlikely that technological innovation can compensate for continued population growth.

Inevitably, the human population will stop growing. Hope for the future lies in recognizing the signs of human overgrazing and responding by reducing our population before we cause further damage to the biosphere, diminishing its ability to support people and the other precious and irreplaceable forms of life on Earth.

THINK CRITICALLY Much of the easily visible ecological damage caused by humans occurs in less developed countries: overgrazed pastures, rain-forest devastation, and critically endangered species such as rhinos and orangutans. Some of this damage results from economic demand from more developed countries. Research the origins and ecological impacts of an imported product such as palm oil, gold, mahogany, or teak. Do developed countries export ecological damage when we import goods from less developed countries?

▶ **FIGURE 27-19 U.S. population growth** Since 1790, U.S. population growth has produced a J-shaped curve typical of exponential growth, with some slight slowing in recent decades. The U.S. Census Bureau predicts that the U.S. population will reach 334 million by 2020. Data from the U.S. Census Bureau.

THINK CRITICALLY At what stage of the S-curve is the U.S. population? What factors do you think might cause it to stabilize? Might the recent recession reduce population growth?

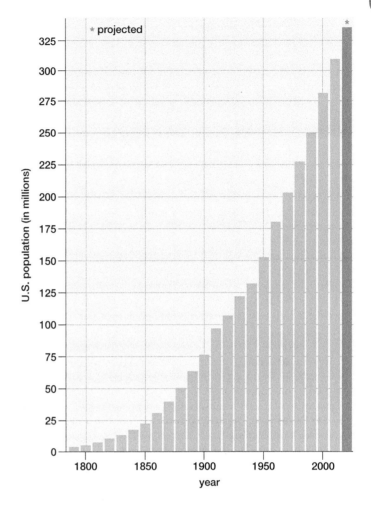

The U.S. Population Is Growing Rapidly

In 2015, the United States had a population of more than 321 million and a growth rate of about 0.8% per year (**FIG. 27-19**). The U.S. is one of the fastest-growing developed countries in the world. Continued immigration, which accounts for more than 30% of the population increase, will ensure growth for the indefinite future, unless the U.S. fertility rate (2.0 in 2015) drops sufficiently below RLF to compensate for the influx of people. Because the average U.S. resident has a large ecological footprint—about 2.5 times the global average—continued population growth in the U.S. has significant impact on both local and global environments.

CHECK YOUR LEARNING

Can you ...

- describe the advances that have allowed exponential growth of the human population?
- explain why rapid population growth continues today?
- explain the demographic transition?
- sketch age structure diagrams and describe how their shape predicts future changes in population size?

CASE STUDY REVISITED

The Return of the Elephant Seals

The rapid recovery of elephant seal populations, from near-extinction in 1892 to about 200,000 animals today, is a triumph of wildlife conservation, with an invaluable role played by the exponential growth of a small population with abundant food, safe breeding sites, and few predators.

However, all modern elephant seals are the offspring of at most 20 ancestors in the 1890s. Therefore, all modern elephant seals may have descended from just one bull and a few females. Passing through such a "population bottleneck" (see Chapter 16) reduces the genetic diversity of future generations, because only the alleles that were present in this minuscule population were available to pass on to the entire present-day population. Indeed, when molecular biologists compared the genetic diversity of modern elephant seals with that of specimens collected before 1892, they found that today's elephant seals are almost genetically identical to one another. Much greater diversity was found

in pre-bottleneck specimens. It may take hundreds or even thousands of years for mutations to replenish allele diversity in elephant seals.

Does this matter? Right now, probably not very much, although elephant seals do have about 2 to 10 times more congenital abnormalities, such as cleft palate and defects in the heart or brain, than harbor seals and California sea lions do. A high incidence of congenital defects is fairly common in inbred populations with low genetic diversity.

CONSIDER THIS As a genetically homogeneous species, elephant seals have a diminished capacity to evolve in response to environmental changes that may occur in the future—the entire population will be affected, to about the same degree, by any adverse changes. Do you think that elephant seals, regardless of their abundance, should be considered potentially endangered for the foreseeable future? Why or why not?

CHAPTER REVIEW

Go to **MasteringBiology** for practice quizzes, activities, eText, videos, current events, and more.

Answers to Figure Caption questions, Multiple Choice questions, and Fill-in-the-Blank questions can be found in the Answers section at the back of the book.

Summary of Key Concepts

27.1 What Is a Population and How Does Population Size Change?

Populations change size through births and deaths, which result in natural increase, and through immigration and emigration, which produce net migration. Ignoring migration, the population growth rate (r) is its birth rate (b) minus its death rate (d). Population growth (G), the increase during a given time interval, equals the growth rate (r) multiplied by the population size (N). All organisms have the biotic potential to more than replace themselves over their lifetimes, resulting in population growth. A constant growth rate produces exponential growth.

27.2 How Is Population Growth Regulated?

Carrying capacity (K) is the maximum size at which a population may be sustained indefinitely by an ecosystem. K is determined by limited resources such as space, nutrients, and energy. Environmental resistance generally maintains populations at or below the carrying capacity. Above K, populations deplete their resource base, leading to (1) the population stabilizing near K; (2) reduction of K and a permanently reduced population; or (3) the population being eliminated from the area. Population growth is restrained by density-independent forms of environmental resistance (principally weather and climate) and density-dependent forms of resistance (competition, predation, and parasitism).

27.3 How Do Life History Strategies Differ Among Species?

r-selected species tend to live in unpredictable environments, mature early, produce large numbers of small offspring, and provide little or no parental care, whereas K-selected species tend to live in stable environments, mature slowly, and provide substantial parental care to small numbers of offspring. The life history strategies of most species fall between these two extremes. Late-loss survivorship curves are characteristic of K-selected species. Species with constant-loss curves have an equal chance of dying at any age. Early-loss curves are typical of r-selected species, or any species that produce numerous offspring, most of which die before reaching maturity.

27.4 How Are Organisms Distributed in Populations?

Clumped distribution may occur for social reasons or around limited resources. Uniform distribution is often the result of territorial spacing. Random distribution is rare, occurring when individuals do not interact socially and when resources are abundant and evenly distributed.

27.5 How Is the Human Population Changing?

The human population exhibited exponential growth for an unprecedented time, the result of a combination of high birth rates and technological, agricultural, industrial, and medical advances that have reduced the effects of environmental resistance and increased Earth's carrying capacity for humans. Age structure diagrams depict numbers of males and females in groups of increasing age. Expanding populations, mostly in less developed countries, have triangular age structures with a broad base. More developed countries typically have stable populations with relatively straight-sided age structures or shrinking populations with age structures that are narrow at the base. Most people live in less developed countries with growing populations and birth rates greater than replacement level fertility (RLF). Even if birth rates decline to RLF, momentum from earlier high birth rates and the resulting large number of children and reproductive adults ensure decades of continued population growth.

Key Terms

age structure diagram   *505*
biosphere   *491*
biotic potential   *492*
birth rate (b)   *491*
boom-and-bust cycle   *493*
carrying capacity (K)   *495*
clumped distribution   *502*
community   *491*
competition   *498*
constant-loss population   *502*
death rate (d)   *491*
demographic transition   *504*
density-dependent   *497*
density-independent   *497*
early-loss population   *502*
ecology   *491*
ecosystem   *491*
emigration   *491*
environmental resistance   *493*
exponential growth   *492*
growth rate (r)   *491*
host   *498*
immigration   *491*
interspecific competition   *499*
intraspecific competition   *499*

invasive species   *495*
J-curve   *492*
K-selected species   *501*
late-loss population   *502*
less developed
  country   *504*
life history   *500*
logistic population
  growth   *495*
more developed
  country   *504*
natural increase   *491*
parasite   *498*
population   *491*
population cycle   *498*
predator   *497*
prey   *497*
r-selected species   *500*
random distribution   *503*
replacement level fertility
  (RLF)   *504*
S-curve   *495*
survivorship curve   *501*
survivorship table   *501*
uniform distribution   *503*

Thinking Through the Concepts

Multiple Choice

1. Density-independent environmental resistance includes
   a. predation.
   c. parasitism.
   b. floods.
   d. competition.

2. Exponential growth often occurs when
   a. a population nears carrying capacity.
   b. a population exceeds carrying capacity.
   c. organisms invade a new habitat.
   d. the birth rate exceeds the death rate for a single generation.

3. Which of the following did *not* contribute to increasing Earth's carrying capacity for humans?
   a. birth control
   c. medical advances
   b. agriculture
   d. improved sanitation

4. A population is likely to increase in size if
   a. there are more postreproductive adults than juveniles.
   b. parasites increase in abundance.
   c. its population pyramid is narrower at the base than in the middle.
   d. its reproductive rate is greater than replacement level fertility.

5. Boom-and-bust populations
   a. do not experience exponential growth.
   b. are usually controlled by density-dependent environmental resistance.
   c. may briefly exceed the carrying capacity of their environment.
   d. level off at the carrying capacity of their environment.

Fill-in-the-Blank

1. Graphs that plot how the numbers of individuals born at the same time change over time are called _____. The specific type of curve that applies to a dandelion that releases 300 seeds, most of which never germinate, is called _____. The curve for humans is an example of _____.

2. The type of growth that occurs in a population that grows by a constant percentage per year is _____. Does this form of growth add the same number of individuals each year? _____ What shape of curve is generated if this type of growth is graphed? _____ Can this type of growth be sustained indefinitely? _____

3. The maximum population size that can be sustained indefinitely without damaging the environment is called the _____. A growth curve in which a population first grows exponentially and then levels off at (or below) this maximum sustainable size is called a(n) _____ curve, or a(n) _____ curve.

4. The type of spatial distribution likely to occur when resources are localized is _____. The type of spatial distribution that results when pairs of animals defend breeding territories is _____. The least common form of distribution is _____.

5. A population grows whenever the number of _____ plus _____ exceeds the number of _____ plus _____. The growth rate of a population increases when the frequency of reproduction _____.

Review Questions

1. Define *biotic potential*, list the factors that influence it, and explain why natural selection may favor a high biotic potential.

2. Write and describe the meaning of the equation for population growth using the variables *G, r,* and *N*.

3. Draw, name, and describe the properties of a growth curve of a population without environmental resistance.

4. Define *environmental resistance* and distinguish between density-independent and density-dependent forms of environmental resistance. Describe three examples of each.

5. What is logistic population growth? What is *K*?

6. Describe three different possible consequences of exceeding carrying capacity. Sketch these scenarios on a graph. Explain your answer.

7. Distinguish between populations showing concave and convex survivorship curves. What are their typical life history strategies?

8. Explain why environmental resistance has not prevented exponential human population growth since prehistoric times; provide examples. Can this continue? Explain why or why not.

9. Draw the general shape of age structure diagrams characteristic of (a) expanding, (b) stable, and (c) shrinking populations. Label all the axes. Explain why you can predict the next several decades of growth by the current age structure of populations.

10. Sketch and label the graph showing the general stages of the demographic transition and explain the changes that influence the growth and size of the population over time.

Applying the Concepts

1. Research a developing country (such as Nigeria, Afghanistan, or Uganda) with rapid population growth and find out what factors sustain that growth and why. Explain these factors and assess the likelihood that the fertility rate of this country will drop in the near future.

2. The U.S. Endangered Species Act (ESA) seeks to increase the population of threatened species to the point where they have a self-sustaining population that no longer needs special protection. Research two species that have been listed as endangered: one that has recovered to the extent that it has been "delisted" and one that has remained on the list for more than 20 years. Based on what you have learned in this chapter, what characteristics of the two species and their environment have significantly contributed to their differing fates?

28 COMMUNITY INTERACTIONS

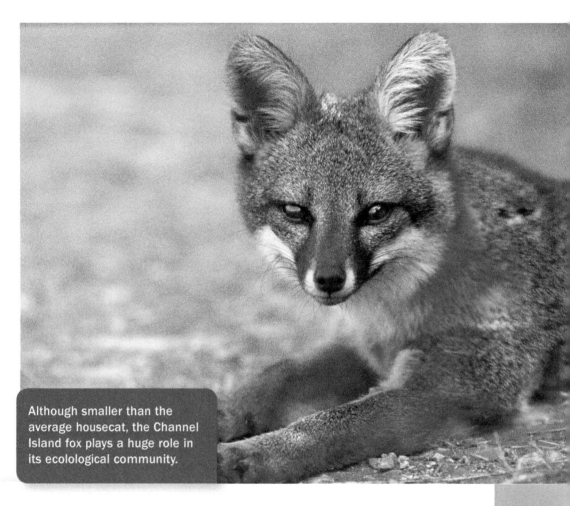

Although smaller than the average housecat, the Channel Island fox plays a huge role in its ecolological community.

CASE STUDY

The Fox's Tale

The eight Channel Islands lie in the Pacific Ocean, scattered in an arc 11 to 70 miles off the southern California coast from Santa Barbara to Los Angeles. For thousands of years, the Channel Island fox, topping out at 4 to 6 pounds, was the largest terrestrial predator on the islands. The foxes ate everything from mice and large insects to fruit and seeds, and they flourished. They shared the islands with bald eagles, which are large enough to prey on the tiny foxes, but which fed primarily on the abundant fish in the surrounding ocean waters and posed no threat to the foxes. In the late 1900s, however, catastrophe struck the foxes, whose population crashed from more than 6,000 in the mid-1900s to just a few hundred by 2000. What happened?

Because the Channel Islands have never been connected to the mainland, their native animals and plants arrived by swimming, flying, rafting on mats of vegetation, or blowing in the wind. The islands became home to a unique collection of organisms adapted to the local conditions and containing some species found nowhere else on Earth, including the Channel Island fox. But starting in the 1800s, the tapestry of life on the islands began to unravel. Settlers in search of farmland cleared large areas of native vegetation and brought in cattle, pigs, and sheep. Some of the pigs and sheep escaped, colonizing the remaining wild areas of the islands, where they consumed or uprooted native plants. In the mid-1900s, most of the bald eagles were wiped out by the insecticide DDT (see Chapter 27). The cumulative effects of these changes devastated the islands' native flora and fauna, particularly the foxes, which almost became extinct. Some islands were down to their last 15 or 20 foxes, while populations of mice, skunks and non-native weeds increased.

These changes illustrate the interconnectedness of the species on the islands. Why would the addition of herbivores such as sheep and pigs, or the loss of fish-eating bald eagles, harm the foxes? How might the loss of foxes affect other island species? Is there any way of restoring connections that have been torn apart?

AT A GLANCE

28.1 WHY ARE COMMUNITY INTERACTIONS IMPORTANT?

An ecological **community** consists of all the populations of multiple species living and interacting with one another in a defined area. All community interactions involve access to resources. Interactions between species may be classified into three major categories (TABLE 28-1).

In **interspecific competition,** two or more species utilize the same resources (*interspecific* means "between species"). For example, acorn woodpeckers defend territories not only against other woodpeckers, but also against jays and squirrels, which may compete with them for acorns, and starlings, which compete with them for nesting holes. Plants of many different species often compete with one another for light, water, or nutrients such as soil nitrogen. Interspecific competition is detrimental to all of the species involved because it reduces their access to resources they need.

In **consumer–prey interactions,** one species (the consumer) uses another species (the prey) as a food source. Consumer–prey interactions include predation and parasitism. Obviously, predators and parasites benefit from their relationships with their prey, whereas the prey are harmed.

In **mutualism,** two species cooperate in ways that increase both species' access to resources. Therefore, mutualism may make it possible for species to thrive together where neither could survive alone.

Species interactions are typically sporadic, as when a lion chases down a zebra or a deer walks along nipping buds off bushes. In **symbiosis,** however, the relationships are prolonged and intimate, so that members of the two species are almost always found together. Unlike the common English meaning of symbiosis, in biology the relationship may be beneficial to both (mutualism) or beneficial to one and harmful to the other (parasitism).

Community interactions exert strong evolutionary forces on the species involved. For example, by killing the prey that are easiest to catch, predators spare those individuals with better defenses against predation. These better-adapted individuals then produce offspring, and over time, their inherited characteristics increase within the prey population. This process, by which interacting species act as agents of natural selection on one another, is called **coevolution.**

CHECK YOUR LEARNING

Can you ...

- define a *community* and explain why community interactions are important?
- name the three major types of community interactions and describe their effects on the species involved?
- define *coevolution*?

28.2 HOW DOES THE ECOLOGICAL NICHE INFLUENCE COMPETITION?

Each species occupies a unique **ecological niche** that encompasses all aspects of its way of life. An important part of an ecological niche is the species' physical home, or habitat, including all of the environmental conditions necessary for its survival and reproduction. These can include nesting or denning sites, climate, the type of nutrients the species requires, its optimal temperature range, the amount of water it needs, the pH and salinity of the water or soil it may inhabit, and (for plants) the degree of sun or shade it can tolerate. An ecological niche also encompasses the entire "role" that a given species performs in an ecosystem, including what it eats (or whether it obtains energy from photosynthesis), which species prey upon it or parasitize it, and the other species with which it competes.

Although different species may share many aspects of their ecological niches, interspecific competition prevents any two species from occupying exactly the same niche.

Resource Partitioning Reduces the Overlap of Ecological Niches Among Coexisting Species

What happens if two species compete to precisely the same extent for every required resource—that is, if they attempt to occupy exactly the same niche? We might consider three possible outcomes: (1) the two species will coexist in the same

TABLE 28-1	Interactions Between Species	
Type of Interaction	**Effect on Species A**	**Effect on Species B**
Interspecific competition between A and B	Harms	Harms
Consumer–prey interactions (A is the consumer, B is the prey)	Benefits	Harms
Mutualism between A and B	Benefits	Benefits

(a) Grown in separate flasks

(b) Grown in the same flask

▲ **FIGURE 28-1 Interspecific competition in the lab (a)** Raised separately with a constant food supply, both *Paramecium aurelia* and *P. caudatum* show the S-curve typical of a population that initially grows rapidly and then stabilizes. **(b)** Raised together and forced to occupy the same niche, *P. aurelia* always eventually outcompetes *P. caudatum* and causes that population to die off. Data from Gause, G. F. 1934. *The Struggle for Existence.* Baltimore: Williams & Wilkins.

niche indefinitely; (2) one species will displace the other, which will go extinct (at least locally); or (3) one or both species will evolve slightly different niche requirements, thus avoiding complete competition.

In 1934, the Russian biologist G. F. Gause tested the first two possibilities. Gause grew two species of the protist *Paramecium* (*P. aurelia* and *P. caudatum*) in laboratory cultures. Grown separately, with bacteria as their only food, both species thrived (**FIG. 28-1a**). However, when Gause placed the two species together, they could not coexist: *P. aurelia* grew more rapidly and always eliminated *P. caudatum* (**FIG. 28-1b**). Gause's conclusion came to be known as the **competitive exclusion principle:** Two species with exactly the same niche cannot coexist indefinitely.

Can species coexist if their niches differ slightly? To find out, Gause repeated the experiment, but this time pairing *P. caudatum* with a different species, *P. bursaria*. *P. caudatum* feeds on bacteria suspended in the culture medium, but *P. bursaria* feeds mostly on bacteria that settle to the bottom of the cultures. These two species of *Paramecium* were able to coexist indefinitely because they preferred feeding in different places and thus occupied slightly different niches.

Gause didn't raise enough generations of *Paramecium* for significant evolution to occur, so he could not test the third possibility, the evolution of different niche requirements. In nature, however, there is plenty of time for competing species to evolve. Ecologist Robert MacArthur carefully observed five species of North American warbler under natural conditions. These birds all nest and hunt for insects in spruce trees. Although their niches overlap, MacArthur found that each species concentrates its search for food in different regions of the spruce trees, employs different hunting tactics, and nests at a slightly different time (**FIG. 28-2**). The five species of warblers have evolved behaviors that reduce the overlap of their niches, thereby reducing interspecific competition.

This phenomenon of dividing up resources, called **resource partitioning,** is often the outcome of the coevolution of different species with extensive (but not complete) niche overlap. A famous example of resource partitioning was discovered by Charles Darwin among related species of finches on the Galápagos Islands. Different finch species that share the same island evolved different bill sizes and shapes and different feeding behaviors that reduce competition among them (see Chapter 15).

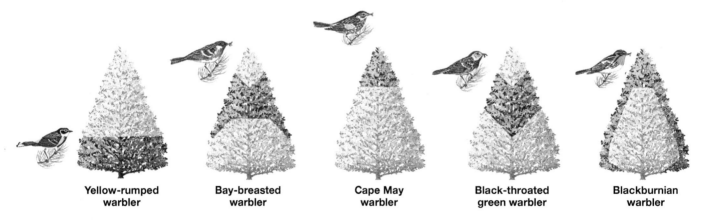

| Yellow-rumped warbler | Bay-breasted warbler | Cape May warbler | Black-throated green warbler | Blackburnian warbler |

▲ **FIGURE 28-2 Resource partitioning** Each of these five insect-eating species of North American warblers searches for food in a slightly different part of a spruce tree. This reduces niche overlap and competition. Adapted from MacArthur, R. H. 1958. Population ecology of some warblers of Northeastern coniferous forest. *Ecology* 39:599–619.

(a) Eurasian red squirrel

(b) Eastern gray squirrel

▲ FIGURE 28-3 **Competition limits population size and distribution (a)** Native red squirrels have been pushed out of most of England by competition from **(b)** gray squirrels imported from the United States. Gray squirrels may also have brought squirrelpox with them, which they resist better than red squirrels can.

Interspecific Competition Between Species May Limit the Population Size and Distribution of Each

Although natural selection often reduces niche overlap, there are still many species with similar niches; these species compete for limited resources. For example, lions and hyenas compete for prey in the African savanna, both by eating similar prey and by direct aggression toward the other species. In North America, similar competition occurs between wolves and coyotes and between bobcats, goshawks, and lynx.

Interspecific competition may restrict the population size and distribution of species, as is currently happening in Great Britain. The native squirrel in Britain and much of Europe is the Eurasian red squirrel, *Sciurus vulgaris* (FIG. 28-3a). In the late 1800s, rich landowners in Britain imported Eastern gray squirrels, *Sciurus carolinensis*, from the United States as "ornaments" for their manors (FIG. 28-3b). Gray squirrels, however, outcompete red squirrels in the deciduous forests of southern England. Gray squirrels are more efficient at eating acorns, often consuming them even before they are ripe, and raid red squirrels' seed caches. As a result, red squirrels are practically extinct in southern England. Red squirrels do much better in coniferous forests, probably because the large gray squirrels don't get enough nutrition from small conifer seeds, whereas the much smaller red squirrels can flourish on this diet. As a result of

these interactions, gray squirrels by the millions now dominate southern England, both species coexist in the mixed deciduous/conifer forests of northern England (although grays are probably still increasing), and red squirrels seem to be holding their own in the coniferous forests of Scotland.

Gray squirrels, of course, are not the only species that humans have moved across our planet. In "Earth Watch: Invasive Species Disrupt Community Interactions" on page 516, we describe what sometimes happens when people transport predatory or competing organisms into ecological communities whose members have not evolved to deal with them.

Competition Within a Species Is a Major Factor Controlling Population Size

Individuals of the same species have the same requirements for resources and thus occupy the same ecological niche. For this reason, **intraspecific competition** (*intra* means "within") is the most intense form of competition, because every member of the species competes for all of the same resources. Intraspecific competition exerts strong density-dependent environmental resistance, limiting population size (see Chapter 27). Intraspecific competition is one of the main factors driving evolution by natural selection, in which individuals that are better equipped to obtain scarce resources are more likely to reproduce successfully, passing their heritable traits to their offspring.

Earth
WATCH

Invasive Species Disrupt Community Interactions

Invasive species are non-native species that have been introduced into an ecosystem in which they did not evolve and that harm human health, the environment, or the local economy. Not all introduced species become invasive; ones that do typically reproduce rapidly, disperse widely, and thrive under a wide range of environmental conditions. Invasive species often encounter few competitors, predators, or parasites in their new environment. Their unchecked population growth may seriously damage the ecosystem as they outcompete or prey on native species.

English house sparrows were introduced into the United States on several occasions, starting in the 1850s, to control caterpillars feeding on shade trees. In 1890, European starlings were released into Central Park in New York City by a group attempting to introduce all the birds mentioned in the works of Shakespeare. Both bird species have spread throughout the continental United States. Their success has reduced populations of native songbirds, such as bluebirds and purple martins, with which they compete for nesting sites. Burmese pythons, probably released by pet owners, have become significant threats to natural communities in the Everglades of Florida (FIG. E28-1a). These huge predatory snakes have caused precipitous declines in populations of raccoons, opossums, deer, and rabbits.

Invasive plants also threaten natural communities. In the 1930s and 1940s, kudzu, a Japanese vine, was planted extensively in the southern United States to control soil erosion. Today, kudzu is a major pest, covering trees and engulfing abandoned buildings (FIG. E28-1b). Both water hyacinth and purple loosestrife were introduced into the United States as ornamental plants. Water hyacinth now clogs waterways in southern states, slowing boat traffic and displacing natural vegetation. Purple loosestrife aggressively invades wetlands, where it outcompetes native plants and reduces food and habitat for native animals.

Invasive species rank second only to habitat destruction in pushing endangered species toward extinction. Governments and land managers have sometimes tried to control invasive species by importing the species' natural predators or parasites (called *biocontrols*). However, biocontrols sometimes have unpredicted and even disastrous effects on native wildlife. The cane toad, for example, was introduced into Australia in the 1930s to control non-native beetles that threatened the sugarcane crop. Unfortunately, the toads have proven to be worse than the beetles; about 200 million toads now occupy northeastern Australia, outcompeting native frogs (FIG. E28-1c).

Despite the risks of biocontrols, there are often few realistic alternatives. Biologists now carefully screen proposed biocontrols to make sure they are likely to attack only the intended invasive species, and there have been successful introductions of biocontrols. For example, Eurasian beetles, released by the millions each year, are now among the most effective methods of controlling purple loosestrife in North America.

CONSIDER THIS Many invasive species were deliberately imported as pets or landscape plants and entered natural communities accidentally (escaped pets), deliberately (by owners who could no longer care for their exotic pets), or through natural spread (landscape plants). But probably the vast majority of non-native plants and animals never cause a major problem. Would you support laws to restrict the importation of non-native plants and animals? Why or why not?

(a) Burmese python

(b) Kudzu

(c) Cane toad

▲ **FIGURE E28-1 Invasive species (a)** Huge Burmese pythons introduced to the Florida Everglades can eat adult deer and even small alligators. **(b)** Kudzu, a Japanese vine imported to the southern United States, can rapidly cover entire trees and small buildings. **(c)** The cane toad (native to central and South America) was imported to Australia, where it outcompetes native toads and frogs and preys on many indigenous animals, such as this pygmy possum. Poisonous secretions on its skin protect the cane toad from predators.

CHECK YOUR LEARNING

Can you ...

- compare interspecific and intraspecific competition and explain which is more intense?
- explain how competitive exclusion leads to resource partitioning?

CASE STUDY \ **CONTINUED**

The Fox's Tale

Channel Island foxes do not encounter significant interspecific competition. Although foxes do compete with skunks for insects and mice, the competition seems to be very one-sided—the foxes suppress skunk populations, but skunks do not have much effect on fox populations. Bald and golden eagles, however, do seem to compete on the Channel Islands. When bald eagles were abundant, their presence apparently prevented golden eagles from settling on the islands. After bald eagles were eliminated by DDT, golden eagles colonized the islands. Around the same time, the fox population plummeted. Did the switch from bald to golden eagles cause the decline in foxes?

28.3 HOW DO CONSUMER–PREY INTERACTIONS SHAPE EVOLUTIONARY ADAPTATIONS?

Consumer–prey interactions are usually divided into two major categories: predation and parasitism. A **predator** is a free-living organism that eats other organisms. Although people generally think of predators as being *carnivores* (animals that eat other animals; FIG. 28-4a), we will include *herbivores* (animals that eat plants; FIG. 28-4b) in this category. An amoeba that eats bacteria or protists by phagocytosis is also a predator (FIG. 28-4c). A **parasite** usually lives in or on its prey (called its **host**) for a significant part of the parasite's life cycle, typically deriving all of its nourishment from its host. In these cases, the parasitism would be a special case of symbiosis. Tapeworms, fleas, and the many disease-causing protists, fungi, bacteria, and viruses are all parasites. There are very few parasitic vertebrates, but the lamprey (see Fig. 25-6), which attaches itself to a host fish and sucks its blood, is one example.

Not all organisms can be conveniently categorized as predators or parasites, but a few characteristics help to distinguish parasites from predators. Parasites are smaller and much more abundant than their hosts. Predators are often, but not always, larger than their prey, and they are generally less abundant than their prey, as explained in Chapter 29. Predators and parasites frequently differ in how much damage they do to their prey. Carnivorous predators, such as lions, eagles, and weasels, typically kill their prey. Herbivorous predators, such as deer and insects, usually do not immediately kill the plants they feed on; in fact, if herbivore numbers are low enough, they may never kill the plants. Parasites harm or weaken their host, but often do not immediately kill it. However, the weakened host may be more susceptible to predators, scarce food supplies, or harsh winter weather, so the parasite may hasten the death of the host.

Predators and Prey Coevolve Counteracting Adaptations

To survive and reproduce, predators must feed, and prey must avoid becoming food. Therefore, predator and prey are powerful forces of natural selection on one another, resulting in coevolution. Coevolution has produced the keen eyesight of the hawk and owl, which is countered by the earthy colors of their mouse and ground squirrel prey. Plants and their predators have also coevolved. For example, grasses embed tough silica substances in their blades that make them difficult to chew. In turn, natural selection has favored the evolution of long, hard teeth in grazing animals, such as horses.

(a) Eagle owl

(b) Pika

(c) Amoeba

▲ **FIGURE 28-4 Forms of predation (a)** An eagle owl feasts on a mouse. **(b)** A pika, whose preferred food is grass, is a small relative of the rabbit and lives in the Rocky Mountains. **(c)** Amoebas are microscopic protists that eat bacteria and smaller protists.

▲ **FIGURE 28-5 Coevolution between bats and moths** A long-eared bat uses a sophisticated echolocation system to hunt moths, which in turn have evolved specialized sound detectors and behaviors to avoid capture.

The adaptations of echolocating bats and their moth prey (**FIG. 28-5**) provide excellent examples of how both body structures and behaviors are molded by coevolution. Echolocating bats are usually nighttime hunters that emit pulses of sound, so high pitched that people can't hear them. The sounds bounce back from nearby objects. Bats use these echoes to produce a sonar "image" of their surroundings, allowing them to navigate around objects and detect prey.

As a result of natural selection imposed by echolocating bats, several species of moths have evolved ears that are particularly sensitive to the sounds produced by the bats. When they hear a bat, these moths take evasive action, flying erratically or dropping to the ground. Some species of bats, in turn, have evolved the ability to counter this defense by switching the frequency of their sound pulses away from the moth's sensitivity range.

Predators and Prey May Engage in Chemical Warfare

The evolution of counteracting defenses may give rise to a kind of "chemical warfare" between predators and prey. Many plants, including milkweeds, synthesize toxic and distasteful chemicals that deter predators. As plants evolved these defensive toxins, certain insects evolved increasingly efficient ways to detoxify or even use these substances. The result is that nearly every toxic plant is eaten by at least one type of insect. For example, monarch butterflies lay their eggs on milkweeds; after the eggs hatch, the monarch caterpillars eat nothing but milkweed (**FIG. 28-6**). The caterpillars not only tolerate the milkweed poison but also store it in their tissues as a defense against their own predators.

Other defensive chemicals include the clouds of ink that certain mollusks (including squid, octopuses, and some sea slugs) emit when a predator attacks. These chemical "smoke screens" confuse predators and mask the prey's escape. Another dramatic example of chemical defense is seen in the bombardier beetle. In response to the bite of an ant, the beetle releases secretions from defensive glands into a chamber in its abdomen. There, enzymes catalyze an explosive chemical reaction that shoots a toxic, boiling-hot spray onto the attacker. Toxins can be used to attack as well as to defend. The venom of spiders and some snakes, such as rattlesnakes and cobras, both paralyzes their prey and deters predators.

Looks Can Be Deceiving for Both Predators and Prey

Have you ever heard the saying that the best hiding place may be in plain sight? Both predators and prey have evolved colors, patterns, and shapes that resemble their surroundings (**FIG. 28-7**). Such disguises, called **camouflage**, render plants and animals inconspicuous, even when they are in full view.

Some animals closely resemble generally inedible objects such as leaves, twigs, seaweed, thorns, or even bird droppings (**FIGS. 28-8a–c**). Camouflaged animals tend to remain motionless; a crawling bird dropping would ruin the disguise. Whereas many camouflaged animals resemble parts of plants, a few succulent desert plants look like small rocks, which hides them from animals seeking the water stored in the plants' bodies (**FIG. 28-8d**).

▲ **FIGURE 28-6 Chemical warfare** A monarch caterpillar feeds on milkweed that contains a powerful toxin.

THINK CRITICALLY Why might the caterpillar be colored with conspicuous stripes?

(a) Sand dab fish adjust camouflage to different backgrounds   **(b) A camouflaged horned lizard**

▲ FIGURE 28-7 **Camouflage by blending in (a)** Sand dabs are flat, bottom-dwelling ocean fish whose mottled colors closely resemble the sand on which they rest. Both their colors and patterns can be modified by nervous signals to better blend with their backgrounds. **(b)** This horned lizard helps protect itself from predation by snakes and hawks by resembling its surroundings of leaf litter.

THINK CRITICALLY How might predators evolve to detect camouflaged prey?

(a) Caterpillar of viceroy butterfly   **(b) Leafy sea dragon**

(c) Thorn treehoppers   **(d) Living rock succulents**

▲ FIGURE 28-8 **Camouflage by resembling specific objects (a)** A Viceroy butterfly caterpillar, whose color and shape resemble a bird dropping, sits motionless on a leaf. **(b)** The leafy sea dragon (a fish related to the seahorse) has evolved extensions of its body that mimic the algae in which it hides. **(c)** Thorn treehopper insects avoid detection by resembling thorns on a branch. **(d)** These South African succulents are appropriately called "living rocks."

THINK CRITICALLY How might such camouflage have evolved?

(a) A camouflaged snow leopard

(b) A camouflaged frogfish

▲ **FIGURE 28-9 Camouflage assists predators (a)** As it waits for prey, such as gazelles, wild sheep, and deer, the snow leopard in the mountains of Mongolia avoids detection with camouflage coloration. **(b)** Combining camouflage and aggressive mimicry, a frogfish waits in ambush, its lumpy, yellow body matching the sponge-encrusted rock on which it rests. Above its mouth dangles a tiny lure that closely resembles a small fish. The lure attracts small predators, which will suddenly find themselves to be prey instead.

Predators that ambush prey are also aided by camouflage. For example, the spotted snow leopard is almost invisible on a mountainside as it watches for prey (FIG. 28-9a). The frogfish, lurking motionless on the ocean floor awaiting smaller fish to swallow, closely resembles sponges and algae-covered rocks (FIG. 28-9b).

Some prey animals have evolved very different visual defenses: bright **warning coloration.** These animals may taste bad or make the predator sick (as monarch butterflies and their caterpillars do; see Fig. 28-6), inflict a venomous sting or bite (as bees and coral snakes do), or produce stinking chemicals when bothered (FIG. 28-10). The eye-catching colors seem to declare "Attack at your own risk!" An uneducated predator might attack, or even kill and eat, such a brightly colored prey once, but would avoid similar prey in the future, thus sparing others of the same species.

Mimicry refers to a situation in which members of one species have evolved to resemble another species. By sharing a similar warning-color pattern, several poisonous species may all benefit. Mimicry among different distasteful species is called *Müllerian mimicry.* For example, toxins from milkweed plants are stored in monarch butterfly caterpillars (see Fig. 28-6) and retained in the metamorphosed adult butterflies, which deters birds from preying on them. Similarly, the caterpillars of viceroy butterflies eat willow and poplar leaves, which contain bitter salicylic acid. Both the caterpillars and the adult viceroys store salicylic acid in their bodies. The wing patterns of monarch and viceroy butterflies are strikingly similar (FIG. 28-11). Birds that become ill from consuming one species are likely to avoid the other as well. Similarly, a toad that is stung while attempting to eat a honeybee is likely to avoid not only honeybees but other black and yellow striped insects (such as yellow jacket wasps) without ever tasting one.

Once warning coloration evolved, there arose a selective advantage for harmless animals to resemble venomous or distasteful ones, an adaptation called *Batesian mimicry.* For example, the harmless hoverfly avoids predation by resembling a bee (FIG. 28-12a), and the nonvenomous scarlet king snake is protected by brilliant warning coloration that closely resembles that of the highly venomous coral snake (FIG. 28-12b).

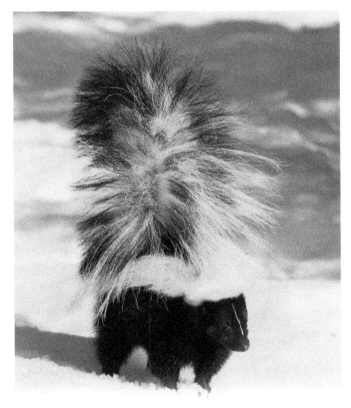

▲ **FIGURE 28-10 Warning coloration** The vivid stripe and the tail display behavior of the skunk advertise its ability to make any attacker miserable.

(a) Monarch

(b) Viceroy

▲ FIGURE 28-11 **Müllerian mimicry** Nearly identical warning coloration protects both **(a)** the distasteful monarch and **(b)** the equally distasteful viceroy butterfly. Their caterpillars, however, look very different from one another; see Figs. 28-6 and 28-8a.

(a) Bee (venomous)

Hoverfly (nonvenomous)

(b) Coral snake (venomous)

Scarlet king snake (nonvenomous)

▲ FIGURE 28-12 **Batesian mimicry (a)** A stinging bee (left) is mimicked by the stingless hoverfly (right). **(b)** The warning coloration of the venomous coral snake (left) is mimicked by the harmless scarlet king snake (right).

(a) False-eyed frog

(b) Peacock moth

(c) Swallowtail caterpillar

▲ FIGURE 28-13 **Startle coloration (a)** When threatened, the false-eyed frog of South America raises its rump, which resembles the eyes of a large predator. **(b)** The peacock moth from Trinidad is well camouflaged, but should a predator approach, it suddenly opens its wings to reveal spots resembling large eyes. **(c)** Predators of this caterpillar larva of the Eastern tiger swallowtail butterfly are deterred by its resemblance to a snake. Just behind the caterpillar's head is a bulge that resembles a snake's head, but—even more frightening—it bears two pairs of "eyes," not just one.

Some prey species use another form of mimicry: **startle coloration.** Several insects and even some vertebrates have evolved color patterns that closely resemble the eyes of a much larger, possibly dangerous animal (FIG. 28-13). If a predator gets close, the prey suddenly reveals its eyespots, startling the predator and sometimes allowing the prey to escape.

Some predators have evolved **aggressive mimicry,** in which they entice their prey to come close by resembling something attractive to the prey. For example, by using a rhythm of flashes that is unique to each species, female fireflies attract males to mate. But in one species, the females sometimes mimic the flashing pattern of a different species, attracting males that they kill and eat. The frogfish (see Fig. 28-9b) not only is camouflaged but also exhibits aggressive mimicry by dangling a wriggling lure that resembles a small fish just above its mouth. Small fish attracted by the lure are engulfed in a split second if they get too close.

CASE STUDY \ **CONTINUED**

The Fox's Tale

Predation played a major role in the decline of Channel Island foxes. The loss of bald eagles opened up the islands to invasion by golden eagles. Meanwhile, pigs that escaped from farms on the islands multiplied, bearing litters year-round and providing a steady supply of piglets for the golden eagles to eat. Although piglets were the main course, foxes were tasty snacks. For thousands of years, island foxes had no predators. As a result, unlike their mainland relatives, Channel Island foxes hunt during the day and spend a lot of time in the open—traits that made them easy targets for the eagles. As we will see, the loss of foxes reverberated throughout the islands' communities.

Parasites Coevolve with Their Hosts

Parasites can only survive and reproduce in suitable hosts; the hosts, in turn, are harmed by the parasites. Therefore, natural selection favors parasites that are better at invading hosts and hosts that can resist parasitic invasion, resulting in coevolution of parasites and hosts. For example, natural selection favored the evolution of the itch–scratch reflex because scratching an itch often dislodges blood-sucking parasites such as ticks and mosquitoes. These parasites, in turn, have evolved chemicals in their saliva that reduce the itch response, so that they are more likely to complete a blood meal before the host becomes aware of their attack and scratches them off.

Perhaps the best-studied example of parasite–host coevolution is the cellular warfare between infectious microorganisms and their mammalian hosts. Mammals defend themselves against these parasites by secreting antimicrobial molecules onto the skin and into the respiratory and digestive tracts; producing several types of white blood cells that eat and destroy microbes or secrete antibodies that help to kill microbes; and even killing their own body cells that have been infected by viruses (see Chapter 37). In response, microbes have evolved coatings that prevent the immune system from recognizing them; cluster together in *biofilms* that help to keep antimicrobial secretions from reaching them (see Chapter 20); and sometimes even invade and destroy parts of the immune system, as the human immunodeficiency virus (HIV) does.

Coevolution between parasite and host can result in a variety of outcomes: devastating disease; a truce of sorts, in which the host provides nutrients and housing for the parasite, but the parasite causes little harm; or even mutualism, in which both parasite and host derive some benefits, as we explore in "Health Watch: Parasitism, Coevolution, and Coexistence."

Health WATCH

Parasitism, Coevolution, and Coexistence

A parasite inevitably weakens its host to some extent, at the very least by robbing nutrients from the host, thereby making it more vulnerable to predators or other parasites, less able to feed itself, or more susceptible to cold weather or drought. Sooner or later, when the host dies, the parasite must find a new host or perish. Until fairly recently, this observation led many biologists to conclude that natural selection will favor parasites that cause less harm to their hosts, postponing the day when the parasite must leave a dead host and find a new, live one. Recent research, however, has shown that this is not necessarily the case. If a parasite (or its offspring) can easily find a new host before its old host dies, then gobbling up the host and reproducing as fast as possible can be a winning evolutionary strategy.

Epidemic typhus is a good example. This type of typhus is caused by a bacterium that infects lice and is excreted in their feces (**FIG. E28-2**). When a person scratches an itchy louse bite, some louse feces may enter the scratch, infecting the person with typhus. Both louse and human often die within a few weeks, but by then the bacterium has moved on. How? Infected lice leave people with high fevers and seek out other, healthy people as new hosts. Before it dies, the sick louse may infect its new host with typhus. Uninfected lice may bite the newly infected person, ingesting the typhus bacterium and starting the cycle over again. Rapid bacterial reproduction at the expense of its host's health helps, rather than harms, the typhus bacterium.

Sometimes humans coevolve with their parasites, resulting in an uneasy truce. An example is *Helicobacter pylori*, a bacterium that colonizes the human stomach and often causes ulcers, sometimes even cancer. More than 3 billion people have *Helicobacter* in their stomachs. Strains of *Helicobacter* that have coevolved with particular human groups seem to cause little harm to their "home team" but may be deadly to outsiders. For example, Tumaco and Tuquerres, two villages in Colombia separated by only 125 miles, have a 25-fold difference in the incidence of stomach cancer, most of which is caused by *Helicobacter*. Researchers discovered that Tumaco, with a very low rate of stomach cancer, is mostly populated by the descendants of freed African slaves. Molecular evidence shows that these people also have *Helicobacter* strains that originated in Africa. In contrast, Tuquerres, which has an extremely high rate of stomach cancer, is populated mostly by native Americans. Their *Helicobacter* strains are European, probably an accidental legacy of conquistadors from Spain. The researchers hypothesize that coevolution of African people with African *Helicobacter* has reduced their cancer risk, while the nearby native Americans struggle to cope with introduced European *Helicobacter*.

▲ **FIGURE E28-2 A human body louse feeds on the blood of its host** Infected lice leave behind feces packed with the bacteria that cause epidemic typhus.

Humans and *Helicobacter* may even be coevolving into mutualism. In the human stomach, *Helicobacter* gets lots of nutrition. People infected with *Helicobacter* seem to benefit by having a lower incidence of acid reflux disease. They also have lower rates of asthma, allergies, and chronic inflammation, apparently because *Helicobacter* damps down their immune responses.

The incidence of asthma and allergies among children has steadily increased in recent years. Evidence is mounting for the "hygiene hypothesis": Being extremely sanitary might not be such a good idea, because people benefit from some of the microbes we pick up from our environment. Growing up in homes with dogs and cats—or even mice and cockroaches—decreases the risk of allergies and asthma. Perhaps the "10-second rule" is actually good for kids?

THINK CRITICALLY Malaria is a common, often lethal, disease of tropical countries, with about 200 million cases worldwide, resulting in more than 600,000 deaths. Malaria is carried by a few species of mosquitoes and transmitted to people when they are bitten by infected mosquitoes. In many parts of the Tropics, the dominant malaria-carrying mosquitoes feed mostly indoors, at night. Therefore, an effective tool for reducing malaria infections is the insecticide-treated bednet, which protects people while they sleep. Do you think that bednets will be a permanent solution to the transmission of malaria by mosquitoes?

CHECK YOUR LEARNING

Can you ...

- define *predator* and *parasite*, and distinguish these two types of consumer–prey interactions from one another?
- provide examples of how predators and prey have coevolved?
- describe some examples of chemical warfare between predators and prey?
- define and provide examples of camouflage, warning coloration, Batesian and Müllerian mimicry, startle coloration, and aggressive mimicry?
- describe coevolution between parasites and hosts?

28.4 HOW DO MUTUALISMS BENEFIT DIFFERENT SPECIES?

Mutualism is an interaction between species in which both benefit. Many, but not all, mutualistic relationships are symbiotic. You may have seen colored patches on rocks; they are probably lichens, a symbiotic mutualistic association between an alga and a fungus (FIG. 28-14a). The fungus provides support and protection while obtaining food from the brightly colored, photosynthetic alga. Mutualistic associations also occur in the digestive tracts of cattle and termites, where

(a) Lichen

(b) Clownfish

▲ FIGURE 28-14 **Mutualism (a)** This brightly colored lichen growing on bare rock is a mutualistic relationship between an alga and a fungus. **(b)** The clownfish is coated with a protective coat of mucus, allowing it to snuggle unharmed among the stinging tentacles of an anemone.

protists and bacteria find food and shelter. The microorganisms break down cellulose, making its component sugar molecules available both to themselves and to the animals that harbor them. In human intestines, mutualistic bacteria synthesize vitamins, such as vitamin K, which we absorb and use.

In many other mutualisms, one partner does not live inside the other. For example, the clownfish of the southern Pacific Ocean shelters amidst the venomous tentacles of certain species of anemones (FIG. 28-14b). In this mutualistic symbiotic association, the anemone provides the clownfish with protection from predators, while the clownfish cleans the anemone and brings it bits of food.

Finally, many mutualistic relationships are not intimate and extended, so are not symbiotic. Consider the relationship between plants and the animals that pollinate them, including bees, moths, hummingbirds, and even some bats. The animals fertilize the plants by carrying plant sperm (found in pollen grains) from one plant to another and benefit by sipping nectar and sometimes eating pollen, so the relationship is mutualistic, but the partners actually spend very little time together.

CHECK YOUR LEARNING

Can you ...

- define *mutualism* and explain why the relationship benefits both species?
- explain why some mutualisms are not symbiotic?

28.5 HOW DO KEYSTONE SPECIES INFLUENCE COMMUNITY STRUCTURE?

In some communities, a particular species, called a **keystone species,** plays a major role in determining community structure—a role that is out of proportion to the species' abundance in the community. If the keystone species is removed, community interactions are significantly altered and the relative abundance of other species often changes dramatically.

In the African savanna, the bush elephant is a keystone species. By grazing on small trees and bushes (FIG. 28-15a), elephants prevent the encroachment of forests and help maintain the grassland community, along with its diverse population of grazing mammals and their predators.

Although elephants alter plant communities directly, large carnivores, such as wolves and cougars (FIG. 28-15b), may also have a major impact on plant communities. By keeping populations of deer and elk in check, wolves and cougars can help maintain the health of forests and stream banks that would otherwise be overgrazed. Because this vegetation provides food, nesting sites, and shelter for many species of smaller animals, the entire community structure depends on the presence of the predators.

Identifying a keystone species can be difficult. Many have been recognized only after their loss has had dramatic, unforeseen consequences. The intricate web of community interactions is illustrated by the effects of enormous fluctuations in populations of the northern sea otter (FIG. 28-15c)

(a) African elephant   (b) Cougar   (c) Northern sea otter

▲ FIGURE 28-15 **Keystone species (a)** The bush elephant is a keystone species on the African savanna.
(b) The cougar, found in isolated habitats throughout North and South America, helps to control herbivores such
as deer. **(c)** The northern sea otter rests in a kelp bed while cradling a sea urchin, one of its favorite foods.

along the coast of southwestern Alaska, including the Aleutian Islands, in the last 250 years. Between the mid-1700s and the early 1900s, fur hunters reduced the sea otter population, formerly numbering 200,000 to 300,000 animals, by about 99%. After otter hunting was banned in 1911, the population rebounded to about 100,000 animals. Kelp forests, sometimes described as the "rain forests of the ocean," flourished around islands in coastal waters where the otters were abundant. But starting in the mid-1990s, otter numbers plummeted again, with some populations declining by 90%. As a result, the numbers of sea urchins, a favored food of otters, skyrocketed. Sea urchins are a major predator of kelp, and they rapidly deforested the seabed, eliminating the diverse community of fish, mollusks, and crustaceans that the kelp forests once fed and sheltered. Clearly, sea otters are a keystone species near the Aleutian Islands. But what is killing them now? Killer whales, which had coexisted with sea otters in the past, have been increasingly observed dining on otters. Why? One hypothesis is that populations of seals and Steller sea lions—the whales' preferred prey—have declined drastically, forcing the whales to eat smaller prey, such as otters. Seal and sea lion populations have fallen, at least in part, because commercial fishing in the North Pacific has depleted their food supply.

CASE STUDY CONTINUED
The Fox's Tale

Foxes are keystone species on the Channel Islands. Predation by foxes controls deer mouse populations and probably limits the types and numbers of ground-nesting birds. Foxes control skunk populations by competing with them for food. Foxes also disperse the seeds of many island plants by eating fruits and expelling the undigested seeds in their feces, often a considerable distance from the parent plant. When fox populations plummeted while pig populations skyrocketed, community interactions changed dramatically, and ecological communities on many parts of the islands became barely recognizable shadows of their former selves. Can such disturbed communities ever recover?

CHECK YOUR LEARNING
Can you ...
- explain the concept of a keystone species?
- provide some examples of the effects that removing keystone species can have on their communities?

28.6 HOW DO SPECIES INTERACTIONS CHANGE COMMUNITY STRUCTURE OVER TIME?

In a mature terrestrial ecosystem, the populations that make up the community interact with one another and with their nonliving environment in intricate ways. But this tangled web of life did not spring fully formed from bare rock or naked soil; rather, it emerged in stages over a long period of time. These stages are called **succession:** a gradual change in a community and its nonliving environment in which groups of species replace one another in a reasonably predictable sequence. During succession, early-stage organisms modify the environment in ways that favor later organisms, while end-stage organisms suppress earlier organisms but tolerate one another's influences, producing a stable community. In general, succession produces a trend toward greater species diversity and species with longer life spans.

Succession begins with an ecological disturbance, an event that disrupts the ecosystem by altering its community, its *abiotic* (nonliving) environment, or both. The precise changes that occur during succession are as diverse as the environments in which succession occurs, but we can recognize certain general stages. Succession starts with a few hardy lichens or plants of species collectively known as **pioneers.** The pioneers alter the environment in ways that favor competing plants, which gradually displace the pioneers. If allowed to continue, succession progresses to a diverse and relatively stable **climax community.** Alternatively, recurring disturbances can maintain a community in an earlier, or **subclimax,** stage of succession. Our discussion of succession will focus on plant communities, which dominate the

(a) Kilauea, in Hawaii (primary succession)

(b) Yellowstone National Park, Wyoming (secondary succession)

▲ FIGURE 28-16 **Succession in progress (a)** Primary succession. (Left) The Hawaiian volcano Kilauea has erupted repeatedly since 1983, sending rivers of lava over the surrounding countryside. (Right) A pioneer fern takes root in a crack in hardened lava. **(b)** Secondary succession. (Left) In the summer of 1988, extensive fires swept through the forests of Yellowstone National Park in Wyoming. (Right) Trees and flowering plants are thriving in the sunlight, and wildlife populations are increasing as secondary succession occurs.

THINK CRITICALLY People have suppressed fires for decades. How might fire suppression affect forest ecosystems and succession?

landscape and provide both food and habitat for animals, fungi, and microorganisms.

There Are Two Major Forms of Succession: Primary and Secondary

During **primary succession,** a community gradually forms in a location where there are no remnants of a previous community and often no trace of life at all. The disturbance that sets the stage for primary succession may be a glacier scouring the landscape down to bare rock or a volcano producing a new island in the ocean or creating a layer of newly hardened lava on land (FIG. 28-16a). Building a community from scratch through primary succession typically requires thousands or even tens of thousands of years.

During **secondary succession,** a new community develops after an existing ecosystem is disturbed in a way that leaves significant remnants of the previous community behind, such as soil and seeds. For example, an abandoned farm typically has fertile soil and seeds from both crops and weeds. A clear-cut forest usually has soil, shrubs, and small trees remaining. Even a forest fire leaves behind the ingredients for secondary succession, such as residues of burnt trees that are high in plant nutrients. Fires also spare some trees and many healthy roots. Some plants produce seeds that can withstand fire or may even require it in order to sprout. The heat of a forest fire opens the cones of lodgepole pines, releasing their seeds. Thus, fires may promote rapid regeneration of forests and other communities (FIG. 28-16b).

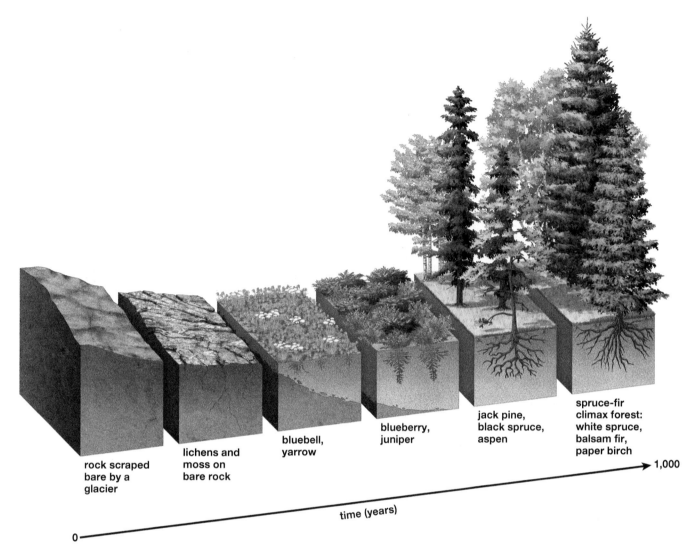

rock scraped
bare by a
glacier

lichens and
moss on
bare rock

bluebell,
yarrow

blueberry,
juniper

jack pine,
black spruce,
aspen

spruce-fir
climax forest:
white spruce,
balsam fir,
paper birch

1,000

time (years)

0

▲ **FIGURE 28-17** **Primary succession** Primary succession on bare rock exposed as glaciers retreated from Isle Royale in Lake Superior in upper Michigan. Notice that the soil deepens over time, gradually burying the bedrock and allowing trees to take root.

Primary Succession May Begin on Bare Rock

FIGURE 28-17 illustrates primary succession on Isle Royale, Michigan, an island in northern Lake Superior that was scraped down to bare rock by glaciers that retreated roughly 10,000 years ago. Weathering includes cycles of freezing and thawing that cracks rocks and erodes their surface layers, producing small particles. Rainwater dissolves some of the minerals from rock particles, making them available to pioneer organisms.

Weathered rock provides an attachment site for lichens, which obtain energy through photosynthesis and acquire some of their mineral nutrients by dissolving rock with an acid that they secrete. As the lichens spread over the rock surface, drought-tolerant mosses begin growing in cracks. Fortified by nutrients liberated by the lichens, the mosses form a dense mat that traps dust, tiny rock particles and bits of organic debris. The mosses eventually cover and kill many of the lichens that made their growth possible.

The mat of mosses acts like a sponge, absorbing and trapping moisture. As mosses die and decompose, their bodies add nutrients to a thin layer of new soil. Within the moss mat, seeds of larger plants, such as bluebell and yarrow, germinate. As these plants die, their decomposing bodies further thicken the layer of soil.

As woody shrubs such as blueberry and juniper take advantage of the deeper soil, the mosses and remaining lichens may be shaded out and buried by decaying leaves and vegetation. Eventually, trees such as jack pine, black spruce, and aspen take root in the deeper crevices, and the sun-loving shrubs are shaded out. Within the forest, shade-tolerant seedlings of taller or faster-growing trees thrive, including balsam fir, paper birch, and white spruce. In time, these trees tower over and replace the earlier trees, which are intolerant of shade. After hundreds of years, a climax forest thrives on what was once bare rock.

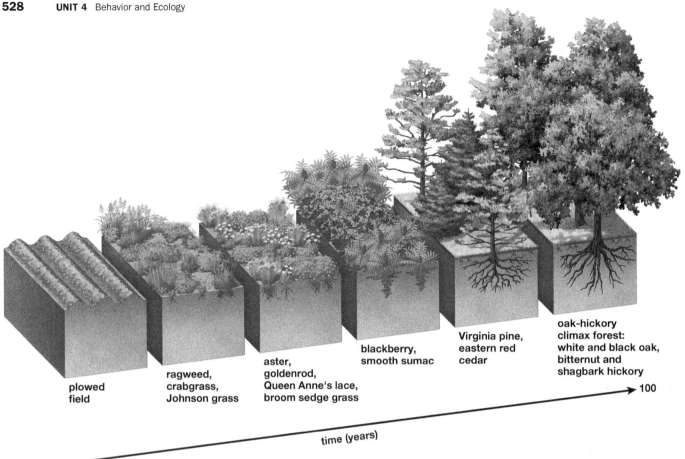

plowed
field

ragweed,
crabgrass,
Johnson grass

aster,
goldenrod,
Queen Anne's lace,
broom sedge grass

blackberry,
smooth sumac

Virginia pine,
eastern red
cedar

oak-hickory
climax forest:
white and black oak,
bitternut and
shagbark hickory

time (years)

0

100

▲ FIGURE 28-18 **Secondary succession** Secondary succession as it might occur on a plowed, abandoned farm field in North Carolina, in the southeastern United States. Notice that a thick layer of soil is present from the beginning, which greatly speeds up the process compared to primary succession.

An Abandoned Farm Undergoes Secondary Succession

FIGURE 28-18 illustrates secondary succession on an abandoned farm in the southeastern United States. The pioneer species are sun-loving, fast-growing plants such as ragweed, crabgrass, and Johnson grass. Such species generally produce large numbers of easily dispersed seeds that help them colonize open spaces. However, they don't compete well against longer-lived species that grow larger over the years and shade them out, so after a few years, plants such as asters, goldenrod, Queen Anne's lace, and perennial grasses move in, followed by woody shrubs such as blackberry and smooth sumac. Eventually, pine and cedar trees become established. About two decades after a field is abandoned, an evergreen forest dominated by pines takes over. However, the new forest alters conditions in ways that favor its successors. The shade of the pine forest inhibits the growth of its own seedlings while favoring the growth of hardwood trees, whose seedlings are shade tolerant and can grow beneath the pines. After about 70 years, slow-growing hardwoods, such as oak and hickory trees, begin to replace the aging pines. Roughly a century after the field was abandoned, the former farm is covered by relatively stable climax forest dominated by oak and hickory.

Succession Also Occurs in Ponds and Lakes

Succession in freshwater ponds and lakes occurs as soil and rock particles, washed in from the shore or carried in by streams entering the pond, settle to the bottom. This sediment gradually makes the pond more and more shallow. Eventually, moisture-loving plants take root along the shore. As more sediment fills the pond, the shoreline slowly moves toward the center of the pond. The soil of the original shoreline becomes drier, and plants from the surrounding land take over (FIG. 28-19). Eventually, no open water remains.

In forests, meadows are often produced by small lakes undergoing succession. As the lake fills in from the edges, grasses colonize the newly formed soil. As the lake shrinks and the area of meadow expands, trees encroach around the meadow's edges, eventually converting the meadow to forest.

Succession Culminates in a Climax Community

Succession ends with a reasonably stable climax community, which perpetuates itself if it is not disturbed by external forces (such as fire, parasites, invasive species, or human activities). The populations within a climax community have ecological niches that allow them to coexist without supplanting one another. In general, climax communities have more species and more types of community interactions than early stages of succession do. The plant species that dominate climax communities generally live longer and tend to be larger than pioneer species, particularly in climax forests.

Climax communities are determined by geological and climatic variables, including temperature, rainfall, elevation, latitude, type of rock (which determines the type of nutrients available in the soil), and exposure to sun and wind. These factors vary dramatically from one area to the next. For example, if you drive through Colorado or Wyoming, you will see a shortgrass prairie climax community on the eastern plains (in those rare areas where it has not been replaced by farms), pine-spruce forests in the mountains, tundra on the mountain summits, and sagebrush-dominated communities in the western valleys.

Natural events such as windstorms, avalanches, and fires started by lightning may destroy sections of climax communities, initiating secondary succession and producing a patchwork of various successional stages within an ecosystem. In many forests throughout the United States, rangers allow fires set by lightning to run their course, recognizing that fires are important for the maintenance of the ecosystem. Fires liberate nutrients and kill some (but usually not all) of the trees. As a result, more nutrients and sunlight reach the forest floor, encouraging the growth of subclimax plants. The combination of climax and subclimax communities in different parts of the ecosystem provides habitats for a larger number of species of plants and animals than would either climax or subclimax vegetation alone.

Some Ecosystems Are Maintained in Subclimax Stages

Frequent disturbances can maintain some ecosystems in subclimax stages for very long periods of time. The tallgrass prairie that once covered northern Missouri and most of Illinois was a subclimax stage of an ecosystem whose climax community is deciduous forest. The subclimax prairie was maintained by periodic fires, some set by lightning and others deliberately set by Native Americans centuries ago to provide grazing land for bison. Where they have not been converted to farms, forest now encroaches on the grasslands, but people maintain some tallgrass prairie preserves with controlled burns.

Farms, gardens, and lawns are subclimax communities maintained by frequent, intentional disturbance. Grains are specialized grasses characteristic of the early stages of succession, and farmers spend a great deal of time, energy, and

▼ FIGURE 28-19 **Succession in a freshwater pond** This pond is rapidly being converted to dry land. Although there is a little open water in the center of the pond, water lilies dominate the pond, showing that it is only a few feet deep in most places. Shrubs and small trees are beginning to grow around the drier edges of the pond.

herbicides to prevent competitors, such as weeds, wildflowers, and woody shrubs, from taking over. The suburban lawn is a subclimax ecosystem maintained by regular mowing, which destroys woody colonizers, and the application of herbicides that selectively kill pioneer species such as crabgrass and dandelions.

CASE STUDY REVISITED
The Fox's Tale

Five of the Channel Islands are included in the Channel Islands National Park. Dismayed by scarred landscapes, invasive weeds replacing rare native plants, and especially by drastic declines in the island fox population, the National Park Service, in collaboration with other government and private organizations, set out to restore the islands' communities. Santa Cruz Island, the largest of the Channel Islands, has been a major focus of restoration efforts.

First, the cattle were removed. However, there were more than 20,000 feral sheep roaming the island. The sheep were rounded up or shot, and by the late 1990s, Santa Cruz was sheep-free. The feral pigs that plagued the island were shot by skilled hunters; the last pig was eliminated in 2007. Finally, golden eagles, which colonized the island and became major predators of foxes, were all trapped and relocated to the mainland, and a few bald eagles were successfully reintroduced. Conservation biologists hope that the bald eagles will keep golden eagles from returning.

Free of predators, the island fox population has rebounded—Santa Cruz alone is now home to about 1,300–1,500 foxes, and the combined fox population on the islands is more than 6,000. Now that the pigs are gone, many native plants are making a comeback. Acorns, a favorite food of pigs, once again sprout into oak seedlings. Campaigns to control invasive weeds have helped the recovery of some of the Channel Islands' endangered plants, although several had already become extinct. The Channel Islands will probably always bear signs of past abuse, but future generations of visitors may see nearly intact, native climax communities once again.

THINK CRITICALLY Ecological succession sounds automatic—a farm is abandoned or a glacier retreats, and eventually the ecosystem regains its original communities. However, as in the Channel Islands, "letting nature take its course" doesn't always work, and ecosystems often need some help from restoration ecologists. If a disturbed ecosystem is simply left alone, what environmental conditions tend to favor natural succession, and what conditions may slow succession or even allow the ecosystem to remain permanently degraded?

CHAPTER REVIEW

 Go to **MasteringBiology** for practice quizzes, activities, eText, videos, current events, and more.

Answers to Think Critically, Evaluate This, Multiple Choice, and Fill-in-the-Blank questions can be found in the Answers section at the back of the book.

Summary of Key Concepts

28.1 Why Are Community Interactions Important?

Ecological communities consist of all the interacting populations of different species within an ecosystem. Community interactions influence population size, and the interacting populations act on one another as agents of natural selection. Thus, community interactions shape the bodies and behaviors of the interacting populations.

28.2 How Does the Ecological Niche Influence Competition?

The ecological niche includes all aspects of a species' habitat and interactions with its living and nonliving environments. Each species occupies a unique ecological niche. Interspecific competition occurs whenever the niches of two species within a community overlap. When two species with the same niche are forced (under laboratory conditions) to occupy the same ecological niche, one species always outcompetes the other. Species in natural communities have evolved in ways that avoid extensive niche overlap, with behavioral and physical adaptations that allow resource partitioning. Interspecific competition limits both the population size and the distribution of competing species. Intraspecific competition also limits population size because individuals of the same species occupy the same ecological niche and compete with one another for all of their needs.

28.3 How Do Consumer–Prey Interactions Shape Evolutionary Adaptations?

Predators and parasites are consumers of other organisms. In general, predators are free-living organisms that are less abundant than their prey, while parasites live in or on their hosts for a significant part of their life cycle and are much more abundant than their prey. Both types of consumers and their prey act as strong agents of natural selection on one another. Predators and prey have evolved a variety of toxic chemicals for attack and defense. Plants have evolved defenses ranging from poisons to overall toughness. These defenses, in turn, have selected for predators that can detoxify poisons and grind down tough tissues. Many prey animals have evolved protective colorations that render them either inconspicuous (camouflage) or startling (startle coloration) to their predators. Some prey are poisonous, distasteful, or venomous and exhibit warning coloration by which they are readily recognized and avoided by predators. Some harmless species have evolved to resemble distasteful organisms. Parasite–host coevolution includes the mammalian immune response against disease microbes and the many ways that these microbes have evolved to avoid detection or destruction by the immune response.

28.4 How Do Mutualisms Benefit Different Species?

Mutualism benefits two or more interacting species. Some mutualistic interactions are symbiotic, such as those of cows and their cellulose-digesting microorganisms. Other mutualistic interactions are more temporary, such as those that occur between plants and the animals that pollinate them.

28.5 How Do Keystone Species Influence Community Structure?

Keystone species have a greater influence on community structure than can be predicted by their numbers. If a keystone species is removed from a community, the structure of the community is significantly altered.

28.6 How Do Species Interactions Change Community Structure over Time?

Succession is a change in a community and its nonliving environment over time. During succession, plants alter the environment in ways that favor their competitors, thus producing a somewhat predictable progression of dominant species. Primary succession, which may take thousands of years, occurs where no remnant of a previous community exists, such as on bare rock. Secondary succession occurs much more rapidly because it builds on the remains of a disrupted community, such as an abandoned field or the remnants of a forest after a fire. Uninterrupted succession ends with a climax community, which tends to be self-perpetuating unless acted on by outside forces. Some ecosystems, including tallgrass prairie and farm fields, are maintained in relatively early, subclimax stages of succession by periodic disruptions.

Key Terms

aggressive mimicry *522*
camouflage *518*
climax community *525*
coevolution *513*
community *513*
competitive exclusion
   principle *514*
consumer–prey interaction *513*
ecological niche *513*
host *517*
interspecific
   competition *513*
intraspecific
   competition *515*
keystone species *524*
mimicry *520*
mutualism *513*
parasite *517*
pioneer *525*
predator *517*
primary succession *526*
resource partitioning *514*
secondary succession *526*
startle coloration *522*
subclimax *525*
succession *525*
symbiosis *513*
warning coloration *520*

Thinking Through the Concepts

Multiple Choice

1. The orderly progress of communities, starting from bare rock with no soil or traces of a previous community, is called
   a. primary succession.
   b. secondary succession.
   c. subclimax community.
   d. climax community.

2. Which of the following statements is *not* true of an ecological niche?
   a. A niche includes the physical environment, such as climate and water availability.
   b. A niche includes predators and parasites.
   c. Niche overlap may help to drive evolution.
   d. Two species cannot have overlapping niches.

3. A keystone species
   a. is always a carnivore.
   b. has a minor influence on community structure.
   c. has a major influence on community structure out of proportion to its numbers.
   d. has a major influence on community structure only when present in large numbers.

4. Which of the following statements regarding invasive species is True?
   a. All introduced species are invasive.
   b. Almost all invasive species are plants.
   c. Invasive species have no predators or parasites in their new ecosystem.
   d. Invasive species multiply rapidly and may displace native species in a community.

5. Which of the following statements about predators and parasites is *not* true?
   a. Predators and parasites harm their prey.
   b. Predators live on or in their hosts for a significant part of their life cycle.
   c. Predators and parasites coevolve with their prey.
   d. Parasites may kill their prey.

Fill-in-the-Blank

1. Organisms that interact serve as agents of _____ on one another. This results in _____, which is the process by which species evolve adaptations to one another.

2. Predators may be meat-eaters, called _____, or plant-eaters, called _____. Both predators and their prey may blend into their surroundings by using _____.

3. The concept that no two species with identical niches can coexist indefinitely is called the _____ principle.

4. Fill in the types of coloration or mimicry: used by prey to signal that it is distasteful: _____; used by a moth with large eyespots on its wings:_____   ; mimicry of a poisonous animal by a nonpoisonous animal: _____; mimicry used by a predator to attract its prey: _____.

5. Fill in the appropriate type of community interaction: bacteria, living in the human gut, that synthesize vitamin K: _____; bacteria that cause illness: _____; a deer eating grass: _____; a bee pollinating a flower:_____.

6. A somewhat predictable change in community structure over time is _____. This process takes two forms. Which of these forms would start with bare rock? _____ Which would occur after a forest fire? _____ A relatively stable community that is the end product of this process is called a _____ community. A mowed lawn in suburbia is an example of a _____ community.

Review Questions

1. Define an *ecological community*, and describe the three major categories of community interactions, including the benefits and harms to the interacting species.

2. Explain how resource partitioning is a logical outcome of the competitive exclusion principle.

3. Describe examples of coevolution between consumers and their prey.

4. Define *succession*. Which type of succession would occur on a clear-cut forest (where all trees have been logged) and why?

5. Provide examples of two climax and two subclimax communities. How do they differ?

6. What is an invasive species? Why are they destructive? What general adaptations do invasive species possess?

7. What is a keystone species? How can a keystone species within a community be identified?

Applying the Concepts

1. An ecologist visiting an island finds two species of birds, one of which has a slightly larger bill than the other. Interpret this finding with respect to the ecological niche and the competitive exclusion principle, and explain both concepts.

2. Why is it difficult to study succession? Choose a specific location and describe how you would study succession there.

ENERGY FLOW AND NUTRIENT CYCLING IN ECOSYSTEMS

A brown bear intercepts a salmon on its journey upstream to spawn.

Dying Fish Feed an Ecosystem

THE SOCKEYE SALMON in Katmai National Park in Alaska have a remarkable life cycle. After hatching in shallow depressions in the gravel bed of a swiftly flowing stream, the juvenile salmon spend 1 to 3 years in fresh water, often in a nearby lake. Then the young fish begin the physiological changes that will prepare them for life in the ocean. They head downstream to estuaries, where fresh water and salt water mix. In the estuary, the salmon complete their transformation, then head out to sea.

In the ocean, the young salmon grow rapidly, feeding on small fish and crustaceans. A few years later, when they reach sexual maturity, an instinctive drive compels them to return to their home streams to spawn. If they are lucky enough to escape the jaws of brown bears and the talons of eagles on their journey, the salmon carry their precious payload of sperm and eggs upstream to renew the cycle of life. The salmon die soon after spawning.

The fishes' trip back to their birthplace is remarkable in another way: Nutrients almost always move downstream, washed from the land into the ocean. But salmon, filled with muscle and fat acquired from feeding in the ocean, bring ocean nutrients back to the land. They bring energy upstream, too. From bears to eagles to spruce trees, this upstream movement of nutrients and energy supports the extraordinarily rich terrestrial ecosystems of the southern coast of Alaska. Where do nutrients and energy originate? How do living organisms acquire nutrients and energy and transfer them among the members of biological communities?

AT A GLANCE

29.1 HOW DO NUTRIENTS AND ENERGY MOVE THROUGH ECOSYSTEMS?

All **ecosystems** consist of two components. The **biotic** components are the communities of living organisms in a given area. The **abiotic** components of an ecosystem consist of all the nonliving aspects of the environment, such as climate, light, temperature, water, and minerals in the soil. Interactions within biological communities and between communities and their abiotic environment determine the movement of energy and nutrients through ecosystems. Two basic principles underlie this movement: Nutrients cycle within and between ecosystems, whereas energy flows through ecosystems (**FIG. 29-1**).

Nutrients are atoms and molecules that organisms obtain from their environment. The same nutrient atoms have been sustaining life on Earth for about 3.5 billion years. Your body includes oxygen, carbon, hydrogen, and nitrogen atoms that were once part of a dinosaur or a woolly mammoth. Nutrients are transported around the planet and converted to different molecular forms, but they do not leave Earth.

Energy, in contrast, takes a one-way journey through ecosystems. Solar energy is captured by photosynthetic bacteria, algae, and plants and then flows from organism to organism. However, all chemical reactions are inefficient. Every time an organism synthesizes a protein or moves its body, some of the useful, concentrated energy found in the chemical bonds of biological molecules is converted to low-level heat given off to the environment (see Chapter 6). Therefore, life on Earth requires a continuous input of energy.

CHECK YOUR LEARNING
Can you ...
- explain why nutrients cycle within and between ecosystems, whereas energy flows through ecosystems?

29.2 HOW DOES ENERGY FLOW THROUGH ECOSYSTEMS?

Thermonuclear reactions in the sun transform a relatively small amount of matter into enormous quantities of energy. Much of this energy is in the form of electromagnetic radiation, including heat (infrared light), visible light, and ultraviolet light. However, the sun emits its energy equally in all directions and is 93 million miles away, so Earth intercepts only about 45 billionths of a percent of this energy. Still, that's almost as much energy per hour as humanity uses in a year. The atmosphere and its clouds absorb or reflect about half of this solar radiation. About half reaches Earth's surface as visible light. A small fraction of the light reaching the surface is used in photosynthesis.

Energy and Nutrients Enter Ecosystems Through Photosynthesis

Plants, algae, and photosynthetic bacteria acquire nutrients such as carbon, nitrogen, oxygen, and phosphorus from the abiotic portions of ecosystems. These photosynthetic organisms capture energy in sunlight and use it to join nutrient atoms into carbohydrates, proteins, nucleic acids, and the other biological molecules of their bodies, storing some of the sun's energy in the chemical bonds of these molecules. Thus, photosynthesis brings both energy and nutrients into ecosystems. Here, we will focus our attention on the flow of energy.

Energy Passes Through Ecosystems from One Trophic Level to the Next

In an ecosystem, each category of organisms through which energy passes is called a **trophic level** (literally, "feeding level"). Photosynthetic organisms form the first trophic level. These organisms are called **producers,** or **autotrophs** (Greek, meaning "self-feeders"), because they produce food for themselves using inorganic nutrients and solar energy. Through photosynthesis, producers directly or indirectly provide food for nearly all other forms of life. Organisms that cannot photosynthesize, called **consumers,** or **heterotrophs** ("other-feeders"), acquire energy and most of their nutrients prepackaged in the molecules that make up the bodies of the organisms that they eat.

There are several levels of consumers. **Primary consumers** feed directly on producers. These **herbivores** (from Latin words meaning "plant-eaters"), which include animals such as grasshoppers, mice, and zebras, form the second trophic level. **Carnivores** ("meat-eaters"), such as spiders, hawks, and salmon, are higher-level consumers. Carnivores act as **secondary consumers** when they prey on herbivores. Some carnivores at least occasionally eat other carnivores; when doing so, they occupy the fourth trophic level and are called **tertiary consumers.** In some instances, particularly in the oceans, there are even higher trophic levels.

▶FIGURE 29-1 **Energy flow, nutrient cycling, and feeding relationships in ecosystems** The energy of sunlight (yellow arrow) enters an ecosystem during photosynthesis by organisms called producers, which store some of the energy in the biological molecules of their bodies. This biologically available energy (red arrows) is then passed to nonphotosynthetic organisms called consumers. Energy in wastes and dead bodies supports detritivores and decomposers. Every organism loses some energy as heat (orange arrows), so useful energy gradually becomes unavailable to living organisms. Therefore, ecosystems require a continuous input of energy. In contrast, nutrients (purple arrows) are recycled.

Net Primary Production Is a Measure of the Energy Stored in Producers

The amount of life that an ecosystem can support is determined by the amount of energy captured by its producers. The energy that photosynthetic organisms in a given area store in their bodies over a given period of time (for example, calories per square meter per year) is called **net primary** **production.** However, mass is much easier to determine than energy, and **biomass,** or dry biological material, is generally a good measure of the energy stored in organisms' bodies. Therefore, net primary production is usually given as grams of biomass per square meter per year.

The net primary production of an ecosystem is influenced by many factors, including the amount of sunlight reaching

◀ **FIGURE 29-2 Net primary production in ecosystems** The average net primary production of some terrestrial and aquatic ecosystems is shown, measured in grams of biological material produced per square meter per year.

THINK CRITICALLY What factors contribute to the differences in primary production among ecosystems?

the producers, the availability of water and nutrients, and the temperature (**FIG. 29-2**). In deserts, for example, lack of water limits production. In the open ocean, light is a limiting factor in deep waters, and lack of nutrients limits production in most surface waters. In ecosystems where all resources are abundant, such as tropical rain forests, production is high.

An ecosystem's contribution to Earth's total production is determined both by the ecosystem's production per unit area and by the portion of Earth that the ecosystem covers. Although the oceans generally have low net primary production, they cover about 70% of Earth's surface, so they contribute about 25% of Earth's total production. This is about the same overall contribution as tropical rain forests, which have high net primary production, but which cover less than 5% of Earth's surface.

Food Chains and Food Webs Describe Feeding Relationships Within Communities

A **food chain** is a linear feeding relationship that includes a single species in each trophic level that is fed upon by a single species in the trophic level just above it (**FIG. 29-3**). Different ecosystems support radically different food chains. Plants are the dominant producers in land-based (terrestrial) ecosystems (**FIG. 29-3a**). Plants support plant-eating insects, reptiles, birds, and mammals, each of which may be preyed on by other animals. In contrast, microscopic photosynthetic protists and bacteria collectively called **phytoplankton** are the dominant producers in most aquatic food chains, such as those found in lakes and oceans (**FIG. 29-3b**). Phytoplankton support a diverse group of consumers called **zooplankton,** which consist mainly of protists and small shrimp-like crustaceans. These are eaten primarily by fish, which in turn are eaten by larger fish.

Animals in natural communities seldom fit neatly into simple food chains. A **food web** shows many interconnected food chains and more accurately describes the actual feeding relationships in a community (**FIG. 29-4**). Some animals, such as raccoons, bears, rats, and humans, are **omnivores** ("everything-eaters"); they act as primary, secondary, and occasionally tertiary consumers. A raccoon, for instance, is a primary consumer when it eats fruits and nuts, a secondary

consumer when it eats grasshoppers, and a tertiary consumer when it eats frogs or carnivorous fish. A carnivorous plant such as the Venus flytrap can tangle the food web further by acting as both a photosynthesizing producer and a spider-trapping tertiary consumer.

Detritivores and Decomposers Recycle Nutrients

Detritivores and decomposers are usually either left out of food webs or described as the final level because they feed on the wastes, dead bodies, or discarded body parts (such as fallen leaves) of all the other levels. **Detritivores** ("debris-eaters") are an army of mostly small and often unnoticed organisms, including nematode worms, earthworms, millipedes, dung beetles, and the larvae of some flies. A few large vertebrates such as vultures are also detritivores.

Decomposers are primarily fungi and bacteria. They feed mostly on the same material as detritivores, but they do not ingest chunks of organic matter, as detritivores do. Instead, they secrete digestive enzymes outside their bodies, where the enzymes break down organic material. The decomposers absorb some of the resulting nutrient molecules, but many of the nutrients remain in the environment.

Because they recycle nutrients, detritivores and decomposers are absolutely essential to life on Earth. They reduce the bodies and wastes of other organisms to simple molecules, such as carbon dioxide, ammonia, and minerals, that return to the atmosphere, soil, and water. Without detritivores and decomposers, ecosystems would gradually be buried by accumulated wastes and dead bodies, whose nutrients would be unavailable to other living organisms, including producers. If the producers died from a lack of nutrients, energy would cease to enter the ecosystem, and organisms at higher trophic levels, including people, would die as well.

Energy Transfer Between Trophic Levels Is Inefficient

A fundamental principle of thermodynamics is that energy use is never completely efficient (see Chapter 6). For example, as your car burns gasoline, only about 20% of the energy

(a) A simple terrestrial food chain

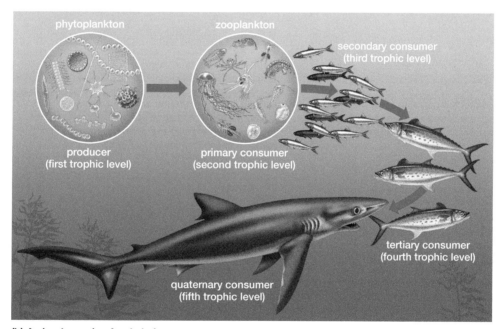

(b) A simple marine food chain

▲ FIGURE 29-3 **Food chains on land and sea**

is used to move the car; the other 80% is lost as heat. Inefficiency is also the rule in living systems: Waste heat is produced by all the biochemical reactions that keep cells alive. For example, splitting the chemical bonds of adenosine triphosphate (ATP) to power muscle contraction releases heat; that is why shivering or walking briskly on a cold day warms your body.

Most of the energy stored in the organisms at a given trophic level is not available to organisms in the next higher trophic level. When a grasshopper (a primary consumer) eats grass (a producer), only some of the solar energy trapped by the grass is available to the insect. The grass converted some

of the solar energy into the chemical bonds of cellulose, which a grasshopper cannot digest. In addition, although grasses don't feel warm to the touch, virtually every chemical reaction in the grass's leaves, stems, and roots gives off some energy as low-level heat, which thus isn't available to any other organism. Therefore, only a fraction of the energy captured by the producers of the first trophic level can be used by organisms in the second trophic level. If the grasshopper is eaten by a robin (the third trophic level), the bird will not obtain all the energy that the insect acquired from the plants. Some of the energy will have been used up to power hopping, flying, and eating. Some energy will be

▲ **FIGURE 29-4 A simplified grassland food web** The animals pictured in the foreground include a vulture (a detritivore), a bull snake, a ground squirrel, a burrowing owl, a badger, a mouse, and a shrew (which looks like a small mouse but is carnivorous). In the middle distance you'll see a grouse, a meadowlark, a grasshopper, and a jackrabbit. In the distance, look for pronghorn antelope, a hawk, pheasants, a wolf, and bison.

found in the grasshopper's indigestible exoskeleton. Most of the energy will have been lost as heat. Similarly, most of the energy in a robin's body will be unavailable to a hawk that may consume it.

Although energy transfer between trophic levels varies significantly among communities, the average net transfer of energy from one trophic level to the next is roughly 10%. This means that, in general, the amount of energy stored in primary consumers is only about 10% of the energy stored in the bodies of producers. In turn, the bodies of secondary consumers contain roughly 10% of the energy stored in primary consumers. This inefficient energy transfer between trophic levels is called the "10% law." An **energy pyramid** illustrates the energy relationships between trophic levels—widest at the base and progressively narrowing in higher trophic levels (**FIG. 29-5**). A biomass pyramid for a given community typically has the same general shape as the community's energy pyramid.

The dominant organisms in a community are almost always photosynthesizers because they have the most energy available to them, as sunlight. The most abundant animals are herbivores. Carnivores are relatively scarce because there is far less energy available to support them.

Energy losses within and between trophic levels mean that long-lived animals at higher trophic levels often eat

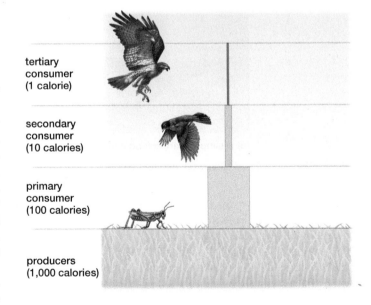

tertiary consumer (1 calorie)

secondary consumer (10 calories)

primary consumer (100 calories)

producers (1,000 calories)

▲ **FIGURE 29-5 An energy pyramid for a grassland ecosystem** The width of each rectangle is proportional to the energy stored at that trophic level. Representative organisms for the first four trophic levels in a U.S. grassland ecosystem illustrated here are grass, a grasshopper, a robin, and a red-tailed hawk.

many times their body weight in organisms that occupy lower trophic levels—consider, for example, how much food you eat in a year, even if you stay the same weight. As long-lived animals continue to eat for months or years, they may consume, and often store, toxic substances that aren't easily broken down or excreted. Thus, toxic chemicals in plants may become concentrated in the bodies of high-level consumers. This **biological magnification** can lead to debilitating, even fatal, effects, as we explore in "Health Watch: Biological Magnification of Toxic Substances" on page 540.

CHECK YOUR LEARNING

Can you ...

* name the trophic levels in a community and give examples of organisms found in each trophic level?
* describe how energy flows through an ecosystem?
* explain why detritivores and decomposers are essential to ecosystem function?
* explain how the inefficiency of energy transfer between trophic levels determines the relative abundance of organisms in different trophic levels?

CASE STUDY \ CONTINUED

Dying Fish Feed an Ecosystem

When a sockeye salmon eats a smaller fish, the salmon is typically a tertiary consumer on the fourth trophic level, because the small fish was a secondary consumer that ate zooplankton, which were primary consumers that fed on photosynthetic phytoplankton. When an Alaskan brown bear eats a salmon, it is therefore feeding on the fifth trophic level. In a simplified food chain with only one type of organism at each trophic level, the 10% law means that a food chain containing a single 1,000-pound bear will also contain 10,000 pounds of salmon, 100,000 pounds of smaller fish, a million pounds of zooplankton, and 10 million pounds of phytoplankton.

All organisms contain not only energy, but also many types of nutrients. How are these nutrients recycled to future generations of living things?

29.3 HOW DO NUTRIENTS CYCLE WITHIN AND AMONG ECOSYSTEMS?

As noted earlier, nutrients are elements and small molecules that form the chemical building blocks of life. Some, called **macronutrients,** are required by organisms in large quantities. These include water, carbon, hydrogen, oxygen, nitrogen, phosphorus, sulfur, and calcium. **Micronutrients,** including zinc, molybdenum, iron, selenium, and iodine, are required only in trace quantities. **Nutrient cycles,** also called *biogeochemical cycles,* describe the pathways that nutrients take as they move from their major sources in the abiotic parts of ecosystems, called **reservoirs,** through living communities and back again. In the following sections, we describe the cycles of water, carbon, nitrogen, and phosphorus.

The Hydrologic Cycle Has Its Major Reservoir in the Oceans

The **hydrologic cycle** (FIG. 29-6) is the pathway by which water travels from its major reservoir—the oceans—through the atmosphere, to smaller reservoirs in freshwater lakes, rivers, and groundwater, and then back again to the oceans. The oceans contain more than 97% of Earth's water. Another 2% of the total water is trapped in ice, leaving only 1% as liquid fresh water.

▲ **FIGURE 29-6 The hydrologic cycle**

Biological Magnification of Toxic Substances

The U.S. Food and Drug Administration advises that pregnant and breastfeeding women should avoid eating swordfish, shark, and king mackerel and limit eating albacore (white) tuna to no more than one can a week. But isn't eating fish supposed to be good for you? That depends on what fish you eat. These particular fish often contain a high concentration of mercury, which can damage the developing brains of fetuses and infants. Where does the mercury come from, and why do certain fish have so much of it?

Most mercury in the environment comes from two sources. Many small-scale gold mining operations, especially in less-developed countries, use mercury to separate gold from crude ore. In developed countries, including the United States, coal-fired power plants are the largest source of mercury contamination. Mercury, found in trace amounts in coal, is vaporized when the coal is burned and may be wafted thousands of miles on the winds. As a result, nowhere on Earth is free of mercury contamination.

Except in very localized areas, environmental concentrations of mercury are extremely low. Mercury becomes a health problem through *biological magnification*, the process by which toxic substances become concentrated in animals occupying high trophic levels. Most substances that undergo biological magnification share two properties. First, substances that biomagnify are stored in living tissue, particularly in fat. (Mercury is also stored in muscle.) Second, neither animals nor decomposers can readily break these substances down into harmless materials—they are not easily *biodegradable*. Mercury is an element, so it can never be broken down. When mercury becomes attached to certain organic functional groups, it becomes much more toxic. Although "organomercury" forms can be broken down, the process is very slow.

Biological magnification occurs because energy transfer between trophic levels is inefficient. By eating large quantities of producers that contain low levels of toxic chemicals and absorbing and storing the toxins in its body, an herbivore accumulates higher concentrations of the toxins. This sequence—eat, absorb, and store—continues up the trophic levels. Sharks, swordfish, and king mackerel are long-lived, predatory fish that feed at the top of long food chains, so they have ample opportunity to accumulate high concentrations of mercury. In ecological terms, the FDA's advice is for people to avoid eating at an even higher trophic level.

Organic compounds, including several pesticides, may also build up in animals that occupy high trophic levels. Biological magnification first came to public attention in the 1950s and 1960s, when wildlife biologists witnessed an alarming decline in populations of several fish-eating birds such as cormorants, ospreys, brown pelicans, and bald eagles. They were being poisoned by a pesticide called DDT. To control insects, many aquatic ecosystems had been sprayed with low amounts of DDT. However, these fish-eating birds contained DDT in concentrations a million times greater than the concentration in the water (**FIG. E29-1**). As a result, the birds laid thin-shelled eggs that broke under the

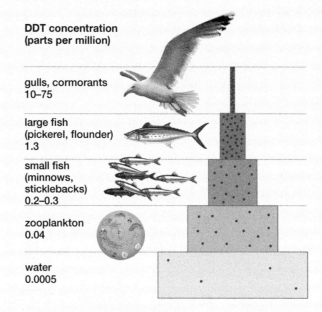

DDT concentration (parts per million)

gulls, cormorants 10–75

large fish (pickerel, flounder) 1.3

small fish (minnows, sticklebacks) 0.2–0.3

zooplankton 0.04

water 0.0005

▲ **FIGURE E29-1 Biological magnification of DDT** During the time when DDT was widely used as an insecticide, concentrations of DDT in a marsh on Long Island, New York, increased about a million-fold with increasing trophic levels, from extremely low levels in the water to toxic levels in predatory birds. Based on Woodwell, et al., *Science*, 1967.

parents' weight during incubation. Some other pesticides, and certain natural toxins produced by bacteria and algae, can also become concentrated as they move up the food chain.

Fortunately, there is good news. Populations of fish-eating birds have recovered significantly since DDT was banned in the United States in 1973. About 180 countries worldwide have agreed to ban or restrict the production and use of a dozen "persistent organic pollutants," including DDT and several other highly toxic pesticides. And in 2011, the U.S. Environmental Protection Agency issued new rules that require reductions in emissions of many toxic substances from power plants, including mercury, arsenic, nickel, and selenium, which should benefit both people and the other animals with which we share our planet.

EVALUATE THIS As you're having lunch with your friend Victoria, she confides in you that she's planning to become pregnant this year. You notice that Victoria is eating a tuna sandwich, and you remember reading that pregnant women should limit tuna intake because of mercury concerns. When you mention this to Victoria, she asks if there are fish that pose less risk. To answer Victoria's question, research the mercury levels typically found in catfish, salmon, light meat tuna and white meat tuna. Why might different species contain different levels of mercury?

The hydrologic cycle is driven by solar heat energy, which evaporates water from oceans, lakes, and streams. When water vapor condenses in the atmosphere, the water falls back to Earth as rain or snow. Because the oceans cover about 70% of Earth's surface, most evaporation occurs from them and most precipitation falls back onto them. Of the water that falls on land, some is absorbed by the roots of plants; much of this water is returned to the atmosphere by evaporation from plant leaves. Most of the rest of the water that falls on land evaporates from soil, lakes, and streams; a portion runs downhill in rivers back to the oceans; a minuscule fraction is stored in the bodies of living organisms; and some enters natural underground reservoirs called **aquifers.**

Aquifers are composed of sand, gravel, or water-permeable rock, such as sandstone, which are saturated with water. They are often tapped to supply water for household use and for irrigating crops. Water movement from the surface into aquifers is usually slow. In many areas of the world—including China, India, North Africa, California, and the Great Plains of the United States—water is being pumped out of aquifers faster than it is being replenished. If these aquifers are depleted, the resulting water shortages will force significant changes in agriculture. How do we know that aquifers are being depleted? There is the obvious way, of course, when wells go dry or have to be drilled deeper to reach water. But satellites can now survey underground water storage—and

much more—from space, as we explore in "How Do We Know That? Monitoring Earth's Health" on page 548.

The hydrologic cycle is crucial for terrestrial ecosystems because it provides the fresh water needed for land-based life. As you study the nutrient cycles that follow, keep in mind that nutrients in the soil must be dissolved in soil water to be taken up by the roots of plants or to be absorbed by bacteria. Plant leaves can take up carbon dioxide gas only after it has dissolved in a thin layer of water coating the cells inside the leaf. Without the hydrologic cycle, terrestrial organisms would rapidly disappear.

The Carbon Cycle Has Major Reservoirs in the Atmosphere and Oceans

Carbon atoms form the framework of all organic molecules. The **carbon cycle** (FIG. 29-7) is the pathway that carbon takes from its major short-term reservoirs in the atmosphere and oceans, through producers and into the bodies of consumers, detritivores, and decomposers, and then back to its reservoirs. Carbon enters a community when producers capture carbon dioxide (CO_2) during photosynthesis. On land, photosynthetic organisms acquire CO_2 from the atmosphere. Aquatic producers such as phytoplankton take up CO_2 dissolved in water.

Photosynthesizers "fix" carbon in biological molecules such as sugars and proteins (see Chapter 7). Producers return some of this carbon to the atmosphere or water as CO_2

▲ **FIGURE 29-7 The carbon cycle**

generated by cellular respiration (see Chapter 8), but much of the carbon remains stored in the biological molecules of their bodies. When primary consumers eat the producers, they acquire this stored carbon. Primary consumers and the organisms in higher trophic levels release CO_2 during respiration, excrete carbon compounds in their feces, and store the rest of the carbon in their bodies. When organisms die, their bodies are broken down by detritivores and decomposers, whose cellular respiration returns CO_2 to the atmosphere and oceans. The complementary processes of uptake by photosynthesis and release by cellular respiration continually recycle carbon from the abiotic to the biotic portions of ecosystems and back again.

Some carbon, however, cycles much more slowly. Much of Earth's carbon is bound up in limestone, formed from calcium carbonate ($CaCO_3$) deposited on the ocean floor in the shells of prehistoric phytoplankton. The movement of carbon from this source to the atmosphere and back again takes millions of years. **Fossil fuels,** which include coal, oil, and natural

gas, are also long-term reservoirs for carbon. These substances were produced from the remains of prehistoric organisms buried deep underground and subjected to high temperature and pressure. In addition to carbon, the energy of prehistoric sunlight (originally captured by photosynthetic organisms) is trapped in these deposits, in the chemical bonds of carbon compounds. When humans burn fossil fuels to tap this stored energy, CO_2 is released into the atmosphere, with potentially serious consequences, as we describe in Section 29.4.

The Nitrogen Cycle Has Its Major Reservoir in the Atmosphere

Nitrogen is a crucial component of proteins, many vitamins, nucleotides (such as ATP), and nucleic acids (such as DNA). The **nitrogen cycle** (FIG. 29-8) is the pathway taken by nitrogen from its primary reservoir—nitrogen gas (N_2) in the atmosphere—to much smaller reservoirs of ammonia and

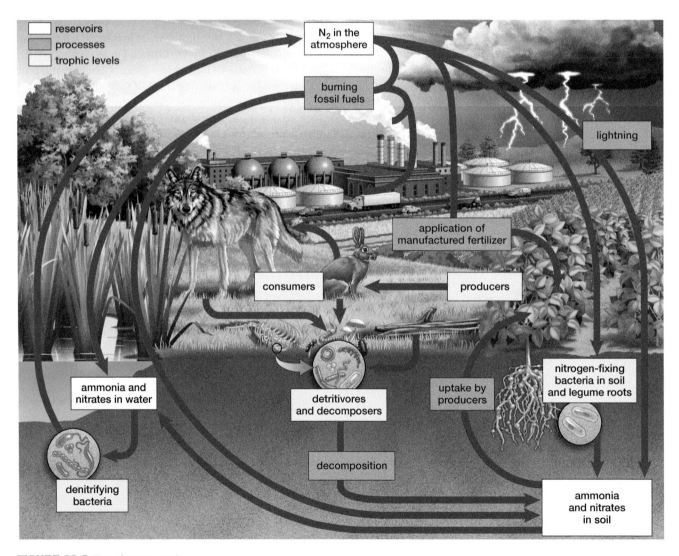

▲ **FIGURE 29-8 The nitrogen cycle**

THINK CRITICALLY What incentives cause humans to capture nitrogen from the air and pump it into the nitrogen cycle? What are some consequences of human augmentation of the nitrogen cycle?

nitrate in soil and water, through producers, consumers, detritivores and decomposers, and back to its reservoirs.

The atmosphere contains about 78% nitrogen gas, but plants and most other producers cannot use nitrogen in this form—they require either ammonia (NH_3) or nitrate (NO_3^-). A few types of bacteria that live in soil or water can convert N_2 into ammonia in a process called **nitrogen fixation.** Some nitrogen-fixing bacteria enter into a mutually beneficial relationship with certain plants, called *legumes*, in which the bacteria live in swellings on the plants' roots. Legumes such as alfalfa, soybeans, clover, and peas are extensively planted on farms, in part because they release excess ammonia produced by the bacteria, thus fertilizing the soil. Other bacteria in soil and water convert ammonia to nitrate. A small amount of nitrate is also produced during electrical storms, when the energy of lightning combines nitrogen and oxygen gases to form nitrogen oxide compounds. These nitrogen oxides fall to the ground dissolved in rain and are eventually converted to nitrate.

Producers absorb ammonia and nitrate and incorporate the nitrogen into biological molecules such as proteins and nucleic acids. The nitrogen passes through successively higher trophic levels as primary consumers eat the producers and are themselves eaten. At each trophic level, bodies and wastes are broken down by decomposers, which liberate ammonia back into the soil and water. The nitrogen cycle is completed by **denitrifying bacteria.** These residents of wet soil, swamps, and estuaries break down nitrate, releasing nitrogen gas back into the atmosphere (see Fig. 29-8).

CASE STUDY CONTINUED

Dying Fish Feed an Ecosystem

Nitrogen-fixing bacteria take up atmospheric nitrogen dissolved in ocean waters and produce ammonia, most of which is taken up by photosynthetic plankton. From the phytoplankton, nitrogen travels up the trophic levels, with some entering the bodies of salmon. As we will see in the Case Study Revisited, salmon bring nitrogen to the terrestrial ecosystems of the Alaskan coast.

People significantly manipulate the nitrogen cycle, both deliberately and unintentionally. As noted earlier, farmers plant legumes to fertilize their fields. Fertilizer factories combine N_2 from the atmosphere with hydrogen generated from natural gas, producing ammonia, which is then often converted to nitrate or urea (an organic nitrogen compound) for fertilizer. In addition, the heat produced by burning fossil fuels combines atmospheric N_2 and O_2, generating nitrogen oxides that form nitrates. These human activities now dominate the nitrogen cycle.

The Phosphorus Cycle Has Its Major Reservoir in Rock

Phosphorus is found in biological molecules such as nucleic acids and the phospholipids of cell membranes. It also forms a major component of vertebrate teeth and bones. The **phosphorus cycle** (FIG. 29-9) is the pathway taken by phosphorus from its primary reservoir in rocks to much smaller

▲ **FIGURE 29-9 The phosphorus cycle**

reservoirs in soil and water, through living organisms, and then back to its reservoirs.

Throughout its cycle, almost all phosphorus is bound to oxygen, forming phosphate (PO_4^{3-}). There are no gaseous forms of phosphate, so there is no atmospheric reservoir in the phosphorus cycle. As phosphate-rich rocks are exposed by geological processes, some of the phosphate is dissolved by rain and flowing water, which carry it into soil, lakes, and the ocean, forming the smaller reservoirs of phosphorus that are available to ecological communities. Dissolved phosphate is absorbed by producers, which incorporate it into biological molecules. From producers, phosphate is passed through food webs; at each level, excess phosphate is excreted. Ultimately, detritivores and decomposers return the phosphate to the soil and water, where it may then be reabsorbed by producers or become bound to sediments and eventually re-formed into rock. Human production of phosphate fertilizers now dominates the phosphorus cycle: We extract about two to eight times more phosphate from rocks than was produced by natural processes in prehistoric times.

CHECK YOUR LEARNING

Can you ...

- explain why nutrients cycle within and among ecosystems?
- describe the hydrologic, nitrogen, carbon, and phosphorus cycles?

29.4 WHAT HAPPENS WHEN HUMANS DISRUPT NUTRIENT CYCLES?

Ancient peoples, with small populations and limited technology, had relatively little impact on nutrient cycles. However, as the human population grew and new technologies were developed, people began to significantly alter many nutrient cycles. Today, human use of fossil fuels and chemical fertilizers has disrupted the global nutrient cycles of nitrogen, phosphorus, sulfur, and carbon.

Overloading the Nitrogen and Phosphorus Cycles Damages Aquatic Ecosystems

Each year, fertilizers containing about 45 million tons of phosphate and 115 million tons of nitrogen (as ammonium, nitrate, and urea) are applied to farm fields to help satisfy the agricultural demands of a growing human population. When water washes over the land from rainfall or irrigation, it dissolves and carries away some of the nitrogen and phosphate. As the water drains into lakes, rivers, and ultimately the oceans, these nutrients can overstimulate the growth of phytoplankton. The resulting *harmful algal blooms* can turn clear water into an opaque green soup. As the phytoplankton die, their bodies sink into deeper water, where they provide a feast for decomposer bacteria. Cellular respiration by decomposers uses up most of the oxygen in the water, creating what is often called a dead zone. Deprived of oxygen, aquatic

▲ **FIGURE 29-10 Harmful algal blooms** Nutrients, especially nitrate and phosphate, wash off farmland in the Midwest and move down the Mississippi River, which flows from upper left to the center of the image, where it ends in the Mississippi Delta. When these nutrients enter the Gulf, they fertilize an explosive growth of algae, visible in this satellite photo as hazy green swirls near the coast.

invertebrates and fish either leave the area or die and decompose (making the problem worse).

Each summer, a huge dead zone occurs in the Gulf of Mexico off the coast of Louisiana. In spring, enormous quantities of nitrates and phosphates wash off fertilized farm fields into streams that flow into the Mississippi River. The Mississippi then empties the fertilizers into the Gulf of Mexico. In summer, when sunlight strengthens and the Gulf warms, the fertilizers create an algal bloom (**FIG. 29-10**), which soon produces a dead zone. Hurricanes and tropical storms break up the dead zone each autumn, but it reappears the following summer. The summer dead zone in the Gulf of Mexico now typically covers 5,000 to 8,000 square miles, an area about the size of Connecticut. Worldwide, dead zones are increasing in both size and number as agricultural activities intensify.

Overloading the Sulfur and Nitrogen Cycles Causes Acid Deposition

Natural processes put both nitrogen oxides and sulfur oxides into the atmosphere. Fires and lightning produce several types of nitrogen oxides, including nitrate; volcanoes, hot springs, and decomposers release sulfur dioxide (SO_2). However, combustion of fossil fuels now produces most of the nitrogen and sulfur oxides entering the atmosphere. When combined with water vapor in the atmosphere, nitrogen oxides and sulfur dioxide are converted into nitric acid and sulfuric acid. Days later and often hundreds of miles away, these acids fall to Earth in rain or snow. This **acid deposition** was first recognized in New Hampshire, where a sample of rain collected in 1963 had a pH of 3.7—about the same as orange juice, and 20 to 200 times more acidic than unpolluted rain, which usually has a pH between 5 and 6.

▲ **FIGURE 29-11 Acid deposition is corrosive** These identical building decorations in Brooklyn, New York, show the effects of acid deposition. On the left, the decoration has been restored to its original state; on the right, an unrestored decoration has eroded almost completely away.

▲ **FIGURE 29-12 Acid deposition can destroy forests** On the Camel's Hump in Vermont, virtually all of the older, mature trees are dead and bare. Since the 1990s, lower sulfur and nitrogen emissions from power plants have reduced acid rain in New England, and young trees are beginning to recolonize the forest.

Acid deposition damages forests, can render lakes lifeless, and even eats away at buildings and statues (FIG. 29-11). Acid deposition is most damaging to ecosystems where the soils have little buffering capacity to neutralize acids, such as much of New England, the mid-Atlantic states, the upper Midwest, Western mountains, and Florida. Upstate New York and New England are doubly vulnerable, because the prevailing westerly winds that sweep across North America carry sulfates and nitrates from coal-burning power plants in the Midwest directly over these states.

Acid deposition increases the exposure of organisms to toxic metals, such as aluminum, mercury, lead, and cadmium, which are far more soluble in acidified water than in water of neutral pH. Dissolved aluminum in the soil, for example, inhibits plant growth. When it runs off into lakes, it kills fish.

Plants growing in acidified soil often become weak and vulnerable to infection and damage by insects. Calcium and magnesium, which are essential nutrients for plants, are leached out of the soil by acid precipitation. Sugar maples in the Northeastern United States, often found in soils that are already low in calcium, have declined as a result. Acid rain directly damages the needles of conifers such as spruce and fir. About half of the red spruce and one-third of the sugar maples in the Green Mountains of Vermont have been killed over the past 40 years (FIG. 29-12).

Since 1990, government regulations have resulted in substantial reductions in emissions of both sulfur dioxide and nitrogen oxides from U.S. power plants—sulfur dioxide emissions are down about 40%, and nitrogen oxide levels have been reduced by more than 50%. Air quality has improved and rain has become less acidic, although large areas of the northeastern United States still receive rain with a pH below 5.0.

Damaged ecosystems recover slowly. If acid deposition is eliminated, eventually lakes in upstate New York and New England will return to their normal pH. Most aquatic life should then recover in 3 to 10 years, depending on the species, although the lakes may need to be restocked with fish. Forests usually take longer to recover because the life span of trees is so long and because soil chemistry changes slowly. Red spruce, however, is bouncing back more quickly than expected. In some locations, red spruce trees are growing faster than at any time in the past two centuries, although no one is sure why.

Interfering with the Carbon Cycle Is Changing Earth's Climate

The reservoir of carbon dioxide in the atmosphere not only provides producers with the starting material for photosynthesis, but also significantly affects Earth's climate. To understand why, let's begin with the fate of sunlight entering Earth's

HAVE YOU EVER
WONDERED ...

Each of us affects Earth through the choices we make. A *carbon footprint* is a measure of the impact that human activities have on climate based on the quantity of greenhouse gases they emit. Our personal carbon footprints give us a sense of our individual impacts.

How Big Your Carbon Footprint Is?

For example, each gallon of gasoline burned releases 19.6 pounds (8.9 kg) of CO_2 into the air. So, if your car gets 20 miles to the gallon, each mile that you drive will add about a pound of CO_2 to the atmosphere.

The Web sites of the U.S. Environmental Protection Agency and several environmental organizations provide online carbon footprint calculators. Some calculators evaluate how your daily choices affect carbon emissions by asking questions such as: What kind of foods do you eat? How fuel efficient is your car? How well is your home insulated, and what temperature is your thermostat set to?

Sun

1 Sunlight energy enters the atmosphere.

2 Some energy is reflected back into space.

3 About half of the sunlight strikes Earth's surface and is converted into heat.

4 Heat is radiated back into the atmosphere.

5 Most heat is radiated into space.

6 Some atmospheric heat is retained by greenhouse gases.

volcanoes

forest fires

power plants and factories

vehicle emissions

agricultural activities

homes and other buildings

▲ FIGURE 29-13 **The greenhouse effect** Incoming sunlight warms Earth's surface and is radiated back to the atmosphere. Greenhouse gases, released by natural processes and substantially augmented by human activities (both shown in yellow rectangles), absorb increasing amounts of this heat, raising global temperatures.

atmosphere (FIG. 29-13). Some of the energy from sunlight 1 is reflected back into space by the atmosphere and by Earth's surface, especially by areas covered with snow or ice 2. About half of the sunlight strikes relatively dark surfaces (land, vegetation, and open water) and is converted into heat 3 that is radiated into the atmosphere 4. Most of this heat continues on into space 5, but water vapor, CO_2 and several other **greenhouse gases** trap some of the heat in the atmosphere 6. This natural process is called the **greenhouse effect,** and it keeps our atmosphere relatively warm. Without the natural greenhouse effect, the average temperature of Earth's surface would be far below freezing, and Earth would probably be lifeless.

The release of greenhouse gases by human activities increases the greenhouse effect. For Earth's temperature to remain constant, the total amount of energy entering and leaving Earth's atmosphere must be equal. When atmospheric concentrations of greenhouse gases increase, more heat is retained than is radiated into space, causing Earth to warm. Since burning fossil fuels began in earnest about 150 years ago during the Industrial Revolution, greenhouse gases, particularly CO_2, have increased. Other greenhouse gases have also increased, including methane (CH_4) and nitrous oxide (N_2O). At the present time, however, CO_2 contributes by far the largest share of the greenhouse effect caused by humans.

Burning Fossil Fuels Causes Climate Change

Human activities release about 35 to 40 billion tons of CO_2 into the atmosphere each year. Burning fossil fuels accounts for about 80% to 85% of this CO_2. A second source of added CO_2 is **deforestation,** which destroys tens of millions of forested acres annually and accounts for about 10% to 15% of humanity's CO_2 emissions. Deforestation is occurring principally in the Tropics, where rain forests are cleared for crops and cattle grazing. The carbon stored in the trees returns to the atmosphere when they are cut down and burned. A third, very minor source of CO_2 is volcanic activity. The U.S. Geological Survey estimates that less than 1% as much CO_2 enters the atmosphere from volcanoes as from human activities.

About half of the CO_2 released each year is absorbed by the oceans and terrestrial plants. The rest of the CO_2 remains in the atmosphere. Since 1850, the CO_2 content of the atmosphere has increased by over 40%—from 280 parts per million (ppm) to about 400 ppm in 2014—and is growing by about 2 ppm annually (FIG. 29-14a). Atmospheric CO_2 is now higher than at any time in the past 800,000 years.

A large and growing body of evidence indicates that human release of CO_2 and other greenhouse gases has amplified the natural greenhouse effect, altering the global climate. Air temperatures at Earth's surface, recorded at thousands of

(a) Atmospheric CO₂

(b) Global surface temperature

▲ **FIGURE 29-14 Global temperature increases parallel atmospheric CO₂ increases (a)** Yearly average CO_2 concentrations in parts per million, measured 11,141 feet (3,396 meters) above sea level, on Mauna Loa, Hawaii. **(b)** Although global average temperatures fluctuate considerably from year to year, there is a clear upward trend over time. Data for both graphs from the National Oceanic and Atmospheric Administration.

THINK CRITICALLY If people stopped emitting CO_2 next year, do you think that global temperature would begin to decline immediately? Why or why not?

sites on land and sea, show that Earth has warmed by about 1.4°F (0.8°C) since the late 1800s, including an increase of 1°F (0.6°C) just since the 1970s (FIG. 29-14b). All but 1 of the 15 warmest years on record have occurred since 2000.

The widely reported "pause" in increasing temperatures since about 1998 (see Fig. 29-14b) is puzzling. Some researchers have hypothesized that the pause was caused by more heat being stored in the oceans rather than in the atmosphere during this time period. On the other hand, a study in mid-2015 suggested that warming has not actually slowed down—the apparent hiatus may be an artifact of outdated temperature recording methods, particularly in the oceans, and insufficient

data from the Arctic, which is warming more rapidly than the rest of the planet. If this study is correct, Earth's atmosphere is a little warmer than climate scientists had previously realized. Pauses do happen, though, such as the one that occurred from about 1960 through 1978, and then was followed by rapid warming between 1980 and 1998.

The overall impact of increased greenhouse gases is usually called **climate change,** reflecting the fact that greenhouse gases and the resulting global warming have many effects on our climate and Earth's ecosystems. Although a 1.4°F increase may not seem like much, our warming climate has already caused widespread changes. For example, glaciers are retreating worldwide: About 90% of the world's mountain glaciers are shrinking, and the trend seems to be accelerating (FIG. 29-15). Glacier National Park, Montana, named for its spectacular abundance of glaciers, had 150 glaciers in 1910; now, only 25 remain—and these are significantly smaller than they were in the recent past. During the past 30 years, the Arctic ice cap has become almost 50% thinner and 35% smaller in area. On the continent of Antarctica, although some ice sheets are shrinking while others are expanding, the total volume of ice has dramatically decreased in recent years

(a) Muir Glacier, 1941

(b) Muir Glacier, 2004

▲ **FIGURE 29-15 Glaciers are melting** Photos taken from the same vantage point in **(a)** 1941 and **(b)** 2004 document the retreat of the Muir Glacier in Glacier Bay National Park, Alaska.

Carbon dioxide concentrations in the atmosphere are increasing; Earth is getting warmer; oceans are acidifying; glaciers are retreating; Arctic sea ice is decreasing. You may wonder—how do we know all this?

Estimating some conditions on Earth is fairly straightforward. For example, atmospheric CO_2 is measured at hundreds of stations in dozens of countries, including Mauna Loa in Hawaii (see Fig. 29-14a). Estimates of CO_2 concentrations in the distant past are obtained by analyzing gas bubbles trapped in ancient Antarctic ice.

In some places on Earth, people began keeping accurate temperature records well over a century ago. Now, air temperatures are measured at about 1,500 locations, on both land and sea, each day. Sophisticated computational methods compensate for the uneven distribution of weather stations (more in England than in the Arctic or Sahara Desert) and produce global average temperatures. Ancient temperatures can be estimated by "natural proxies"—natural phenomena that vary with temperature and leave long-lasting records. For example, isotopes of oxygen in air trapped in bubbles inside ice vary with the air temperature at the time the bubble formed. Ice cores collected from glaciers in Antarctica or Greenland can therefore be used to estimate "paleotemperatures." Chemical measurements of corals and mollusk shells, and even some types of sediments and fossils, also provide estimates of paleotemperatures.

However, some measurements of Earth's environment wouldn't have been possible even 20 to 40 years ago. Many involve data collected by satellites. For example, measuring areas of forest is a simple, if tedious, matter of carefully examining satellite photos. Other measurements are much more sophisticated. Accurate estimates of Arctic sea ice started in 1979, with the launch of satellites that measure microwave

radiation emitted from Earth's surface. Ice emits more microwave radiation than liquid water does, so the satellites can easily distinguish the two. Satellite data show that the extent of Arctic sea ice has declined about 13% per decade since 1979 (FIG. E29-2). Many other features of Earth have distinctive "signature wavelengths" that satellites can detect, from sulfur dioxide emitted by power plants to chlorophyll in the oceans (FIG. E29-3).

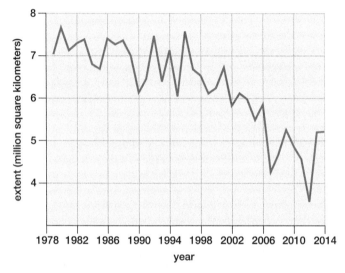

▲ FIGURE E29-2 **Changes in Arctic sea ice** Satellite measurements of Arctic sea ice began in 1979. By 2014, the area covered by ice at the end of the summer (September) had declined by more than a third.

(see "How Do We Know That? Monitoring Earth's Health"). The oceans are warming, which causes their water to expand and occupy more volume. This expansion, coupled with water flowing into the oceans from melting glaciers and ice sheets, causes sea levels to rise.

Continued Climate Change Will Disrupt Ecosystems and Endanger Many Species

What does the future hold? Climate scientists predict that a warming atmosphere will cause more severe storms, including stronger hurricanes; greater amounts of rain or snow in single storms (a phenomenon already observed in the northeastern United States during the past half-century); and more frequent, severe, and prolonged droughts. Increased CO_2 also makes the oceans more acidic, which disturbs many natural processes, including the ability of many marine

animals, such as snails and corals, to make their shells and skeletons.

Predictions of continued climate change are based on sophisticated computer models developed and run independently by climate scientists around the world. As the models continue to improve, they match past climate with ever-greater accuracy, providing increasing confidence in their predictions for the future. The models also provide evidence that natural causes, such as changes in the output of the sun, cannot account for the recent warming. The models match the data only when human greenhouse gas emissions are included in the calculations.

The Intergovernmental Panel on Climate Change (IPCC) is a consortium of hundreds of climate scientists and other experts from 130 nations who work together to address climate change. In their 2014 report, the IPCC predicted that even under the best-case scenario in which a

Chlorophyll _a_ Concentration (mg/m³)

0.01   0.1   1.0   10   60

▲ **FIGURE E29-3 Ocean chlorophyll** Satellite measurements of chlorophyll show which areas of the ocean have the greatest amount of phytoplankton. Purple/blue represent low chlorophyll concentrations, green/yellow intermediate amounts, and orange/red the highest concentrations.

Perhaps the most amazing measurements come from NASA's GRACE satellites—the Gravity Recovery and Climate Experiment. A satellite's orbiting speed is determined, in part, by the force of gravity exerted on it. Water and ice are heavy. Large volumes of ice on the land increase local gravity, tugging ever-so-slightly on the satellites, which then measure the extra gravitational pull. GRACE has found that land ice sheets in Antarctica and Greenland have declined dramatically over the past decade. Antarctica is losing about 150 billion tons of ice per year; Greenland is losing about 260 billion tons. GRACE can even measure water underground: the combination of prolonged drought and groundwater pumping for agriculture in California's Central Valley has greatly depleted the aquifers underlying the Valley (**FIG. E29-4**).

California Drying
Cumulative water storage changes from NASA GRACE (2002–2014)

June 2002   June 2008   June 2014

▲ **FIGURE E29-4 Changes in gravity show depletion of water in California's aquifers** Underground aquifers in California's Central Valley are losing about 4 trillion gallons of water each year. The transition from green to red in these false-color images shows water lost between 2002 and 2014.

THINK CRITICALLY People tend to be much more attuned to what's happening right now and less aware of long-term trends. Every time there's a blast of cold weather in winter or hot weather in summer, opinion polls show lesser or greater concern about global warming. Climatologists, however, take a very long view and look for trends in climate data. Using a ruler, estimate trend lines for the data in Figures 29-14 and E29-2. What do the trend lines predict about the future of atmospheric CO_2 concentrations, global temperatures, and Arctic sea ice? If these trends persist, will the Arctic become ice-free in late summer? If so, in what year? When will CO_2 concentrations double from preindustrial levels and reach 560 parts per million? Is it reasonable to extrapolate straight (linear) trend lines into the future? Why or why not?

concerted worldwide effort is made to reduce greenhouse gas emissions, the average global temperature will rise by another 1.3°F (0.7°C) by the year 2100. Without major reductions in emissions, global temperatures might rise as much as 5.8°F (3.2°C). These changes in climate will be difficult to stop, let alone reverse, as we explore in "Earth Watch: Climate Intervention—A Solution to Climate Change?" on page 550.

Even if the more optimistic predictions are correct, the consequences for natural ecosystems will be profound. In 2011, scientists compiled the results of 53 studies that examined changes in the distribution of more than 1,000 species of terrestrial plants and animals. The species' ranges are moving toward the poles at an average rate of about 10.5 miles (17 kilometers) per decade—just what would be expected if they are moving in response

to a warming planet. As climate change continues, some plants and animals will find it easier to move than others will, either because they are intrinsically more mobile (such as some birds) or because they can move great distances while reproducing (such as some plants that produce lightweight, wind-borne seeds). Some species may not be able to move rapidly enough and will become rare or even go extinct.

Species on mountains or in the Arctic and Antarctic may have nowhere to go. For example, the loss of summer sea ice is bad news for polar bears and other marine mammals that rely on ice floes as nurseries for their young and as staging platforms for hunting fish or seals. As summer ice diminishes, both walrus and polar bear populations are moving onto land to give birth, putting the adults farther away from their prime hunting grounds. As walrus crowd together onto

Earth WATCH

Climate Intervention—A Solution to Climate Change?

What should be done about climate change? The obvious solution is to reduce our emissions of CO_2 and other greenhouse gases. But that isn't as simple as it sounds. Modern societies depend on the energy of fossil fuels and cannot just stop burning them overnight. As a result, some scientists and policymakers are pondering a temporary fix while we make the transition to carbon-neutral, renewable energy sources. Perhaps we can slow down climate change with *climate intervention—* altering fundamental characteristics of Earth to reduce, or counteract the warming effect of, greenhouse gases. Although climate intervention is a complex subject, there are two main approaches: shading the planet and removing CO_2 from the atmosphere.

Shading the Planet

Some molecules, such as a few sulfur compounds, can reflect sunlight back into space, cooling the planet. Whenever a massive volcano erupts, it spews millions of tons of sulfur dioxide miles high into the atmosphere. In 1991, when Mt. Pinatubo erupted in the Philippines (FIG. E29-5), it blasted about 20 million tons of sulfur dioxide as high as 22 miles skyward. For the next couple of years, global temperatures were slightly cooler. In the early 2000s, global emissions of sulfur from power plants, especially in China, rose by about 25%. At the same time, there appeared to be a pause in the upward trend of planetary temperatures. Although most of the pause was probably due to the oceans taking up more heat, the shading effect of added sulfur in the atmosphere may have contributed. Based on data such as these, some have suggested that governments could slow global warming by sending planes loaded with sulfur compounds high into the atmosphere, where they would release the sulfur. Other potential methods of shading the planet include spewing reflective metal particles from jet exhaust or modifying Earth's cloud cover.

Capturing and Storing CO_2

There are both engineering and biological approaches to capturing and storing carbon. For example, to reduce CO_2 in the atmosphere, air could be sucked through thousands of towers, planet-wide, in which CO_2 would be removed, concentrated, and then either injected underground or converted to solid forms (similar to limestone) that could be stored on land. Although technically feasible, this approach would be enormously expensive. However, the exhaust gases from power plants have a very high CO_2 concentration. It would be much less expensive to remove CO_2 at the emission source rather than from the atmosphere as a whole. In 2014, a coal-fired power plant in Canada became the first large-scale facility to capture and store carbon in this way.

A biological approach to removing CO_2 is to fertilize the oceans. In many parts of the open ocean, the nutrient that limits phytoplankton growth is iron, which is an essential part of enzymes involved in ATP production in mitochondria, chloroplasts, and bacteria. The proposal is to spread powdered iron on open ocean waters, triggering phytoplankton blooms. The phytoplankton would then take up CO_2 during

▲ **FIGURE E29-5** **Sulfur emissions both cool and pollute** The 1991 eruption of Mt. Pinatubo in the Philippines injected millions of tons of sulfur dioxide miles into the atmosphere. The sulfur compounds reflected sunlight and cooled the planet for a few years.

photosynthesis and store some of the carbon in their bodies. When the phytoplankton die, they would sink, carrying the carbon to the ocean depths, where it should remain for many years.

Will Climate Intervention Work? Is It Worth the Risks?

Many people question the feasibility and desirability of climate intervention. As a panel of experts commissioned by the U.S. National Academy of Sciences put it, "Climate intervention is no substitute for reductions in carbon dioxide emissions." Why not? Atmospheric sulfur causes respiratory damage in people, decreases the ozone layer, and generates acid deposition that injures ecosystems. In addition, shading the planet would do nothing to reduce acidification of the oceans. Although small-scale tests have been promising, no one really knows if ocean fertilization would remove enough CO_2 to help very much, or what effects it might have on ocean ecosystems. Removing CO_2 from the atmosphere by chemical means would be extremely expensive. Nevertheless, the expert panel recommends studying both planetary shading and carbon storage: If climate change gets bad enough, people are likely to demand action—and action informed by careful research is far preferable to blundering about, with little understanding of the consequences.

CONSIDER THIS Investigate a climate intervention proposal in some depth. How much temperature change can be achieved, how fast, and at what cost? What are the likely health or environmental side effects? Compare these costs and benefits to "business as usual" emissions and to efforts to reduce carbon emissions.

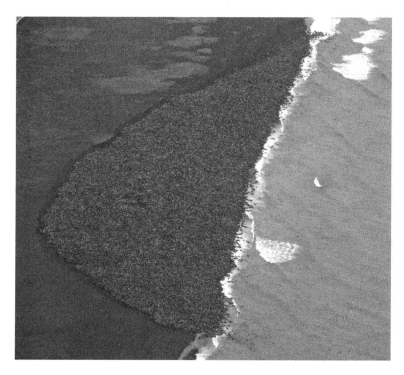

▲ **FIGURE 29-16 Walrus pack the beach at Point Lay, Alaska** Walrus are normally dispersed on floating sea ice in the summer. As the Arctic warms and sea ice disappears during the summer, they now congregate on a few beaches, a phenomenon first seen in 2007.

small beaches (**FIG. 29-16**), instead of being spread out over sea ice, they sometimes endanger their own young. In 2009, for example, stampeding adults trampled 131 walrus calves to death. Complete loss of Arctic sea ice during the summer, which climate models predict could occur by mid-century, may cause the extinction of polar bears in the wild.

Some of the movement of species may have direct impacts on human health. Many diseases, especially those carried by mosquitoes and ticks, are currently restricted to tropical or subtropical parts of the planet. Like other animals, these disease vectors will probably spread poleward as a result of warming temperatures, bringing their diseases, such as malaria, dengue fever, yellow fever, and Rift Valley fever, with them. On the other hand, it may become so hot and dry in parts of the Tropics that mosquitoes and some other insects may have shortened life spans, thus reducing vector-borne diseases in these regions. At this time, no one can confidently predict the overall effects on human health.

CHECK YOUR LEARNING

Can you ...

- explain how human activities have disrupted nutrient cycles?
- describe how human interference with nutrient cycles causes acid deposition, damages aquatic ecosystems, enhances the greenhouse effect, and causes climate change?
- describe some of the evidence that Earth is warming and some of the impacts of climate change on Earth's ecosystems?

CASE STUDY REVISITED

Dying Fish Feed an Ecosystem

The sockeye salmon's return to an Alaskan stream is unforgettable (**FIG. 29-17**). Even after the fish have run the gauntlet of brown bears and bald eagles, hundreds remain, their brilliant red bodies writhing in water so shallow that it barely covers them. A female excavates a depression in the gravel where she releases her eggs; a male then showers them with sperm. But sperm and eggs aren't the only cargo the salmon carry upstream from the ocean. About 95% of a sockeye's body mass was acquired during its years of feeding in the ocean, so it carries enormous amounts of energy and nutrients upstream with it. Sunlight energy, originally captured by phytoplankton, then transferred to zooplankton and smaller fish, is now stored in the bodies of the salmon, where it becomes available to terrestrial predators and scavengers. During a summer gorging on salmon, a brown bear may put on as much as 400 pounds of fat, which serves as its vital energy supply while it hibernates during the long Alaskan winter. Minks also profit. Females nurse their young during the salmon runs, taking advantage of the virtually inexhaustible supply of half-eaten salmon carcasses left behind by the bears.

Of the nutrients that salmon transport from the ocean to the land, nitrogen is especially important. Nitrogen from ocean sources can be distinguished from terrestrial nitrogen by the

▲ **FIGURE 29-17 Spawning sockeye salmon**

ratio of two isotopes of nitrogen, ^{14}N and ^{15}N. Ecologists have found that 50% to 70% of the nitrogen near some streams in Alaska originated in the ocean and was brought upstream in the bodies of salmon. In some places, more than half of this salmon-derived nitrogen is carried some distance away from the streams by bears, which often eat only the choicest parts of the fish and leave the rest. Salmon-derived nitrogen is important to Sitka spruce, which can grow three times faster near salmon streams than near streams without salmon runs. It's also important to the next generation of salmon. Because salmon carcasses fertilize nearby lakes, stimulating the growth of phytoplankton and conse quently the zooplankton upon which newly hatched salmon feed, the adult salmon indirectly feed their young.

CONSIDER THIS Dams, river pollution, and overfishing have depleted many salmon populations—some are listed as endangered or threatened under the Endangered Species Act. Some people argue that because these salmon are also raised commercially in fish farms, the depletion of wild populations doesn't really matter. Based on what you have learned in this chapter, do you think that wild populations of salmon should be protected and efforts made to increase their numbers?

CHAPTER REVIEW

 MB Go to MasteringBiology for practice quizzes, activities, eText, videos, current events, and more.

Answers to Think Critically, Evaluate This, Multiple Choice, and Fill-in-the-Blank questions can be found in the Answers section at the back of the book.

Summary of Key Concepts

29.1 How Do Nutrients and Energy Move Through Ecosystems?

Ecosystems are sustained by a continuous input of energy from sunlight and the recycling of nutrients. Energy enters the biotic portion of ecosystems through photosynthesis and then flows through the ecosystem. Nutrients are obtained by organisms from their living and nonliving environments and are recycled within and among ecosystems.

29.2 How Does Energy Flow Through Ecosystems?

Photosynthetic organisms act as conduits of both energy and nutrients into biological communities. The energy of sunlight is captured by photosynthetic organisms (producers), the first trophic level in an ecosystem. Herbivores (plant-eaters, also called primary consumers) form the second trophic level. Carnivores (meat-eaters) are secondary consumers when they prey on herbivores and tertiary or higher-level consumers when they eat other carnivores. Omnivores occupy multiple trophic levels. Detritivores and decomposers feed on dead bodies and wastes. Decomposers (mostly bacteria and fungi) liberate nutrients as simple molecules that reenter nutrient cycles.

The higher the trophic level, the less energy is available to sustain it. In general, only about 10% of the energy captured by organisms at one trophic level is available to organisms in the next higher level.

29.3 How Do Nutrients Cycle Within and Among Ecosystems?

A nutrient cycle depicts the movement of a particular nutrient from its reservoir, usually in the abiotic portion of an ecosystem, through the biotic portion, and back to its reservoir.

In the hydrologic cycle, the major reservoir of water is the oceans. Solar energy evaporates water, which returns to Earth as precipitation. Water flows into lakes and underground aquifers and is carried by rivers to the oceans.

In the carbon cycle, the short-term reservoirs are CO_2 in the oceans and the atmosphere. Carbon enters producers via photosynthesis. From producers, carbon is passed through the food web and released to the atmosphere as CO_2 during cellular respiration. Burning fossil fuels also releases CO_2 into the atmosphere.

In the nitrogen cycle, the major reservoir is N_2 in the atmosphere. N_2 is captured by nitrogen-fixing bacteria, which produce ammonia. Other bacteria convert ammonia to nitrate. Plants obtain nitrogen from nitrates and ammonia. Nitrogen passes from producers to consumers and is returned to the environment through excretion and the activities of detritivores and decomposers. N_2 is returned to the atmosphere by denitrifying bacteria.

In the phosphorus cycle, the principal reservoir consists of phosphate in rocks. Phosphate dissolves in water, is absorbed by photosynthetic organisms, and is passed through food webs. Some phosphate is excreted, and the rest is returned to the soil and water by decomposers. Some is carried to the oceans, where it may be deposited in marine sediments.

29.4 What Happens When Humans Disrupt Nutrient Cycles?

Human activities often produce and release more nutrients than nutrient cycles can efficiently process. Fertilizer use in agriculture has disrupted many aquatic ecosystems. By burning fossil fuels, humans have overloaded the natural cycles for sulfur, nitrogen, and carbon. In the atmosphere, sulfur dioxide and nitrogen oxide are converted to sulfuric acid and nitric acid, which fall to Earth as acid deposition, with harmful effects on lakes and forests.

Burning fossil fuels has substantially increased atmospheric carbon dioxide. Climate scientists have concluded that increased CO_2 causes increased global temperatures. Increased temperatures cause climate change that is manifested in more extreme weather, melting glaciers, thinning Arctic sea ice, warming and acidifying oceans, rising sea levels, and changing distributions and seasonal activities of wildlife.

Key Terms

abiotic   *534*
acid deposition   *544*
aquifer   *541*
autotroph   *534*
biological magnification   *539*
biomass   *535*
biotic   *534*
carbon cycle   *541*

carnivore   *534*
climate change   *547*
consumer   *534*
decomposer   *536*
deforestation   *546*
denitrifying bacteria   *543*
detritivore   *536*
ecosystem   *534*

Thinking Through the Concepts

Multiple Choice

1. Which trophic level(s) must be present to sustain any ecosystem?
a. producers only
b. producers and consumers
c. producers, detritivores, and decomposers
d. producers, consumers, detritivores, and decomposers

2. Which of the following is *not* a major reservoir in the carbon cycle?
a. consumers
b. the atmosphere
c. the oceans
d. fossil fuels

3. Denitrifying bacteria
a. convert ammonia to nitrate.
b. convert nitrate to ammonia.
c. convert N_2 to ammonia.
d. convert nitrate to N_2.

4. Net primary production per unit area is likely to be highest in which of the following ecosystems?
a. grasslands
b. deserts
c. temperate deciduous forests
d. tropical rain forests

5. The effect of CO_2 emissions from burning fossil fuels is likely to be
a. nothing; photosynthesis by plants will remove all the added CO_2 from the atmosphere.
b. nothing; the carbon cycle will simply run faster.
c. planetary warming due to an increased greenhouse effect.
d. planetary cooling due to a reduced greenhouse effect.

Fill-in-the-Blank

1. Nearly all life gets its energy from _____, which is captured by the process of _____. In contrast, _____ are constantly recycled during processes called _____.

2. Photosynthetic organisms are called either _____ or _____. The energy that these store and make available to other organisms is called _____.

3. Feeding levels within ecosystems are also called _____. An illustration of these levels with only one organism at each level is called a(n) _____. Feeding relationships are most accurately depicted as _____.

4. In general, only about _____ percent of the energy available in one trophic level is captured by the level above it.

5. Photosynthetic organisms make up the first trophic level. Organisms in higher trophic levels are collectively called _____ or _____. Photosynthetic organisms are consumed by organisms collectively called _____ or _____. Animals that feed on other animals are called _____ or _____. Organisms that feed on wastes and dead bodies are called _____ and _____.

6. During the nitrogen cycle, nitrogen gas is captured from its atmospheric reservoir by _____ in the soil, and is then returned to this reservoir by _____. The two forms of nitrogen that are used by plants are _____ and _____.

7. Two relatively short-term reservoirs for carbon are the _____ and _____. Carbon in these reservoirs is in the form of _____. Two long-term reservoirs for carbon are _____ and _____.

Review Questions

1. What makes the movement of energy through ecosystems fundamentally different from the movement of nutrients?

2. What is a producer? What trophic level does it occupy, and what is its importance in ecosystems?

3. Define *net primary production*. Would you predict higher productivity in a farm pond or an alpine lake? Explain your answer.

4. Name the first three trophic levels. Among the consumers, which are most abundant? Use the "10% law" to explain why you would predict that there will be a greater biomass of plants than herbivores in an ecosystem.

5. How do food chains and food webs differ? Which is the more accurate representation of feeding relationships in ecosystems?

6. Define *detritivore* and *decomposer* and explain their importance in ecosystems.

7. Trace the movement of carbon from one of its reservoirs through the biotic community and back to the reservoir. How have human activities altered the carbon cycle, and what are the implications for Earth's future climate?

8. Explain how nitrogen gets from the atmosphere into a plant's body.

9. Trace a pathway of a phosphorus molecule from a phosphate-rich rock into a carnivore. What makes the phosphorus cycle fundamentally different from the carbon and nitrogen cycles?

Applying the Concepts

1. Humans are omnivores who can feed on several trophic levels. Discuss how the inefficiency of energy transfer between trophic levels might apply to how many humans can be fed, with what environmental impacts, by people eating fundamentally different diets.

2. Discuss the contribution of human population growth to (a) acid precipitation and (b) global climate change.

30

EARTH'S DIVERSE ECOSYSTEMS

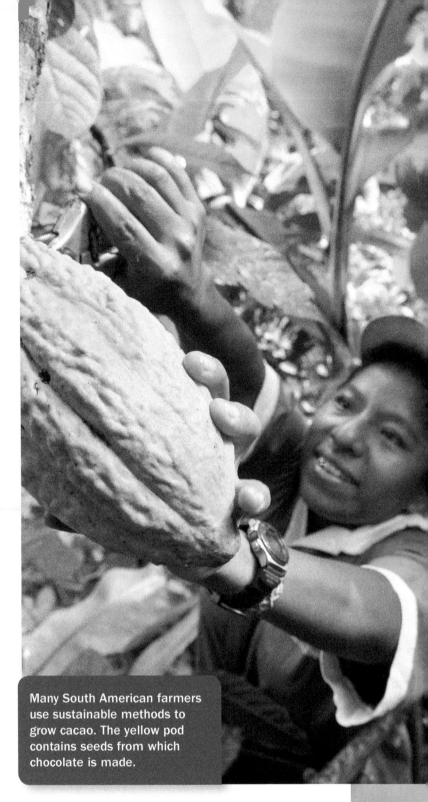

Food of the Gods

WHAT DO CHOCOLATE AND COFFEE have in common? Some would say they are both necessities of life. Every year, the average person in the United States eats about 11 pounds of chocolate and drinks about 340 cups of coffee. Scandinavians devour about twice as much chocolate and coffee as Americans do. Indeed, there must have been chocoholics in Sweden at least 300 years ago: Carolus Linnaeus, the Swedish scientist who invented scientific taxonomy, named the cacao tree *Theobroma cacao*—in Greek, "theobroma" means "food of the gods."

Cocoa is produced from the seeds of the cacao tree, originally from rain forests in South and Central America. Coffee "beans" are the seeds of two species of coffee plants, native to upland forests in the African country of Ethiopia. Both cacao and coffee are now widely cultivated in the Tropics, including South and Central America, Africa, and Southeast Asia. Worldwide, about 4.4 million tons of cacao seeds and 9 million tons of coffee beans are produced each year.

The original varieties of both cacao and coffee grew in the shade of taller trees—in fact, full sunlight killed the plants, especially seedlings. In Central and South America, cacao and coffee were traditionally cultivated as an understory plant in the rain forest. These plantations provided a multilevel, diverse habitat that supported monkeys, frogs, flowers, and about 200 species of birds. The forest vegetation absorbed water and protected the soil from erosion. The shade discouraged weed growth, and detritivores and decomposers recycled fallen leaves into plant nutrients.

Many South American farmers use sustainable methods to grow cacao. The yellow pod contains seeds from which chocolate is made.

In the 1960s and 1970s, however, new varieties of cacao and coffee plants were developed that thrived in full sun and yielded more seeds. As world demand for chocolate and coffee increases, more and more cacao and coffee plants are grown in full-sun plantations. What is lost when rain forests are cut down to make room for full-sun plantations? Or when we alter, or even destroy, natural communities in other ways, such as draining wetlands for agriculture or housing? To answer these questions, we must first understand the properties of the communities that make up life on Earth.

AT A GLANCE

30.1 WHAT DETERMINES THE DISTRIBUTION OF LIFE ON EARTH?

Both the type of living organisms—cacti or redwood trees, lobsters or jaguars—and their abundance vary enormously from place to place. This variability arises from an uneven distribution of four requirements for life on Earth: (1) energy, (2) nutrients, (3) liquid water, and (4) suitable temperatures.

Energy enters almost all ecosystems as sunlight, captured by plants and other photosynthetic organisms and transferred through food webs to consumers (see Chapter 29). Therefore, the distribution of life on Earth is largely determined by the requirements of the photosynthesizers. Although there are exceptions, we can make two major generalizations about how the location and abundance of the four requirements of life affect photosynthetic organisms.

First, in aquatic ecosystems, liquid water is almost always available, so sunlight energy, nutrients, and temperature are usually the factors that determine the distribution of life. Only the top 650 feet (200 meters) of a body of water, and usually much less, receives enough sunlight for photosynthesis. Even there, photosynthesis may be limited because surface waters usually contain low levels of many nutrients. Temperature may also be a limiting factor because many aquatic organisms, such as corals, thrive only within a fairly narrow temperature range.

Second, in terrestrial ecosystems, sunlight energy and most nutrients are relatively plentiful, so precipitation and temperature largely determine the distribution of life. Terrestrial plants require liquid water in the soil, at least during part of the year, because plants require water for their metabolic activities and to replace water that evaporates from their leaves. Soil moisture depends on precipitation and temperature. Generally speaking, the more precipitation, the more moisture the soil contains, but temperature also strongly influences soil moisture: High temperatures evaporate water from the soil, while prolonged freezing temperatures turn soil water to ice, making it unavailable to plants.

These requirements for life occur in specific patterns on our planet, resulting in characteristic communities of living organisms that extend over thousands, sometimes (in the oceans) even millions, of square miles. These large-scale communities are called **biomes,** often named after their principal types of vegetation, such as deciduous forests or grasslands.

The types of vegetation that dominate a terrestrial biome are determined by long-term patterns of temperature and precipitation. Measured over hours or days, temperature and precipitation are two of the principal components of weather. Weather patterns that prevail for years or centuries in a particular region make up its **climate.** Therefore, the climate in any particular region is a good predictor of its biome (**FIG. 30-1**). Before we begin our survey of terrestrial biomes, we will explore how the physical features of Earth and its movement in the solar system affect climate.

CHECK YOUR LEARNING
Can you ...
- name the four requirements for life on Earth?
- explain which of these requirements are most important in determining the distribution of life in aquatic and terrestrial ecosystems?

30.2 WHAT FACTORS INFLUENCE EARTH'S CLIMATE?

Weather and climate are driven by a great thermonuclear engine: the sun. Solar energy reaches Earth in a range of wavelengths—from short, high-energy ultraviolet (UV) rays, through visible light, to the long infrared wavelengths that we experience as heat (see Chapter 7). When sunlight enters the atmosphere, some is reflected back into space, but most solar energy is absorbed either by molecules in the atmosphere or by Earth's surface, thereby heating the planet. Fortunately, most UV radiation, which can damage biological molecules, including DNA, does not reach the surface. UV is absorbed by an **ozone layer** in the middle atmosphere, or stratosphere. During the twentieth century, humans produced a number of chemicals that began to deplete the ozone layer. In a remarkable case of international cooperation, almost all the nations of the world agreed to limit the production of ozone-depleting chemicals, as we explore in "Earth Watch: Plugging the Ozone Hole" on page 558.

The climate of different locations on Earth varies tremendously. These variations arise from the physical properties of our planet. Among the most important are Earth's curvature, its tilted axis, and the fact that it orbits the sun rather than staying in one place. As we will see, these factors cause uneven heating of Earth's surface. Uneven heating, in conjunction with Earth's rotation on its axis, generates air and ocean currents, which are in turn modified by the presence, location, and topography of the continents.

◀ **FIGURE 30-1 Rainfall and temperature influence the distribution of terrestrial ecosystems** Rainfall and temperature determine the amount of soil moisture available to support plant growth.

Earth's Curvature and Tilt on Its Axis Determine the Angle at Which Sunlight Strikes the Surface

Average yearly temperatures are determined by the amount of sunlight that reaches the surface in different regions, which in turn depends on latitude (FIG. 30-2a). Latitude is a measure of the distance north or south of the equator, expressed in degrees. The equator is defined as 0° latitude, and the poles are at 90° north and south latitudes. Sunlight hits the equator relatively directly (perpendicular to the surface) throughout the year. However, because Earth is a sphere, the farther away from the equator, the more slanted the sunlight, so a given amount of sunlight is spread out over a larger area. In addition, slanting sunlight at high latitudes must travel through more of Earth's atmosphere than vertical sunlight at the equator does, further reducing the amount of solar energy that reaches the surface. Earth is also tilted on its axis, about 23.5° relative to a line perpendicular to the plane of its orbit around the sun (FIG. 30-2b). During the course of a year, the tilted axis causes latitudes north and south of the equator to experience

significant changes in the angle and duration of sunlight, resulting in pronounced seasons. When Earth's position in its orbit causes the Northern Hemisphere to be tilted toward the sun, this hemisphere receives relatively direct sunlight and experiences summer (Fig. 30-2b, left). Simultaneously, the Southern Hemisphere is tilted away from the sun, receives slanted sunlight, and thus experiences winter. Six months later, conditions are reversed: It is summer in the Southern Hemisphere and winter in the Northern Hemisphere (Fig. 30-2b, right). Because sunlight hits the equator fairly directly throughout the year, the Tropics remain warm year-round.

Air Currents Produce Large-Scale Climatic Zones That Differ in Temperature and Precipitation

The angle at which sunlight strikes Earth's surface produces climatic zones with markedly different temperatures and precipitation (FIG. 30-3). Averaged over the course of a year, sunlight has the greatest warming effect at the equator ❶. The heat evaporates water from Earth's surface, especially from

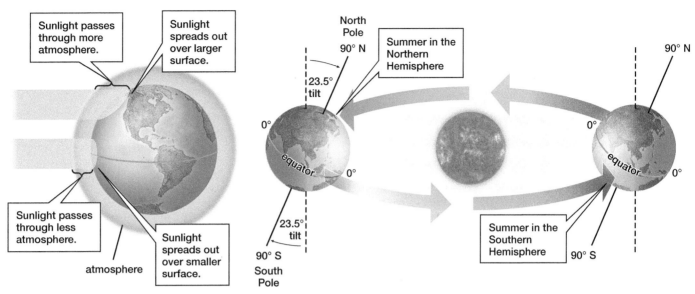

(a) The intensity of sunlight hitting Earth's surface varies with latitude.

(b) The intensity of sunlight hitting different latitudes on Earth's surface varies with the seasons.

▲ FIGURE 30-2 **Earth's curvature and tilt cause temperature to vary with latitude and season of the year (a)** At the equator, sunlight passes through a minimum thickness of atmosphere and strikes Earth's surface nearly vertically year-round. Further toward the poles, sunlight passes through more atmosphere and hits Earth's surface at an angle that spreads a given amount of sunlight over a much larger land surface. Therefore, average temperatures are highest at the equator and lowest at the poles. **(b)** The tilt of Earth on its axis causes seasonal variations in how directly sunlight strikes different latitudes.

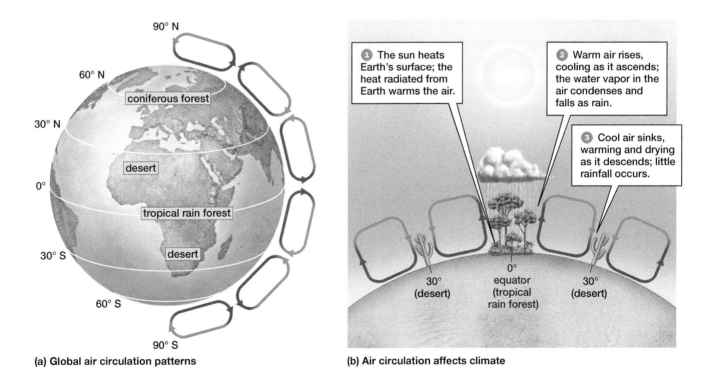

(a) Global air circulation patterns

(b) Air circulation affects climate

▲ FIGURE 30-3 **Air currents and climatic zones (a)** Warm air (red) rises at about 0° and 60° latitudes, and cool air (blue) falls at about 30° and 90° latitudes. **(b)** Air circulation patterns produce broad climatic zones.

Earth WATCH   Plugging the Ozone Hole

Ultraviolet light is so energetic that it can damage biological molecules. UV causes sunburn, premature aging of the skin, and skin cancer. Fortunately, more than 97% of UV radiation is filtered out by an ozone-enriched region of the stratosphere called the ozone layer, which begins about 6 miles (10 kilometers) above Earth's surface and extends up to about 30 miles (50 kilometers). UV light striking ozone and oxygen gas causes reactions that both break down and regenerate ozone. In the process, the UV radiation is converted to heat, and the overall level of ozone remains reasonably constant—or it did before humans intervened.

In 1985, British atmospheric scientists published the startling news that springtime levels of stratospheric ozone over Antarctica had declined by more than 30% since 1979. By the mid-1990s, the **ozone hole** over Antarctica had worsened, with springtime ozone only about 50% of its original levels (**FIG. E30-1**). Higher levels of UV light beneath the ozone hole reduce photosynthesis by phytoplankton—the producers in marine ecosystems, and the basis of food webs that support penguins, seals, and whales. Although ozone layer depletion is most severe over Antarctica, the ozone layer is somewhat reduced over most of the world. The ozone layer at mid-latitudes is about 5% less than its original level.

The ozone hole is caused primarily by human production and release of chlorofluorocarbons (CFCs). These chemicals were once widely used in the production of foam plastic, as coolants in refrigerators and air conditioners, as aerosol spray propellants, and as cleansers for electronic parts. CFCs are very stable and were considered safe. Their stability, however, proved to be a major problem because they remain chemically unchanged as they slowly rise into the stratosphere. In the stratosphere, UV light causes them to break down and release chlorine atoms, which in turn catalyze the breakdown of ozone.

Fortunately, major steps have been taken toward plugging the ozone hole. The 1987 Montreal Protocol set limits and established phase-out periods for several ozone-depleting chemicals. In a remarkable worldwide effort, 197 countries have signed the treaty. Since 2000, the ozone layer has begun to show signs of recovery. However, because CFCs persist in the atmosphere for many years, full recovery is not expected until 2050, possibly even later.

THINK CRITICALLY UV light damages some of the molecules involved in photosynthesis, not only in phytoplankton, but also in many terrestrial plants. Assume that the Montreal Protocol had not been implemented and that ozone-depleting chemicals had been released in ever-increasing amounts. In this situation, how would you expect ozone depletion to affect global climate change?

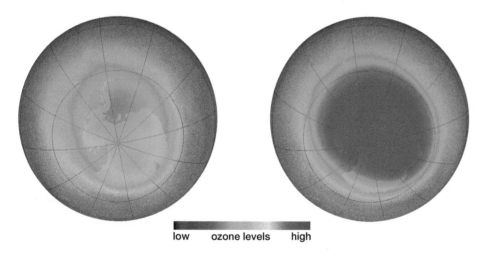

low   ozone levels   high

(a) Antarctic ozone hole, September 1979   (b) Antarctic ozone hole, September 2014

◀ **FIGURE E30-1 The Antarctic ozone hole** Satellite images show ozone concentrations above the Antarctic in September 1979, before significant ozone depletion occurred, and in September 2014. Low concentrations of ozone are shown in blue and purple. There are fluctuations from year to year, but the area of the hole (about 9.5 million square miles; 25 million square kilometers) and its ozone concentration (about 50% of the concentration before depletion began) are currently both about the same as they were in the mid-1990s. Images courtesy of NASA.

the oceans, so equatorial air contains a lot of moisture. Warm air is less dense than cool air, so near the equator this warm, moist air rises. As it rises, the air cools, and water condenses out, falling as rain ❷. The direct rays of the sun and abundant rainfall at the equator create a warm, wet climate, where rain forests flourish.

After the moisture has fallen from the rising equatorial air, cooler, drier air remains. The continuing upward flow of air from the equator pushes this cool, dry air north and south. By about 30° N and 30° S latitudes, the air has cooled enough to sink. As it sinks, the air is warmed by heat radiated from Earth's surface. This warm, dry air produces very little rainfall ❸. As a result, the major deserts of the world are found near these latitudes. After reaching the desert surface, the warm air flows north and south, some moving back toward the equator and some moving toward the poles. As the air flows near the surface, its warmth evaporates water, so the air gradually becomes moist. This moderately warm, moist air rises at about 60° N and 60° S. The air cools as it rises, so water precipitates out as rain or (in winter) as snow. These climatic conditions favor the growth of coniferous and deciduous forests. Finally, the remaining dry air flows to the poles and sinks once more, producing very little precipitation. With highly slanted sunlight in summer and no sunlight at all in the winter, the poles are also extremely cold.

These patterns of air circulation predict that climate zones should occur in bands corresponding to latitude. The actual locations of Earth's biomes agree fairly well with this overall pattern, but the fit isn't perfect by any means (FIG. 30-4). The differences are largely caused by three factors: the rotation of Earth on its axis, the existence of the

continents, and the presence of large mountain ranges on the continents.

Terrestrial Climates Are Affected by Prevailing Winds and Proximity to Oceans

The interaction between Earth's rotation and air flowing north and south from 30° N and 30° S latitudes determines average wind directions: east to west between the equator and 30° N and 30° S latitudes, and west to east north of 30° N and south of 30° S latitudes. Friction between winds and the ocean surface produces ocean currents. If there were no continents, then ocean currents would flow around the globe, east to west near the equator, and west to east north of 30° N and south of 30° S. However, the continents interrupt the currents, breaking them into roughly circular patterns called

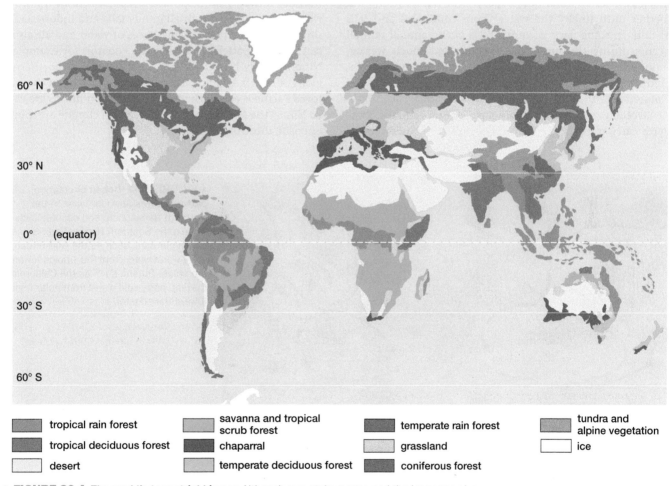

▲ **FIGURE 30-4 The world's terrestrial biomes** Although mountain ranges and the immense size of continents complicate the distribution of biomes, fairly consistent patterns remain. Tundra and coniferous forests are in the northernmost parts of the Northern Hemisphere, whereas the deserts of Mexico, the Sahara, Saudi Arabia, Southern Africa, and Australia are located around 30° N and 30° S latitudes. Tropical rain forests are found near the equator. Note that there is little land in the Southern Hemisphere between 45° S and the Antarctic continent; therefore, coniferous forest and tundra biomes are rare in the Southern Hemisphere.

gyres, which circulate clockwise in the Northern Hemisphere and counterclockwise in the Southern Hemisphere (FIG. 30-5).

Interactions between prevailing winds, ocean currents, and the sheer sizes of the continents profoundly affect terrestrial climates. Because water both heats and cools more slowly than land or air does, the interiors of continents have much more extreme temperatures than coastal regions at similar latitudes experience. For example, the average high temperatures in San Francisco, on the coast of California, range from 58°F (14°C) in winter to 71°F (22°C) in summer. Sacramento, only about 80 miles inland, has average high temperatures of 54°F (12°C) in winter and 92°F (33°C) in summer. In St. Louis, Missouri, about 1,700 miles east of San Francisco and 600 miles from the nearest ocean, high temperatures average about 38°F (3°C) in winter and 90°F (32°C) in summer.

The differential heating of land versus water causes the *monsoons* that bring summer rainfall to India and much of southeastern Asia. As the summer sun heats the land, hot air rises, pulling cooler, moist air inland off the ocean. The moist air rises up mountain slopes on the land, cooling still further until finally the water vapor condenses and falls as rain. In some parts of India, 80% of the annual rainfall occurs during the monsoons. Similar, but much weaker, monsoons bring rain to the southwestern United States, including parts of Arizona, New Mexico, Utah, Nevada, and Colorado.

Ocean gyres further modify some coastal climates. Some gyres carry warm water from the Tropics to coastal regions located relatively far from the equator. This creates warmer, moister climates than would be expected at these latitudes. For example, the Gulf Stream, carrying warm water from the Caribbean up the coast of North America and across the Atlantic (see Fig. 30-5), is responsible for the mild, infamously moist climate of the British Isles. Other ocean currents, such as the California current, move cold water from near the poles down toward the equator, causing cooler climates than would be expected in regions adjacent to these currents.

Finally, changes in water temperature in the central and eastern Pacific Ocean drive the *El Niño/Southern Oscillation,* a major shift in global climate that recurs every few years. Sporadically, surface waters in the equatorial Pacific warm and move eastward toward South America. Because the warm ocean water often appears off the coast of South America around Christmas, the local fishermen called it El Niño, "the (male) child," referring to Jesus. Evaporation from this pool of warm water causes increased winter precipitation in northern South America, Mexico, and the southern United States. In the western Pacific, cooler water replaces the warm water that has moved east. Less water evaporates from this cooler water, producing less rainfall in Australia and Indonesia. The shifting paths of these huge masses of water and air also affect weather patterns far from the equator; for example, El Niño typically brings warmer, drier winters to northern regions of North America. There are also years when the equatorial Pacific is cooler than usual; these conditions are called La Niña, "the female child." Its effects on climate are roughly opposite those of El Niño.

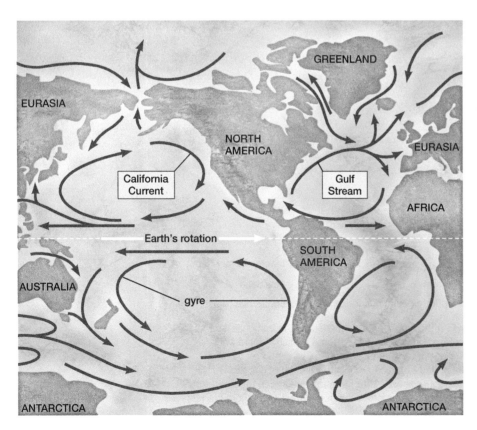

◀ FIGURE 30-5 **Ocean circulation patterns** Gyres flow clockwise in the Northern Hemisphere and counterclockwise in the Southern Hemisphere. Some ocean currents, such as the Gulf Stream, carry warm water from the Tropics toward the poles. Others, such as the California Current, carry cold water from polar regions toward the equator.

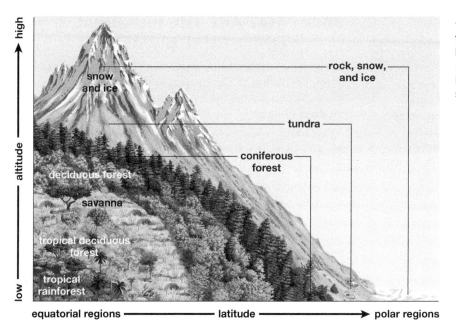

FIGURE 30-6 The similar effects of altitude and latitude on the distribution of the biomes Climbing a mountain in the Northern Hemisphere is like heading north; in both cases, increasingly cool temperatures produce a similar series of biomes.

Mountains Complicate Climate Patterns

Variations in elevation within continents significantly affect climate. As elevation increases, air becomes thinner and cooler. The temperature drops approximately 3.5°F (2°C) for every 1,000 feet (305 meters) in elevation, so increasing elevation and increasing latitude have similar effects on terrestrial ecosystems (FIG. 30-6). Even near the equator, lofty mountains, such as Mount Kilimanjaro in Tanzania (19,341 feet) and Chimborazo in Ecuador (20,565 feet), may be snowcapped much of the year.

Mountains also modify patterns of precipitation. When water-laden air is forced to rise as it meets a mountain, it cools. Because cooling reduces the air's ability to hold water, the water condenses and falls as rain or snow on the windward side of the mountain. The air warms again as it travels down the far (lee) side of the mountain, so it absorbs water from the land, creating a local dry area called a **rain shadow** (FIG. 30-7). For example, the Sierra Nevada range of California wrings moisture from westerly winds blowing off the Pacific Ocean. On the western side of the mountains, heavy winter snows provide moisture for forests of pine, fir, and massive sequoias. The Great Basin Desert, the Owens Valley, and the northern Mojave Desert, in the rain shadow on the east side of the Sierra Nevada, receive only 5 to 7 inches of rain a year and support mostly cacti and drought-resistant bushes.

CHECK YOUR LEARNING
Can you ...
- distinguish between weather and climate?
- explain how Earth's curvature, tilt on its axis, and orbit around the Sun affect climate?
- explain how temperature and precipitation interact to determine soil moisture and the distribution of terrestrial biomes?
- describe how winds, ocean currents, continents, and mountains affect climate and the distribution of terrestrial biomes?

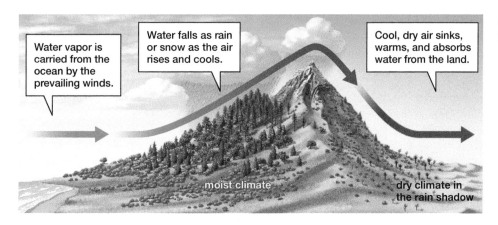

◀ **FIGURE 30-7 Mountains create rain shadows**

Water vapor is carried from the ocean by the prevailing winds.

Water falls as rain or snow as the air rises and cools.

Cool, dry air sinks, warms, and absorbs water from the land.

moist climate

dry climate in the rain shadow

CASE STUDY \ **CONTINUED**

Food of the Gods

In recent years, a fungus called coffee rust has become a major threat to coffee production in Central America. The fungus infects the leaves of the coffee plant, preventing photosynthesis. If enough leaves are infected, the entire plant may die. Coffee rust is typically a major problem in full-sun plantations at warm temperatures. It grows slowly, if at all, at temperatures below 59°F (15°C). In the past, coffee rust was not a significant problem for farms in many Central American countries, where coffee is mostly grown in cool climates at altitudes above 4,000 feet. However, climate change has brought warmer temperatures and wetter weather, and the rust has proliferated, even in high-altitude farms.

Coffee rust has been known to occur in Africa for at least 150 years, generally without destroying the coffee plants. Can growing coffee in a more natural rain forest habitat help modern farmers to defeat coffee rust?

30.3 WHAT ARE THE PRINCIPAL TERRESTRIAL BIOMES?

In the following sections, we discuss the major terrestrial biomes, beginning at the equator and working our way poleward. We also discuss some of the impacts of human activities on these biomes.

Tropical Rain Forests

Near the equator, the average temperature is between 77° and 86°F (25° and 30°C), with little variation during the year. Rainfall ranges from 100 to 160 inches (250 to 400 centimeters) annually. These evenly warm, moist conditions create the most productive biome on Earth, the **tropical rain forest,** dominated by broadleaf evergreen trees (**FIG. 30-8**). Extensive rain forests are found in Central and South America, Africa, and Southeast Asia.

Rain forests have the highest **biodiversity,** or total number of species, of any biome on Earth. Although rain forests cover less than 5% of Earth's total land area,

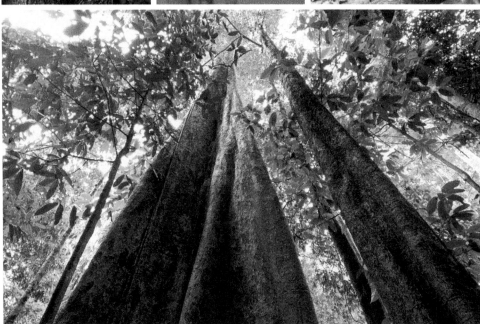

◀ **FIGURE 30-8 The tropical rain-forest biome** Towering trees reach for the light in the dense tropical rain forest. Amid their branches dwells the most diverse assortment of life on Earth, including (from left to right) tree-dwelling orchids, red-eyed tree frogs, and fruit-eating toucans.

THINK CRITICALLY How does a biome with such poor soil support the highest plant productivity and the greatest animal diversity on Earth?

ecologists estimate that they contain half of the world's biodiversity. For example, in a 3-square-mile tract of rain forest in Peru (about 8 square kilometers), scientists counted more than 1,300 butterfly species and 600 bird species. For comparison, the entire continental United States is home to only about 600 butterfly species and 800 bird species.

Tropical rain forests typically have several layers of vegetation. The tallest trees may be more than 200 feet (60–70 meters) high, towering above the rest of the forest. Below these giants sits a fairly continuous canopy of treetops at about 90 to 120 feet (30 to 40 meters). Another layer of shorter trees typically stands below the canopy. Woody vines grow up the trees. Collectively, these plants capture most of the sunlight. Only about 2% of the sunlight reaches the forest floor, where the plants often have enormous, dark-green leaves, an adaptation that allows them to carry out photosynthesis in dim light.

Because of the lack of sunlight, edible plant material close to the ground is scarce, so most of the animals—including birds, monkeys, and insects—inhabit the trees. Competition for the nutrients that do reach the ground is intense among both plants and animals. For example, when a monkey defecates high up in the canopy, hundreds of dung beetles converge on the droppings within minutes after the waste hits the ground. Plants absorb nutrients almost as soon as soil decomposers release them from wastes or dead plants and animals. This rapid recycling means that almost all the nutrients in a rain forest are stored in the vegetation, leaving the soil relatively infertile.

Human Impacts Because of infertile soil and heavy rains, agriculture in rain forests is risky and often destructive. If the trees are cut and carried away for lumber, few nutrients remain to support crops. If the trees are burned, releasing nutrients into the soil, the heavy year-round rainfall quickly dissolves the nutrients and carries them away, leaving the soil depleted after only a few seasons of cultivation.

Nevertheless, rain forests are being felled for lumber or burned for ranching or farming at an alarming rate. Satellite images indicate that about 20 to 30 million acres of tropical rain forest are lost each year—the area of a football field every 1 to 1.5 seconds. About half of the world's rain forests have now been lost. In addition, like all forests, rain forests absorb carbon dioxide and release oxygen. About 10% of the CO_2 released into the atmosphere by human activities comes from cutting and burning tropical rain forests, intensifying the greenhouse effect and accelerating climate change. Fortunately, some areas have been set aside as protected preserves, and some reforestation efforts are underway.

Tropical Deciduous Forests

Slightly farther from the equator, annual rainfall is still high, but there are pronounced wet and dry seasons. In these

---

Food of the Gods

When coffee is grown in the shade of tall trees in a rain forest environment, coffee rust fungus, other diseases, and even some insect predators often cause relatively little damage, compared to full-sun plantations. Ecologists Ivette Perfecto and John Vandermeer have found that a second fungus, called the white halo, attacks the coffee rust fungus without harming the coffee plants. White halo is common in shady environments, but not in full-sun plantations. Birds, which are much more abundant in shady plantations, eat coffee berry borers, which are beetles whose larvae live in, and eat, coffee beans. Even the supposed advantage of full-sun plantations—higher yields—can be problematic. When grown in full sun with lots of fertilizer, coffee plants often produce so many berries that they stress themselves, becoming weaker and more susceptible to coffee rust. Full-sun cacao, too, is more susceptible to various fungal diseases, including witch's broom and frosty pod rot.

Although an ever-increasing demand for coffee and chocolate means that more rain forest is likely to be converted to plantations, shady plantations with a diverse assortment of forest trees can both produce these delicious foods and help to preserve many of the benefits of an intact rain forest for future generations. Can similar strategies that combine production and preservation be applied to other biomes?

---

areas, which include much of India as well as parts of Southeast Asia, South America, and Central America, **tropical deciduous forests** grow. During the dry season, the trees cannot get enough water from the soil to replace what evaporates from their leaves. Many shed their leaves during the dry season ("deciduous" literally means "falling off"), minimizing water loss.

Human Impacts Human activities impact tropical deciduous forests in much the same ways that they affect tropical rain forests. Logging, burning to clear land for agriculture, and cutting for firewood all contribute to deforestation of tropical deciduous forests. Fortunately, many tropical deciduous trees "stump-sprout" after logging. Therefore, if disturbances are not too severe and not too frequent, tropical deciduous forests often recover fairly quickly, with nearly the same species as were present before the disturbances occurred.

Tropical Scrub Forests and Savannas

Along the edges of the tropical deciduous forest, reduced rainfall produces the **tropical scrub forest** biome, dominated by deciduous trees that are shorter and more widely spaced than in tropical deciduous forests. Between the scattered trees, sunlight penetrates to ground level, which allows grass to grow. Still farther from the equator, the climate grows drier, and grasses become the dominant vegetation, with only scattered trees; this biome is the **savanna** (**FIG. 30-9**).

Rainfall in tropical scrub forests and savannas ranges from about 12 to 40 inches (30 to 100 centimeters) a year, almost all falling during a rainy season lasting 3 or 4 months. When the dry season arrives, rain might not fall for months, and the soil becomes hard, dry, and dusty. Grasses are well adapted to this type of climate, growing very rapidly during the rainy season and dying back to drought-resistant roots during the dry season. Only a few specialized trees, such as the thorny acacia or the water-storing baobab, can survive the dry seasons.

The African savanna supports the most diverse array of large mammals on Earth. These include herbivores such as antelope, wildebeest, rhinos, elephants, and giraffes and carnivores such as lions, leopards, hyenas, and wild dogs.

Human Impacts Africa's rapidly expanding human population threatens the wildlife of the savanna. The abundant grasses that make the savanna a suitable habitat for so much wildlife also make it suitable for grazing domestic cattle. Fences erected to contain cattle disrupt the migration of herds of wild herbivores as they search for food and water. In addition, black market sales, usually in Asia, of products derived from rare African animals may be the death knell for some species. Black market demand for rhino horns has already driven the black rhinoceros to the brink of extinction,

◀ **FIGURE 30-9 The African savanna** Giraffes feed on savanna trees and share this biome with (from left to right) lions, rare black rhinos, and zebras.

(a) Sahara dunes   (b) Utah desert

◀ FIGURE 30-10 **The desert biome**
(a) Under the most extreme conditions of heat and drought, deserts can be almost devoid of life, such as these sand dunes of the Sahara Desert in Africa. **(b)** Throughout much of Utah and Nevada, the Great Basin Desert presents a landscape of widely spaced shrubs, such as sagebrush and greasewood.

(a) Cactus   (b) Euphorb

▲ FIGURE 30-11 **Environmental demands shape physical characteristics** Evolution in response to similar desert conditions has molded the bodies of **(a)** cacti and **(b)** euphorbs into nearly identical shapes, although they are not closely related to one another.

and poaching for ivory endangers African elephants; about 20,000 were killed in 2013, a number that far exceeds the elephants' reproductive rate.

Deserts

Even drought-resistant grasses need at least 10 to 20 inches (25 to 50 centimeters) of rain a year, depending on the temperature and the precipitation's seasonal distribution. Biomes where annual rainfall is 10 inches or less are called **deserts.** Although we tend to think of them as hot, deserts are defined by their lack of precipitation rather than by their temperatures. In the Gobi Desert of Asia, for example, although the summers are very hot, average temperatures are below freezing for half the year. Desert biomes are found on every continent, typically at around 30° N and 30° S latitudes, and in the rain shadows of mountain ranges.

Deserts vary in just how dry they are. At one extreme are the Atacama Desert in Chile and parts of the Sahara Desert in Africa, where it almost never rains and no vegetation grows (FIG. 30-10a). More commonly, deserts are characterized by widely spaced vegetation and large areas of bare ground (FIG. 30-10b).

Only highly specialized plants can grow in deserts. Although not closely related to each other, cacti (mostly in the Western Hemisphere) and euphorbs (mostly in the Eastern Hemisphere; FIG. 30-11) have shallow, spreading roots that rapidly absorb rainwater before it evaporates. Their thick stems store water when it is available. Spines protect the plants from herbivores that would otherwise eat the stems for both nutrition and water. Evaporation is minimized because the leaves, if any, are very small; typically, most photosynthesis occurs in the green, fleshy stem. A heavy wax coating on the stem further reduces water loss.

Some deserts have a very brief rainy season, in which a whole year's rain falls in just a few storms. Annual wildflowers take advantage of the brief period of moisture to sprout from seed, grow, flower, and produce seeds of their own in a month or two (FIG. 30-12).

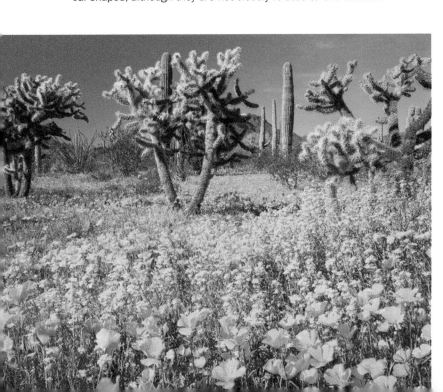

◀ FIGURE 30-12 **Desert wildflowers** After a relatively wet spring, this Arizona desert is carpeted with wildflowers. Through much of the year—and sometimes for several years—annual wildflower seeds lie dormant, waiting for adequate rains to fall.

Desert animals are also adapted to survive heat and drought. Few animals are active during the hot summer days. Many desert denizens take refuge from the heat in underground burrows that stay relatively cool and moist. In North American deserts, nocturnal (night-active) animals include jackrabbits, bats, kangaroo rats, and burrowing owls (FIG. 30-13). Reptiles such as snakes, turtles, and lizards adjust their activity cycles depending on the temperature. In summer, they may be active only around dawn and dusk. Kangaroo rats and many other small desert animals survive without ever drinking. They obtain water from their food and as a by-product of cellular respiration (see Chapter 8). Larger animals, such as desert bighorn sheep, depend on permanent water holes during the driest times of the year.

Human Impacts Desert ecosystems are fragile. Desert soil is stabilized by strands of bacteria that intertwine among sand grains. Driving motorized vehicles on the desert destroys this crucial bacterial network, causing soil erosion and reducing the nutrients available to the desert's slow-growing plants. Regeneration is extremely slow: In the Mojave Desert of California, tread marks left by tanks during World War II are still visible today. Desert soil may require hundreds of years to fully recover from heavy vehicle use.

(a) A kangaroo rat

(b) A burrowing owl

▲ **FIGURE 30-13 Desert dwellers (a)** Kangaroo rats and **(b)** burrowing owls spend the hottest part of the day in burrows, emerging at night to feed.

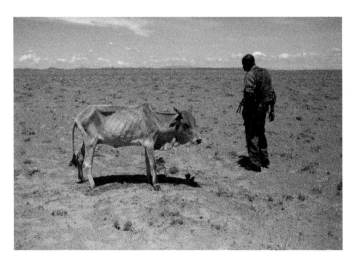

▲ **FIGURE 30-14 Desertification in the Sahel** A rapidly growing human population, coupled with drought and poor land use, has reduced the ability of many dry regions to support life.

Human activities also contribute to **desertification,** the process by which relatively dry regions are converted to desert as a result of drought coupled with misuse of the land. When people overharvest bushes and trees for firewood, graze too many livestock, and deplete both surface and groundwater to grow crops, the native vegetation becomes extremely vulnerable to drought. Loss of vegetation in turn allows the soil to erode, further decreasing the land's productivity. Desertification has severely impacted the Sahel region in Africa just south of the Sahara Desert (FIG. 30-14). In 2011, 11 African countries proposed building a "Great Green Wall" of trees and bushes, about 9 miles (15 kilometers) wide, clear across the continent, in an effort to revegetate the degraded environment and stop desertification in the Sahel. Senegal, on the Atlantic coast, has planted 50,000 acres of drought-resistant trees, including acacia trees that provide food for livestock and gum arabic that can be sold overseas as a food additive. In Niger, preventing overgrazing and planting grasses and bushes has reduced erosion and helped forests to grow back naturally.

Chaparral

Many coastal regions that border deserts, such as those in southern California and much of the Mediterranean, support the **chaparral** biome (FIG. 30-15). The annual rainfall is up to 30 inches (about 75 centimeters), nearly all of which falls during cool, wet winters. Summers are hot and dry. Chaparral plants consist mainly of drought-resistant shrubs and small trees. Their leaves are usually small and are often coated with tiny hairs or waxy layers that reduce evaporation during the dry summer months. Chaparral is adapted to fire. Many shrubs regrow from their roots after fires. Others have seeds that are stimulated to germinate by chemicals found in smoke.

Human Impacts People enjoy living in warm, dry climates adjacent to oceans, so development for housing is a major threat to chaparral biomes. In more rugged terrain, especially in

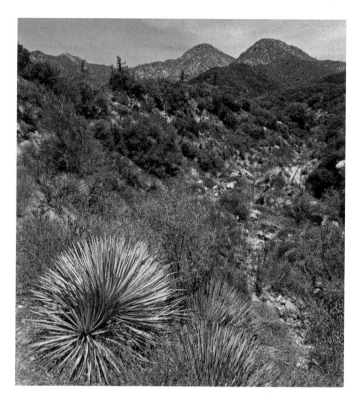

▲ **FIGURE 30-15** **The chaparral biome** Limited to warm, dry coastal regions and maintained by fires caused by lightning, this biome is characterized by drought-resistant shrubs and small trees, such as these seen here in the foothills of the San Gabriel mountains in Southern California.

southern Europe, chaparral has been cleared for grazing, olive groves, and other types of agriculture.

Grasslands

In the centers of continents, such as North America and Eurasia, **grassland,** or *prairie,* biomes predominate (FIG. 30-16). Grassland biomes typically have hot summers and cold winters and receive 15 to 30 inches of rain annually. In general, these biomes have a continuous cover of grass and virtually no trees, except along rivers. In tallgrass prairie—in North America, originally found from Texas to southern Canada—grasses reach up to 6 feet in height. An acre of natural tallgrass prairie may support 200 to 400 different species of native plants. Areas further west, which receive less rainfall, support midgrass and shortgrass prairies. In these grasslands, prairie dogs and ground squirrels provide food for eagles, foxes, coyotes, and bobcats. Pronghorns browse in western grasslands, and bison survive in preserves.

Why do grasslands lack trees? Water and fire are the crucial factors in the competition between grasses and trees. The hot, dry summers and frequent droughts of the midgrass and shortgrass prairies can be tolerated by grass but are fatal to trees. In tallgrass prairies with more precipitation, forests are the climax ecosystems.

Historically, however, tree growth was suppressed by a combination of occasional severe drought and frequent fires caused by lightning or set by Native Americans. Although fire kills trees, the root systems of grasses survive.

Human Impacts Grasses growing and decomposing for thousands of years produced the most fertile soil in the world. In the early nineteenth century, North American grasslands supported an estimated 60 million bison. Today, the Midwestern U.S. grasslands have been largely converted to farm and range land, and cattle have replaced bison.

Prairie dog colonies and the eagles and ferrets that hunted them have become a rare sight as their habitat shrinks. In some regions, overgrazing has destroyed the native grasses, allowing woody sagebrush to flourish (FIG. 30-17). Undisturbed grasslands are now largely confined to protected areas. Tallgrass prairie is one of the most endangered ecosystems in the world. Only about 1% remains, in tiny remnants restored by planting native species and maintained by controlled burning.

▼ **FIGURE 30-16** **Shortgrass prairie** Shortgrass prairie is characterized by low-growing grasses. In addition to many wildflowers, life in shortgrass prairies includes (from left to right) bison (in preserves), prairie dogs, and pronghorns.

▲ **FIGURE 30-17 Sagebrush desert or shortgrass prairie?**
Biomes are influenced by human activities as well as by temperature, rainfall, and soil. The shortgrass prairie field on the right has been overgrazed by cattle, causing the grasses to be replaced by sagebrush.

Temperate Deciduous Forests

At their eastern edge, the North American grasslands merge into the **temperate deciduous forest** biome (**FIG. 30-18**). Temperate deciduous forests are also found in much of Europe and eastern Asia. More precipitation occurs in temperate deciduous forests than in grasslands (30 to 60 inches, or 75 to 150 centimeters). The soil retains enough moisture for trees to grow, shading out most grasses.

Winters in temperate deciduous forests often have long periods of below-freezing weather, when liquid water is not available. Deciduous trees drop their leaves in the fall and remain dormant through the winter, thus conserving their water. During the brief time in spring when the ground has thawed but emerging leaves on the trees have not yet blocked off the sunlight, abundant wildflowers grace the forest floor.

Decaying leaf litter on the forest floor provides food and suitable habitat for bacteria, earthworms, fungi, and small plants. A variety of vertebrates—including mice, shrews, squirrels, raccoons, deer, bears, and many species of birds—dwell in deciduous forests.

Human Impacts Large predatory mammals such as black bears, wolves, bobcats, and mountain lions were formerly abundant in the eastern United States, but hunting and habitat loss have severely reduced their numbers. Consequently, in many areas deer populations have skyrocketed due to a lack of predators. Clearing for lumber, agriculture, and housing dramatically reduced deciduous forests in the United States. Virgin (uncut) deciduous forests are almost nonexistent, but the last century has seen extensive regrowth of deciduous forests on abandoned farms and formerly logged land.

Temperate Rain Forests

On the Pacific coast of the United States and Canada, from northern California to southeast Alaska, lies a **temperate rain forest**

◄ **FIGURE 30-18 The temperate deciduous forest biome** Temperate deciduous forests of the eastern United States are inhabited by (from top to bottom) white-tailed deer and birds such as this blue jay; in spring, a profusion of woodland wildflowers (such as these hepaticas) blooms briefly before the trees produce leaves that shade the forest floor.

THINK CRITICALLY Both tropical deciduous and temperate deciduous forests are dominated by trees that drop their leaves for part of the year. Explain how dropping leaves is an effective adaptation in these two very different biomes.

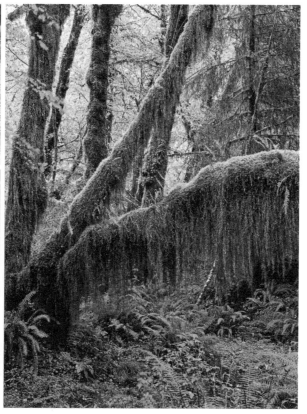

▲ **FIGURE 30-19 The temperate rain-forest biome** The Hoh River temperate rain forest in Olympic National Park receives about 12 feet of rain annually. Ferns, mosses, and wildflowers grow in the pale green light of the forest floor. Denizens of this rain forest include (from top to bottom) ferns, such as this lady fern, elk, and flowering foxglove.

(**FIG. 30-19**). Temperate rain forests are also located along the southeastern coast of Australia, the southwestern coast of New Zealand, and parts of Chile and Argentina. In North America, these biomes typically receive more than 55 inches (140 centimeters) of rain annually—and as much as 12 feet a year in some areas. The nearby ocean keeps the temperature moderate.

Most of the trees in the temperate rain forest are huge conifers, such as spruce, Douglas fir, and hemlock, commonly 250 to 300 feet tall. The forest floor and tree trunks are typically covered with mosses and ferns. Fungi thrive in the moisture and enrich the soil. As in tropical rain forests, so little light reaches the forest floor that tree seedlings usually cannot become established. Whenever one of the forest giants falls, however, it opens up a patch of light, and new seedlings quickly sprout, often right atop the fallen log.

Human Impacts Tall, straight trees are extremely valuable for lumber, and consequently many temperate rain forests have been logged. In the mild, wet climate, the forests regrow quickly, providing a renewable supply of lumber. However, some animals, such as the spotted owl, dwell mainly in old-growth forests that are hundreds of years old. Fortunately, some pristine temperate rain forest is preserved in national parks, including Olympic in Washington and Glacier Bay in Alaska.

Northern Coniferous Forests

North of the grasslands and temperate forests stretches the **northern coniferous forest** (also called the *taiga;* **FIG. 30-20**). The northern coniferous forest, which is the largest terrestrial biome on Earth, stretches across Scandinavia, Siberia, central Alaska, Canada, and parts of the northern United States. Similar forests occur in many mountain ranges, including the Cascades, the Sierra Nevada, and the Rocky Mountains.

Conditions in the northern coniferous forest are much harsher than in temperate deciduous forests, with long, cold winters and short growing

◀ **FIGURE 30-20 The northern coniferous forest biome** The small needles and conical shape of conifers allow them to shed heavy snows. (Upper left) A Canada lynx catches a snowshoe hare. (Upper right) A great horned owl waits for nightfall, when it will begin to hunt.

▲ **FIGURE 30-21 Clear-cutting** Coniferous forests are vulnerable to clear-cutting, as seen in this forest in Alberta, Canada. Clear-cutting is a relatively simple and inexpensive means of logging compared to selective harvesting of trees, but its environmental costs are high. Erosion diminishes the fertility of the soil, slowing new growth. Further, the dense stands of similarly aged trees that typically regrow are more susceptible to fires and parasites than a natural stand of trees of various ages would be.

seasons. About 16 to 40 inches (40 to 100 centimeters) of precipitation occur annually, much of it as snow. The conical shape and narrow, stiff needles of evergreen conifers allow them to shed snow efficiently. The waxy coating on the needles minimizes water loss during the long winters, when water remains frozen. By retaining their leaves during the winter, evergreen conifers conserve the energy that deciduous trees must expend to grow new leaves in the spring. Therefore, when spring arrives, conifers can begin photosynthesis immediately. Large mammals—including black bears, moose, deer, and wolves—still roam the northern coniferous forest, as do wolverines, lynxes, foxes, bobcats, and snowshoe hares. These forests also serve as breeding grounds for many migratory bird species.

Human Impacts Clear-cutting for papermaking and lumber has leveled huge expanses of northern coniferous forest in both Canada and the U.S. Pacific Northwest (**FIG. 30-21**). Demand is also increasing to extract natural gas and oil, often from unconventional sources such as oil sands. Nevertheless, much of Canada's coniferous forest remains intact. Encouragingly, the provincial governments of Ontario and Quebec have pledged to protect half of the publicly owned coniferous forest and to manage the remainder sustainably.

Tundra

The biome furthest north is the arctic **tundra,** a vast treeless region bordering the Arctic Ocean (**FIG. 30-22**). Conditions in the tundra are severe. Winter temperatures are often −40°F (−55°C) or below, with howling winds. Precipitation averages 10 inches (25 centimeters) or less each year, making this region a freezing desert. Even during the summer, frosts are frequent, and the growing season may last only a few weeks. Similar climates and tundra vegetation are found at high elevations on mountains worldwide.

The cold climate of the arctic tundra results in **permafrost,** a permanently frozen layer of soil. Soil above the permafrost thaws each summer, often to a

◀ **FIGURE 30-22 The tundra biome** Life on the tundra is seen here in Denali National Park, Alaska, turning color in autumn. (From left to right) Perennial plants such as this frost-covered bearberry grow low to the ground, avoiding the chilling tundra wind. Tundra animals, such as arctic fox and caribou, can regulate blood flow in their legs, keeping them just warm enough to prevent frostbite while preserving precious body heat for the brain and other vital organs.

depth of 2 feet (60 centimeters) or more. When the summer thaws arrive, the underlying permafrost limits the ability of soil to absorb the water from melting snow and ice, and so the tundra becomes a marsh.

Trees do not grow in the tundra because of the extreme cold, the brief growing season, and the permafrost, which limits the depth of roots. Nevertheless, the ground is carpeted with small perennial flowers, dwarf willows, and large lichens called "reindeer moss," a favorite food of caribou. The summer marshes also provide superb mosquito habitat. These and other insects feed about 100 different species of birds, most of which migrate here to nest and raise their young during the brief summer feast. The tundra vegetation also supports arctic hares and lemmings (small rodents) that are eaten by wolves, owls, and arctic foxes.

Human Impacts The tundra is among the most fragile of all terrestrial biomes because of its short growing season. A willow 4 inches (10 centimeters) high may be 50 years old. Alpine tundra is easily damaged by off-road vehicles and even hikers. Fortunately for the inhabitants of the arctic tundra, the impacts of civilization are mostly localized around oil-drilling sites, pipelines, mines, and scattered military bases. The most significant threat to the tundra is climate change. Shrubs and trees are replacing tundra along its southern margins. Climate models suggest that more than a third of Earth's tundra may be lost by the end of this century.

CHECK YOUR LEARNING
Can you ...
- describe the principal terrestrial biomes and discuss how temperature and precipitation interact to determine their characteristic plant life?
- describe human impacts on terrestrial biomes?

30.4 WHAT ARE THE PRINCIPAL AQUATIC BIOMES?

Of the four requirements for life, aquatic ecosystems typically provide abundant water and appropriate temperatures. However, sunlight in aquatic ecosystems decreases with depth, as it is absorbed by water and blocked by suspended particles. In addition, nutrients in aquatic ecosystems tend to be concentrated in sediments on the bottom, so where nutrients are high, light levels tend to be low.

Freshwater Lakes

Freshwater lakes form when natural depressions fill with water from groundwater seepage, streams, and runoff from rain or melting snow. Large lakes in temperate climates have distinct zones of life (**FIG. 30-23**). Near the shore is the shallow **littoral zone,** which receives abundant sunlight and

▼ **FIGURE 30-23** **Lake life zones** A typical large lake has three life zones: a nearshore littoral zone with rooted plants, an open-water limnetic zone, and a deep, dark profundal zone.

littoral zone

limnetic zone

profundal zone

Remember *Jurassic Park* and *Jurassic World*? OK, maybe the idea of resurrecting *T. rex* and *Velociraptor* is a little far-fetched. But how about a Pleistocene Park? Russian scientist Sergey Zimov thinks that the present-day Siberian tundra, dominated by mosses and shrubs, is an artificial landscape created when prehistoric people wiped out most of Siberia's large herbivores,

If People Can Re-create Ancient Biomes?

Yakutian horses are an essential component of Pleistocene Park

including mammoths, bison, and woolly rhinos, about 10,000 years ago. Zimov hypothesizes that grazing and trampling by these large herbivores destroyed mosses, bushes, and tree seedlings, but grasses thrived. When the megafauna were killed off, the whole ecosystem changed. Zimov wants to recreate the "mammoth steppe"—a vast grassland supporting herds of herbivores and the carnivores that prey on them. Of course, there aren't any mammoths or woolly rhinos anymore, but Zimov has introduced Yakutian horses, musk ox, European bison, and elk to a large protected area in Siberia called Pleistocene Park. Horses seem to be crucial to restoring the grasslands. Wherever there are enough horses, grasslands are returning. The "re-wilding" of Pleistocene Park is well under way.

dominate in the limnetic zone. Organisms that live in the profundal zone are nourished by organic matter that drifts down from the littoral and limnetic zones and by sediment washed in from the land. Inhabitants of the profundal zone include catfish, which mainly feed on the bottom, and detritivores and decomposers such as crayfish, aquatic worms, clams, leeches, and bacteria.

Freshwater Lakes Are Classified According to Their Nutrient Content

Freshwater lakes may be described as *oligotrophic* (Greek, "poorly fed"), *eutrophic* ("well fed"), or *mesotrophic* (between these two extremes, or "middle fed"). Here, we describe the characteristics of oligotrophic and eutrophic lakes.

Oligotrophic lakes contain few nutrients and support relatively little life. Many oligotrophic lakes were formed by glaciers that scraped depressions in bare rock and are now fed by mountain streams and snowmelt. Because there is little sediment or microscopic life to cloud the water, oligotrophic lakes are clear, and light penetrates deeply. Fish that require well-oxygenated water, such as trout, thrive in oligotrophic lakes.

Eutrophic lakes receive relatively large inputs of sediments, organic material, and inorganic nutrients (such as phosphates and nitrates) from their surroundings, allowing them to support dense plant communities (**FIG. 30-24**). They are murky from suspended sediment and dense phytoplankton populations, so the limnetic zone is shallow. The dead bodies of limnetic zone inhabitants sink into the profundal zone, where they feed decomposer organisms. The metabolic activities of these decomposers use up oxygen, so the

nutrients. Plants in the littoral zone include cattails, bullrushes, and water lilies, anchored in the bottom near the shore, and fully submerged plants that flourish in slightly deeper waters. Littoral waters are home to small organisms collectively called **plankton** (from a Greek word meaning "drifters"). Photosynthetic protists and bacteria are called **phytoplankton.** Nonphotosynthetic protists and tiny crustaceans that feed on phytoplankton make up the **zooplankton.**

A great diversity of animal life is also found in the littoral zone, although many of the animals, especially fish, spend time in more than one zone. Littoral vertebrates include frogs, aquatic snakes, turtles, and fish such as pike, bluegill, and perch; invertebrates include insect larvae, snails, flatworms, and crustaceans such as crayfish.

As the water increases in depth, plants are unable to anchor themselves to the bottom and still receive enough sunlight for photosynthesis. This open-water region is divided into an upper **limnetic zone,** in which enough light penetrates to support photosynthesis by phytoplankton, and a lower **profundal zone,** in which light is too weak for photosynthesis to occur (see Fig. 30-23). Plankton and fish

▲ **FIGURE 30-24 A eutrophic lake** Rich in dissolved nutrients carried from the land, eutrophic lakes support dense growths of algae, phytoplankton, and both floating and rooted plants.

profundal zone of eutrophic lakes is often very low in oxygen and supports little other life.

Gradually, as nutrient-rich sediment accumulates, oligotrophic lakes tend to become mesotrophic and then eutrophic, a process called eutrophication. Although large lakes may persist for millions of years, eutrophication may eventually cause lakes to undergo succession to dry land (see Chapter 29).

Human Impacts Nutrients carried into lakes from farms, feedlots, sewage, and even fertilized suburban lawns accelerate eutrophication. Overfertilized lakes sometimes experience massive algal blooms, followed by die-offs and decomposition that deplete the water of oxygen and kill most of the fish. Phosphate-free detergents, more effective sewage treatment, reduced fertilizer use, and proper location and operation of feedlots lessen the danger of eutrophication.

Streams and Rivers

Streams often originate in mountains, the *source region* shown in FIGURE 30-25, where runoff from rain and melting snow cascades over impervious rock. Little sediment reaches the streams, phytoplankton is sparse, and the water is clear and cold. Algae grow on rocks in the streambed, where insect larvae find food and shelter. Turbulence keeps mountain streams well oxygenated, providing a home for trout that feed on insect larvae and smaller fish.

At lower elevations, in the *transition zone,* small streams merge, forming wider, slower-moving streams and small rivers. The water warms slightly, and more sediment is carried in by tributaries, providing nutrients that allow aquatic plants, algae, and phytoplankton to proliferate. Fish such as bass, bluegills, and yellow perch (all of which require less oxygen than trout do) are found in such waterways.

As the land becomes lower and flatter, the river warms, widens, and slows, meandering back and forth. The water becomes murky with dense populations of phytoplankton. Decomposer bacteria deplete the oxygen in deeper water, but carp and catfish can still thrive despite the low oxygen levels. When precipitation or snowmelt is high, the river may flood the surrounding flat land, called a *floodplain,* depositing sediment over the adjoining terrestrial ecosystem.

Rivers drain into lakes or into other rivers that ultimately lead to an estuary, the area where a river meets the ocean (described below). Close to sea level, most rivers move slowly, depositing their sediment. In many cases, the sediment interrupts the river's flow, breaking it into small winding channels before it finally empties into the sea.

Human Impacts Rivers are sometimes channelized (deepened and straightened) to facilitate boat traffic, to prevent

▲ **FIGURE 30-25**

From stream to river to sea

At high elevations, precipitation feeds fast-flowing, clear streams, which grow and slow as they are joined by tributaries at lower elevations. Many become rivers that weave through a floodplain, dropping nutrient-rich sediment. Most rivers eventually flow into estuaries, where they meet the ocean. The communities of freshwater organisms change as the water flows from mountains to the ocean.

flooding, and to allow farming along their banks. Channelization increases erosion of the riverbed and banks because water flows more rapidly in straightened rivers. In addition, where natural flooding has been prevented, floodplain soil no longer receives the nutrients formerly deposited by floodwaters.

In the United States, both Pacific and Atlantic salmon populations have been greatly reduced by hydroelectric dams, water diversion for agriculture, erosion from logging operations, and overfishing. On both coasts of the United States, federal, state, and local groups are working to restore clean, free-flowing rivers that support salmon and rich wildlife communities. Some dams in Washington State and Maine have been removed to allow salmon once again to migrate upstream to spawn, in some cases for the first time in more than 150 years.

Freshwater Wetlands

Freshwater **wetlands,** which include marshes, swamps, and bogs, are regions where the soil is covered or saturated with water. Wetlands support dense growths of algae and phytoplankton, as well as both floating and rooted plants, including cattails, marsh grasses, and water-tolerant trees, such as bald cypress. Wetlands provide breeding grounds, food, and shelter for a great variety of birds (cranes, grebes, herons, kingfishers, and ducks), mammals (beavers, muskrats, and otters), freshwater fish, and invertebrates such as crayfish and dragonflies.

Freshwater wetlands are among the most productive ecosystems in North America. Many occur around the margins of lakes or in the floodplains of rivers. Wetlands act as giant sponges, absorbing water and then gradually releasing it into rivers, making wetlands important safeguards against flooding and erosion. Wetlands also serve as natural water filters and purifiers. As water flows slowly through wetlands, suspended particles fall to the bottom. Wetland plants and phytoplankton absorb nutrients such as nitrates and phosphates that have washed from the land. Bacteria break down many organic pollutants, rendering them harmless.

Human Impacts About half of the freshwater wetlands in the United States (outside of Alaska) have been lost as a result of being drained and filled for agriculture, housing, and commercial uses. Destruction of wetlands makes nearby water more susceptible to pollutants, reduces wildlife habitat, and may increase the severity of floods.

Fortunately, local, state, and federal agencies have cooperated to protect existing wetlands and restore some that have been degraded. These actions have combined to slow wetland loss in the United States. A survey by the U.S. Fish and Wildlife Service found that, although individual types of freshwater wetlands have expanded or shrunk, their total area has remained fairly constant in recent years.

Marine Biomes

The oceans can be divided into life zones characterized by the amount of light they receive and their proximity to the shore (FIG. 30-26). The **photic zone** consists of relatively shallow waters (to a depth of about 650 feet, or 200 meters) where the light is strong enough to support photosynthesis. Below the photic zone lies the **aphotic zone,** which extends to the ocean floor, with a maximum depth of about 36,000 feet (11,000 meters) in the Marianas Trench in the Pacific Ocean. Light in the aphotic zone is inadequate for photosynthesis. Therefore, nearly all the energy to support life must be extracted from the excrement and bodies of organisms that sink down from the photic zone above.

Because their water levels rise and fall with the tides, oceans do not have a defined shoreline. Instead, the **intertidal zone,** where the land meets the ocean, is alternately covered and exposed by the tides. The **nearshore zone** extends out to sea from the low-tide line, with gradually increasing depth as the continental shelf slopes downward. The nearshore zone is usually considered to end, and the **open ocean** to begin, where the water is deep enough that wave action no longer affects the bottom, even during strong storms.

Shallow Water Marine Biomes

As in freshwater lakes, the major concentrations of life in the oceans are found in shallow waters where both nutrients and light are abundant. Such locations include estuaries, the intertidal zone, and kelp forests and coral reefs, which are mostly located in the nearshore zone.

Estuaries An **estuary** is an area of brackish water where fresh water from one or more rivers mixes with seawater (FIG. 30-27a). The waters of estuaries vary in salinity. High tides, for example, bring an influx of seawater, while heavy rains bring a pulse of fresh water down the river. Estuaries support enormous biological productivity and diversity. Many commercially important animal species, including shrimp, oysters, clams, crabs, and a variety of fish, spend part of their lives in estuaries. Dozens of species of birds, including ducks, swans, and shorebirds, feed and nest in estuaries.

Intertidal Zones In the intertidal zone, organisms must be adapted to survive both submerged in seawater and exposed to the air as the tides rise and fall. During heavy rains, organisms in tide pools and mudflats may also experience significant dilution of the seawater. On rocky shores, barnacles (shelled crustaceans) and mussels (mollusks) filter phytoplankton from the water at high tide and close their shells at low tide to resist drying. At high tide, sea stars pry open mussels to eat, sea urchins feast on algae coating the rocks, and anemones spread their tentacles to catch passing crustaceans and small fish (FIG. 30-27b). The intertidal zone of sandy shores and mudflats typically has less diversity but still

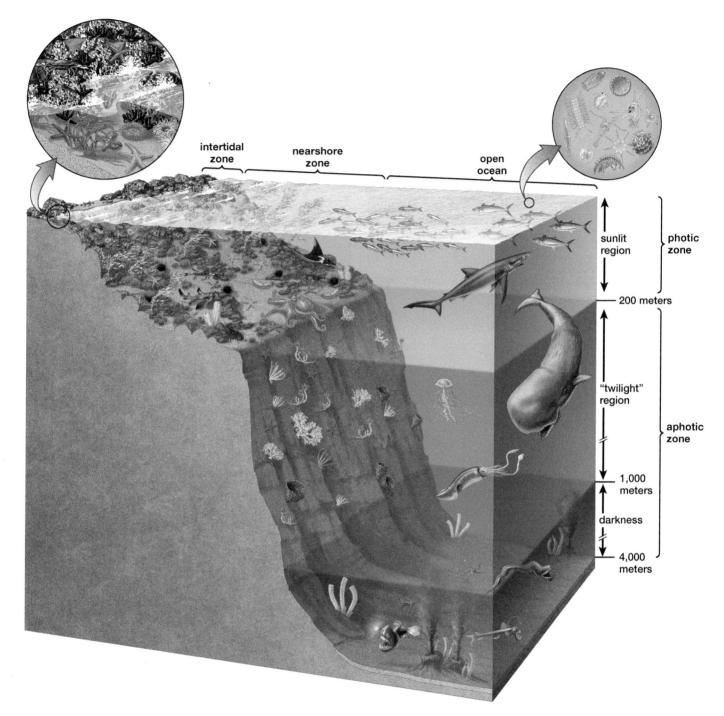

intertidal zone

nearshore zone

open ocean

sunlit region

photic zone

200 meters

"twilight" region

aphotic zone

1,000 meters

darkness

4,000 meters

▲ FIGURE 30-26 **Ocean life zones** Photosynthesis can occur only in the sunlit photic zone, which includes the intertidal zone, nearshore zone, and the upper waters of the open ocean. Approximate depths of various regions are shown, although these vary considerably depending on the clarity of the water; note that the depths are not drawn to scale. Nearly all the organisms that spend their lives in the aphotic zone rely on organic material that drifts down from the photic zone above.

contains life, including organisms such as sand crabs and burrowing worms.

Kelp Forests Kelp are enormous brown algae that can grow as tall as 160 feet (50 meters; see Chapter 21). Kelp often occur in dense stands called **kelp forests,** found throughout the world in cool waters of the nearshore zone (**FIG. 30-27c**). Kelp forests provide food and shelter for an amazing variety of animals, including annelid worms, sea anemones, sea urchins, snails, sea stars, lobsters, crabs, fish, seals, and otters.

(a) An estuary

(b) A tide pool

(c) An underwater kelp forest

(d) A tropical coral reef

▲ FIGURE 30-27 **Shallow water marine biomes (a)** Life flourishes in estuaries, where fresh river water mixes with seawater. Salt marsh grasses provide shelter for fish and invertebrates that are eaten by egrets (shown here) and many other birds. **(b)** Although pounded by waves and baked by the sun, tide pools in the intertidal zone harbor a brilliant diversity of invertebrates. **(c)** Kelp forests are home to a stunning array of invertebrates and fish, such as these bright orange Garibaldis. **(d)** Coral reefs provide habitat for many species of fish and invertebrates.

THINK CRITICALLY Why do estuaries and other coastal ecosystems have higher productivity than the open ocean?

Coral Reefs Corals are relatives of anemones and sea jellies. Some corals build skeletons of calcium carbonate. These skeletons accumulate over hundreds or thousands of years, building **coral reefs** (FIG. 30-27d). Coral reefs are most abundant in tropical waters, where temperatures typically range between 68° and 86°F (20° and 30°C). Large reefs are found in the Pacific and Indian Oceans, the Caribbean, and the Gulf of Mexico as far north as southern Florida. Coral reefs provide anchorage, shelter, and food for a diverse community of algae, fish, and invertebrates such as shrimp, sponges, and octopuses. The reefs are home to more than 90,000 known species, with possibly a million yet to be discovered.

Most reef-building corals harbor unicellular photosynthetic protists, called dinoflagellates, in their bodies. The relationship is mutually beneficial: The dinoflagellates benefit from high nutrient and carbon dioxide levels within the corals, and the dinoflagellates provide the corals with food produced by photosynthesis. Because their dinoflagellates require sunlight for photosynthesis, reef-building corals can thrive only within the photic zone, usually at depths of less than 130 feet (40 meters). Dinoflagellates give many corals their brilliant colors.

Human Impacts Human population growth is increasing the conflict between preserving coastal ecosystems as wildlife habitat and developing these areas for energy extraction, housing, harbors, and marinas. Estuaries are threatened by runoff from farming operations, which often provide a glut of nutrients from fertilizer and livestock excrement. This fosters excessive growth of algae and photosynthetic bacteria. When these organisms die, they provide nutrients that stimulate the growth of decomposers, whose metabolism depletes the water of oxygen, killing both fish and invertebrates.

Coral reefs face multiple threats. Anything that diminishes the water's clarity harms the coral's photosynthetic partners and hinders coral growth. Runoff from farming, agriculture, logging, and construction carries silt and excess nutrients. Mollusks, turtles, fish, crustaceans, and the corals themselves are often harvested from reefs faster than they can reproduce. Removing parrotfish and invertebrates often leads to an explosion of algae that smother the reefs.

Even though they require warm water, coral reefs are vulnerable to global warming caused by increased CO_2 in the atmosphere. When waters become too warm, corals expel their colorful photosynthetic dinoflagellates and appear to be bleached (see Chapter 31). The dinoflagellates return if the water cools, but when water temperatures remain too high for too long, the corals may starve. Increased CO_2 also slowly acidifies the oceans, reducing the ability of corals to build their skeletons of calcium carbonate.

There is some good news. Many countries now recognize the enormous benefits of coral reefs, including economic benefits from tourism, and are working to protect their reefs. Australia's Great Barrier Reef Marine Park and the Papahānaumokuākea Marine National Monument in the Hawaiian Islands protect enormous reef systems. Collectively, about 20,000 known species thrive in these two hotspots of biodiversity.

The Open Ocean

Beyond the coastal regions lie vast areas of the ocean in which the bottom is too deep to allow plants to anchor and still receive enough light to grow. Therefore, most life in the open ocean depends on photosynthesis by phytoplankton drifting in the photic zone. Phytoplankton are consumed by zooplankton, such as tiny shrimp-like crustaceans, which in turn are eaten by larger invertebrates, small fish, and even some marine mammals, such as humpback and blue whales (**FIG. 30-28**).

Even in the photic zone, the amount of life in the open ocean varies tremendously from place to place, largely due to differences in nutrient availability. Nutrients are provided by two major sources: runoff from the land and upwelling from

◀ **FIGURE 30-28 The open ocean** The open ocean supports fairly abundant life in the photic zone, including whales, such as these humpbacks feeding on krill (lower left). The animals in open ocean, including whales, krill, and sea jellies (lower middle), all ultimately depend on phytoplankton, the photic zone's photosynthetic producers (lower right).

◀ FIGURE 30-29 **Denizens of the deep** The skeleton of a whale provides an undersea nutrient bonanza. A zombie worm (upper left) inserts its rootlike lower body into the bones of the decomposing whale carcass. Other denizens of the deep include viperfish (upper middle), whose huge jaws and sharp teeth allow it to grasp and swallow its prey whole, and nearly transparent squid with short tentacles below bulging eyes (upper right).

the ocean depths. **Upwelling** brings cold, nutrient-laden water from the ocean depths to the surface. Major areas of upwelling occur around Antarctica and along western coastlines, including those of California, Peru, and West Africa. Nutrient-rich waters that support a large phytoplankton community are greenish and relatively murky. In contrast, the blue clarity of many tropical waters is due to a lack of nutrients, which limits the concentration of phytoplankton in the water.

Human Impacts Two major threats to the open ocean are pollution and overfishing. For example, plastic refuse, blown off the land or deliberately dumped at sea, is often mistaken for food by sea turtles, gulls, porpoises, seals, and whales. Animals that consume this refuse may die from clogged digestive tracts. Oil from oil-tanker spills, runoff from improper disposal on land, and leakage from offshore oil wells contaminates the open ocean. Some components of oil cause lethal developmental defects in a variety of marine organisms.

Many fish populations are harvested unsustainably as a result of increased demand for fish and highly efficient fishing technologies (see Chapter 31). For example, the once abundant cod populations off eastern Canada collapsed in 1992,

prompting a fishing moratorium that still continues. In 2013, cod fishing was severely restricted off the coast of New England as well, with further restrictions enacted in 2014. Populations of Pacific bluefin tuna, haddock, mackerel, and many other fish have also declined dramatically because of overfishing. In 2014, the United Nations Food and Agriculture Organization estimated that 30% of marine fish stocks were being fished at unsustainable levels.

Efforts are now being made to prevent overfishing. Many countries have established quotas on fish whose populations are threatened. Fishing restrictions have succeeded in rebuilding the stocks of fish such as the Acadian redfish and Atlantic swordfish. Marine reserves, where fishing is prohibited, are increasingly being established throughout the world, causing substantial improvements in the diversity, number, and size of marine animals. Nearby areas also benefit because the reserves act as nurseries, helping to restore populations outside the reserves.

The Ocean Floor

Because the amount of light in the aphotic zone is inadequate for photosynthesis, most of the food on the ocean floor comes from the excrement and dead bodies that drift down from above. Nevertheless, life is found on the ocean floor in amazing quantity and variety, including worms, sea cucumbers, sea stars, mollusks, squid, and fish of bizarre shapes (FIG. 30-29). Little is known of the behavior and ecology of these exotic creatures, which almost never survive being brought to the surface.

Entire communities feed on the dead bodies of whales, each of which contains an average of 40 tons of food. When a whale carcass reaches the ocean floor, fish, crabs, worms, and snails swarm over it, extracting nutrients from its flesh and bones. Bone-eating zombie worms tunnel into the bone

◀ **FIGURE 30-30 Hydrothermal vent communities** Hydrothermal vents spew superheated water rich in minerals that provide both energy and nutrients to the vent community. Giant red tube worms may reach 9 feet (nearly 3 meters) in length and live up to 250 years (left). The foot of this snail is protected by scales coated with iron sulfide (right).

and absorb nutrients. Anaerobic bacteria complete the breakdown of bone, and the bacteria themselves provide food for clams, worms, mussels, and crustaceans.

Hydrothermal Vent Communities In 1977, geologists exploring the Galápagos Rift (an area of the Pacific floor where the plates that form Earth's crust are separating) found cracks in the seafloor, called hydrothermal ("hot water") vents. Hydrothermal vents emit superheated water containing sulfides and other minerals (**FIG. 30-30**). Surrounding the vents are **hydrothermal vent communities** of pink fish, blind white crabs, enormous mussels, white clams, sea anemones, giant tube worms, and a species of snail sporting iron-laden armor plates (Fig. 30-30, right). Hundreds of species have been found near vents, which have now been discovered in many deep-sea regions where separating tectonic plates allow material from Earth's interior to spew out.

In this unique, completely dark ecosystem, sulfur bacteria serve as the producers. Instead of photosynthesis, sulfur bacteria use **chemosynthesis** to manufacture organic molecules from carbon dioxide, harvesting energy from a source that is deadly to most other forms of life—hydrogen

sulfide, discharged from the vents. Many vent animals consume the sulfur bacteria directly; others, such as the giant tube worm, harbor chemosynthetic bacteria within their bodies and live off the by-products of bacterial metabolism. The tube worms derive their red color from a unique form of hemoglobin that transports hydrogen sulfide to its symbiotic bacteria.

The bacteria and archaea that inhabit the vent communities can survive at remarkably high temperatures; some can live at 248°F (106°C; the tremendous pressure in the deep ocean prevents water from boiling at temperatures well above its sea-level boiling point). Scientists are investigating how the enzymes and other proteins of these heat-loving microbes can continue to function at such high temperatures.

CHECK YOUR LEARNING

Can you ...

- describe the principal freshwater and marine biomes?
- explain how water depth and proximity to the shore help to determine the nature and abundance of life in each?
- describe some effects humans have on aquatic biomes?

Food of the Gods

World demand for both coffee and chocolate will probably continue to soar. Can coffee and cacao farmers meet this demand, enjoy a reasonable income, and simultaneously help to preserve rain forests? That largely depends on how the coffee and cacao plants are grown.

Full-sun plantations, in which the original vegetation has been completely removed and replaced with monocultures of coffee or cacao, often have the highest coffee or cocoa production, but at the cost of lower quality, substantial inputs of fertilizers and pesticides, and little biodiversity. Shady plantations typically provide higher quality product and more biodiversity, but some shady plantations are better than others. For example, most coffee from Mexico is grown in shady plantations ("shade-grown coffee"), but often under only a sparse cover of a few species of trees, which does not provide a sufficiently diverse habitat for rain-forest birds and other species. In contrast, in rustic plantations, the canopy remains mostly intact, because only low-growing plants are removed from the rain forest to make way for coffee or cocoa plants. Rustic plantations that promote diversity and sustainable production can be certified by the Smithsonian Migratory Bird Center, the Rainforest Alliance, and similar organizations. To

achieve certification, plantations must include a diversity of tree species. Some rustic plantations provide a home for more than 150 different species of birds, which feast on fruit, or on insects that thrive in the trees and moist soil.

Are rustic plantations good for biodiversity but bad deals for farmers? Not if they're well managed. In many cases, the canopy trees serve as an additional source of food or income for the farmers, providing citrus fruit, bananas, guavas, and lumber. Higher quality cocoa and coffee, combined with certification by the Bird Center or Rainforest Alliance, usually bring farmers a higher price for their products and, consequently, higher incomes.

CONSIDER THIS Ecologists argue that it is both ecologically and economically advantageous to manage Earth's ecosystems as a long-term investment rather than for short-term profit, letting natural ecosystems thrive while simultaneously providing needed products for people. Research one sustainable natural product (for example, a forest product or a type of fish). Was the source of this product ever overexploited? What measures have been taken to ensure sustainability? What challenges might the future bring, and how might those challenges be overcome?

CHAPTER REVIEW

 Go to **MasteringBiology** for practice quizzes, activities, eText, videos, current events, and more.

Answers to Think Critically, Evaluate This, Multiple Choice, and Fill-in-the-Blank questions can be found in the Answers section at the back of the book.

Summary of Key Concepts

30.1 What Determines the Distribution of Life on Earth?

The requirements for life on Earth include nutrients, energy, liquid water, and an appropriate temperature range. In aquatic ecosystems, liquid water is readily available; sunlight, nutrients, and temperature determine the distribution and abundance of life. On land, sunlight energy and nutrients are usually plentiful; the distribution of life is largely determined by soil moisture, which in turn is determined by precipitation and temperature. The requirements for life occur in specific patterns on Earth, resulting in characteristic large-scale communities called biomes.

30.2 What Factors Influence Earth's Climate?

Because of Earth's curvature, the sun's rays are nearly vertical and pass through the least amount of atmosphere at the equator; toward the poles, the rays are more slanted and must penetrate more atmosphere. Thus, the equator is uniformly warm, whereas higher latitudes have lower overall temperatures. Earth's tilt on its axis causes seasonal variations in climate at northern and southern latitudes as Earth orbits the sun. Rising warm air and sinking cool air in regular patterns from north to south produce

areas of low and high moisture. These patterns are modified by prevailing winds, the presence and topography of continents, and proximity to oceans.

30.3 What Are the Principal Terrestrial Biomes?

The tropical rain-forest biome, located near the equator, is warm and wet year-round. Tropical rain forests are dominated by broadleaf evergreen trees. Most nutrients are found in the vegetation. Most animals live in the trees. Rain forests have the highest productivity and biodiversity on Earth. Slightly farther from the equator, wet seasons alternate with dry seasons during which trees shed their leaves, producing tropical deciduous forests. Scrub forests and savannas receive less rain than tropical deciduous forests and have extended dry seasons. Savannas are characterized by widely spaced trees with grass growing beneath. Most deserts, which receive less than 10 inches of rain annually, are located around 30° N and 30° S latitudes, or in the rain shadows of mountain ranges. In deserts, plants are widely spaced and have adaptations to conserve water. Animals have both behavioral and physiological mechanisms to avoid excessive heat and to conserve water. Chaparral exists in desert-like conditions that are moderated by their proximity to a coastline, allowing drought-resistant bushes and small trees to thrive. Grasslands occur in the centers of continents. These biomes have a continuous grass cover and few trees. Relatively low precipitation, fires, and severe droughts prevent the growth of trees. Grasslands have the world's richest soils and have largely been converted to agriculture. Temperate deciduous forests, whose broadleaf trees drop their leaves in winter, dominate the eastern half of the United States and are also found in Europe and eastern Asia. Moderate precipitation and lack of severe droughts allow the growth of deciduous trees, which shade the forest floor, preventing the growth of grasses. Temperate rain forests, dominated by conifers, occur in coastal regions with both high rainfall and moderate temperatures. The northern coniferous forest nearly encircles Earth below the arctic region. It is dominated by conifers whose small, waxy needles are adapted to conserve water and take advantage of the short growing season. The tundra is a frozen desert where permafrost prevents the growth of trees and the bushes remain stunted. Tundra is found both in the Arctic and on mountain peaks.

30.4 What Are the Principal Aquatic Biomes?

Sunlight is strong enough for photosynthesis only in shallow waters. Nutrients are found in bottom sediments, washed in from surrounding land or provided by upwelling in nearshore ocean waters.

In freshwater lakes, the littoral zone receives both sunlight and nutrients and supports the most life. The limnetic zone is the well-lit region of open water where photosynthetic protists thrive. In the deep profundal zone of large lakes, light is inadequate for photosynthesis, and most energy is provided by detritus. Oligotrophic lakes are clear, are low in nutrients, and support sparse communities. Eutrophic lakes are rich in nutrients and support dense communities. During succession, lakes shift from an oligotrophic to a eutrophic condition.

Streams begin at a source region, often in mountains, where water is provided by rain and snow. Source water is generally clear, high in oxygen, and low in nutrients. In the transition zone, streams join to form rivers that carry sediment from land and support a larger community. On their way to lakes or oceans, rivers enter relatively flat floodplains, where they deposit nutrients, take a meandering path, and spill over the land during floods.

Most life in the oceans is found in shallow water, where sunlight can penetrate, and is concentrated near the continents, particularly in areas of upwelling, where nutrients are most plentiful. Estuaries are highly productive areas where rivers meet the ocean. The intertidal zone, alternately covered and exposed by tides, harbors organisms that can withstand waves and exposure to air. Kelp forests grow in cool, nutrient-rich coastal areas and provide food and shelter for many animals. Coral reefs, formed by the skeletons of corals, are primarily found in shallow water in warm tropical seas. Coral reefs support an extremely diverse ecosystem. In the open ocean, most life is found in the photic zone, where light supports photosynthesis by phytoplankton. In the aphotic zone, life is supported by nutrients that drift down from the photic zone. The deep ocean floor lies within the aphotic zone. Whale carcasses provide a nutrient bonanza that supports a succession of unique communities. Specialized hydrothermal vent communities, supported by chemosynthetic bacteria, thrive at great depths in geothermally heated water.

Key Terms

Thinking Through the Concepts

Multiple Choice

1. Which of the following does *not* characterize the tropical rain-forest biome?
  a. warm temperatures year-round
  b. abundant rainfall
  c. nutrient-rich soil
  d. high biodiversity

2. The biome that is mostly covered by grass and scattered trees, with warm temperatures year-round and pronounced wet and dry seasons, is the
  a. tropical deciduous forest.
  b. savanna.
  c. desert.
  d. tropical scrub forest.

3. The part of a freshwater lake that typically contains the most abundant plant and animal life is the
  a. profundal zone.
  b. aphotic zone.
  c. limnetic zone.
  d. littoral zone.

4. Which of the following is True about ocean ecosystems?
  a. Surface waters typically have abundant sunlight but low levels of nutrients.
  b. Because there isn't enough sunlight for photosynthesis, deep waters typically have no life.
  c. Surface waters in the open ocean have the highest productivity.
  d. Life near hydrothermal vents relies on photosynthesis for energy.

5. As the global climate warms, which of the following changes in the distribution of biomes is likely to occur?
  a. spread of coniferous forests to lower elevations on mountains
  b. spread of tundra to lower elevations on mountains
  c. spread of northern coniferous forests farther north
  d. spread of northern coniferous forests farther south

Fill-in-the-Blank

1. The tilt of Earth on its axis produces _____. Coastal climates are more moderate because of _____. A dry region on the side of a mountain range that faces away from the direction of prevailing winds is called a(n) _____.

2. Of the four major requirements of life, which are the most important in determining the nature and distribution of terrestrial biomes? _____, _____ Which are most important for aquatic ecosystems? _____, _____, _____

3. The most biologically diverse terrestrial ecosystems are _____. The most biologically diverse aquatic ecosystems are _____.

4. The shallow portion of a large freshwater lake is called the _____. Photosynthetic plankton are called _____; nonphotosynthetic plankton are called _____. The open-water portion of a lake is divided into two zones, the upper _____ and the lower _____. Lakes that are low in nutrients are described as _____. Lakes high in nutrients are described as _____. The most diverse freshwater ecosystems are _____.

5. The primary producers of the open ocean are mainly _____. Hydrothermal vent communities are supported by bacteria that obtain energy from the process of _____, using the compound _____ as an energy source. Water may be at temperatures above the surface boiling point near hydrothermal vents, but it does not boil because of the _____.

Review Questions

1. Explain how air currents contribute to the formation of rain forests and large deserts.

2. What are large, roughly circular ocean currents called? What effect do they have on climate, and where is that effect strongest?

3. Explain why traveling up a mountain in the Northern Hemisphere takes you through biomes similar to those you would encounter by traveling north for a long distance.

4. Where are the nutrients of the tropical rain-forest biome concentrated? Why is life in the tropical rain forest concentrated high above the ground?

5. List some adaptations of desert cactus plants and desert animals to heat and drought.

6. What is desertification?

7. How are trees of the northern coniferous forest adapted to a lack of water and a short growing season?

8. How do deciduous and coniferous biomes differ?

9. What environmental factor best explains why the natural biome is shortgrass prairie in eastern Colorado, tallgrass prairie in Illinois, and deciduous forest in Ohio?

10. Where is life in the oceans most abundant, and why?

11. Distinguish among the littoral, limnetic, and profundal zones of lakes in terms of their location and the communities they support.

12. Distinguish between oligotrophic and eutrophic lakes. Describe a natural scenario and a human-created scenario under which an oligotrophic lake might be converted to a eutrophic lake.

13. Compare the source, transition, and floodplain zones of streams and rivers.

14. Distinguish between the photic and aphotic zones of the ocean. How do organisms in the photic zone obtain nutrients? How are nutrients obtained in the aphotic zone?

Applying the Concepts

1. Fairbanks, Alaska, the plains of eastern Montana, and Tucson, Arizona, all have about the same annual precipitation. Explain why these locations contain very different vegetation.

2. Using Figures 30-3 and 30-4 as starting points, explain why terrestrial biomes are not evenly distributed in bands of latitude across Earth's surface. Explain how your proposed mechanisms apply to two specific locations.

31 CONSERVING EARTH'S BIODIVERSITY

Exterminating the wolves in Yellowstone National Park put an entire ecosystem in jeopardy.

The Wolves of Yellowstone

IN 1926, THE LAST TWO WOLVES in Yellowstone National Park were killed by park rangers. Why were wolves intentionally exterminated in a national park? Because, when Congress established the park in 1872, the Secretary of the Interior had been instructed to "provide against the wanton destruction of the fish and game." Wolf predation on elk was considered "wanton destruction," so all the wolves were killed. But it turned out that no wolves meant too many elk, which in turn devastated the park. As early as the 1930s, scientists noted that aspen, cottonwoods, and willows were being overgrazed. In fact, from the mid-1930s through 1997, at 87 study sites in northern Yellowstone, not a single aspen sapling survived.

In 1987, the U.S. Fish and Wildlife Service, charged with restoring endangered species, proposed transplanting wolves from Canada to Yellowstone. After considerable debate, 31 wolves were released in Yellowstone in 1995 and 1996. Since 2000, wolf populations in the park have ranged from about 100 to 170. Within a few years after wolves were reintroduced to the park, elk populations started to decline. Elk behavior changed, as well. They spent more time looking around and less time feeding. Aspen saplings suffered less browsing and began to grow again, providing increased habitat for many other species, including wildflowers and songbirds. Although it is very difficult to prove that wolf restoration is the cause of the decline in elk and the rebound in aspen, most ecologists studying the Yellowstone ecosystem have concluded that wolves indeed caused these profound changes.

The impact of wolves in Yellowstone is just one example of the importance of **biodiversity:** the sum total of Earth's tremendous variety of life, including genes, species, communities, and ecosystems. When wolves were exterminated from Yellowstone in 1926, there were still grizzly bears, coyotes, foxes, and mountain lions in the park, but all of these predators put together could not fill the role of the wolf in the Yellowstone ecosystem.

Is biodiversity truly important to ecosystem function, or are just a few species the key players? If biodiversity is essential, why is that so? How do human activities endanger biodiversity, and potentially the functioning of the ecosystems upon which all life on Earth depends?

AT A GLANCE

31.1 WHAT IS CONSERVATION BIOLOGY?

Conservation biology is the scientific discipline devoted to understanding and preserving Earth's biodiversity, including:

- *Genetic Diversity*   The long-term survival of a species depends on the variety of different alleles in its gene pool. Genetic diversity is crucial for a species to adapt to changing environments.
- *Species Diversity*   The variety and relative abundance of the different species that make up a community are important for the functioning of the community. Species diversity helps to buffer communities against disturbances such as drought, climate change, and even invasive species.
- *Ecosystem Diversity*   Ecosystem diversity includes the variety of communities and the nonliving environments on which the communities depend. Ecosystem diversity also includes the different types of ecosystems, both terrestrial and aquatic, found throughout the biosphere.

CHECK YOUR LEARNING

Can you ...

- describe the goals of conservation biology?
- explain the importance of the three levels of biodiversity that conservation biologists study and seek to protect?

31.2 WHY IS BIODIVERSITY IMPORTANT?

The vast majority of people in developed countries, such as most of the countries in North America and Europe, live in cities or suburbs. Why should preserving biodiversity be important to us? Many people would say that species and natural ecosystems are worth preserving for their own sake. But even if you disagree, a very practical reason for preserving biodiversity is simple self-interest: Ecosystems, and the biodiversity that sustains them, are essential for human well-being.

Ecosystem Services Are Practical Uses for Biodiversity

Ecosystem services are the benefits that people obtain from ecosystems. The *Millennium Ecosystem Assessment*

groups ecosystem services into four interconnected categories: (1) provisioning services, (2) regulating services, (3) cultural services, and (4) supporting services. Here we provide a few examples of each type of ecosystem service.

Provisioning Services Are Products Directly Obtained from Ecosystems

Ecosystems provide many materials and sources of energy that are used by people. Provisioning services are often called "natural resources."

- *Food*   Most of our food comes from farms (agricultural ecosystems), but people throughout the world also eat wild-grown food. For example, the United Nations Food and Agriculture Organization estimates that about 20 pounds (9 kilograms) of wild fish and other seafood are caught per person per year, worldwide. In parts of Africa, Asia, and South America, wild animals provide an important source of protein for an often poorly nourished population.
- *Raw Materials*   Wood is used for construction, furniture, and paper worldwide. Natural ecosystems provide almost all of the fresh water used for agriculture, industry, and drinking.
- *Energy*   Hydroelectric power provides electricity in almost every country with enough rainfall and suitable dam sites. In less-developed countries, rural residents often rely on wood for heating and cooking.

Regulating Services Control Ecosystem Processes

Regulating services affect the quality or abundance of many of the products people obtain from ecosystems, including water, soil, and food. Regulating services also help to control weather and climate.

- *Water Purification*   Natural ecosystems, including forests, grasslands, and wetlands, purify water by removing sediments and pollutants.
- *Pollination*   Bees and other insects pollinate most plants, including important agricultural products such as coffee, cocoa, and many fruits.
- *Pest Control*   Animals as diverse as bats, frogs, birds, and wasps feed on insects that are often agricultural pests or carry human diseases such as malaria.
- *Erosion and Flood Control*   Vegetation helps to hold soil in place and prevent erosion. Plant roots also increase the

▲ **FIGURE 31-1 Loss of flood control services** Although triggered by heavy monsoon rains, the catastrophic flooding in northern India in 2014 was worsened by massive deforestation. Hundreds of people were killed.

soil's capacity to hold water, reducing both erosion and flooding. Deforestation is thought to have contributed to massive flooding triggered by heavy rains in India and Brazil in 2014 (FIG. 31-1).

- *Climate Regulation* By providing shade, reducing temperatures, and serving as windbreaks, plant communities affect local climates. Forests dramatically influence the water cycle, as water evaporating from leaves returns to the atmosphere. In the Amazon rain forest, one-third to one-half of the rain is water that evaporated from leaves.
- *Carbon Storage* Plants remove CO_2 from the atmosphere during photosynthesis. Some of this CO_2 is stored in the plants, especially in the trunks and roots of trees. Thus, forests slow down the increase in atmospheric CO_2 that causes climate change and acidifies the oceans. If forests are cut down or burned, they release CO_2 again. About 10% to 15% of the CO_2 produced by human activities results from deforestation.

Cultural Services Are Nonmaterial Benefits Desired by People

People use natural ecosystems to increase their enjoyment of life, in many cases returning home not with material products, but with pleasant memories and reduced stress.

- *Recreation* Many, perhaps most, people take pleasure in "returning to nature." In the United States, more than 430 million visitors flock to national parks and national forests each year. Hundreds of millions more go to wildlife refuges and state parks.
- *Tourism* Ecotourism, in which people travel to observe unique biological communities, is a rapidly growing recreational industry. Examples of ecotourism destinations include tropical coral reefs and rain forests, the Galápagos Islands, the African savanna, and even Antarctica (FIG. 31-2).
- *Mental and Physical Health* Scientific studies have found that being in, or often just looking at, natural environments hastens healing after surgery, reduces stress hormone levels, improves mental focus in children with ADHD, and boosts the immune system.

Supporting Services Are Crucial to Providing Other Ecosystem Services

Ecosystem services that either affect people only indirectly or take a very long time to affect human welfare are usually classed as supporting services.

- *Habitat* Ecosystems provide habitat for the organisms that supply provisioning and regulating services, including wild foods, wood, and pollinators.
- *Photosynthesis* Photosynthesis by plants, algae, and cyanobacteria provides all of the oxygen needed for life on Earth and is the first step in providing food for almost all living organisms, including people.
- *Genetic Resources* The wealth of genes found in wild plants is an often-overlooked ecosystem service that may help to protect our food supply. According to the UN Food and Agriculture Organization, most of our food is supplied

(a) Scuba diving in a coral reef in the Red Sea   (b) Spotting penguins in Antarctica

▲ **FIGURE 31-2 Ecotourism** Carefully managed ecotourism represents a sustainable use of natural ecosystems, generating revenue and providing an incentive to preserve wildlife habitat.

by only 12 crop plants, including rice, wheat, and corn. Researchers have identified genes in wild relatives of these domesticated plants that might be transferred into crops to increase their productivity or provide greater resistance to disease, drought, or salty soil.

- *Soil Formation* It can take hundreds of years to build up a single inch of soil. For example, the rich soils of the Midwestern United States accumulated under natural grasslands over thousands of years. Farmers have converted these grasslands into one of the most productive agricultural regions in the world.
- *Nutrient Cycling* As we described in Chapter 29, nutrients cycle within and between ecosystems, often moving from reservoirs that are not available to living organisms to chemical forms that organisms can use. For example, nitrogen-fixing bacteria in soil convert atmospheric nitrogen into ammonia and nitrate, which plants can then use in the synthesis of proteins and nucleic acids.

Ecological Economics Attempts to Measure the Monetary Value of Ecosystem Services

Historically, people have assumed that ecosystem services are free and unlimited. Therefore, the value of ecosystem services has seldom been taken into account when making decisions about land use, farming practices, power generation, and a host of other human activities. Fortunately, that is beginning to change. **Ecological economics** attempts to determine the monetary value of ecosystem services and to assess the trade-offs that occur when natural ecosystems are damaged to make way for human activities.

For example, a farmer planning to divert water from a wetland to irrigate a crop would traditionally weigh the benefit of increased crop production against the cost of the project's labor and materials. This analysis ignores the many services an intact wetland provides, such as neutralizing pollutants, controlling floods, and providing breeding grounds for fish, birds, and many other animals. If the loss of ecosystem services were factored into the cost–benefit analysis, the intact wetland might well be more valuable than the crop. In a market economy, however, the economic benefits from projects that damage ecosystems usually go to individuals, whereas the costs are borne by society as a whole. Thus, it is difficult to apply the principles of ecological economics except in projects designed and funded by government agencies.

New York City offers an excellent example of government planning to preserve ecosystem services. The city obtains most of its water from the Catskill Mountains, a 1600-square-mile watershed 120 miles away in upstate New York. In 1997, realizing that its water would be polluted by sewage and agricultural runoff as the Catskills were developed, city officials calculated that it would cost $6 billion to $8 billion to build a water filtration plant, plus an additional $250 million annually to run it. Recognizing that the same water purification service was provided by the ecosystems of the Catskill

Mountains, city officials decided to invest about $1.5 billion in protecting them, purchasing large tracts of land and keeping them in a reasonably natural state

Earth's Ecosystem Services Have Enormous Monetary Value

In 2014, an international team of ecologists, economists, and geographers calculated that ecosystem services provide benefits to humanity worth between $125 trillion and $145 trillion per year, about twice the world's annual gross domestic product (an estimate of the market value of all goods and services produced everywhere in the world). However, humanity isn't taking very good care of our biosphere. For example, the *Millennium Ecosystem Assessment* concluded that 60% of Earth's ecosystem services were being degraded.

Biodiversity Supports Ecosystem Function

Several studies have concluded that areas with the highest biodiversity also tend to be areas providing the greatest ecosystem services. Why is biodiversity important to ecosystem function? More diverse communities tend to have higher productivity (see Chapter 29). Diverse communities are also better able to withstand disturbances, such as drought, severe winters, episodes of pollution, or delivery of excess nutrients, such as farm fertilizer runoff. When a community has a large number of different species, each with its own niche, resources are often used very efficiently, leaving few resources available for invasive species to gain a foothold.

One way in which biodiversity might protect ecosystems, sometimes called the "redundancy hypothesis," is that several species in a community may have functionally equivalent roles. For example, several species of bees in an ecosystem may pollinate flowers. If a few of these species are lost, the remaining ones may increase their population size and pollinate most or all of the flowers, as long as the ecosystem operates under typical conditions. If, however, the ecosystem is stressed—by drought, for example—some of the remaining bee species may not survive the stress, resulting in significantly less pollination and, hence, less plant reproduction.

The "rivet hypothesis" postulates that ecosystem function is analogous to an airplane wing, in which the loss of a couple of rivets may not be catastrophic, but the loss of rivets in strategic places causes the entire wing to fall apart. In an ecosystem, superficially similar species may have somewhat different positions in the web of ecosystem stability, and the loss of a few critical species may cause collapse. Returning to our bee example, some species of bees specialize in pollinating specific species of flowers. Eliminating one of these bee species may mean that some species of plants no longer reproduce. Any animals that specialize in feeding on those plants will die along with them. If just a few critical bee species disappear, then many plant and animal species will also die off.

Earth WATCH   Whales—The Biggest Keystones of All?

The oceans are a lot emptier than they used to be. No one knows for sure how many whales originally roamed the seas, but it is believed that commercial whaling reduced many whale populations by 90%. Even now, decades after almost all commercial whaling ceased, most whale populations are much less than half their pre-whaling size. Because whales swim at the top of the food chain, you would think that whale prey, from giant squid to shrimp-like krill, should be experiencing a population boom, right?

Actually, they're not. Populations of krill have not increased and may have even declined a little, despite the fact that the pre-whaling population of filter-feeding baleen whales probably ate something like 150 million tons of krill each year. How can that be? Studies by marine ecologists suggest an answer: The nutrients required by krill are carried from ocean depths to surface waters by whales.

Krill eat photosynthetic phytoplankton, which can only live in well-lit waters near the surface. Phytoplankton require nutrients such as iron and nitrogen, which tend to be scarce in surface waters. Why are nutrients scarce at the surface? Because most organisms and their feces are denser than seawater. For example, single-celled algae sink a few yards each day. Feces and dead animals sink much faster, some as much as a half-mile a day. As they sink, algae, dead animals, and feces all carry nutrients from the surface down to the depths. Ocean currents and winter storms bring some of these nutrients back up to the surface, but not all.

Enter the great whales. Many whales feed at substantial depths, from a few hundred feet to as much as a half mile below the surface. Whales, of course, return to the surface to breathe—and to poop (**FIG. E31-1**). Whales release huge plumes of buoyant feces that effectively bring nutrients from the depths back to the surface. Whale feces have about 10 million times as much iron as seawater does. Whale feces and urine also bring nitrogen up to the surface in the form of ammonia and urea. By bringing nutrients to sunlit surface water,

◀ **FIGURE E31-1**
Whale feces fertilize the oceans Whales, such as the sperm whale shown here, release huge plumes of semi-liquid feces that drift in surface waters, providing essential nutrients for photosynthetic algae.

the "whale pump" enhances the productivity of the oceans and may actually increase krill populations.

Fortunately, almost all whaling has ceased, and most whale populations are increasing, some by as much as 5% to 7% a year. As these giant keystones rise up, they will likely bring ocean ecosystems up with them.

THINK CRITICALLY How would you test the whale pump hypothesis? Assume that you can measure populations of whales and phytoplankton and the concentrations of iron, nitrogen, and other nutrients in ocean waters.

In some ecosystems, one or two "rivets," called **keystone species,** may be crucially important to ecosystem function. Think of the analogy that inspired the phrase: A keystone sits at the top of a stone arch and holds all the other pieces in place. Remove the keystone, and the whole arch collapses. Similarly, in a biological community, a keystone species is one whose role is much more important than would be predicted by the size of its population or by a superficial glance at its position in the food web. In the oceans, the great whales may be keystone species, as we explore in "Earth Watch: Whales—The Biggest Keystones of All?"

CHECK YOUR LEARNING

Can you ...

- describe the major categories of ecosystem services provided to humanity and provide examples of each?
- explain why biodiversity helps to maintain functioning ecosystems?

CASE STUDY \ **CONTINUED**
The Wolves of Yellowstone

In Yellowstone, the wolf is a top predator and keystone species that helps to determine populations not only of its direct prey, but also of other species in the ecosystem. In the early twentieth century, no one expected that exterminating wolves would wreak havoc on aspens and the many species that depend on them. Unfortunately, in many parts of the world, loss of biodiversity, including keystone predators, continues today. What are the principal causes?

31.3 IS EARTH'S BIODIVERSITY DIMINISHING?

No species lasts forever. Over the course of evolutionary time, species arise, flourish for various periods of time, and go extinct. If all species are fated to eventual extinction, why should we worry about modern extinctions? Because the rate of extinction during modern times has become extraordinarily high.

Extinction Is a Natural Process, but Rates Have Risen Dramatically in Recent Years

The fossil record indicates that, in the absence of cataclysmic events, extinctions occur naturally at a very low rate. This *background extinction rate* ranges from about 0.1 to 1 extinction per million species per year. However, the fossil record also provides evidence of five major **mass extinctions,** during which many species were eradicated in a relatively short period of time (see Chapter 18). The most recent mass extinction happened roughly 66 million years ago, abruptly ending the age of dinosaurs. Sudden changes in the environment, such as might be caused by enormous meteor impacts or rapid climate change, are the most likely reasons for these mass extinctions.

A recent study estimates that the modern extinction rate is about 1,000 times the background rate: 100 to 1,000 extinctions per million species per year. And species aren't

HAVE YOU EVER

WONDERED ...

You may feel helpless to prevent extinction, but in fact, you can do a lot. You can purchase coffee, chocolate, fish, and many other products that have been grown or harvested in a sustainable manner and certified by organizations such as the Marine Stewardship Council, Seafood Watch, the Forest Stewardship Council, or the Rainforest Alliance. You can contribute to organizations, such as the Nature Conservancy, the World Wildlife Fund,

What You Can Do to Prevent Extinctions?

or Saving Species, that work directly to protect biodiversity. For example, Saving Species was the driving force behind preserving wildlife corridors that connect cloud forest habitat in Ecuador, home of the olinguito, a 2-pound relative of raccoons that was first discovered in the wild in 2013. The same habitat also supports 14 species of endangered hummingbirds and many other rare and endangered animals and plants.

Olinguito

being replaced; new ones appear at a far slower rate. As a result, many biologists are convinced that humans are causing a sixth mass extinction. Extinctions of birds and mammals are best documented, although these represent only about 0.1% of the world's species. Since the 1500s, we have lost about 1.7% of all mammal species and 1.6% to 2% of all bird species, an extinction rate probably more than 100 times the background rate.

Each year, a Red List of at-risk species is published by the International Union for Conservation of Nature (IUCN), the world's largest conservation network. Species are described as **vulnerable, endangered,** or **critically endangered,** depending on how likely they are to become extinct in the near future. Species that fall into any of these categories are described as **threatened.** In 2014, the Red List contained 22,176 threatened species, including 13% of all birds, 26% of mammals, and 41% of amphibians. The U.S. Fish and Wildlife Service lists more than 1,500 threatened and endangered species in the United States alone. Why are so many species in danger of extinction?

CHECK YOUR LEARNING

Can you ...

- define *mass extinction*?
- explain why biologists fear that a mass extinction is occurring as a result of human activities?

31.4 WHAT ARE THE MAJOR THREATS TO BIODIVERSITY?

The 2014 edition of the *Living Planet Report,* a joint project of the World Wildlife Fund, the Zoological Society of London, the Global Footprint Network, and the Water Footprint Network, estimated that the total population of wild vertebrate animals on Earth is only about half of what it was 40 years earlier. This loss was primarily caused by habitat destruction and overexploitation by hunting and fishing, with smaller contributions from climate change, invasive species, pollution, and disease. Much of the loss of habitat is essentially irreversible, as people convert wildlands to farms, cities, and roads.

Humanity's Ecological Footprint Exceeds Earth's Resources

The human **ecological footprint** is an estimate of the area of Earth's surface required to produce the resources we use and absorb the wastes we generate. A complementary concept, **biocapacity,** is an estimate of the sustainable resources and waste-absorbing capacity actually available on Earth. Although related to the concept of carrying capacity (explained in Chapter 28), both footprint and biocapacity calculations are subject to change as new technologies influence the way people use resources. The calculations assume that humans can use the entire planet, without reserving any of it for the rest of life on Earth.

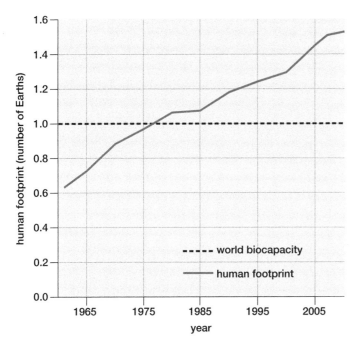

In 2010, the biocapacity available for each of the
6.7 billion people then living on Earth was 4.2 acres, but
the average human footprint was 6.4 acres. In other words,
we exceeded biocapacity by about 50%: In the long run,
we would need about 1.5 Earths to support humanity at
2010 consumption and popula-
tion levels (FIG. 31-3). Countries
vary enormously in their ecological footprints, from about 12 to
24 acres per person for wealthy
countries, such as most of Europe,
Canada, Australia, New Zealand,
and the United States, to as little
as 1 to 2 acres per person for poor
countries, such as most of those in
Africa. Since these estimates were
made, the human population
has grown by about 400 million,
while Earth's total biocapacity has
not significantly increased.

Running such an ecological
deficit is possible only on a temporary basis. Imagine a savings account that must support you for
the rest of your life. If you preserve
the capital and live on the interest,
the account will last forever. But if you withdraw the capital
to support an extravagant lifestyle or a growing family, you
will soon run out of money. By degrading Earth's ecosystems, humanity is drawing down Earth's ecological capital.
As the human population grows and highly populated countries such as India and China raise their living standards, the
strain on Earth's resources will increase. By using up so much
biocapacity, people inevitably reduce the resources available
for the rest of life on Earth.

Many Human Activities Directly Threaten Biodiversity

Habitat destruction, overexploitation, invasive species, pollution, and global climate change pose the greatest dangers
to biodiversity. Threatened species often face several of these
perils simultaneously. For example, coral reefs, home to
about one-third of marine fish species, suffer from a combination of overharvesting, pollution, ocean acidification, and
global warming.

Habitat Destruction Is the Most Serious Threat to Biodiversity

Habitat loss imperils more than 85% of all endangered mammals, birds, and amphibians. The most serious threat is the
loss of tropical rain forests, home to about half of Earth's
plant and animal species. Satellite images indicate that about
30,000 to 45,000 square miles of rain forest are lost each year
(the state of Kentucky is about 40,000 square miles), or the
area of a football field every 1 to 1.5 seconds (FIG. 31-4). The
primary cause of the destruction of tropical rain forests is
converting the land to agriculture, to create both small sub-
sistence farms and huge plantations and ranches that supply
beef, soybeans, palm oil, sugarcane, and biofuels, mostly to
developed countries (see "Earth Watch: Biofuels—Are Their
Benefits Bogus?" in Chapter 7).

| 1975 | 2012 |

▲ **FIGURE 31-4 Habitat destruction** The loss of habitat due to human activities is the greatest single threat to biodiversity worldwide. These satellite images show a section of rain forest in
Brazil in 1975 (left) and 2012 (right). More than half of the original rain forest has been cut down.

▲ **FIGURE 31-5 Habitat fragmentation** Fields isolate patches of forest in Paraguay.

THINK CRITICALLY Which types of species do you think are most likely to disappear from small patches of forest? What do you think would be the resulting effect on the ecosystem?

Even when a natural ecosystem is not destroyed, it may become broken into small pieces, separated by roads, farms, or housing developments (**FIG. 31-5**). This **habitat fragmentation** is a serious threat to wildlife. Some species of U.S. songbirds, such as the ovenbird and Acadian flycatcher, need as much as 300 acres of continuous forest to find food, mates, and breeding sites; in smaller forest patches, reproductive success is much lower. Big cats are also threatened by habitat fragmentation. Starting in the 1970s, India has set aside 47 forest reserves intended to protect the endangered Bengal tiger. However, many of the reserves have become islands in a sea of development, forcing the tigers into isolated patches of woodland.

To be truly functional, a preserve must support a **minimum viable population (MVP),** the smallest isolated population that can persist in spite of natural events, including disease, fires, floods, and the loss of genetic diversity through inbreeding and genetic drift. The MVP for any species is influenced by many factors, including the quality of the environment, the species' average life span, its fertility, and the number of young that typically reach maturity. Most wildlife experts think that an MVP of Bengal tigers must include at least 50 females—more than are found in most of India's tiger reserves.

Many countries are working to preserve critical habitat. One of the largest protected habitats is the Pāpahánaumokuákea Marine National Monument in the Hawaiian Islands, designated in 2006. This national monument covers 84 million acres of the Pacific Ocean and is home to about 7,000 species of birds, fish, and marine mammals. Some species depend on

CASE STUDY CONTINUED
The Wolves of Yellowstone

As you learned in Chapter 29, large predators at the top of food webs, such as wolves and grizzly bears, are always relatively rare, because of energy losses between trophic levels. Even a national park the size of Yellowstone—almost 3,500 square miles—often cannot sustain a minimum viable population of such animals over long time periods, primarily because of the loss of genetic diversity and the dangers of epidemic diseases. How can an MVP be provided for these animals? We will return to this crucial concern in Section 31.5.

such huge reserves; for others, critical habitat may be a few patches of sandy beach. "Earth Watch: Saving Sea Turtles" on page 594 discusses an innovative sea turtle conservation program in Brazil, which not only preserves turtle nesting sites but also helps local communities to prosper.

Overexploitation Threatens Many Species

Overexploitation is the hunting or harvesting of natural populations at a rate that exceeds their ability to replenish their numbers. Overexploitation of many species has increased as a growing demand for wild animals and plants has been coupled with technological advances that have increased our efficiency at harvesting them. For example, overharvesting is the single greatest threat to marine life, causing dramatic declines of many species, including invertebrates such as abalone, oyster, and corals, and fish such as cod, many sharks, haddock, Pacific bluefin tuna, and mackerel. The UN Food and Agriculture Organization estimates that about 30% of global fish populations are overexploited, and another 60% are being fished to their maximum sustainable yield.

Both poverty and wealth can contribute to overexploitation, particularly of endangered species. Rapidly growing populations in less-developed countries increase the demand for animal products, as hunger and poverty drive people to harvest all that can be sold or eaten, legally or illegally, without regard to its rarity. Rich consumers often fuel the exploitation of endangered species by paying high prices for illegal products such as elephant-tusk ivory, rare orchids, and exotic birds. Although good data about black market activities are difficult to come by (for obvious reasons), the sale of endangered species, or products derived from them, is extremely lucrative, thought to total about $19 billion a year.

Invasive Species Displace Native Wildlife and Disrupt Community Interactions

Humans have transported a multitude of species around the world—everything from thistles to camels. In many cases, the introduced species cause no great harm. Sometimes, however, non-native species become invasive: They increase

(a) Blue rock hunter cichlid

(b) Nile perch

▲ **FIGURE 31-6 Invasive species endanger native wildlife (a)** Lake Victoria was home to hundreds of species of stunningly colored cichlid fish, such as the blue rock hunter cichlid pictured here. **(b)** The Nile perch, introduced into Lake Victoria for fishermen, has proven to be a disaster for native fish.

in number at the expense of native species, competing with them for food or habitat or preying on them directly (see Chapter 29). According to the Center for Invasive Species and Ecosystem Health, there are almost 2,900 invasive species in North America, mostly plants and insects. About half of all threatened U.S. species suffer from competition with or predation by invasive species.

Island ecosystems are particularly vulnerable to invasive species, because populations of native plants and animals are usually low, the native species are often found nowhere else in the world, and, if they can't compete with the invaders, the natives cannot easily move to new habitat. For example, the Hawaiian Islands have lost about 1,000 species of native plants and animals since their settlement by humans. Many of the losses have been caused by competition and predation by invasive species, beginning with pigs and rats brought by the original Polynesian settlers and accelerating in the nineteenth and twentieth centuries. Most of the native wildlife of Hawaii remains in danger: According to the U.S. Fish and Wildlife Service, more than 430 plant and animal species in Hawaii are endangered, by far the largest number in any state.

Lakes are also especially vulnerable to invasive species. For example, Lake Victoria in Africa was once home to about 400 to 500 different species of cichlid fish that were found nowhere else on Earth (**FIG. 31-6a**). Enormous predatory Nile perch (**FIG. 31-6b**) and much smaller plankton-feeding tilapia were introduced into Lake Victoria in the mid-1900s. The combination of predation by Nile perch, competition from tilapia, pollution, and algal blooms (brought on by nutrients from surrounding farms draining into the lake) has caused a mass extinction of cichlids; only about 200 species remain.

Pollution Is a Multifaceted Threat to Biodiversity

Pollution takes many forms, including synthetic chemicals such as plasticizers, flame retardants, and pesticides; toxic metals such as mercury, lead, and cadmium; and high levels of nutrients, usually from sewage or agricultural runoff.

Because synthetic chemicals are often lipid soluble, even small amounts in the environment may accumulate to toxic levels in the fatty tissue of animals (see Chapter 29). In the mid-twentieth century, for example, the insecticide DDT accumulated in many predatory birds, causing them to lay eggs with shells so thin that they cracked when the parents sat on them during incubation. Fortunately, DDT and 11 other persistent organic pollutants have been banned or heavily restricted by a treaty signed by about 180 countries. Disputes continue over possible environmental and human health effects of several other synthetic organic chemicals. Although the evidence is still controversial, bisphenol A, used in the manufacture of certain types of plastics, is suspected of causing reproductive and developmental abnormalities. A class of insecticides called neonicotinoids has been implicated in massive declines in honeybee populations.

Many heavy metals are naturally bound up in rocks and thus rendered harmless. However, mining, industrial processes, and burning fossil fuels release heavy metals into the environment. Even extremely low levels of certain heavy metals, such as mercury and lead, are toxic to virtually all organisms.

Finally, nutrients in excessive amounts become pollutants. For example, burning fossil fuels releases nitrogen and sulfur compounds, disrupting their natural biogeochemical cycles and causing acid precipitation that threatens forests and lakes (see Fig. 29-12). Fertilizer runoff from farms and lawns often enters nearby waters and may cause harmful algal blooms (see Fig. 29-10).

Global Climate Change Is an Emerging Threat to Biodiversity

The rapid pace of human-induced climate change challenges the ability of species to adapt. Scientists at the Convention on Biological Diversity, an international organization with more than 150 member countries, have concluded that warmer conditions have already contributed to some extinctions and are likely to cause many more. Although it is difficult to predict all the impacts of global climate change, they likely include the following:

- Deserts may become hotter and drier.
- Warmer conditions are forcing some species to retreat toward the poles or up mountains to stay within the climate zones in which they can survive and reproduce. Relatively immobile species, especially plants, may be unable to retreat fast enough to stay within a suitable temperature range, because they typically only "move" as far and as fast as wind or animals disperse their seeds.
- Cool habitat will probably disappear completely from mountaintops. Animals that live at high altitudes, such as pikas in the Rocky Mountains (FIG. 31-7a), face shrinking habitat as the mountains warm. Some local populations on isolated mountains have already vanished.
- Insect pests that were previously killed by frost or sustained freezes may spread and thrive. For example, in the northern and central Rocky Mountains, populations of pine bark beetles were formerly limited by sustained extremely cold weather in the winter. In the past 20 years, however, these beetles have reached epidemic levels, with over 4 million acres infested. The infestation in British Columbia, Canada, is much worse: over 40 million acres (FIG. 31-7b).
- Parasites and insect-borne diseases are spreading closer to the poles. From lungworms in musk ox in Arctic Canada to disease-carrying mosquitoes infecting people in Sweden with tularemia, a warmer climate allows many pathogens and their carriers both to move northward and often to reproduce faster.
- Coral reefs require warm water, but too much warming causes bleaching and coral death (FIG. 31-7c; see Chapter 24). Coral reefs have already suffered massive damage in the Seychelles Islands, American Samoa, Sri Lanka, the coasts of Tanzania and Kenya, and parts of the Australian Great Barrier Reef.

(a) A pika gathers plants for the winter

(b) Pine bark beetles are killing pine trees

(c) Bleached corals (white) are usually dead or dying

▲ **FIGURE 31-7 Global climate change threatens biodiversity**
(a) Pikas live at high altitudes in the Rocky Mountains; as the climate warms, suitable pika habitat may disappear off the tops of the mountains. **(b)** A forest infested with pine bark beetles often consists of a mosaic of uninfected trees (with green needles), newly killed trees (with reddish needles), and trees killed several years earlier (gray, without needles). **(c)** Corals usually contain photosynthetic algae that provide nourishment for the coral. When the water warms too much, corals eject their algae and become white; without the algae to help feed them, they often die.

CHECK YOUR LEARNING

Can you ...

- explain the concepts of ecological footprint and biocapacity, and how they are interrelated?
- describe how habitat destruction, overexploitation, invasive species, pollution, and global climate change threaten biodiversity?

31.5 WHY IS HABITAT PROTECTION NECESSARY TO PRESERVE BIODIVERSITY?

As we have seen, human activities pose many threats to biodiversity. Reversing some of these activities, for example, by reducing overexploitation and curbing greenhouse gas emissions, is crucial to preserving biodiversity. Without suitable natural habitat, however, many species cannot survive. Therefore, it is essential to set aside habitat in protected reserves and to connect small, fragmented reserves with wildlife corridors.

Core Reserves Preserve All Levels of Biodiversity

Core reserves are natural areas protected from most human uses except low-impact recreation. Ideally, a core reserve encompasses enough space to preserve ecosystems with all their biodiversity, withstanding storms, fires, and floods without losing species.

To establish effective core reserves, ecologists must estimate the smallest areas required to sustain MVPs of the species that require the most space. The sizes of these *minimum critical areas* vary significantly among species and also depend on the availability of food, water, and shelter. In general, large predators in arid environments need a larger minimum critical area than small herbivores in lush environments.

Wildlife Corridors Connect Habitats

One fact stands out in estimating minimum critical areas, especially for reserves that include large predators: In today's crowded world, an individual core reserve, even a large national park, is seldom large enough to maintain biodiversity by itself. **Wildlife corridors,** which are strips of protected land linking core reserves, allow animals to move relatively freely and safely between habitats that would otherwise be isolated. Corridors thereby increase the effective size of small reserves by connecting them. In India, for example, government and private groups are working to preserve forested corridors linking some tiger reserves. Researchers have found genetic evidence that tigers are traveling through the corridors to mate with other tigers in reserves as far as 230 miles away. In the increasingly fragmented Atlantic forest of Brazil, forested corridors connect reserves that are home to endangered black lion tamarins and golden lion tamarins (**FIG. 31-8**).

▶ **FIGURE 31-8 Wildlife corridors connect habitat** These continuous strips of forest winding through pastures provide vital corridors for the movement of jaguars, ocelots, and endangered black lion tamarins (inset) between larger patches of forest.

THINK CRITICALLY What would be the likely effect of isolated small reserves on the genetic diversity of endangered species? How would genetic diversity be affected by connecting the small reserves with wildlife corridors?

CHECK YOUR LEARNING
Can you ...
• describe some strategies that can preserve natural ecosystems and their associated biodiversity?
• define the terms *core reserve* and *wildlife corridor*, and explain the relationship between them?

CASE STUDY \ **CONTINUED**

The Wolves of Yellowstone

Wildlife corridors are often the only way to provide enough habitat for a minimum viable population of large predators such as wolves, grizzlies, and mountain lions. A coalition of conservation groups and scientists has proposed the Yellowstone to Yukon Conservation Initiative, which would provide corridors connecting habitat in the Rocky Mountains all the way from Yellowstone and Grand Teton National Parks in Wyoming to the Yukon Territory in northwestern Canada.

Wildlife corridors such as these must include private land interspersed between national parks and national forests. Can private landowners preserve wildlife habitat while still making a living and enjoying their land?

31.6 WHY IS SUSTAINABILITY ESSENTIAL FOR A HEALTHY FUTURE?

Natural ecosystems share certain features that allow them to persist and flourish. Important characteristics of sustainable ecosystems include diverse communities, relatively stable populations that remain within the carrying capacity of the environment, recycling and efficient use of raw materials, and reliance on renewable sources of energy. Environments

Earth
WATCH

Saving Sea Turtles

Six of the seven species of sea turtles are threatened with extinction, endangered by their unusual life history, losses to predators, and human activities.

Most sea turtles don't begin to breed until they are 20 to 50 years old. When they reach reproductive age, the females must swim hundreds, even thousands, of miles to reach their nesting grounds, often on the same beaches where they hatched. The turtles drag themselves ashore, excavate a hole in the sand, deposit their eggs, and return to the sea (FIG. E31-2a). The eggs may be eaten by domestic dogs, foxes, wild pigs, raccoons, and a host of other predators. After about 2 months, baby turtles emerge from the surviving eggs and begin their difficult journey to adulthood. Seabirds and crabs attack them as they crawl to the ocean (FIG. E31-2b). Once there, the hatchlings may become a tasty morsel for fish.

As if these natural dangers weren't enough, female turtles and their eggs are easy prey for human poachers. Turtle meat and eggs are a delicacy in many cultures, turtle shells make beautiful jewelry, and turtle skin makes fancy leather. Turtles are also caught, both deliberately and accidentally, in fish lines and nets. The beautiful beaches attract tourists who may frighten nesting females. Finally, hatchlings find the sea by crawling toward the brightest area in sight—but the brightest place on the beach may now be not the moon reflecting off the ocean, but the lights of a resort.

These dangers plagued the five species of sea turtles that nest on the beaches of Brazil—until the late 1970s, when some students from a Brazilian university were vacationing on Rocas Atoll just off the coast. They watched a group of sea turtles come ashore to lay eggs, only to be slaughtered by the very fishermen who had been hired as the students' guides. Two of the students, José Albuquerque and Guy Marcovaldi, founded Projeto Tartarugas Marinhas (TAMAR for short, from the Portuguese tartarugas marinhas, or "sea turtles").

Albuquerque and Marcovaldi realized that for sea turtle conservation to succeed, fishermen and local villagers had to participate. Today, TAMAR has 22 bases on the Brazilian coast. Most of TAMAR's employees are former fishermen. Instead of hunting sea turtles, they free turtles caught in nets and patrol the beaches during nesting season. TAMAR biologists tag females and trace their travels. The fishermen

(a) A green turtle excavating a nest

(b) A turtle hatchling heads for the sea

▲ **FIGURE E31-2 Endangered sea turtles (a)** A female green turtle scoops sand with powerful flippers, creating a cavity where she will bury about 100 eggs. **(b)** After incubating in the sand for about 2 months, the eggs hatch. Here a hatchling heads for the sea, where (if it survives) it will spend 20 to 50 years before reaching sexual maturity.

that have been modified by human development often do not possess these characteristics. As a result, many human-modified ecosystems may not be sustainable in the long run. How can we meet our needs in ways that sustain the ecosystems on which we depend?

Sustainable Development Promotes Long-Term Ecological and Human Well-Being

In *Caring for the Earth: A Strategy for Sustainable Living,* the IUCN stated that **sustainable development** "meets the needs of the present without compromising the ability of future generations to meet their own needs" by "improving the quality of human life while living within the carrying capacity of supporting ecosystems." Therefore, sustainable development must minimize the use of nonrenewable resources and use renewable resources in a manner that allows them to be utilized year after year, far into the future. Here we will explore three specific issues of sustainability: the use of renewable resources, sustainable agriculture, and the preservation of reasonably natural ecosystems while still providing desired goods for people.

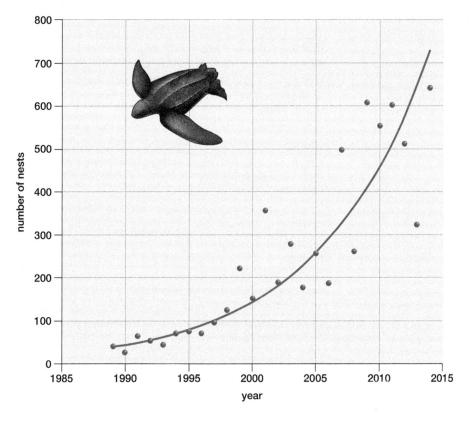

◀ FIGURE E31-3 **Atlantic leatherback sea turtle populations in Florida are growing** Atlantic leatherback sea turtle nests on a group of beaches in Florida have been surveyed each year from 1989 to 2014. Because sea turtles are difficult to count at sea, nests are used as an indicator of population size. The population has been growing exponentially since the late 1980s (smooth curve).

fend off the (now rare) turtle poachers, identify nests in risky locations, and relocate the eggs to better beach sites or to a nearby hatchery. As of 2014, TAMAR had helped more than 15 million hatchlings reach the sea.

TAMAR has been successful because the project organizers have engaged local communities as partners in turtle protection. Money flows into the local economies as ecotourists come to see baby turtles, visit turtle museums, and buy souvenirs made by local residents. TAMAR also sponsors communal gardens, day-care centers, and environmental education activities. Recognizing that the economic benefits derived from preserving turtles far outweigh the money that can be made by hunting them, local residents eagerly participate in turtle conservation. As IUCN sea turtle specialist

Neca Marcovaldi put it, "Brazil's sea turtles are now worth more alive."

THINK CRITICALLY In 1970, Atlantic leatherback sea turtle populations were very low, and the U.S. Fish and Wildlife Service listed the species as endangered. Over the next several decades, steps were taken to protect turtle nests and prevent accidental killing of turtles at sea by fishing fleets. As a result, the population of leatherbacks nesting on beaches in Florida has been growing exponentially (**FIG. E31-3**). What factors probably contributed to this exponential growth? Can exponential growth continue? If not, what factors are likely to cause the population to stabilize?

Sustainable Development Relies on Renewable Resources

In principle, minerals such as aluminum, iron, and copper can be recycled by humans, just as nutrients are recycled in ecosystems, so that we never run out. Further, many minerals can substitute for each other in various uses, with enough ingenuity by inventors, engineers, and materials scientists. However, substitution cannot overcome absolute limits on supply. Some minerals, such as copper, are typically used in large quantities; certain rare minerals used in devices such as cell phones and computers are already in short supply. Other

minerals are highly toxic when dumped into the environment. For all of these reasons, the adage "reduce, reuse, and recycle" is very apt when applied to minerals.

Fossil fuels cannot be recycled. Further, burning fossil fuels releases carbon dioxide, which is the principal cause of global climate change, with profound effects on humans and natural ecosystems alike, as outlined in Section 31.4 and Chapter 30. Therefore, a concerted effort to switch from fossil fuels to renewable energy sources, such as solar, wind, and geothermal power, is an essential part of sustainable development.

Sustainable Agriculture Preserves Productivity with Reduced Impact on Natural Ecosystems

Agricultural land is by far the largest proportion of land appropriated by people for their own use, so how we farm is an important component of sustainable development. The goals of sustainable agriculture are to produce sufficient food to feed humankind, to ensure economic benefits to farmers, and to maintain ecosystem services so that both future generations of people and the rest of life on Earth can flourish. Many of the practices of sustainable agriculture differ significantly from those of traditional agriculture (TABLE 31-1). Farms differ in many of these practices, but two stand out: how fields are prepared for planting and whether synthetic fertilizers and pesticides are used.

Tillage There are two major methods of treating fields to grow crops: conventional tillage, in which all residues of last year's crop are removed and the fields are completely plowed each year, and conservation tillage, in which at least 30% of the previous crop's residue remains on the surface of the soil, with soil disturbance by plowing or other forms of cultivation. **No-till** farming is the most complete form of conservation tillage. No-till farming usually leaves all the residue of harvested crops in the fields as mulch for the next year's crops and/or grows a cover crop—plants that are typically grown during the fall or early spring and are not the main cash crop for the farmer. In the United States, no-till methods are used on about 35% of all croplands. Another 27% of farmlands use other types of conservation tillage.

No-till farming reduces soil erosion from both wind and rain and reduces fertilizer runoff. It also helps to improve soil structure and increase the amount of organic matter in the soil. The combination of crop mulch and increased organic matter also keeps the soil cooler and more moist during the hottest parts of the summer, helping crops to withstand drought. Because it requires less plowing, no-till farming also saves labor, wear and tear on tractors, and up to 14 gallons of diesel fuel per acre.

On the other hand, no-till farmers often spray herbicides to kill weeds. The herbicides may blow off farm fields and damage nearby natural habitats. In some situations, cover crops can suppress weeds fairly effectively. Herbicides may then be used to kill the cover crop in the spring before planting the cash crop (FIG. 31-9). In other situations, the cover crop may die during the winter or can be cut or crushed in spring, so herbicides are not needed. Depending on the cover and cash crop species and the climate, soil, and common weeds in a given locale, cover crops can reduce, or even eliminate, the need for herbicides.

Fertilizer and Pesticide Use The vast majority of farms use synthetic herbicides, insecticides, and fertilizers; organic farmers do not. Organic farming relies on natural predators to control pests and on soil microorganisms to degrade animal and crop wastes, thereby recycling their nutrients. Rotating an assortment of different crops each year reduces outbreaks of pests and diseases that attack a single type of plant. Although most organic farmers plow their fields at least every other year to help control weeds, a growing number employ no-till methods and control weeds with cover crops that do not need to be killed with herbicides.

There is an ongoing debate about the relative productivity of organic versus conventional farming. A recent analysis of over 100 studies found that organic farms average about 19% smaller yields compared to conventional farming, although for some crops the difference is much smaller. For

TABLE 31-1	Agricultural Practices Affect Sustainability	
	Unsustainable Agriculture	**Sustainable Agriculture**
Soil erosion	Allows soil to erode far faster than it can be replenished because the remains of crops are plowed under, leaving the soil exposed until new crops grow.	No-till agriculture greatly reduces soil erosion. Planting strips of trees as windbreaks reduces wind erosion.
Pest control	Uses large amounts of pesticides to control crop pests.	Trees and shrubs near fields provide habitat for insect-eating birds and predatory insects. Reducing insecticide use helps to protect birds and insect predators.
Fertilizer use	Uses large amounts of synthetic fertilizer.	No-till agriculture retains nutrient-rich soil. Animal wastes are used as fertilizer. Legumes that replenish soil nitrogen (such as soybeans and alfalfa) are alternated with crops that deplete soil nitrogen (such as corn and wheat).
Water quality	Allows runoff from bare soil to contaminate water with pesticides and fertilizers. Allows excessive amounts of animal wastes to drain from feedlots.	Animal wastes are used to fertilize fields. Plant cover left by no-till agriculture reduces nutrient runoff.
Irrigation	May excessively irrigate crops, often using groundwater pumped from aquifers at a rate faster than the water is replenished by precipitation.	Modern irrigation technology reduces evaporation and delivers water only when and where it is needed. No-till agriculture reduces evaporation.
Crop diversity	Relies on a small number of high-profit crops, which encourages outbreaks of insects or plant diseases and leads to reliance on large quantities of pesticides.	Alternating crops and planting a wider variety of crops reduce the likelihood of major outbreaks of insects and diseases.
Fossil fuel use	Uses large amounts of nonrenewable fossil fuels to run farm equipment, produce fertilizer, and apply fertilizers and pesticides.	No-till agriculture reduces the need for plowing and fertilizing.

(a) Cotton seedlings emerge in a no-till field in North Carolina

(b) The same field one month later

▲ **FIGURE 31-9 No-till agriculture (a)** A cover crop of wheat has been killed with an herbicide. Cotton seedlings thrive amid the dead wheat, which anchors soil and reduces evaporation. **(b)** Later in the season, the same field shows a healthy cotton crop mulched by the dead wheat.
Photos courtesy of Dr. George Naderman, Former Extension Soil Specialist (retired), College of Agriculture and Life Sciences, North Carolina State University, Raleigh, NC.

beans, peas, and lentils, organic and conventional farming produce the same yields. Organic food is usually sold at a higher price than nonorganic food, so the farmer may receive a higher income even if yields are lower. In addition, conventional farming has benefitted from decades of intensive research into crops that produce high yields under a high-fertilizer, and often high-pesticide, regime. Research into crop varieties that might produce higher yields in organic farming has barely begun; research into weed control in no-till fields without using herbicides is also in its infancy.

In the best-case scenario, farmers would grow a variety of crops, use agricultural practices that retain soil fertility, and use as little energy and as few potentially toxic chemicals as possible. Insect pests would be controlled by birds and predatory insects and by crop rotation, so that pests that specialize on particular crop plants would not find a feast laid out for them year after year. Fields would be relatively small, separated by strips of natural habitat for native plants and animals. Many projects, such as the University of California's Sustainable Agriculture Research and Education Program, support research and educate farmers about the advantages of sustainable agriculture and how to practice it.

Sustainable Development Balances Preservation of Natural Ecosystems with Providing Goods for People

With rare exceptions, most farms provide more wildlife habitat than cities do. To help keep rural land undeveloped, many states and counties offer conservation easements, whereby a landowner gives up the right to develop property, usually in return for some sort of tax credit. Conservation easements can be powerful tools for preserving natural habitat at low cost. As of 2014, more than 22 million acres of woods, farmland, and wildlife habitat in the United States have been preserved through conservation easements.

Although woods, fields, and farms typically provide more wildlife habitat, even cities and suburbs can provide homes for some types of wildlife. From apartment balconies to large suburban gardens, growing the right plants can provide nectar, pollen, berries, seeds, and nuts for birds, insects, and a variety of small mammals such as chipmunks and squirrels. The National Wildlife Federation offers free advice on how to make your home wildlife-friendly.

Providing for People and Wildlife: The Case of the Migrating Monarchs Monarch butterflies, probably the most recognizable butterfly in North America, provide a case study in preserving wildlife while providing for people's needs. Each fall, hundreds of millions of monarch butterflies in eastern North America migrate south to spend the winter in just a handful of forest groves in the mountains of central Mexico (FIG. 31-10a). Without these wintering sites, the entire monarch population east of the Rocky Mountains would vanish. Conditions in these stands of fir and pine trees are just right for the overwintering monarchs. A thick canopy of needles protects them from snow and rain. The groves are cool enough to slow down the butterflies' metabolism so they don't starve to death but are not so cold that they freeze.

However, the groves are owned not by the Mexican government but by the local people, most of whom are poor farmers. The stands of large trees that are essential to monarch survival have also traditionally been an important economic resource for the farmers, providing firewood and lumber. How can people provide for both butterflies and farmers? Several organizations are helping Mexican agricultural experts to train the farmers in sustainable agriculture. One of the most profitable "crops" in the reserve is, ironically, trees. The soil and climate provide ideal conditions

(a) Monarch butterflies at their wintering groves in Mexico

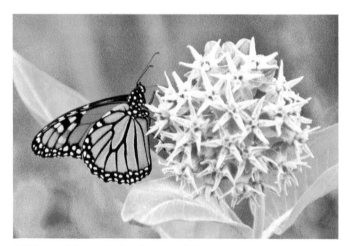

(b) Monarch butterfly feeding on milkweed

▲ **FIGURE 31-10 Preserving monarch butterflies (a)** In the winter, so many monarchs roost in a handful of forest groves in the mountains of central Mexico that their weight bends the branches of the trees. **(b)** Monarchs sip nectar from milkweed flowers and lay their eggs on the leaves, which are the only food eaten by monarch caterpillars.

for rapid tree growth. Some conifers mature in less than 20 years. Planting seedlings today allows some harvesting in only 5 years, for firewood and Christmas trees. After 15 years, the trees are large enough for commercial lumber. If, meanwhile, the trees are continually replanted, the cycle can continue indefinitely, and the old-growth groves can be left alone. Environmental and social organizations, in collaboration with the Mexican government, have planted more than 5 million trees in the past decade. The World Wildlife Fund has set up a $5,000,000 trust fund to help farmers find alternate sources of income rather than log their land.

The fund is also used to establish forested corridors connecting the groves where the monarchs overwinter. Meanwhile, ECOLIFE is building stoves that are 60% more fuel efficient for cooking and home heating than traditional open fires, which reduces deforestation, saves money, and reduces respiratory illness caused by indoor smoke from open fires.

Another source of income for the farmers is ecotourism. Tourists flock to the reserve each year to see the butterflies. If properly regulated, ecotourism can both preserve the forest and provide significant income opportunities for the local people, who serve as guides to the monarch groves and offer food, accommodations, and souvenirs for the tourists.

These efforts seem to have slowed, perhaps stopped, the loss of monarchs in recent years. Nevertheless, monarch populations are only about 20% as large as they were 15 or 20 years ago. One reason is the loss of summer habitat in the United States and Canada. Monarch caterpillars eat only milkweeds, which grow mainly in disturbed areas such as roadsides and pastures. Mowing roadsides, intensive farming, and especially the widespread use of herbicides have greatly reduced the milkweed population; one study estimates that milkweeds are about 60% less abundant in the Midwestern United States than they were 20 years ago. People in the United States and Canada can help by planting milkweeds (*Asclepias* species) in their gardens (**FIG. 31-10b**). Most have beautiful pink or orange flowers, with lots of nectar for both butterflies and hummingbirds. Several organizations provide seeds or seedlings and advice on planting. Environmental organizations and some states are planting milkweeds along roadsides and railroads. Iowa has restored 10,000 acres of roadsides to natural vegetation, including milkweeds. Such "milkweed highways" can provide vital habitat for monarchs both during the summer and during their autumn migration.

The Future of Earth Is in Your Hands

How should we manage our planet so that it provides a healthy, satisfying life for the current generation of people, while simultaneously retaining biodiversity and the resources needed for future generations? No one can give a simple, certain answer. However, three interrelated questions must be considered: (1) What should human lifestyles look like? (2) What technologies can support those lifestyles in a sustainable way? (3) How many people can Earth support and in what lifestyle?

Changes in Lifestyle and Use of Appropriate Technologies Are Essential

The billions of people on Earth will never all agree on exactly what is needed for a happy, fulfilling life. Nearly everyone would agree, however, that a minimal lifestyle should include adequate food and clothing, clean air and water, good health care and working conditions, educational and career opportunities, and access to natural environments. Most of Earth's people live in less-developed countries and lack at least some of these necessities.

Without a sustainable approach to development, there can be no long-term improvement in the quality of human life—in fact, it might even decline. We must make choices about which technologies are sustainable and how to make the transition from the realities of today to a hoped-for tomorrow.

Human Population Growth Is Unsustainable

The root causes of environmental degradation are simple: too many people using too many resources and generating too much waste. As the IUCN eloquently stated in *Who Will Care for the Earth?* ". . . the central issue [is] how to bring human populations into balance with the natural ecosystems that sustain them."

In the long run, that balance cannot be achieved if the human population continues to grow. Given the lifestyle to which the vast majority of people on Earth aspire, many are convinced that the balance cannot be maintained even with our current population, and yet we add 75 to 80 million people each year. No matter how simple our diets, how efficient our housing, how low-impact our farming techniques, or how much we reuse and recycle, continued population growth will eventually overwhelm our best efforts.

Let's return to our comparison of Earth's biocapacity and the human ecological footprint (**FIG. 31-11**). As you can see, the rapid increase in humanity's ecological footprint between 1961 and 2010 (red line) is roughly paralleled by our rapid population increase (blue line). The ecological footprint *per person* (green line), however, was only about 10% higher in 2010 than it was in 1961. In fact, the average person was using a bit less of Earth's biocapacity in 2010

than in 1970. If the human population had not increased, the total human ecological footprint would still be well below Earth's biocapacity, but because there are so many more of us today, the total human footprint has climbed far above Earth's biocapacity. Eliminating, and probably reversing, population growth is essential if we wish to improve the quality of life for the 7 billion of us already here, provide the potential for a similar quality of life for our descendants, and save what is left of Earth's biodiversity for future generations.

The Choices Are Yours

It is all too easy to assume that "sustainable development" is solely the responsibility of industry, commercial farms, or governments, but we can all promote sustainable living by our individual actions. As Canadian educator and philosopher Marshall McLuhan noted 50 years ago, "There are no passengers on Spaceship Earth. We are all crew." Here are some ways to make a difference.

Conserve Energy

- *Heating and Cooling* Don't heat your house over 68°F in winter or air condition it below 78°F in summer. Reduce the heating or cooling while you're away. When you purchase or remodel a home, consider energy-efficient features such as passive solar heating, good insulation, an attic fan, double-glazed windows (with "low-E" coating to reduce heat transfer), and tight weather stripping. Plant deciduous trees on the south side of your home for shade in summer (when the trees are covered with leaves) and sun in winter (after the leaves have dropped off). If possible, purchase renewable energy, usually wind or solar power, from your energy provider.
- *Lighting* Use energy-efficient compact fluorescent or LED bulbs, which typically use about a quarter to a sixth as much energy as an incandescent bulb with the same light output and also last 8 to 30 times longer.
- *Hot Water* Take shorter showers and switch to low-flow shower heads. Wash only full loads in your washing machine and dishwasher; use cold water to wash clothes; don't prewash your dishes. Insulate and turn down the temperature on your water heater.
- *Appliances* When you choose a major appliance, look for the most energy-efficient models. Don't use your dryer in the summer—put up a clothesline.
- *Transportation* Choose the most fuel-efficient car that meets your needs and use it efficiently by combining errands. Use public transit, carpool, walk, bicycle, or telecommute when possible.

Conserve Materials

- *Recycling* Look into recycling options in your community and recycle everything that is accepted. Don't forget to recycle your cell phone when you replace it. Purchase recycled paper products. You can also buy decking and carpet made from recycled plastic bottles.

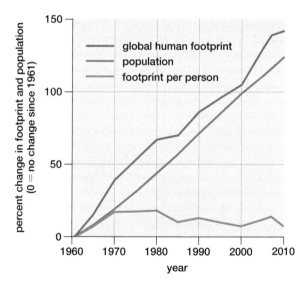

▲ **FIGURE 31-11 Human population growth threatens sustainability** Between 1961 and 2010, human population growth (blue line) increased at approximately the same rate as the global human ecological footprint (red line). The footprint per person (green line) has remained almost the same since 1970: The increase in our global footprint has resulted almost entirely from population growth. Data from the World Wildlife Fund, the Zoological Society of London, and the Global Footprint Network (2014), *The Living Planet Report.*

- *Reuse* Reuse anything possible, such as manila envelopes, file folders, and both sides of paper. Consider buying used furniture. Refill your water bottle. Reuse your grocery bags. Give away—rather than throw away—serviceable clothing, toys, and furniture. Make rags out of unusable old clothes and use them instead of disposable cleaning materials.
- *Conserve Water* If you live in a dry area, plant drought-resistant vegetation around your home to reduce water usage. A low-flow shower head not only saves energy, but also saves water.

Support Sustainable Practices

- *Food Choices* When possible, buy locally grown produce that does not require long-distance shipping. Look for coffee with the "Bird-Friendly™" or "Rainforest Alliance Certified" seal of approval, or other evidence of sustainable production such as the Starbucks "Coffee and Farmer Equity" program. Reduce your meat consumption. Search Internet sites such as the Seafood Watch of the Monterey Bay Aquarium to find out which fish at your local supermarket have been harvested sustainably.
- *Avoid Harmful Chemicals* Limit your use of harsh cleaners, insecticides, and herbicides that may contaminate water and soil.

Magnify Your Efforts

- *Support Organized Conservation Efforts* Join conservation groups and donate money to conservation efforts.

Sign up for e-mail alerts that educate you about environmental legislation and make it easy for you to contact your government representatives and express your views.

- *Volunteer* Volunteer for local campus and community projects that improve the environment.
- *Make Your Vote Count* Investigate candidates' stands and voting records on environmental issues and consider this information when choosing which candidate to support.
- *Educate* Through your words and actions, share your concern for sustainability with your family, friends, and community. Write letters to the editor of your school or local newspaper, to local businesses, and to elected officials. Talk with your campus administrators about reducing energy use on your campus. Recruit other concerned people and lobby for change.
- *Reduce Population Growth* Consider the consequences of human population growth when you plan your family. Adoption, for example, allows people to raise large families while simultaneously contributing to the welfare of humanity and the environment.

CHECK YOUR LEARNING

Can you ...
- describe the principles of sustainable development?
- explain how population, technology, and lifestyle choices interact to affect sustainability?

CASE STUDY REVISITED

The Wolves of Yellowstone

The simple trophic cascade from wolves to elk to aspen is far from the only impact of wolves on the Yellowstone ecosystem. Remember, real feeding relationships almost always form a web, not a chain (see Chapter 29). In the Yellowstone food web, wolves affect many trophic levels. For example, grizzly bears often scavenge on wolf-killed elk carcasses. Grizzlies also eat a lot of berries in the summer, and berry-producing bushes thrive without constant grazing by elk—again thanks to the wolves. Before wolf reintroduction, berries provided about 4% of the grizzlies' summer diet; now they provide about 10%.

Wolves also reduce coyote populations by chasing them away and sometimes killing them. Coyotes are major predators on pronghorn fawns, while wolves are not. In areas of the park with wolves, there are few coyotes, and four times as many pronghorn fawns survive as in areas without wolves. Wolves indirectly benefit birds, too. Crows and vultures scavenge on elk carcasses. Several types of songbirds are more abundant in aspen groves and willow thickets, many of which have grown only since wolves reduced elk populations.

According to the Green World Hypothesis, Earth is so green because top predators keep populations of herbivores in check, which in turn allows more plant growth. If this hypothesis is correct, then many ecosystems benefit from the presence of top predators. And they do. In the Pacific Ocean off the coast of

British Columbia, sea otters were hunted extensively for their fur. The decline in otters allowed an explosive increase in sea urchins, a favored prey of otters (FIG. 31-12). The urchins then virtually

▲ **FIGURE 31-12 A sea otter dines on sea urchins** Otters keep the urchin population in check and thereby promote the health of kelp forests.

eliminated kelp forests (see Chapter 28). When otter hunting was stopped and the otters returned, urchin populations declined drastically, and the kelp forests came back. In Venezuela, the construction of a hydroelectric dam isolated a number of hilltops, which became small islands in the resulting reservoir. Within just a few years, large predators vanished from the islands, herbivore numbers increased tremendously, and reproduction by canopy tree species almost ceased. As the research article describing these findings stated, there was "ecological meltdown in predator-free forest fragments."

CONSIDER THIS Before 1700, wolves roamed over almost all of North America; coyotes were found mostly west of the Mississippi. White-tailed deer lived throughout the eastern half of the continent. In the eastern United States, most of the land was covered with coniferous or deciduous forests. When Europeans arrived, they cleared most of the forests, planted crops, raised livestock, and exterminated the wolves. Based on what you have learned in this chapter and its Case Study, what do you think happened to the populations of coyotes and white-tailed deer between 1700 and now, in terms of their range and abundance, and to the types of vegetation in much of the eastern states (outside of cities, suburbs, and farms)? Why?

CHAPTER REVIEW

 Go to **MasteringBiology** for practice quizzes, activities, eText, videos, current events, and more.

Answers to Think Critically, Evaluate This, Multiple Choice, and Fill-in-the-Blank questions can be found in the Answers section at the back of the book.

Summary of Key Concepts

31.1 What Is Conservation Biology?

Conservation biology is the scientific discipline devoted to understanding and preserving Earth's biodiversity, including diversity at the genetic, species, and ecosystem levels.

31.2 Why Is Biodiversity Important?

Biodiversity provides provisioning, regulating, cultural, and supporting ecosystem services. Biodiversity is a source of goods, such as food, fuel, building materials, and medicines. Other ecosystem services include forming soil, purifying water, controlling floods, moderating climate, and providing genetic reserves and recreational opportunities. The emerging discipline of ecological economics attempts to measure the contribution of ecosystem goods and services to the economy and estimates the costs of losing them to unsustainable development.

31.3 Is Earth's Biodiversity Diminishing?

Natural communities have a low background extinction rate. Many biologists have concluded that human activities are currently causing a mass extinction, increasing extinction rates perhaps 1,000-fold.

31.4 What Are the Major Threats to Biodiversity?

The ecological footprint estimates the area of Earth required to support the human population at any given level of consumption and waste production. Biocapacity estimates the resources and waste-absorbing capacity actually available. The human footprint is already exceeding Earth's biocapacity, leaving less and less to support other forms of life. Major threats to biodiversity include habitat destruction and fragmentation, overexploitation, invasive species, pollution, and global climate change.

31.5 Why Is Habitat Protection Necessary to Preserve Biodiversity?

Conservation efforts include conserving wild ecosystems by establishing core reserves connected by wildlife corridors, which helps to preserve functional communities and self-sustaining wildlife populations.

31.6 Why Is Sustainability Essential for a Healthy Future?

Sustainable development meets present needs without compromising the future. Such development requires that people maintain biodiversity, recycle raw materials, and rely on renewable resources. A shift to sustainable farming is crucial for conserving soil and water, reducing pollution and energy use, and preserving biodiversity. Human population growth is unsustainable and is driving consumption of resources beyond nature's ability to replenish them.

Key Terms

biocapacity *588*
biodiversity *583*
conservation biology *584*
core reserve *593*
critically endangered
    species *588*
ecological economics *586*
ecological footprint *588*
ecosystem services *584*
endangered species *588*
habitat fragmentation *590*

keystone species *587*
mass extinction *588*
minimum viable population
    (MVP) *590*
no-till *596*
overexploitation *590*
sustainable
    development *594*
threatened species *588*
vulnerable species *588*
wildlife corridor *593*

Thinking Through the Concepts
Multiple Choice

1. A factor that increases humanity's ecological footprint is
   a. human population growth.
   b. technological innovations that improve the efficiency with which resources are used.

c.   renewable energy sources.
d.   sustainable agriculture.

2. A species that plays an essential role in an ecosystem, usually out of proportion to its population size, is called a
a.   predator.
b.   keystone species.
c.   rivet species.
d.   redundant species.

3. The modern rate of extinction is
a.   higher than the background rate.
b.   the same as the background rate.
c.   lower than the background rate.
d.   having little effect on biodiversity.

4. Biocapacity is
a.   the carrying capacity of an ecosystem.
b.   the area of Earth required to produce the resources used by humans.
c.   the number of species in an ecosystem.
d.   the amount of sustainable resources and waste-absorbing capacity of Earth.

5. Which of the following is *not* true of a population of large predators in a small reserve?
a.   The species may disappear from the reserve.
b.   The species will probably undergo a population explosion.
c.   The species will probably lose genetic diversity.
d.   The species may overeat its prey, causing a reduction in prey population.

Fill-in-the-Blank

1. Three levels of biodiversity are _____, _____, and _____. If the population of a species becomes too small, it is likely to have lost much of its _____ diversity.

2. Products or processes by which functioning ecosystems benefit humans are collectively called _____. Four important categories of these benefits are _____, _____, _____, and _____.

3. Many of the benefits that humans derive from functioning ecosystems, such as purifying water, have traditionally been considered to be free. The discipline of _____ tries to quantify the monetary value of these benefits.

4. The major threats to biodiversity include _____, _____, _____, _____, and _____. For most endangered species, _____ is probably the major threat.

5. The smallest population of a species that is likely to be able to survive in the long term is called the _____. When suitable habitat for a given species is split up into areas that are too small to support a large enough population, this is called _____. One way to maintain large enough populations is to set up core reserves of suitable habitat, connected by _____.

6. A Native American saying tells us that "We do not inherit the Earth from our ancestors, we borrow it from our children." If this principle guided our activities, we would practice _____ development.

Review Questions

1. What are the three different levels of biodiversity, and why is each one important?

2. What is ecological economics? Why is it important?

3. List the major categories of services that natural ecosystems provide, and give three examples of each.

4. What five specific threats to biodiversity are described in this chapter? Provide an example of each.

5. Why are efforts to protect monarch butterflies a good model for conservation and sustainable development?

Applying the Concepts

1. List some reasons that the ecological footprints of U.S. residents are very large. How could you reduce the size of your own footprint? How does the ecological footprint of U.S. residents extend into the Tropics?

2. Search for and describe some examples of habitat destruction, pollution, and invasive species in the region around your home or campus. Predict how each of these might affect specific local populations of native animals and plants.

APPENDIX I BIOLOGICAL VOCABULARY: COMMON ROOTS, PREFIXES, AND SUFFIXES

Biology has an extensive vocabulary often based on Greek or Latin rather than English words. Rather than memorizing every word as if it were part of a new, foreign language, you can figure out the meaning of many new terms if you learn a much smaller number of word roots, prefixes, and suffixes. We have provided common meanings in biology rather than literal translations from Greek or Latin. For each item in the list, the following information is given: meaning; part of word (prefix, suffix, or root); example from biology.

a–, an–: without, lack of (prefix); *abiotic*, without life

acro–: top, highest (prefix); *acrosome*, vesicle of enzymes at the tip of a sperm

ad–: to (prefix); *adhesion*, property of sticking to something else

allo–: other (prefix); *allopatric* (literally, "different fatherland"), restricted to different regions

amphi–: both, double, two (prefix); *amphibian*, a class of vertebrates that usually has two life stages (aquatic and terrestrial; e.g., a tadpole and an adult frog)

andro: man, male (root); *androgen*, a male hormone such as testosterone

ant–, anti–: against (prefix); *antibiotic* (literally "against life"), a substance that kills bacteria

antero–: front (prefix or root); *anterior*, toward the front of

aqu–, aqua–: water (prefix or root); *aquifer*, an underground water source, usually rock saturated with water

apic–: top, highest (prefix); *apical meristem*, the cluster of dividing cells at the tip of a plant shoot or root

arthr–: joint (prefix); *arthropod*, animals such as spiders, crabs, and insects, with exoskeletons that include jointed legs

–ase: enzyme (suffix); *protease*, an enzyme that digests protein

auto–: self (prefix); *autotrophic*, self-feeder (e.g., photosynthetic)

bi–: two (prefix); *bipedal*, having two legs

bio–: life (prefix or root); *biology*, the study of life

blast: bud, precursor (root); *blastula*, embryonic stage of development, a hollow ball of cells

bronch: windpipe (root); *bronchus*, a branch of the trachea (windpipe) leading to a lung

carcin, –o: cancer (root); *carcinogenesis*, the process of producing a cancer

cardi, –a–, –o–: heart (root); *cardiac*, referring to the heart

carn–, –i–, –o–: flesh (prefix or root); *carnivore*, an animal that eats other animals

centi–: one hundredth (prefix); *centimeter*, a unit of length, 1 one-hundredth of a meter

cephal–, –i–, –o–: head (prefix or root); *cephalization*, the tendency for the nervous system to be located principally in the head

chloro–: green (prefix or root); *chlorophyll*, the green, light-absorbing pigment in plants

chondr–: cartilage (prefix); *Chondrichthyes*, class of vertebrates including sharks and rays, with a skeleton made of cartilage

chrom–: color (prefix or root); *chromosome*, a threadlike strand of DNA and protein in the nucleus of a cell (*Chromosome* literally means "colored body," because chromosomes absorb some of the colored dyes commonly used in microscopy.)

–cide: killer (suffix); *pesticide*, a chemical that kills "pests" (usually insects)

–clast: break down, broken (root or suffix); *osteoclast*, a cell that breaks down bone

co–: with or together with (prefix); *cohesion*, property of sticking together

coel–: hollow (prefix or root); *coelom*, the body cavity that separates the internal organs from the body wall

contra–: against (prefix); *contraception*, acting to prevent conception (pregnancy)

cortex: bark, outer layer (root); *cortex*, outer layer of kidney

crani–: skull (prefix or root); *cranium*, the skull

cuti–: skin (root); *cuticle*, the outermost covering of a leaf

–cyte, cyto–: cell (root or prefix); *cytokinin*, a plant hormone that promotes cell division

de–: from, out of, remove (prefix); *decomposer*, an organism that breaks down organic matter

dendr: treelike, branching (root); *dendrite*, highly branched input structures of nerve cells

derm: skin, layer (root); *ectoderm*, the outer embryonic germ layer of cells

deutero–: second (prefix); *deuterostome* (literally, "second opening"), an animal in which the coelom is derived from the gut

di–: two (prefix); *dicot*, an angiosperm with two cotyledons in the seed

diplo–: both, double, two (prefix or root); *diploid*, having paired homologous chromosomes

dys–: difficult, painful (prefix); *dysfunction*, an inability to function properly

eco–: house, household (prefix); *ecology*, the study of the relationships between organisms and their environment

ecto–: outside (prefix); *ectoderm*, the outermost tissue layer of animal embryos

–elle: little, small (suffix); *organelle* (literally, "little organ"), a subcellular structure that performs a specific function

end–, endo–, ento–: inside, inner (prefix); *endocrine*, pertaining to a gland that secretes hormones inside the body

epi–: outside, outer (prefix); *epidermis*, outermost layer of skin

equi–: equal (prefix); *equidistant*, the same distance

erythro–: red (prefix); *erythrocyte*, red blood cell

eu–: true, good (prefix); *eukaryotic*, pertaining to a cell with a true nucleus

ex–, exo–: out of (prefix); *exocrine*, pertaining to a gland that secretes a substance (e.g., sweat) outside of the body

extra–: outside of (prefix); *extracellular*, outside of a cell

–fer: to bear, to carry (suffix); *conifer*, a tree that bears cones

gastr–: stomach (prefix or root); *gastric*, pertaining to the stomach

–gen–: to produce (prefix, root, or suffix); *antigen*, a substance that causes the body to produce antibodies

glyc–, glyco–: sweet (prefix); *glycogen*, a starch-like molecule composed of many glucose molecules bonded together

gyn, –o: female (prefix or root); *gynecology*, the study of the female reproductive tract

haplo–: single (prefix); *haploid*, having a single copy of each type of chromosome

hem–, hemato–: blood (prefix or root); *hemoglobin*, the molecule in red blood cells that carries oxygen

hemi–: half (prefix); *hemisphere*, one of the halves of the cerebrum

herb–, herbi–: grass (prefix or root); *herbivore*, an animal that eats plants

hetero–: other (prefix); *heterotrophic*, an organism that feeds on other organisms

hom–, homo–, homeo–: same (prefix); *homeostasis*, to maintain constant internal conditions in the face of changing external conditions

hydro–: water (usually prefix); *hydrophilic*, being attracted to water

hyper–: above, greater than (prefix); *hyperosmotic*, having a greater osmotic strength (usually higher solute concentration)

hypo–: below, less than (prefix); *hypodermic*, below the skin

inter–: between (prefix); *interneuron*, a neuron that receives input from one (or more) neuron(s) and sends output to another neuron (or many neurons)

intra–: within (prefix); *intracellular*, pertaining to an event or substance that occurs within a cell

iso–: equal (prefix); *isotonic*, pertaining to a solution that has the same osmotic strength as another solution

–itis: inflammation (suffix); *hepatitis*, an inflammation (or infection) of the liver

kin–, kinet–: moving (prefix or root); *cytokinesis*, the movements of a cell that divide the cell in half during cell division

lac–, lact–: milk (prefix or root); *lactose*, the principal sugar in mammalian milk

leuc–, leuco–, leuk–, leuko–: white (prefix); *leukocyte*, a white blood cell

lip–: fat (prefix or root); *lipid*, the chemical category to which fats, oils, and steroids belong

–logy: study of (suffix); *biology*, the study of life

lyso–, –lysis: loosening, split apart (prefix, root, or suffix); *lysis*, to break open a cell

macro–: large (prefix); *macrophage*, a large white blood cell that destroys invading foreign cells

medulla: marrow, middle substance (root); *medulla*, inner layer of kidney

mega–: large (prefix); *megaspore*, a large, haploid (female) spore formed by meiotic cell division in plants

–mere: segment, body section (suffix); *sarcomere*, the functional unit of a vertebrate skeletal muscle cell

meso–: middle (prefix); *mesophyll*, middle layers of cells in a leaf

meta–: change, after (prefix); *metamorphosis*, to change body form (e.g., developing from a larva to an adult)

micro–: small (prefix); *microscope*, a device that allows one to see small objects

milli–: one-thousandth (prefix); *millimeter*, a unit of measurement of length; 1 one-thousandth of a meter

mito–: thread (prefix); *mitosis*, cell division (in which chromosomes appear as threadlike bodies)

mono–: single (prefix); *monocot*, a type of angiosperm with one cotyledon in the seed

morph–: shape, form (prefix or root); *polymorphic*, having multiple forms

multi–: many (prefix); *multicellular*, pertaining to a body composed of more than one cell

myo–: muscle (prefix); *myofibril*, protein strands in muscle cells

neo–: new (prefix); *neonatal*, relating to or affecting a newborn child

neph–: kidney (prefix or root); *nephron*, functional unit of mammalian kidney

neur–, neuro–: nerve (prefix or root); *neuron*, a nerve cell

neutr–: of neither gender or type (usually root); *neutron*, an uncharged subatomic particle found in the nucleus of an atom

non–: not (prefix); *nondisjunction*, the failure of chromosomes to distribute themselves properly during cell division

oligo–: few (prefix); *oligomer*, a molecule made up of a few subunits (see also *poly–*)

omni–: all (prefix); *omnivore*, an animal that eats both plants and animals

oo–, ov–, ovo–: egg (prefix); *oocyte*, one of the stages of egg development

opsi–: sight (prefix or root); *opsin*, protein part of light-absorbing pigment in eye

opso–: tasty food (prefix or root); *opsonization*, process whereby antibodies and/or complement render bacteria easier for white blood cells to engulf

–osis: a condition, disease (suffix); *atherosclerosis*, a disease in which the artery walls become thickened and hardened

oss–, osteo–: bone (prefix or root); *osteoporosis*; a disease in which the bones become spongy and weak

para–: alongside (prefix); *parathyroid*, referring to a gland located next to the thyroid gland

pater, patr–: father (usually root); *paternal*, from or relating to a father

path–, –i–, –o–: disease (prefix or root); *pathology*, the study of disease and diseased tissue

–pathy: disease (suffix); *neuropathy*, a disease of the nervous system

peri–: around (prefix); *pericycle*, the outermost layer of cells in the vascular cylinder of a plant root

phago–: eat (prefix or root); *phagocyte*, a cell (e.g., some types of white blood cell) that eats other cells

–phil, philo–: to love (prefix or suffix); *hydrophilic* (literally, "water loving"), pertaining to a water-soluble molecule

–phob, phobo–: to fear (prefix or suffix); *hydrophobic* (literally, "water fearing"), pertaining to a water-insoluble molecule

photo–: light (prefix); *photosynthesis*, the manufacture of organic molecules using the energy of sunlight

–phyll: leaf (root or suffix); *chlorophyll*, the green, light-absorbing pigment in a leaf

–phyte: plant (root or suffix); *gametophyte* (literally, "gamete plant"), the gamete-producing stage of a plant's life cycle

plasmo, –plasm: formed substance (prefix, root, or suffix); *cytoplasm*, the material inside a cell

ploid: chromosomes (root); *diploid*, having paired chromosomes

pneumo–: lung (root); *pneumonia*, a disease of the lungs

-pod: foot (root or suffix); *gastropod* (literally, "stomach-foot"), a class of mollusks, principally snails, that crawl on their ventral surfaces

poly-: many (prefix); *polysaccharide*, a carbohydrate polymer composed of many sugar subunits (see also *oligo-*)

post-, postero-: behind (prefix); *posterior*, pertaining to the hind part

pre-, pro-: before, in front of (prefix); *premating isolating mechanism*, a mechanism that prevents gene flow between species, acting to prevent mating (e.g., having different courtship rituals or different mating seasons)

prim-: first (prefix); *primary cell wall*, the first cell wall laid down between plant cells during cell division

pro-: before (prefix); *prokaryotic*, pertaining to a cell without (that evolved before the evolution of) a nucleus

proto-: first (prefix); *protocell*, a hypothetical evolutionary ancestor to the first cell

pseudo-: false (prefix); *pseudopod* (literally, "false foot"), the extension of the plasma membrane by which some cells, such as *Amoeba*, move and capture prey

quad-, quat-: four (prefix); *quaternary structure*, the "fourth level" of protein structure, in which multiple peptide chains form a complex three-dimensional structure

ren: kidney (root); *adrenal*, gland attached to the mammalian kidney

retro-: backward (prefix); *retrovirus*, a virus that uses RNA as its genetic material; this RNA must be copied "backward" to DNA during infection of a cell by the virus

sarco-: muscle (prefix); *sarcoplasmic reticulum*, a calcium-storing, modified endoplasmic reticulum found in muscle cells

scler-: hard, tough (prefix); *sclerenchyma*, a type of plant cell with a very thick, hard cell wall

semi-: one-half (prefix); *semiconservative replication*, the mechanism of DNA replication, in which one strand of the original DNA double helix becomes incorporated into the new DNA double helix

-some, soma-, somato-: body (prefix or suffix); *somatic nervous system*, part of the peripheral nervous system that controls the skeletal muscles that move the body

sperm, sperma-, spermato-: seed (usually root); *gymnosperm*, a type of plant producing a seed not enclosed within a fruit

-stasis, stat-: stationary, standing still (suffix or prefix); *homeostasis*, the physiological process of maintaining constant internal conditions despite a changing external environment

stoma, -to-: mouth, opening (prefix or root); *stoma*, the adjustable pore in the surface of a leaf that allows carbon dioxide to enter the leaf

sub-: under, below (prefix); *subcutaneous*, beneath the skin

sym-: same (prefix); *sympatric* (literally "same father"), found in the same region

tel-, telo-: end (prefix); *telophase*, the last stage of mitosis and meiosis

test-: witness (prefix or root); *testis*, male reproductive organ (derived from the custom in ancient Rome that only males had standing in the eyes of the law; *testimony* has the same derivation)

therm-: heat (prefix or root); *thermoregulation*, the process of regulating body temperature

trans-: across (prefix); *transgenic*, having genes from another organism (usually another species); the genes have been moved "across" species

tri-: three (prefix); *triploid*, having three copies of each homologous chromosome

-trop-, tropic: change, turn, move (suffix); *phototropism*, the process by which plants orient toward the light

troph: food, nourishment (root); *autotrophic*, self-feeder (e.g., photosynthetic)

ultra-: beyond (prefix); *ultraviolet*, light of wavelengths beyond the violet

uni-: one (prefix); *unicellular*, referring to an organism composed of a single cell

vita: life (root); *vitamin*, a molecule required in the diet to sustain life

-vor: eat (usually root); *herbivore*, an animal that eats plants

zoo-, zoa-: animal (usually root); *zoology*, the study of animals

1 **H** 1.008		atomic number (number of protons)															2 **He** 4.003
3 **Li** 6.941	4 **Be** 9.012	element (chemical symbol)			atomic mass (total mass of protons + neutrons + electrons)							5 **B** 10.81	6 **C** 12.01	7 **N** 14.01	8 **O** 16.00	9 **F** 19.00	10 **Ne** 20.18
11 **Na** 22.99	12 **Mg** 24.31											13 **Al** 26.98	14 **Si** 28.09	15 **P** 30.97	16 **S** 32.07	17 **Cl** 35.45	18 **Ar** 39.95
19 **K** 39.10	20 **Ca** 40.08	21 **Sc** 44.96	22 **Ti** 47.87	23 **V** 50.94	24 **Cr** 52.00	25 **Mn** 54.94	26 **Fe** 55.85	27 **Co** 58.93	28 **Ni** 58.69	29 **Cu** 63.55	30 **Zn** 65.39	31 **Ga** 69.72	32 **Ge** 72.61	33 **As** 74.92	34 **Se** 78.96	35 **Br** 79.90	36 **Kr** 83.80
37 **Rb** 85.47	38 **Sr** 87.62	39 **Y** 88.91	40 **Zr** 91.22	41 **Nb** 92.91	42 **Mo** 95.94	43 **Tc** (98)	44 **Ru** 101.1	45 **Rh** 102.9	46 **Pd** 106.4	47 **Ag** 107.9	48 **Cd** 112.4	49 **In** 114.8	50 **Sn** 118.7	51 **Sb** 121.8	52 **Te** 127.6	53 **I** 126.9	54 **Xe** 131.3
55 **Cs** 132.9	56 **Ba** 137.3	57 ***La** 138.9	72 **Hf** 178.5	73 **Ta** 180.9	74 **W** 183.8	75 **Re** 186.2	76 **Os** 190.2	77 **Ir** 192.2	78 **Pt** 195.1	79 **Au** 197.0	80 **Hg** 200.6	81 **Tl** 204.4	82 **Pb** 207.2	83 **Bi** 209.0	84 **Po** (209)	85 **At** (210)	86 **Rn** (222)
87 **Fr** (223)	88 **Ra** (226)	89 **†Ac** (227)	104 **Rf** (261)	105 **Db** (262)	106 **Sg** (263)	107 **Bh** (264)	108 **Hs** (265)	109 **Mt** (268)	110 **Ds** (281)	111 **Rg** (280)	112 ****** (277)	113 ******	114 ****** (285)	115 ******			

*Lanthanide series	58 **Ce** 140.1	59 **Pr** 140.9	60 **Nd** 144.2	61 **Pm** (145)	62 **Sm** 150.4	63 **Eu** 152.0	64 **Gd** 157.3	65 **Tb** 158.9	66 **Dy** 162.5	67 **Ho** 164.9	68 **Er** 167.3	69 **Tm** 168.9	70 **Yb** 173.0	71 **Lu** 175.0
†Actinide series	90 **Th** 232.0	91 **Pa** 231	92 **U** 238.0	93 **Np** (237)	94 **Pu** (244)	95 **Am** (243)	96 **Cm** (247)	97 **Bk** (247)	98 **Cf** (251)	99 **Es** (252)	100 **Fm** (257)	101 **Md** (258)	102 **No** (259)	103 **Lr** (262)

The periodic table of the elements was first devised by Russian chemist Dmitri Mendeleev. The atomic numbers of the elements (the numbers of protons in the nucleus) increase in normal reading order: left to right, top to bottom. The table is "periodic" because all the elements in a column possess similar chemical properties, and such similar elements therefore recur "periodically" in each row. For example, elements that usually form ions with a single positive charge—including H, Li, Na, K, and so on—occur as the first element in each row.

The gaps in the table are a consequence of the maximum numbers of electrons in the most reactive, usually outermost, electron shells of the atoms. It takes only two electrons to completely fill the first shell, so the first row of the table contains only two elements, H and He. It takes eight electrons to fill the second and third shells, so there are eight elements in the second and third rows. It takes 18 electrons to fill the fourth and fifth shells, so there are 18 elements in these rows.

The lanthanide series and actinide series of elements are usually placed below the main body of the table for convenience—it takes 32 electrons to completely fill the sixth and seventh shells, so the table would become extremely wide if all of these elements were included in the sixth and seventh rows.

The important elements found in living things are highlighted in color. The elements in pale red are the six most abundant elements in living things. The elements that form the five most abundant ions in living things are in purple. The trace elements important to life are shown as dark blue (more common) and lighter blue (less common). For radioactive elements, the atomic masses are given in parentheses, and represent the most common or the most stable isotope. Elements indicated as double asterisks have not yet been named.

To Convert Metric Units:	Multiply by:	To Get English Equivalent:
Length		
Centimeters (cm)	0.394	Inches (in)
Meters (m)	3.281	Feet (ft)
Meters (m)	1.094	Yards (yd)
Kilometers (km)	0.621	Miles (mi)
Area		
Square centimeters (cm^2)	0.155	Square inches (in^2)
Square meters (m^2)	10.764	Square feet (ft^2)
Square meters (m^2)	1.196	Square yards (yd^2)
Square kilometers (km^2)	0.386	Square miles (mi^2)
Hectare (ha) (10,000 m^2)	2.471	Acres (a)
Volume		
Cubic centimeters (cm^3)	0.0610	Cubic inches (in^3)
Cubic meters (m^3)	35.315	Cubic feet (ft^3)
Cubic meters (m^3)	1.308	Cubic yards (yd^3)
Cubic kilometers (km^3)	0.240	Cubic miles (mi^3)
Liters (L)	1.057	Quarts (qt), U.S.
Liters (L)	0.264	Gallons (gal), U.S.
Mass		
Grams (g)	0.0353	Ounces (oz)
Kilograms (kg)	2.205	Pounds (lb)
Metric ton (tonne) (t)	1.102	Ton (tn), U.S.
Speed		
Meters/second (mps)	2.237	Miles/hour (mph)
Kilometers/hour (kmph)	0.621	Miles/hour (mph)

To Convert English Units:	Multiply by:	To Get Metric Equivalent:
Length		
Inches (in)	2.540	Centimeters (cm)
Feet (ft)	0.305	Meters (m)
Yards (yd)	0.914	Meters (m)
Miles (mi)	1.609	Kilometers (km)
Area		
Square inches (in^2)	6.452	Square centimeters (cm^2)
Square feet (ft^2)	0.0929	Square meters (m^2)
Square yards (yd^2)	0.836	Square meters (m^2)
Square miles (mi^2)	2.590	Square kilometers (km^2)
Acres (a)	0.405	Hectare (ha) (10,000 m^2)
Volume		
Cubic inches (in^3)	16.387	Cubic centimeters (cm^3)
Cubic feet (ft^3)	0.0283	Cubic meters (m^3)
Cubic yards (yd^3)	0.765	Cubic meters (m^3)
Cubic miles (mi^3)	4.168	Cubic kilometers (km^3)
Quarts (qt), U.S.	0.946	Liters (L)
Gallons (gal), U.S.	3.785	Liters (L)
Mass		
Ounces (oz)	28.350	Grams (g)
Pounds (lb)	0.454	Kilograms (kg)
Ton (tn), U.S.	0.907	Metric ton (tonne) (t)
Speed		
Miles/hour (mph)	0.447	Meters/second (mps)
Miles/hour (mph)	1.609	Kilometers/hour (kmph)

Metric Prefixes

Prefix		Meaning	
giga-	G	$10^9 =$	1,000,000,000
mega-	M	$10^6 =$	1,000,000
kilo-	k	$10^3 =$	1,000
hecto-	h	$10^2 =$	100
deka-	da	$10^1 =$	10
		$10^0 =$	1
deci-	d	$10^{-1} =$	0.1
centi-	c	$10^{-2} =$	0.01
milli-	m	$10^{-3} =$	0.001
micro-	μ	$10^{-6} =$	0.000001

$$°C = \frac{°F - 32}{1.8}$$

$$°F = (1.8 \times °C) + 32$$

CLASSIFICATION OF MAJOR GROUPS OF EUKARYOTIC ORGANISMS*

Kingdom[†]	Phylum or Class	Common Name
Excavata	Parabasalia	parabasalids
	Diplomonadida	diplomonads
Euglenozoa	Euglenida	euglenids
	Kinetoplastida	kinetoplastids
Stramenopila	Oomycota	water molds
	Phaeophyta	brown algae
	Bacillariophyta	diatoms
Alveolata	Apicomplexa	sporozoans
	Pyrrophyta	dinoflagellates
	Ciliophora	ciliates
Rhizaria	Foraminifera	foraminiferans
	Radiolaria	radiolarians
Amoebozoa	Tubulinea	amoebas
	Myxomycota	acellular slime molds
	Acrasiomycota	cellular slime molds
Rhodophyta		red algae
Chlorophyta		green algae
Plantae	Marchantiophyta	liverworts
	Anthocerotophyta	hornworts
	Bryophyta	mosses
	Lycopodiopsida	club mosses
	Polypodiopsida	ferns, horsetails
	Gymnospermae	cycads, ginkgos, gnetophytes, conifers
	Anthophyta	flowering plants
Fungi	Chytridiomycota	chytrids
	Neocallimastigomycota	rumen fungi
	Blastocladiomycota	blastoclades
	Glomeromycota	glomeromycetes
	Ascomycota	sac fungi
	Basidiomycota	club fungi
Animalia	Porifera	sponges
	Cnidaria	hydras, sea anemones, sea jellies, corals
	Ctenophora	comb jellies
	Platyhelminthes	flatworms
	Annelida	segmented worms
	Oligochaeta	earthworms
	Polychaeta	tube worms
	Hirudinea	leeches
	Mollusca	mollusks
	Gastropoda	snails
	Pelecypoda	mussels, clams
	Cephalopoda	squid, octopuses
	Nematoda	roundworms
	Arthropoda	arthropods
	Insecta	insects
	Arachnida	spiders, ticks
	Crustacea	crabs, lobsters
	Myriapoda	millipedes, centipedes
	Chordata	chordates
	Tunicata	tunicates
	Cephalochordata	lancelets
	Myxini	hagfishes
	Petromyzontiformes	lampreys
	Chondrichthyes	sharks, rays
	Actinopterygii	ray-finned fishes
	Actinistia	coelacanths
	Dipnoi	lungfishes
	Amphibia	amphibians (frogs, salamanders)
	Reptilia	reptiles (turtles, crocodiles, birds, snakes, lizards)
	Mammalia	mammals

*This table lists only those taxonomic categories described in the textbook.

†Although the major protist groups are not generally called "kingdoms," they are approximately the same taxonomic rank as the kingdoms Plantae, Fungi, and Animalia.

GLOSSARY

abiotic (ā-bī-ah′-tik): nonliving; the abiotic portion of an ecosystem includes soil, rock, water, and the atmosphere.

abscisic acid (ab-sis′-ik): a plant hormone that generally inhibits the action of other hormones, enforcing dormancy in seeds and buds and causing the closing of stomata.

abscission layer: a layer of thin-walled cells, located at the base of the petiole of a leaf, that produces an enzyme that digests the cell walls holding the leaf to the stem, allowing the leaf to fall off.

absorption: the process by which nutrients enter the body through the cells lining the digestive tract.

accessory pigment: a colored molecule, other than chlorophyll *a*, that absorbs light energy and passes it to chlorophyll *a*.

acellular slime mold: a type of organism that forms a multinucleate structure that crawls in amoeboid fashion and ingests decaying organic matter; also called *plasmodial slime mold*. Acellular slime molds are members of the protist clade Amoebozoa.

acid: a substance that releases hydrogen ions (H⁺) into solution; a solution with a pH less than 7.

acid deposition: the deposition of nitric or sulfuric acid, either in rain (acid rain) or in the form of dry particles, as a result of the production of nitrogen oxides or sulfur dioxide through burning, primarily of fossil fuels.

acidic: referring to a solution with an H⁺ concentration exceeding that of OH⁻; referring to a substance that releases H⁺.

acquired immune deficiency syndrome (AIDS): an infectious disease caused by the human immunodeficiency virus (HIV); attacks and destroys T cells, thus weakening the immune system.

acrosome (ak′-rō-sōm): a vesicle, located at the tip of the head of an animal sperm, that contains enzymes needed to dissolve protective layers around the egg.

actin (ak′-tin): a major muscle protein whose interactions with myosin produce contraction; found in the thin filaments of the muscle fiber; see also *myosin*.

action potential: a rapid change from a negative to a positive electrical potential in a nerve cell. An action potential travels along an axon without a change in amplitude.

activation energy: in a chemical reaction, the energy needed to force the electron shells of reactants together, prior to the formation of products.

active site: the region of an enzyme molecule that binds substrates and performs the catalytic function of the enzyme.

active transport: the movement of materials across a membrane through the use of cellular energy, normally against a concentration gradient.

adaptation: a trait that increases the ability of an individual to survive and reproduce compared to individuals without the trait.

adaptive immune response: a response to invading toxins or microbes in which immune cells are activated by a specific invader, selectively destroy that invader, and then "remember" the invader, allowing a faster response if that type of invader reappears in the future; see also *innate immune response*.

adaptive immune system: a widely distributed system of organs (including the thymus, bone marrow, and lymph nodes), cells (including macrophages, dendritic cells, B cells, and T cells), and molecules (including cytokines and antibodies) that work together to combat microbial invasion of the body; the adaptive immune system responds to and destroys specific invading toxins or microbes; see also *innate immune response*.

adaptive radiation: the rise of many new species in a relatively short time; may occur when a single species invades different habitats and evolves in response to different environmental conditions in those habitats.

adenine (A): a nitrogenous base found in both DNA and RNA; abbreviated as A.

adenosine diphosphate (a-den′-ō-sēn dī-fos′-fāt; ADP): a molecule composed of the sugar ribose, the base adenine, and two phosphate groups; a component of ATP.

adenosine triphosphate (a-den′-ō-sēn trī ī fos′-fāt; ATP): a molecule composed of the sugar ribose, the base adenine, and three phosphate groups; the major energy carrier in cells. The last two phosphate groups are attached by "high-energy" bonds.

adhesion: the tendency of polar molecules (such as water) to adhere to polar surfaces (such as glass).

adhesive junctions: attachment structures that link cells to one another within tissues.

adipose tissue (a′-dipōs): tissue composed of fat cells.

adrenal cortex: the outer part of the adrenal gland, which secretes steroid hormones that regulate metabolism and salt balance.

adrenal gland: a mammalian endocrine gland, adjacent to the kidney; secretes hormones that function in water and salt regulation and in the stress response.

adrenal medulla: the inner part of the adrenal gland, which secretes epinephrine (adrenaline) and norepinephrine (noradrenaline) in the stress response.

adrenocorticotropic hormone (a-drēn-ō-kor-tik-ō-trō′-pik; ACTH): a hormone, secreted by the anterior pituitary, that stimulates the release of hormones by the adrenal cortex, especially in response to stress.

adult stem cell (ASC): any stem cell not found in an early embryo; can divide and differentiate into any of several cell types, but usually not all of the cell types of the body.

aerobic: using oxygen.

age structure diagram: a graph showing the distribution of males and females in a population according to age groups.

aggression: antagonistic behavior, normally among members of the same species, that often results from competition for resources.

aggressive mimicry (mim′ik-rē): the evolution of a predatory organism to resemble a harmless animal or a part of the environment, thus gaining access to prey.

aging: the gradual accumulation of damage to essential biological molecules, particularly DNA in both the nucleus and mitochondria, resulting in defects in cell functioning, declining health, and ultimately death.

albinism: a recessive hereditary condition caused by defective alleles of the genes that encode the enzymes required for the synthesis of melanin, the principal pigment in mammalian skin and hair; albinism results in white hair and pink skin.

alcoholic fermentation: a type of fermentation in which pyruvate is converted to ethanol (a type of alcohol) and carbon dioxide, using hydrogen ions and electrons from NADH; the primary function of alcoholic fermentation is to regenerate NAD⁺ so that glycolysis can continue under anaerobic conditions.

aldosterone: a hormone, secreted by the adrenal cortex, that helps regulate ion concentration in the blood by stimulating the reabsorption of sodium by the kidneys and sweat glands.

alga (al′-ga; pl., algae, al′-jē): any photosynthetic protist.

allantois (al-an-tō′-is): one of the embryonic membranes of reptiles (including birds) and mammals; in reptiles, serves as a waste-storage organ; in mammals, forms most of the umbilical cord.

allele (al-ēl′): one of several alternative forms of a particular gene.

allele frequency: for any given gene, the relative proportion of each allele of that gene in a population.

allergy: an inflammatory response produced by the body in response to invasion by foreign materials, such as pollen, that are themselves harmless.

allopatric speciation (al-ō-pat′-rik): the process by which new species arise following physical separation of parts of a population (geographical isolation).

allosteric regulation: the process by which enzyme action is enhanced or inhibited by small organic molecules that act as regulators by binding to the enzyme at a regulatory site distinct from the active site and altering the shape and/or function of the active site.

alternation of generations: a life cycle, typical of plants, in which a diploid sporophyte (spore-producing) generation alternates with a haploid gametophyte (gamete-producing) generation.

altruism: a behavior that benefits other individuals while reducing the fitness of the individual that performs the behavior.

alveolate (al-vē´-ō-lāt): a member of the Alveolata, a large protist clade. The alveolates, which are characterized by a system of sacs beneath the cell membrane, include ciliates, dinoflagellates, and apicomplexans.

alveolus (al-vē´-ō-lus; pl., alveoli): a tiny air sac within the lungs, surrounded by capillaries, where gas exchange with the blood occurs.

amino acid: the individual subunit of which proteins are made, composed of a central carbon atom bonded to an amino group (–NH₂), a carboxyl group (–COOH), a hydrogen atom, and a variable group of atoms denoted by the letter *R*.

amino acid derived hormone: a hormone composed of one or two modified amino acids. Examples include epinephrine and thyroxine.

ammonia: NH₃; a highly toxic nitrogen-containing waste product of amino acid breakdown. In the mammalian liver, it is converted to urea.

amniocentesis (am-nē-ō-sen-tē´-sis): a procedure for sampling the amniotic fluid surrounding a fetus: A sterile needle is inserted through the abdominal wall, uterus, and amniotic sac of a pregnant woman, and 10 to 20 milliliters of amniotic fluid are withdrawn. Various tests may be performed on the fluid and the fetal cells suspended in it to provide information on the developmental and genetic state of the fetus.

amnion (am´-nē-on): one of the embryonic membranes of reptiles (including birds) and mammals; encloses a fluid-filled cavity that envelops the embryo.

amniotic egg (am-nē-ōt´-ik): the egg of reptiles, including birds; contains a membrane, the amnion, that surrounds the embryo, enclosing it in a watery environment and allowing the egg to be laid on dry land.

amoeba: an amoebozoan protist that uses a characteristic streaming mode of locomotion by extending a cellular projection called a *pseudopod*. Also known as a *lobose amoeba*.

amoeboid cell: a protist or animal cell that moves by extending a cellular projection called a pseudopod.

amoebozoan: a member of the Amoebozoa, a protist clade. The amoebozoans, which generally lack shells and move by extending pseudopods, include the lobose amoebas and the slime molds.

amphibian: a member of the chordate clade Amphibia, which includes the frogs, toads, and salamanders, as well as the limbless caecilians.

amygdala (am-ig´-da-la): part of the forebrain of vertebrates that is involved in the production of appropriate behavioral responses to environmental stimuli.

amylase (am´-i-lās): an enzyme, found in saliva and pancreatic secretions, that catalyzes the breakdown of starch.

anaerobe (an-ə-rōb): an organism that can live and grow in the absence of oxygen.

anaerobic: not using oxygen.

analogous structure: structures that have similar functions and superficially similar appearance but very different anatomies, such as the wings of insects and birds. The similarities are the result of similar environmental pressures rather than a common ancestry.

anaphase (an´-a-fāz): in mitosis, the stage in which the sister chromatids of each chromosome separate from one another and are moved to opposite poles of the cell; in meiosis I, the stage in which homologous chromosomes, consisting of two sister chromatids, are separated; in meiosis II, the stage in which the sister chromatids of each chromosome separate from one another and are moved to opposite poles of the cell.

androgen: a male sex hormone.

angina (an-jī´-nuh): chest pain associated with reduced blood flow to the heart muscle; caused by an obstruction of the coronary arteries.

angiosperm (an´-jē-ō-sperm): a flowering vascular plant.

angiotensin (an-jē-ō-ten-sun): a hormone that functions in water regulation in mammals by stimulating physiological changes that increase blood volume and blood pressure.

annual ring: a pattern of alternating light (early) and dark (late) xylem in woody stems and roots; formed as a result of the unequal availability of water in different seasons of the year, normally spring and summer.

antagonistic muscles: a pair of muscles, one of which contracts and in so doing extends the other, relaxed muscle; this arrangement allows movement of the skeleton at joints.

anterior pituitary: a lobe of the pituitary gland that produces prolactin, growth hormone, follicle-stimulating hormone, luteinizing hormone, adrenocorticotropic hormone, and thyroid-stimulating hormone.

anther (an´-ther): the uppermost part of the stamen, in which pollen develops.

antheridium (an-ther-id´-ē-um; pl., antheridia): a structure in which male sex cells are produced; found in nonvascular plants and certain seedless vascular plants.

antibiotic: chemicals that help to combat infection by destroying or slowing down the multiplication of bacteria, fungi, or protists.

antibody: a protein, produced by cells of the immune system, that combines with a specific antigen and normally facilitates the destruction of the antigen.

anticodon: a sequence of three bases in transfer RNA that is complementary to the three bases of a codon of messenger RNA.

antidiuretic hormone (an-tē-dī-ūr-et´-ik; ADH): a hormone produced by the hypothalamus and released into the bloodstream by the posterior pituitary when blood volume is low; increases the permeability of the distal tubule and the collecting duct to water, allowing more water to be reabsorbed into the bloodstream.

antigen: a complex molecule, normally a protein or polysaccharide, that stimulates the production of a specific antibody.

antioxidant: any molecule that reacts with free radicals, neutralizing their ability to damage biological molecules. Vitamins C and E are examples of dietary antioxidants.

antiviral drug: a medicine that interferes with one or more stages of the viral life cycle, including attachment to a host cell, replication of viral parts, assembly of viruses within a host cell, and release of viruses from a host cell.

anvil: the second of the small bones of the middle ear that link the tympanic membrane (eardrum) to the oval window of the cochlea; also called the *incus*.

aphotic zone: the region of the ocean below 200 meters where sunlight does not penetrate.

apical dominance: the phenomenon whereby a growing shoot tip inhibits the sprouting of lateral buds.

apical meristem (āp´-i-kul mer´-i-stem): the cluster of meristem cells at the tip of a shoot or root (or one of their branches).

apicomplexan (ā-pē-kom-pleks´-an): a member of the protist clade Apicomplexa, which includes mostly parasitic, single-celled eukaryotes such as *Plasmodium*, which causes malaria in humans. Apicomplexans are part of a larger group known as the alveolates.

appendicular skeleton (ap-pen-dik´-ū-lur): the portion of the skeleton consisting of the bones of the extremities and their attachments to the axial skeleton; the appendicular skeleton therefore consists of the pectoral and pelvic girdles and the arms, legs, hands, and feet.

aquaporin: a channel protein in the plasma membrane of a cell that is selectively permeable to water.

aqueous humor (ā´-kwē-us): the clear, watery fluid between the cornea and lens of the eye; nourishes the cornea and lens.

aquifer (ok´-wifer): an underground deposit of fresh water, often used as a source of water for irrigation.

archaea: prokaryotes that are members of the domain Archaea, one of the three domains of living organisms; only distantly related to members of the domain Bacteria.

Archaea: one of life's three domains; consists of prokaryotes that are only distantly related to members of the domain Bacteria.

archegonium (ar-ke-gō´-nē-um; pl., archegonia): a structure in which female sex cells are produced; found in nonvascular plants and certain seedless vascular plants.

arteriole (ar-tēr´-ē-ōl): a small artery that empties into capillaries; constriction of arterioles regulates blood flow to various parts of the body.

artery (ar´-tuh-rē): a vessel with muscular, elastic walls that conducts blood away from the heart.

arthropod: a member of the animal phylum Arthropoda, which includes the insects, spiders, ticks, mites, scorpions, crustaceans, millipedes, and centipedes.

artificial selection: a selective breeding procedure in which only those individuals with particular traits are chosen as breeders; used mainly to enhance desirable traits in domesticated plants and animals; may also be used in evolutionary biology experiments.

ascomycete: a member of the fungus clade Ascomycota, whose members form sexual spores in a saclike case known as an ascus.

ascus (as'-kus; pl., asci): a saclike case in which sexual spores are formed by members of the fungus clade Ascomycota.

asexual reproduction: reproduction that does not involve the fusion of haploid gametes.

atherosclerosis (ath'-er-ō-skler-ō'-sis): a disease characterized by the obstruction of arteries by cholesterol deposits and thickening of the arterial walls.

atom: the smallest unit of an element that retains the properties of the element.

atomic mass: the total mass of all the protons, neutrons, and electrons within an atom.

atomic nucleus: the central part of an atom that contains protons and neutrons.

atomic number: the number of protons in the nuclei of all atoms of a particular element.

ATP synthase: a channel protein in the thylakoid membranes of chloroplasts and the inner membrane of mitochondria that uses the energy of H^+ ions moving through the channel down their concentration gradient to produce ATP from ADP and inorganic phosphate.

atrial natriuretic peptide (ANP) (ā'-trē-ul nā-trē-ū-ret'-ik; ANP): a hormone, secreted by cells in the mammalian heart, that reduces blood volume by inhibiting the release of ADH and aldosterone.

atrioventricular (AV) node (ā'-trē-ō-ven-trik'-ū-lar nōd): a specialized mass of muscle at the base of the right atrium through which the electrical activity initiated in the sinoatrial node is transmitted to the ventricles.

atrioventricular valve: a heart valve that separates each atrium from each ventricle, preventing the backflow of blood into the atria during ventricular contraction.

atrium (ā'-trē-um; pl., atria): a chamber of the heart that receives venous blood and passes it to a ventricle.

auditory canal (aw'-di-tor-ē): a relatively large-diameter tube within the outer ear that conducts sound from the pinna to the tympanic membrane.

auditory nerve: the nerve leading from the mammalian cochlea to the brain; it carries information about sound.

auditory tube: a thin tube connecting the middle ear with the pharynx, which allows pressure to equilibrate between the middle ear and the outside air; also called the *Eustachian tube*.

autoimmune disease: a disorder in which the immune system attacks the body's own cells or molecules.

autonomic nervous system: the part of the peripheral nervous system of vertebrates that synapses on glands, internal organs, and smooth muscle and produces largely involuntary responses.

autosome (aw'-tō-sōm): a chromosome that occurs in homologous pairs in both males and females and that does not bear the genes determining sex.

autotroph (aw'-tō-trōf): literally, "self-feeder"; normally, a photosynthetic organism; a producer.

auxin (awk'-sin): a plant hormone that influences many plant functions, including phototropism, gravitropism, apical dominance, and root branching.

axial skeleton: the skeleton forming the body axis, including the skull, vertebral column, and rib cage.

axon: a long extension of a nerve cell, extending from the cell body to synaptic endings on other nerve cells or on muscles.

B cell: a type of lymphocyte that matures in the bone marrow and that participates in humoral immunity; gives rise to plasma cells, which secrete antibodies into the circulatory system, and to memory cells.

bacteria (sing., bacterium): prokaryotes that are members of the domain Bacteria, one of the three domains of living organisms; only distantly related to members of the domain Archaea.

Bacteria: one of life's three domains; consists of prokaryotes that are only distantly related to members of the domain Archaea.

bacteriophage (bak-tir'-ē-ō-fāj): a virus that specifically infects bacteria.

ball-and-socket joint: a joint in which the rounded end of one bone fits into a hollow depression in another, as in the hip; allows movement in several directions.

bark: the outer layer of a woody stem, consisting of phloem, cork cambium, and cork cells.

Barr body: a condensed, inactivated X chromosome in the cells of female mammals that have two X chromosomes.

basal body: a structure derived from a centriole that produces a cilium or flagellum and anchors this structure within the plasma membrane.

basal ganglion: a cluster of neurons in the interior of the cerebrum, plus the substantial nigra in the midbrain, that functions in the control of movement. Damage to or degeneration of one or more basal ganglia causes disorders such as Parkinson's disease and Huntington's disease.

base: (1) a substance capable of combining with and neutralizing H^+ ions in a solution; a solution with a pH greater than 7; (2) one of the nitrogen-containing, single- or double-ringed structures that distinguishes one nucleotide from another. In DNA, the bases are adenine, guanine, cytosine, and thymine.

basic: referring to a solution with an H^+ concentration less than that of OH^-; referring to a substance that combines with H^+.

basidiomycete: a member of the fungus clade Basidiomycota, which includes species that produce sexual spores in club-shaped cells known as basidia.

basidiospore (ba-sid'-ē-ō-spor): a sexual spore formed by members of the fungus clade Basidiomycota.

basidium (pl., basidia): a diploid cell, typically club-shaped, formed by members of the fungus clade Basidiomycota; produces basidiospores by meiosis.

basilar membrane (bas'-eh-lar): a membrane in the cochlea that bears hair cells that respond to the vibrations produced by sound.

behavior: any observable activity of a living animal.

behavioral isolation: reproductive isolation that arises when species do not interbreed because they have different courtship and mating rituals.

bilateral symmetry: a body plan in which only a single plane through the central axis will divide the body into mirror-image halves.

bile (bīl): a digestive secretion formed by the liver, stored and released from the gallbladder, and used to disperse fats in the small intestine.

binocular vision: the ability to see objects simultaneously through both eyes, providing greater depth perception and more accurate judgment of the size and distance of an object than can be achieved by vision with one eye alone.

binomial system: the method of naming organisms by genus and species, often called the scientific name, usually using Latin or Greek words or words derived from Latin or Greek.

biocapacity: an estimate of the sustainable resources and waste-absorbing capacity actually available on Earth. Biocapacity calculations are subject to change as new technologies change the way people use resources.

biodegradable: able to be broken down into harmless substances by decomposers.

biodiversity: the diversity of living organisms; measured as the variety of different species, the variety of different alleles in species' gene pools, or the variety of different communities and nonliving environments in an ecosystem or in the entire biosphere.

biofilm: a community of prokaryotes of one or more species, in which the prokaryotes secrete and are embedded in slime that adheres to a surface.

biogeochemical cycle: the pathways of a specific nutrient (such as carbon, nitrogen, phosphorus, or water) through the living and nonliving portions of an ecosystem; also called a *nutrient cycle*.

biological clock: a metabolic timekeeping mechanism found in most organisms, whereby the organism measures the approximate length of a day (24 hours) even without external environmental cues such as light and darkness.

biological magnification: the increasing accumulation of a toxic substance in progressively higher trophic levels.

biological molecules: all molecules produced by living things.

biology: the study of all aspects of life and living things.

biomass: the total weight of all living material within a defined area.

biome (bī′-ōm): a terrestrial ecosystem that occupies an extensive geographical area and is characterized by a specific type of plant community; for example, deserts.

bioremediation: the use of organisms to remove or detoxify toxic substances in the environment.

biosphere (bī′-ō-sfēr): all life on Earth and the nonliving portions of Earth that support life.

biotechnology: any industrial or commercial use or alteration of organisms, cells, or biological molecules to achieve specific practical goals.

biotic (bī-ah′-tik): living.

biotic potential: the maximum rate at which a population is able to increase, assuming ideal conditions that allow a maximum birth rate and minimum death rate.

birth rate: the number of births per individual in a specified unit of time, such as a year.

bladder: a hollow muscular organ that stores urine.

blade: the flat part of a leaf.

blastoclade: a member of the fungus clade Blastocladiomycota, whose members have swimming spores with a single flagellum and ribosomes arranged to form a nuclear cap.

blastocyst (blas′-tō-sist): an early stage of human embryonic development, consisting of a hollow ball of cells, enclosing a mass of cells attached to its inner surface, which becomes the embryo.

blastopore: the site at which a blastula indents to form a gastrula.

blastula (blas′-tū-luh): in animals, the embryonic stage attained at the end of cleavage, in which the embryo usually consists of a hollow ball with a wall that is one or several cell layers thick.

blind spot: the area of the retina at which the axons of the ganglion cells merge to form the optic nerve; because there are no photoreceptors in the blind spot, objects focused at the blind spot cannot be seen.

blood: a specialized connective tissue, consisting of a fluid (plasma) in which blood cells are suspended; carried within the circulatory system.

blood–brain barrier: relatively impermeable capillaries of the brain that protect the cells of the brain from potentially damaging chemicals that reach the bloodstream.

blood clotting: a complex process by which platelets, the protein fibrin, and red blood cells block an irregular surface in or on the body, such as a damaged blood vessel, sealing the wound.

blood vessel: any of several types of tubes that carry blood throughout the body.

body mass index (BMI): a number derived from an individual's weight and height that is used to estimate body fat. The formula is weight (in kg) /height^2 (in meters^2).

bone: a hard, mineralized connective tissue that is a major component of the vertebrate endoskeleton; provides support and sites for muscle attachment.

bone marrow: a soft, spongy tissue that fills the cavities of large bones and generates the cell-based components of blood.

boom-and-bust cycle: a population cycle characterized by rapid exponential growth followed by a sudden massive die-off; seen in seasonal species, such as many insects living in temperate climates, and in some populations of small rodents, such as lemmings.

brain: the part of the central nervous system of vertebrates that is enclosed within the skull.

branch root: a root that arises as a branch of a preexisting root; occurs through divisions of pericycle cells and subsequent differentiation of the daughter cells.

bronchiole (bron′-kē-ōl): a narrow tube, formed by repeated branching of the bronchi, that conducts air into the alveoli.

bronchus (bron′-kus; pl., bronchi): a tube that conducts air from the trachea to each lung.

bud: in plants, an embryonic shoot, often dormant until stimulated by specific combinations of hormones. In asexually reproducing animals,

a miniature copy of an animal that develops on some part of the adult animal's body; usually eventually separates from the adult and assumes independent existence.

budding: asexual reproduction by the growth of a miniature copy, or bud, of the adult animal on the body of the parent. The bud breaks off to begin independent existence.

buffer: a compound that minimizes changes in pH by reversibly taking up or releasing H$^+$ ions.

bulbourethral gland (bul-bō-ū-rē′-thrul): in male mammals, a gland that secretes a basic, mucus-containing fluid that forms part of the semen.

bulk flow: the movement of many molecules of a gas or liquid in unison (in bulk, hence the name) from an area of higher pressure to an area of lower pressure.

bundle sheath cells: cells that surround the veins of plants; in C$_4$ (but not in C$_3$) plants, bundle sheath cells contain chloroplasts.

C$_3$ pathway: in photosynthesis, the cyclic series of reactions whereby carbon from carbon dioxide is fixed as phosphoglyceric acid, the simple sugar glyceraldehyde-3-phosphate is generated, and the carbon-capture molecule, RuBP, is regenerated. Also called the *Calvin cycle*.

C$_3$ plant: a plant that relies on the C$_3$ pathway to fix carbon.

C$_4$ pathway: the series of reactions in certain plants that fixes carbon dioxide into a four-carbon molecule, which is later broken down for use in the Calvin cycle of photosynthesis. This reduces wasteful photorespiration in hot, dry environments.

C$_4$ plant: a plant that relies on the C$_4$ pathway to fix carbon.

calcitonin (kal-si-tōn′-in): a hormone, secreted by the thyroid gland, that inhibits the release of calcium from bone.

calorie (kal′-ō-rē): the amount of energy required to raise the temperature of 1 gram of water by 1 degree Celsius.

Calorie: a unit used to measure the energy content of foods; it is the amount of energy required to raise the temperature of 1 liter of water 1 degree Celsius; also called a *kilocalorie*, equal to 1,000 calories.

Calvin cycle: in photosynthesis, the cyclic series of reactions whereby carbon from carbon dioxide is fixed as phosphoglyceric acid, the simple sugar glyceraldehyde-3-phosphate is generated, and the carbon-capture molecule, RuBP, is regenerated. Also called the *C$_3$ pathway*.

cambium (kam′-bē-um; pl., cambia): a lateral meristem, parallel to the long axis of roots and stems, that causes secondary growth of woody plant stems and roots. See also *cork cambium; vascular cambium*.

camouflage (cam′-a-flaj): coloration and/or shape that renders an organism inconspicuous in its environment.

cancer: a disease in which some of the body's cells escape from normal regulatory processes and divide without control.

capillary: the smallest type of blood vessel, connecting arterioles with venules; capillary walls, through which the exchange of nutrients and wastes occurs, are only one cell thick.

capillary action: the movement of water within narrow spaces resulting from its properties of adhesion and cohesion.

carbohydrate: a compound composed of carbon, hydrogen, and oxygen, with the approximate chemical formula $(CH_2O)_n$; includes sugars, starches, and cellulose.

carbon cycle: the biogeochemical cycle by which carbon moves from its reservoirs in the atmosphere and oceans through producers and into higher trophic levels, and then back to its reservoirs.

carbon fixation: the process by which carbon derived from carbon dioxide is captured in organic molecules during photosynthesis.

cardiac cycle (kar′-dē-ak): the alternation of contraction and relaxation of the heart chambers.

cardiac muscle (kar′-dē-ak): the specialized muscle of the heart; able to initiate its own contraction, independent of the nervous system.

carnivore (kar′-neh-vor): literally, "meat-eater"; a predatory organism that feeds on herbivores or on other carnivores; a secondary (or higher) consumer.

carotenoid (ka-rot′-en-oid): a red, orange, or yellow pigment, found in chloroplasts, that serves as an accessory light-gathering pigment in thylakoid photosystems.

carpel (kar′pel): the female reproductive structure of a flower, composed of stigma, style, and ovary.

carrier: an individual who is heterozygous for a recessive condition; a carrier displays the dominant phenotype but can pass on the recessive allele to offspring.

carrier protein: a membrane protein that facilitates the diffusion of specific substances across the membrane. The molecule to be transported binds to the outer surface of the carrier protein; the protein then changes shape, allowing the molecule to move across the membrane.

carrying capacity (*K*): the maximum population size that an ecosystem can support for a long period of time without damaging the ecosystem; determined primarily by the availability of space, nutrients, water, and light.

cartilage (kar'-teh-lij): a form of connective tissue that forms portions of the skeleton; consists consists principally of cartilage cells and their major extracellular secretion, collagen protein.

Casparian strip (kas-par'-ē-un): a waxy, waterproof band, located in the cell walls between endodermal cells in a root, that prevents the movement of water and minerals into and out of the vascular cylinder through the extracellular space.

catalyst (kat'-uh-list): a substance that speeds up a chemical reaction without itself being permanently changed in the process; a catalyst lowers the activation energy of a reaction.

cell: the smallest unit of life, consisting, at a minimum, of an outer membrane that encloses a watery medium containing organic molecules, including genetic material composed of DNA.

cell body: the part of a nerve cell in which most of the common cellular organelles are located; typically a site of integration of inputs to the nerve cell.

cell cycle: the sequence of events in the life of a cell, from one cell division to the next.

cell division: splitting of one cell into two; the process of cellular reproduction.

cell-mediated immunity: an adaptive immune response in which foreign cells or substances are destroyed by contact with T cells.

cell plate: in plant cell division, a series of vesicles that fuse to form the new plasma membranes and cell wall separating the daughter cells.

cell theory: the scientific theory stating that every living organism is made up of one or more cells; cells are the functional units of all organisms; and all cells arise from preexisting cells.

cell wall: a nonliving, protective, and supportive layer secreted outside the plasma membrane of fungi, plants, and most bacteria and protists.

cellular respiration: the oxygen-requiring reactions, occurring in mitochondria, that break down the end products of glycolysis into carbon dioxide and water while capturing large amounts of energy as ATP.

cellular slime mold: a type of organism consisting of individual amoeboid cells that can aggregate to form a slug-like mass, which in turn forms a fruiting body. Cellular slime molds are members of the protist clade Amoebozoa.

cellulose: an insoluble carbohydrate composed of glucose subunits; forms the cell wall of plants.

central nervous system (CNS): in vertebrates, the brain and spinal cord.

central vacuole (vak'-ū-ōl): a large, fluid-filled vacuole occupying most of the volume of many plant cells; performs several functions, including maintaining turgor pressure.

centriole (sen'-trē-ōl): in animal cells, a short, barrel-shaped ring consisting of nine microtubule triplets; a pair of centrioles is found near the nucleus and may play a role in the organization of the spindle; centrioles also give rise to the basal bodies at the base of each cilium and flagellum that give rise to the microtubules of cilia and flagella.

centromere (sen'-trō-mēr): the region of a replicated chromosome at which the sister chromatids are held together until they separate during cell division.

cephalization (sef-ul-ī-zā'-shun): concentration of sensory organs and nervous tissue in the anterior (head) portion of the body.

cerebellum (ser-uh-bel'-um): the part of the hindbrain of vertebrates that is concerned with coordinating movements of the body.

cerebral cortex (ser-ē'-brul kor-tex): a thin layer of neurons on the surface of the vertebrate cerebrum in which most neural processing and coordination of activity occurs.

cerebral hemisphere: one of two nearly symmetrical halves of the cerebrum, connected by a broad band of axons, the corpus callosum.

cerebrum (ser-ē'-brum): the part of the forebrain of vertebrates that is concerned with sensory processing, the direction of motor output, and the coordination of most of the body's activities; consists of two nearly symmetrical halves (the hemispheres) connected by a broad band of axons, the corpus callosum.

cervix (ser'-viks): a ring of connective tissue at the outer end of the uterus that leads into the vagina.

channel protein: a membrane protein that forms a channel or pore completely through the membrane and that is usually permeable to one or to a few water-soluble molecules, especially ions.

chaparral: a biome located in coastal regions, with very low annual rainfall; is characterized by shrubs and small trees.

checkpoint: a mechanism in the eukaryotic cell cycle by which protein complexes in the cell determine whether the cell has successfully completed a specific process that is essential to successful cell division, such as the accurate replication of chromosomes.

chemical bond: an attraction between two atoms or molecules that tends to hold them together. Types of bonds include covalent, ionic, and hydrogen.

chemical digestion: the process by which particles of food within the digestive tract are exposed to enzymes and other digestive fluids that break down large molecules into smaller subunits.

chemical energy: a form of potential energy that is stored in molecules and may be released during chemical reactions.

chemical reaction: a process that forms and breaks chemical bonds that hold atoms together in molecules.

chemiosmosis (ke-mē-oz-mō'-sis): a process of ATP generation in chloroplasts and mitochondria. The movement of electrons down an electron transport system is used to pump hydrogen ions across a membrane, thereby building up a concentration gradient of hydrogen ions; the hydrogen ions diffuse back across the membrane through the pores of ATP-synthesizing enzymes; the energy of their movement down their concentration gradient drives ATP synthesis.

chemoreceptor: a sensory receptor that responds to chemicals in either the internal or external environment.

chemosynthesis (kē-mō-sin-the-sis): the process of oxidizing inorganic molecules, such as hydrogen sulfide, to obtain energy. Producers in hydrothermal vent communities, where light is absent, use chemosynthesis instead of photosynthesis.

chemosynthetic (kēm'-ō-sin-the-tik): capable of oxidizing inorganic molecules to obtain energy.

chiasma (kī-as'-muh; pl., chiasmata): a point at which a chromatid of one chromosome crosses with a chromatid of the homologous chromosome during prophase I of meiosis; the site of exchange of chromosomal material between chromosomes.

chitin (kī'-tin): a compound found in the cell walls of fungi and the exoskeletons of insects and some other arthropods; composed of chains of nitrogen-containing, modified glucose molecules.

chlamydia (kla-mid'-ē-uh): a sexually transmitted disease, caused by a bacterium, that causes inflammation of the urethra in males and of the urethra and cervix in females.

chlorophyll (klor'-ō-fil): a pigment found in chloroplasts that captures light energy during photosynthesis; chlorophyll absorbs violet, blue, and red light but reflects green light.

chlorophyll *a* (klor'-ō-fil): the most abundant type of chlorophyll molecule in photosynthetic eukaryotic organisms and in cyanobacteria; chlorophyll *a* is found in the reaction centers of the photosystems.

chlorophyte (klor'-ō-fīt): a member of Chlorophyta, a protist clade. Chlorophytes are photosynthetic green algae found in marine, freshwater, and terrestrial environments.

chloroplast (klor'-ō-plast): the organelle in plants and plantlike protists that is the site of photosynthesis; is surrounded by a double membrane and contains an extensive internal membrane system that bears chlorophyll.

cholecystokinin (kō'-lē-sis-tō-ki'-nin): a digestive hormone produced by the small intestine that stimulates the release of pancreatic enzymes.

chondrocyte (kon'-drō-sīt): a living cell of cartilage. Together with their extracellular secretions of collagen, chondrocytes form cartilage.

chorion (kor'-ē-on): the outermost embryonic membrane in reptiles (including birds) and mammals. In reptiles, the chorion functions mostly in gas exchange; in mammals, it forms the embryonic part of the placenta.

chorionic gonadotropin (kor-ē-on´-ik gō-nādō-trō´-pin; CG): a hormone secreted by the chorion (one of the fetal membranes) that maintains the integrity of the corpus luteum during early pregnancy.

chorionic villus (kor-ē-on-ik; pl., chorionic villi): in mammalian embryos, a finger-like projection of the chorion that penetrates the uterine lining and forms the embryonic portion of the placenta.

chorionic villus sampling (kōr-ē-on´-ik; CVS): a procedure for sampling cells from the chorionic villi produced by a fetus: A tube is inserted into the uterus of a pregnant woman, and a small sample of villi is suctioned off for genetic and biochemical analyses.

choroid (kor´-oid): a darkly pigmented layer of tissue behind the retina; contains blood vessels and also pigment that absorbs stray light.

chromatid (krō´-ma-tid): one of the two identical strands of DNA and protein that forms a duplicated chromosome. The two sister chromatids of a duplicated chromosome are joined at the centromere.

chromatin (krō´-ma-tin): the complex of DNA and proteins that makes up eukaryotic chromosomes.

chromosome (krō´-mō-sōm): a DNA double helix and associated proteins that help to organize and regulate the use of the DNA.

chylomicron: a particle produced by cells of the small intestine; it consists of proteins, triglycerides, and cholesterol, and it transports the products of lipid digestion into the lymphatic system and ultimately into the circulatory system.

chyme (kīm): an acidic, soup-like mixture of partially digested food, water, and digestive secretions that is released from the stomach into the small intestine.

chytrid: a member of the fungus clade Chytridomycota, which includes species with flagellated swimming spores.

ciliate (sil´-ē-et): a member of a protist group characterized by cilia and a complex unicellular structure. Ciliates are part of a larger group known as the alveolates.

cilium (sil´-ē-um; pl., cilia): a short, hair-like, motile projection from the surface of certain eukaryotic cells that contains microtubules in a 9 + 2 arrangement. The movement of cilia may propel cells through a fluid medium or move fluids over a stationary surface layer of cells.

citric acid cycle: a cyclic series of reactions, occurring in the matrix of mitochondria, in which the acetyl groups from the pyruvic acids produced by glycolysis are broken down to CO_2, accompanied by the formation of ATP and electron carriers; also called the Krebs cycle.

clade: a group that includes all the organisms descended from a common ancestor, but no other organisms; a monophyletic group.

class: in Linnaean classification, the taxonomic rank composed of related orders. Closely related classes form a phylum.

classical conditioning: a type of learning in which an animal learns to associate an innate behavior with a novel stimulus, as when a dog is trained to salivate in response to the sound of a bell.

cleavage: the early cell divisions of embryos, in which little or no growth occurs between divisions; reduces the cell size and distributes gene-regulating substances to the newly formed cells.

climate: patterns of weather that prevail for long periods of time (from years to centuries) in a given region.

climate change: a long-lasting change in weather patterns, which may include significant changes in temperature, precipitation, the timing of seasons, and the frequency and severity of extreme weather events.

climax community: a diverse and relatively stable community that forms the endpoint of succession.

clitoris: an external structure of the female reproductive system that is composed of erectile tissue; a sensitive point of stimulation during the sexual response.

clonal selection: the mechanism by which the adaptive immune response gains specificity; an invading antigen elicits a response from only a few lymphocytes, which proliferate to form a clone of cells that attack only the specific antigen that stimulated their production.

clone: offspring that are produced by mitosis and are, therefore, genetically identical to each other.

cloning: the process of producing many identical copies of a gene; also the production of many genetically identical copies of an organism.

closed circulatory system: a type of circulatory system, found in certain worms and vertebrates, in which the blood is always confined within the heart and vessels.

clumped distribution: the distribution characteristic of populations in which individuals are clustered into groups; the groups may be social or based on the need for a localized resource.

cochlea (kahk´-lē-uh): a coiled, bony, fluid-filled tube found in the mammalian inner ear; contains mechanoreceptors (hair cells) that respond to the vibration of sound.

codominance: the relation between two alleles of a gene, such that both alleles are phenotypically expressed in heterozygous individuals.

codon: a sequence of three bases of messenger RNA that specifies a particular amino acid to be incorporated into a protein; certain codons also signal the beginning or end of protein synthesis.

coelom (sē´-lōm): in animals, a space or cavity, lined with tissue derived from mesoderm, that separates the body wall from the inner organs.

coenzyme: an organic molecule that is bound to certain enzymes and is required for the enzymes' proper functioning; typically, a nucleotide bound to a water-soluble vitamin.

coevolution: the evolution of adaptations in two species due to their extensive interactions with one another, such that each species acts as a major force of natural selection on the other.

cohesion: the tendency of the molecules of a substance to stick together.

cohesion–tension mechanism: a mechanism for the transport of water in xylem; water is pulled up the xylem tubes, powered by the force of evaporation of water from the leaves (producing tension) and held together by hydrogen bonds between nearby water molecules (cohesion).

coleoptile (kō-lē-op´-tīl): a sheath surrounding the shoot in monocot seedlings that protects the shoot from abrasion by soil particles during germination.

collecting duct: a tube within the kidney that collects urine from many nephrons and conducts it through the renal medulla into the renal pelvis. Urine may become concentrated in the collecting ducts if antidiuretic hormone (ADH) is present.

collenchyma tissue (kō-len´-ki-muh): a tissue formed from collenchyma cells which are often elongated, with thickened, flexible cell walls. This cell type is alive at maturity and helps support the plant body.

colon: the longest part of the large intestine; does not include the rectum.

colostrum (kō-los´-trum): a yellowish fluid, high in protein and containing antibodies, that is produced by the mammary glands before milk secretion begins.

communication: the act of producing a signal that causes a receiver, normally another animal of the same species, to change its behavior in a way that is, on average, beneficial to both signaler and receiver.

community: populations of different species that live in the same area and interact with one another.

compact bone: the hard and strong outer bone; composed of osteons. Compare with *spongy bone*.

companion cell: a cell adjacent to a sieve-tube element in phloem; involved in the control and nutrition of the sieve-tube element.

competition: interaction among individuals who attempt to utilize a resource (for example, food or space) that is limited relative to the demand for that resource.

competitive exclusion principle: the concept that no two species can simultaneously and continuously occupy the same ecological niche.

competitive inhibition: the process by which two or more molecules that are somewhat similar in structure compete for the active site of an enzyme.

complement: a group of blood-borne proteins that participate in the destruction of foreign cells, especially those to which antibodies have bound.

complementary base pair: in nucleic acids, bases that pair by hydrogen bonding. In DNA, adenine is complementary to thymine, and guanine is complementary to cytosine; in RNA, adenine is complementary to uracil, and guanine to cytosine.

complete flower: a flower that has all four floral parts (sepals, petals, stamens, and carpels).

compound eye: a type of eye, found in many arthropods, that is composed of numerous independent subunits called *ommatidia*. Each ommatidium contributes a piece of a mosaic-like image perceived by the animal.

concentration: the amount of solute (often in moles, a measurement that is proportional to the number of molecules) in a given volume of solvent.

concentration gradient: a difference in the concentration of a solute between different regions within a fluid or across a barrier such as a membrane.

conclusion: in the scientific method, a decision about the validity of a hypothesis, based on experiments or observations.

conducting portion: the portion of the respiratory system in lung-breathing vertebrates that carries air to the alveoli.

cone: a cone-shaped photoreceptor cell in the vertebrate retina; not as sensitive to light as are the rods. In humans, the three types of cones are most sensitive to different colors of light and provide color vision; see also *rod*.

conifer (kon-eh-fer): a member of a group of nonflowering vascular plants whose members reproduce by means of seeds formed inside cones; retains its leaves throughout the year.

conjugation: in prokaryotes, the transfer of DNA from one cell to another via a temporary connection; in single-celled eukaryotes, the mutual exchange of genetic material between two temporarily joined cells.

connection protein: a protein in the plasma membrane of a cell that attaches to the cytoskeleton inside the cell, to other cells, or to the extracellular matrix.

connective tissue: a tissue type consisting of diverse tissues, including bone, cartilage, fat, and blood, that generally contain large amounts of extracellular material.

conservation biology: the application of knowledge from ecology and other areas of biology to understand and conserve biodiversity.

constant-loss population: a population characterized by a relatively constant death rate; constant-loss populations have a roughly linear survivorship curve.

constant region: the part of an antibody molecule that is similar in all antibodies of a given class.

consumer: an organism that eats other organisms; a heterotroph.

consumer–prey interaction: an interaction between species where one species (the consumer) uses another (the prey) as a food source.

contraception: the prevention of pregnancy.

contractile vacuole: a fluid-filled vacuole in certain protists that takes up water from the cytoplasm, contracts, and expels the water outside the cell through a pore in the plasma membrane.

control: that portion of an experiment in which all possible variables are held constant; in contrast to the "experimental" portion, in which a particular variable is altered.

convergent evolution: the independent evolution of similar structures among unrelated organisms as a result of similar environmental pressures; see also *analogous structures*.

convolution: a folding of the cerebral cortex of the vertebrate brain.

copulation: reproductive behavior in which the penis of the male is inserted into the body of the female, where it releases sperm.

coral reef: an ecosystem created by animals (reef-building corals) and plants in warm tropical waters.

core reserve: a natural area protected from most human uses that encompasses enough space to preserve most of the biodiversity of the ecosystems in that area.

cork cambium: a lateral meristem in woody roots and stems that gives rise to cork cells.

cork cell: a protective cell of the bark of woody stems and roots; at maturity, cork cells are dead, with thick, waterproof cell walls.

cornea (kor'-nē-uh): the clear outer covering of the eye, located in front of the pupil and iris; begins the focusing of light on the retina.

corona radiata (kuh-rō'-nuh rā-dē-a'-tuh): the layer of cells surrounding an egg after ovulation.

corpus callosum (kor'pus kal-ō'-sum): the band of axons that connects the two cerebral hemispheres of vertebrates.

corpus luteum (kor'-pus loo-tē'-um): in the mammalian ovary, a structure that is derived from the follicle after ovulation and that secretes the hormones estrogen and progesterone.

cortex: the part of a primary root or stem located between the epidermis and the vascular cylinder.

cortisol (kor'-ti-sol): a steroid hormone released into the bloodstream by the adrenal cortex in response to stress. Cortisol helps the body cope with short-term stressors by raising blood glucose levels; it also inhibits the immune response.

cotyledon (kot-ul-ē'don): a leaflike structure within a seed that absorbs food molecules from the endosperm and transfers them to the growing embryo; also called *seed leaf*.

countercurrent exchange: a mechanism for the transfer of some property, such as heat or a dissolved substance, from one fluid to another, generally without the two fluids actually mixing; in countercurrent exchange, the two fluids flow past one another in opposite directions, and they transfer heat or solute from the fluid with the higher temperature or higher solute concentration to the fluid with the lower temperature or lower solute concentration.

coupled reaction: a pair of reactions, one exergonic and one endergonic, that are linked together such that the energy produced by the exergonic reaction provides the energy needed to drive the endergonic reaction.

covalent bond (kō-vā'-lent): a chemical bond between atoms in which electrons are shared.

craniate: an animal that has a skull.

crassulacean acid metabolism (CAM): a biochemical pathway used by some plants in hot, dry climates, that increases the efficiency of carbon fixation during photosynthesis. Mesophyll cells capture carbon dioxide at night and use it to produce sugar during the day.

critically endangered species: a species that faces an extreme risk of extinction in the wild in the immediate future.

cross-fertilization: the union of sperm and egg from two individuals of the same species.

crossing over: the exchange of corresponding segments of the chromatids of two homologous chromosomes during meiosis I; occurs at chiasmata.

cuticle (kū'-ti-kul): a waxy or fatty coating on the surfaces of the aboveground epidermal cells of many land plants; aids in the retention of water.

cyclic adenosine monophosphate (cyclic AMP): a cyclic nucleotide, formed within many target cells as a result of the reception of amino acid derived or peptide hormones, that causes metabolic changes in the cell.

cytokine (sī'-tō-kīn): any of several chemical messenger molecules released by cells that facilitate communication with other cells and transfer signals within and among the various systems of the body. Cytokines are important in cellular differentiation and the adaptive immune response.

cytokinesis (sī-tō-ki-nē'-sis): the division of the cytoplasm and organelles into two daughter cells during cell division; normally occurs during telophase of mitotic and meiotic cell division.

cytokinin (sī-tō-ki'-nin): a group of plant hormones that promotes cell division, fruit development, and the sprouting of lateral buds; also delays the senescence of plant parts, especially leaves.

cytoplasm (sī'-tō-plaz-um): all of the material contained within the plasma membrane of a cell, exclusive of the nucleus.

cytosine (C): a nitrogenous base found in both DNA and RNA; abbreviated as C.

cytoskeleton: a network of protein fibers in the cytoplasm that gives shape to a cell, holds and moves organelles, and is typically involved in cell movement.

cytosol: the fluid portion of the cytoplasm; the substance within the plasma membrane exclusive of the nucleus and organelles.

cytotoxic T cell: a type of T cell that, upon contacting foreign cells, directly destroys them.

daughter cell: one of the two cells formed by cell division.

day-neutral plant: a plant in which flowering occurs as soon as the plant has undergone sufficient growth and development, regardless of day length.

death rate: the number of deaths per individual in a specified unit of time, such as a year.

decomposer: an organism, usually a fungus or bacterium, that digests organic material by secreting digestive enzymes into the environment, in the process liberating nutrients into the environment.

deductive reasoning: the process of generating hypotheses about the results of a specific experiment or the nature of a specific observation.

deforestation: the excessive cutting of forests. In recent years, deforestation has occurred primarily in rain forests in the Tropics, to clear space for agriculture.

dehydration synthesis: a chemical reaction in which two molecules are joined by a covalent bond with the simultaneous removal of a hydrogen from one molecule and a hydroxyl group from the other, forming water; the reverse of hydrolysis.

deletion mutation: a mutation in which one or more pairs of nucleotides are removed from a gene.

demographic transition: a change in population dynamic in which a fairly stable population with both high birth rates and high death rates experiences rapid growth as death rates decline and then returns to a stable (although much larger) population as birth rates decline.

demography: the study of the changes in human numbers over time, grouped by world regions, age, sex, educational levels, and other variables.

denature: to disrupt the secondary and/or tertiary structure of a protein while leaving its amino acid sequence intact. Denatured proteins can no longer perform their biological functions.

denatured: having the secondary and/or tertiary structure of a protein disrupted, while leaving the amino acid sequence unchanged. Denatured proteins can no longer perform their biological functions.

dendrite (den'-drīt): a branched tendril that extends outward from the cell body of a neuron; specialized to respond to signals from the external environment or from other neurons.

dendritic cell (den-drit'-ick): a type of phagocytic leukocyte that presents antigen to T and B cells, thereby stimulating an adaptive immune response to an invading microbe.

denitrifying bacteria (dē-nī'-treh-fī-ing): bacteria that break down nitrates, releasing nitrogen gas to the atmosphere.

density-dependent: referring to any factor, such as predation, that limits population size to an increasing extent as the population density increases.

density-independent: referring to any factor, such as floods or fires, that limits a population's size regardless of its density.

deoxyribonucleic acid (dē-ox-ē-rī-bō-noo-klā'-ik; DNA): a molecule composed of deoxyribose nucleotides; contains the genetic information of all living cells.

dermal tissue system: a plant tissue system that makes up the outer covering of the plant body.

dermis (dur'-mis): the layer of skin beneath the epidermis; composed of connective tissue and containing blood vessels, muscles, nerve endings, and glands.

desert: a biome in which less than 10 inches (25 centimeters) of rain fall each year; characterized by cacti, succulents, and widely spaced, drought-resistant bushes.

desertification: the process by which relatively dry, drought-prone regions are converted to desert as a result of drought and overuse of the land, for example, by overgrazing or cutting of trees.

desmosome (dez'-mō-sōm): a strong cell-to-cell junction that attaches adjacent cells to one another.

detritivore (de-trī'-ti-vor): one of a diverse group of organisms, ranging from worms to vultures, that eat the wastes and dead remains of other organisms.

deuterostome (do'-ter-ō-stōm): an animal with a mode of embryonic development in which the coelom is derived from outpocketings of the gut; characteristic of echinoderms and chordates.

development: the process by which an organism proceeds from fertilized egg through adulthood to eventual death.

diabetes mellitus (di-uh-bē'-tēs mel-ī'-tus): a disease characterized by defects in the production, release, or reception of insulin; characterized by high blood glucose levels that fluctuate with sugar intake.

diaphragm (dī'-uh-fram): in the respiratory system, a dome-shaped muscle forming the floor of the chest cavity; when the diaphragm contracts, it flattens, enlarging the chest cavity and causing air to be drawn into the lungs.

diastolic pressure (dī'-uh-stal-ik): the blood pressure measured during relaxation of the ventricles; the lower of the two blood pressure readings.

diatom (dī'-uh-tom): a member of a protist group that includes photosynthetic forms with two-part glassy outer coverings; important photosynthetic organisms in fresh water and salt water. Diatoms are part of a larger group known as the stramenopiles.

dicot (dī'-kaht): short for dicotyledon; a type of flowering plant characterized by embryos with two cotyledons, or seed leaves, that are usually modified for food storage.

differentiate: the process whereby a cell becomes specialized in structure and function.

differentiated cell: a mature cell specialized for a specific function; in plants, differentiated cells normally do not divide.

diffusion: the net movement of solute particles from a region of high solute concentration to a region of low solute concentration, driven by a concentration gradient; may occur within a fluid or across a barrier such as a membrane.

digestion: the process by which food is physically and chemically broken down into molecules that can be absorbed by cells.

digestive system: a group of organs responsible for ingesting food, digesting food into simple molecules that can be absorbed the body into the circulatory system, and expelling undigested wastes from the body.

dinoflagellate (dī-nō-fla'-jel-et): a member of a protist group that includes photosynthetic forms in which two flagella project through armor-like plates; abundant in oceans; can reproduce rapidly, causing "red tides." Dinoflagellates are part of a larger group known as the alveolates.

diploid (dip'-loid): referring to a cell with pairs of homologous chromosomes.

diplomonad: a member of a protist group characterized by two nuclei and multiple flagella. Diplomonads, which include disease-causing parasites such as *Giardia*, are part of a larger group known as the excavates.

direct development: a developmental pathway in which the offspring is born as a miniature version of the adult and does not radically change in body form as it grows and matures.

directional selection: a type of natural selection that favors one extreme of a range of phenotypes.

disaccharide (dī-sak'-uh-rīd): a carbohydrate formed by the covalent bonding of two monosaccharides.

disruptive selection: a type of natural selection that favors both extremes of a range of phenotypes.

dissolve: the process by which solvent molecules completely surround and disperse the individual atoms or molecules of another substance, the solute.

distal tubule: the last section of a mammalian nephron, following the nephron loop and emptying urine into a collecting duct; most secretion and a small amount of reabsorption occur in the distal tubule.

disturbance: any event that disrupts an ecosystem by altering its community, its abiotic structure, or both; disturbance precedes succession.

disulfide bond: the covalent bond formed between the sulfur atoms of two cysteines in a protein; typically causes the protein to fold by bringing otherwise distant parts of the protein close together.

DNA cloning: any of a variety of technologies that are used to produce multiple copies of a specific segment of DNA (usually a gene).

DNA helicase: an enzyme that helps unwind the DNA double helix during DNA replication.

DNA ligase: an enzyme that bonds the terminal sugar in one DNA strand to the terminal phosphate in a second DNA strand, creating a single strand with a continuous sugar-phosphate backbone.

DNA polymerase: an enzyme that bonds DNA nucleotides together into a continuous strand, using a preexisting DNA strand as a template.

DNA probe: a sequence of nucleotides that is complementary to the nucleotide sequence of a gene or other segment of DNA under study; used to locate the gene or DNA segment during gel electrophoresis or other methods of DNA analysis.

DNA profile: the pattern of short tandem repeats of specific DNA segments; using a standardized set of 13 short tandem repeats, DNA profiles identify individual people with great accuracy.

DNA replication: the copying of the double-stranded DNA molecule, producing two identical DNA double helices.

DNA sequencing: the process of determining the order of nucleotides in a DNA molecule.

domain: the broadest category for classifying organisms; organisms are classified into three domains: Bacteria, Archaea, and Eukarya.

dominance hierarchy: a social structure that arises when the animals in a social group establish individual ranks that determine access to resources; ranks are usually established through aggressive interactions.

dominant: an allele that can determine the phenotype of heterozygotes completely, such that they are indistinguishable from individuals homozygous for the allele; in the heterozygotes, the expression of the other (recessive) allele is completely masked.

dormancy: a state in which an organism does not grow or develop; usually marked by lowered metabolic activity and resistance to adverse environmental conditions.

dorsal root ganglion: a ganglion, located on the dorsal (sensory) branch of each spinal nerve, that contains the cell bodies of sensory neurons.

double circulation: the separation of circulatory routes between (1) the heart and lungs and (2) the heart and the rest of the body.

double fertilization: in flowering plants, the fusion of two sperm nuclei with the nuclei of two cells of the female gametophyte. One sperm nucleus fuses with the egg to form the zygote; the second sperm nucleus fuses with the two haploid nuclei of the central cell to form a triploid endosperm cell.

double helix (hē'-liks): the shape of the two-stranded DNA molecule; similar to a ladder twisted lengthwise into a corkscrew shape.

Down syndrome: a genetic disorder caused by the presence of three copies of chromosome 21; common characteristics include learning disabilities, distinctively shaped eyelids, a small mouth, heart defects, and low resistance to infectious diseases; also called *trisomy 21*.

duodenum: the first section of the small intestine, in which most food digestion occurs; receives chyme from the stomach, buffers and digestive enzymes from the pancreas, and bile from the liver and gallbladder.

duplicated chromosome: a eukaryotic chromosome following DNA replication; consists of two sister chromatids joined at the centromeres.

early-loss population: a population characterized by a high birth rate, a high death rate among juveniles, and lower death rates among adults; early loss populations have a concave survivorship curve.

ecdysone (ek-dī'-sōn): a steroid hormone that triggers molting in insects and other arthropods.

ecological economics: the branch of economics that attempts to determine the monetary value of ecosystem services and to compare the monetary value of natural ecosystems with the monetary value of human activities that may reduce the services that natural ecosystems provide.

ecological footprint: the area of productive land needed to produce the resources used and absorb the wastes (including carbon dioxide) generated by an individual person, or by an average person of a specific part of the world (for example, an individual country), or of the entire world, using current technologies.

ecological isolation: reproductive isolation that arises when species do not interbreed because they occupy different habitats.

ecological niche (nitch): the role of a particular species within an ecosystem, including all aspects of its interaction with the living and nonliving environments.

ecology (ē-kol'-uh-jē): the study of the interrelationships of organisms with each other and with their nonliving environment.

ecosystem (ē'-kō-sis-tem): all the organisms and their nonliving environment within a defined area.

ecosystem services: the processes through which natural ecosystems and their living communities sustain and fulfill human life. Ecosystem services include purifying air and water, replenishing oxygen, pollinating plants, reducing flooding, providing wildlife habitat, and many more.

ectoderm (ek'-tō-derm): the outermost embryonic tissue layer, which gives rise to structures such as hair, the epidermis of the skin, and the nervous system.

ectotherm: an animal that obtains most of its body warmth from its environment; body temperatures of ectotherms vary with the temperature of their surroundings.

effector (ē-fek'-tor): a part of the body (normally a muscle or gland) that carries out responses as directed by the nervous system.

egg: the haploid female gamete, usually large and nonmotile; contains food reserves for the developing embryo.

electromagnetic spectrum: the range of all possible wavelengths of electromagnetic radiation, from wavelengths longer than radio waves, to microwaves, infrared, visible light, ultraviolet, X-rays, and gamma rays.

electron: a subatomic particle, found in an electron shell outside the nucleus of an atom, that bears a unit of negative charge and very little mass.

electron carrier: a molecule that can reversibly gain or lose electrons. Electron carriers generally accept high-energy electrons produced during an exergonic reaction and donate the electrons to acceptor molecules that use the energy to drive endergonic reactions.

electron shell: a region in an atom within which electrons orbit; each shell corresponds to a fixed energy level at a given distance from the nucleus.

electron transport chain (ETC): a series of electron carrier molecules, found in the thylakoid membranes of chloroplasts and the inner membrane of mitochondria, that extract energy from electrons and generate ATP or other energetic molecules.

element: a substance that cannot be broken down, or converted, to a simpler substance by ordinary chemical reactions.

elimination: the expulsion of indigestible materials from the digestive tract, through the anus, and outside the body.

embryo (em'-brē-ō): in animals, the stages of development that begin with the fertilization of the egg cell and end with hatching or birth; in mammals, the early stages in which the developing animal does not yet resemble the adult of the species.

embryonic disk: in human embryonic development, the flat, two-layered group of cells that separates the amniotic cavity from the yolk sac; the cells of the embryonic disk produce most of the developing embryo.

embryonic stem cell (ESC): a cell derived from an early embryo that is capable of differentiating into any of the adult cell types.

emerging infectious disease: a previously unknown infectious disease (one caused by a microbe), or a previously known infectious disease whose frequency or severity has significantly increased in the past two decades.

emigration (em-uh-grā'-shun): migration of individuals out of an area.

endangered species: a species that faces a high risk of extinction in the wild in the near future.

endergonic (en-der-gon'-ik): pertaining to a chemical reaction that requires an input of energy to proceed; an "uphill" reaction.

endocrine communication: communication between cells of an animal in which certain cells, usually part of an endocrine gland, release hormones that travel through the bloodstream to other cells (often in distant parts of the body) and alter their activity.

endocrine disrupter: an environmental pollutant that interferes with endocrine function, often by disrupting the action of sex hormones.

endocrine gland: a ductless, hormone-producing gland consisting of cells that release their secretions into the interstitial fluid from which the secretions diffuse into nearby capillaries; most endocrine glands are composed of epithelial cells.

endocrine hormone: a molecule produced by the cells of endocrine glands and released into the circulatory system. An endocrine hormone causes changes in target cells that bear specific receptors for the hormone.

endocrine system: an animal's organ system for cell-to-cell communication; composed of hormones and the cells that secrete them.

endocytosis (en-dō-sī-tō'-sis): the process in which the plasma membrane engulfs extracellular material, forming membrane-bound sacs that enter the cytoplasm and thereby move material into the cell.

endoderm (en'-dō-derm): the innermost embryonic tissue layer, which gives rise to structures such as the lining of the digestive and respiratory tracts.

endodermis (en-dō-der'-mis): the innermost layer of small, close-fitting cells of the cortex of a root that form a ring around the vascular cylinder; see also *Casparian strip*.

endomembrane system: internal membranes that create loosely connected compartments within the eukaryotic cell. It includes the nuclear envelope, the endoplasmic reticulum, vesicles, the Golgi apparatus, and lysosomes.

endometrium (en-dō-mē'-trē-um): the nutritive inner lining of the uterus.

endoplasmic reticulum (en-dō-plaz'-mik re-tik'-ū-lum; ER): a system of membranous tubes and channels in eukaryotic cells; the site of most protein and lipid synthesis.

endoskeleton (en'-dō-skel'-uh-tun): a rigid internal skeleton with flexible joints that allow for movement.

endosperm: a triploid food storage tissue in the seeds of flowering plants that nourishes the developing plant embryo.

endospore: a protective resting structure of some rod-shaped bacteria that withstands unfavorable environmental conditions.

endosymbiont hypothesis: the hypothesis that certain organelles, especially chloroplasts and mitochondria, arose as mutually beneficial associations between the ancestors of eukaryotic cells and captured bacteria that lived within the cytoplasm of the pre-eukaryotic cell.

endotherm: an animal that obtains most of its body heat from metabolic activities; body temperatures of endotherms usually remain relatively constant within a fairly wide range of environmental temperatures.

energy: the capacity to do work.

energy-carrier molecule: high energy molecules that are synthesized at the site of an exergonic reaction, where they capture one or two energized electrons and hydrogen ions. They include nicotinamide adenine dinucleotide (NADH) and flavin adenine dinucleotide ($FADH_2$).

energy pyramid: a graphical representation of the energy contained in succeeding trophic levels, with maximum energy at the base (primary producers) and steadily diminishing amounts at higher levels.

energy-requiring transport: the transfer of substances across a cell membrane using cellular energy; includes active transport, endocytosis, and exocytosis.

entropy (en′-trō-pē): a measure of the amount of randomness and disorder in a system.

environmental resistance: any factor that tends to counteract biotic potential, limiting population growth and the resulting population size.

enzyme (en′zīm): a biological catalyst, usually a protein, that speeds up the rate of specific biological reactions.

epicotyl (ep′-ē-kot-ul): the part of the embryonic shoot located above the attachment point of the cotyledons but below the tip of the shoot.

epidermal tissue: dermal tissue in plants that forms the epidermis, the outermost cell layer that covers leaves, young stems, and young roots.

epidermis (ep-uh-der′-mis): in animals, specialized stratified epithelial tissue that forms the outer layer of the skin; in plants, the outermost layer of cells of a leaf, young root, or young stem.

epididymis (e-pi-di′-di-mus): a series of tubes that connect with and receive sperm from the seminiferous tubules of the testis and empty into the vas deferens.

epigenetics: the study of the mechanisms by which cells and organisms change gene expression and function without changing the base sequence of their DNA; usually, epigenetic controls over DNA expression involve modification of DNA, modification of chromosomal proteins, or alteration of transcription or translation through the actions of noncoding RNA molecules.

epiglottis (ep-eh-glah′-tis): a flap of cartilage in the lower pharynx that covers the opening to the larynx during swallowing; directs food into the esophagus.

epinephrine (ep-i-nef′-rin): a hormone, secreted by the adrenal medulla, that is released in response to stress and that stimulates a variety of responses, including the release of glucose from the liver and an increase in heart rate.

epithelial tissue (eh-puh-thē′-lē-ul): a tissue type that forms membranes that cover the body surface and line body cavities, and that also gives rise to glands.

equilibrium population: a population in which allele frequencies and the distribution of genotypes do not change from generation to generation.

erythrocyte (eh-rith′-rō-sīt): a red blood cell, which contains the oxygen-binding protein hemoglobin and thus transports oxygen in the circulatory system.

erythropoietin (eh-rith′-rō-pō-ē′-tin): a hormone produced by the kidneys in response to oxygen deficiency; stimulates the production of red blood cells by the bone marrow.

esophagus: a muscular, tubular portion of the mammalian digestive tract located between the pharynx and the stomach; no digestion occurs in the esophagus.

essential amino acid: an amino acid that is a required nutrient; the body is unable to manufacture essential amino acids, so they must be supplied in the diet.

essential fatty acid: a fatty acid that is a required nutrient; the body is unable to manufacture essential fatty acids, so they must be supplied in the diet.

essential nutrient: any nutrient that cannot be synthesized by the body, including certain fatty acids and amino acids, vitamins, minerals, and water.

estrogen: a female sex hormone, produced by follicle cells of the ovary, that stimulates follicle development, oogenesis, the development of secondary sex characteristics, and growth of the uterine lining.

estuary (es′-choo-ār-ē): a wetland formed where a river meets the ocean; the salinity is quite variable, but lower than in seawater and higher than in fresh water.

ethylene: a plant hormone that promotes the ripening of some fruits and the dropping of leaves and fruit; promotes senescence of leaves.

euglenid (ū′-gle-nid): a member of a protist group characterized by one or more whip-like flagella, which are used for locomotion, and by a photoreceptor, which detects light. Euglenids are photosynthetic and are part of a larger group known as euglenozoans.

euglenozoan: a member of the Euglenozoa, a protist clade. The euglenozoans, which are characterized by mitochondrial membranes that appear under the microscope to be shaped like a stack of disks, include the euglenids and the kinetoplastids.

Eukarya (ū-kar′-ē-a): one of life's three domains; consists of all eukaryotes (plants, animals, fungi, and protists).

eukaryote (ū-kar′-ē-ōt): an organism whose cells are eukaryotic; plants, animals, fungi, and protists are eukaryotes.

eukaryotic (ū-kar-ē-ot′-ik): referring to cells of organisms of the domain Eukarya (plants, animals, fungi, and protists). Eukaryotic cells have genetic material enclosed within a membrane-bound nucleus, and they contain other membrane-bound organelles.

eutrophic lake: a lake that receives sufficiently large inputs of sediments, organic material, and inorganic nutrients from its surroundings to support dense communities, especially of plants and phytoplankton; contains murky water with poor light penetration.

evolution: (1) the descent of modern organisms, with modification, from preexisting life-forms; (2) the theory that all organisms are related by common ancestry and have changed over time; (3) any change in the genetic makeup (the proportions of different genotypes) of a population from one generation to the next.

excavate: a member of the Excavata, a protist clade. The excavates, which generally lack mitochondria, include the diplomonads and the parabasalids.

excitatory postsynaptic potential (EPSP): an electrical signal produced in a postsynaptic cell that makes the resting potential of the postsynaptic neuron less negative and, hence, makes the neuron more likely to produce an action potential.

excretion: the elimination of waste substances from the body; can occur from the digestive system, skin glands, urinary system, or lungs.

exergonic (ex-er-gon′-ik): pertaining to a chemical reaction that releases energy (either as heat or in the form of increased entropy); a "downhill" reaction.

exhalation: the act of releasing air from the lungs, which results from a relaxation of the respiratory muscles.

exocrine gland: a gland that releases its secretions into ducts that lead to the outside of the body or into a body cavity, such as the digestive or reproductive system; most exocrine glands are composed of epithelial cells.

exocytosis (ex-ō-sī-tō′-sis): the process in which intracellular material is enclosed within a membrane-bound sac that moves to the plasma membrane and fuses with it, releasing the material outside the cell.

exon: a segment of DNA in a eukaryotic gene that codes for amino acids in a protein; see also *intron*.

exoskeleton (ex′-ō-skel′-uh-tun): a rigid external skeleton that supports the body, protects the internal organs, and has flexible joints that allow for movement.

experiment: in the scientific method, the use of carefully controlled observations or manipulations to test the predictions generated by a hypothesis.

exponential growth: a continuously accelerating increase in population size; this type of growth generates a curve shaped like the letter "J."

extensor: a muscle that straightens (increases the angle of) a joint.

external fertilization: the union of sperm and egg outside the body of either parent.

extinction: the death of all members of a species.

extracellular digestion: the physical and chemical breakdown of food that occurs outside a cell, normally in a digestive cavity.

extracellular matrix (ECM): material secreted by and filling the spaces between cells. Animal cells secrete supporting and adhesive proteins embedded in a gel of polysaccharides linked by proteins; plant cells secrete a matrix of cellulose that forms cell walls.

extraembryonic membrane: in the embryonic development of reptiles (including birds) and mammals, one of the following membranes: the chorion (functions in gas exchange), amnion (provision of the watery environment needed for development), allantois (waste storage), or yolk sac (storage of the yolk).

facilitated diffusion: the diffusion of molecules across a membrane, assisted by protein pores or carriers embedded in the membrane.

family: in Linnaean classification, the taxonomic rank composed of related genera. Closely related families make up an order.

farsighted: the inability to focus on nearby objects, caused by the eyeball being slightly too short or the cornea too flat.

fat (molecular): a lipid composed of three saturated fatty acids covalently bonded to glycerol; fats are solid at room temperature.

fatty acid: an organic molecule composed of a long chain of carbon atoms, with a carboxylic acid (–COOH) group at one end; may be saturated (all single bonds between the carbon atoms) or unsaturated (one or more double bonds between the carbon atoms).

feces: semisolid waste material that remains in the intestine after absorption is complete and that is voided through the anus. Feces consist principally of indigestible wastes and bacteria.

feedback inhibition: in enzyme-mediated chemical reactions, the condition in which the product of a reaction inhibits one or more of the enzymes involved in synthesizing the product.

fermentation: anaerobic reactions that convert the pyruvic acid produced by glycolysis into lactic acid or alcohol and CO_2, using hydrogen ions and electrons from NADH; the primary function of fermentation is to regenerate NAD^+ so that glycolysis can continue under anaerobic conditions.

fertilization: the fusion of male and female haploid gametes, forming a zygote.

fetal alcohol syndrome (FAS): a cluster of symptoms, including mental retardation and physical abnormalities, that occur in infants born to mothers who consumed large amounts of alcoholic beverages during pregnancy.

fetus: the later stages of mammalian embryonic development (after the second month for humans), when the developing animal has come to resemble the adult of the species.

fever: an elevation in body temperature caused by chemicals (pyrogens) that are released by white blood cells in response to infection.

fibrillation (fi-bri-lā'-shun): the rapid, uncoordinated, and ineffective contraction of heart muscle cells.

fibrin (fī'-brin): a clotting protein formed in the blood in response to a wound; binds with other fibrin molecules and provides a matrix around which a blood clot forms.

fibrinogen (fī-brin'-ō-jen): the inactive form of the clotting protein fibrin. Fibrinogen is converted into fibrin by the enzyme thrombin, which is produced in response to injury.

fibrous root system: a root system, commonly found in monocots, that is characterized by many roots of approximately the same size arising from the base of the stem.

filament: in flowers, the stalk of a stamen, which bears an anther at its tip.

filtrate: the fluid produced by filtration; in the kidneys, the fluid produced by the filtration of blood through the glomerular capillaries.

filtration: within renal corpuscle in each nephron of a kidney, the process by which blood is pumped under pressure through permeable capillaries of the glomerulus, forcing out water and small solutes, including wastes and nutrients.

first law of thermodynamics: the principle of physics that states that within any isolated system, energy can be neither created nor destroyed, but can be converted from one form to another; also called the law of conservation of energy.

fitness: the reproductive success of an organism, relative to the average reproductive success in the population.

flagellum (fla-jel'-um; pl., flagella): a long, hair-like, motile extension of the plasma membrane; in eukaryotic cells, it contains microtubules arranged in a 9 + 2 pattern. The movement of flagella propels some cells through fluids.

flavin adenine dinucleotide (FAD or FADH₂): an electron-carrier molecule produced in the mitochondrial matrix by the Krebs cycle; subsequently donates electrons to the electron transport chain.

flexor: a muscle that flexes (decreases the angle of) a joint.

florigen: one of a group of plant hormones that may stimulate or inhibit flowering in response to day length.

flower: the reproductive structure of an angiosperm plant.

flower bud: a cluster of meristem cells (a bud) that forms a flower.

fluid: any substance whose molecules can freely flow past one another; "fluid" can describe liquids, cell membranes, and gases.

fluid mosaic model: a model of cell membrane structure; according to this model, membranes are composed of a double layer of phospholipids in which various proteins are embedded. The phospholipid bilayer is a somewhat fluid matrix that allows the movement of proteins within it.

follicle: in the ovary of female mammals, the oocyte and its surrounding accessory cells.

follicle-stimulating hormone (FSH): a hormone, produced by the anterior pituitary, that stimulates spermatogenesis in males and the development of the follicle in females.

food chain: a linear feeding relationship in a community, using a single representative from each of the trophic levels.

food vacuole: a membranous sac, within a single cell, in which food is enclosed. Digestive enzymes are released into the vacuole, where intracellular digestion occurs.

food web: a representation of the complex feeding relationships within a community, including many organisms at various trophic levels, with many of the consumers occupying more than one level simultaneously.

foraminiferan (for-am-i-nif'-er-un): a member of a protist group characterized by pseudopods and elaborate calcium carbonate shells. Foraminiferans are generally aquatic (largely marine) and are part of a larger group known as rhizarians.

forebrain: during development, the anterior portion of the brain. In mammals, the forebrain differentiates into the thalamus, the limbic system, and the cerebrum. In humans, the cerebrum contains about half of all the neurons in the brain.

fossil: the remains of a dead organism, normally preserved in rock. Fossils may be petrified bones or wood shells; eggs; feces; impressions of body forms, such as feathers, skin, or leaves; or markings made by organisms, such as footprints.

fossil fuel: a fuel, such as coal, oil, and natural gas, derived from the remains of ancient organisms.

founder effect: the result of an event in which an isolated population is founded by a small number of individuals; may result in genetic drift if allele frequencies in the founder population are by chance different from those of the parent population.

fovea (fō'-vē-uh): in the vertebrate retina, the central region on which images are focused; contains closely packed cones.

fragmentation: a mechanism of asexual reproduction in which an animal splits its body apart and the resulting pieces regenerate the missing parts of a complete body.

free nucleotide: a nucleotide that has not been joined with other nucleotides to form a DNA or RNA strand.

free radical: a molecule containing an atom with an unpaired electron, which makes it highly unstable and reactive with nearby molecules. By removing an electron from the molecule it attacks, it creates a new free radical and begins a chain reaction that can lead to the destruction of biological molecules crucial to life.

fruit: in flowering plants, the ripened ovary (plus, in some cases, other parts of the flower), which contains the seeds.

functional group: one of several groups of atoms commonly found in an organic molecule, including hydrogen, hydroxyl, amino, carboxyl, and phosphate groups, that determine the characteristics and chemical reactivity of the molecule.

gallbladder: a small sac located next to the liver that stores and concentrates the bile secreted by the liver. Bile is released from the gallbladder to the small intestine through the bile duct.

gamete (gam'-ēt): a haploid sex cell, usually a sperm or an egg, formed in sexually reproducing organisms.

gametic incompatibility: a postmating reproductive isolating mechanism that arises when sperm from one species cannot fertilize eggs of another species.

gametophyte (ga-mēt'-ō-fīt): the multicellular haploid stage in the life cycle of plants.

ganglion (gang'-lē-un; pl., ganglia): a cluster of neurons.

ganglion cell: in the vertebrate retina, the nerve cells whose axons form the optic nerve.

gap junction: a type of cell-to-cell junction in animals in which channels connect the cytoplasm of adjacent cells.

gas-exchange portion: the portion of the respiratory system in lung-breathing vertebrates where gas is exchanged in the alveoli of the lungs.

gastric gland: one of numerous small glands in the stomach lining; contains cells that secrete mucus, hydrochloric acid, or pepsinogen (the inactive form of the protease pepsin).

gastrin: a hormone produced by the stomach that stimulates acid secretion in response to the presence of food.

gastrovascular cavity: a saclike chamber with digestive functions, found in some invertebrates such as cnidarians (sea jellies, anemones, and related animals); a single opening serves as both mouth and anus.

gastrula (gas'-troo-luh): in animal development, a three-layered embryo with ectoderm, mesoderm, and endoderm cell layers. The endoderm layer usually encloses the primitive gut.

gastrulation (gas-troo-la'-shun): the process whereby a blastula develops into a gastrula, including the formation of endoderm, ectoderm, and mesoderm.

gel electrophoresis: a technique in which molecules (such as DNA fragments) are placed in wells in a thin sheet of gelatinous material and exposed to an electric field; the molecules migrate through the gel at a rate determined by certain characteristics, most commonly size.

gene: the unit of heredity; a segment of DNA located at a particular place on a chromosome that usually encodes the information for the amino acid sequence of a protein and, hence, a particular trait.

gene flow: the movement of alleles from one population to another owing to the movement of individual organisms or their gametes.

gene linkage: the tendency for genes located on the same chromosome to be inherited together.

gene pool: the total of all alleles of all genes in a population; for a single gene, the total of all the alleles of that gene that occur in a population.

gene therapy: the attempt to cure a disease by inserting, deleting, or altering a patient's genes.

generative cell: in flowering plants, one of the haploid cells of a pollen grain; undergoes mitotic cell division to form two sperm cells.

genetic code: the collection of codons of mRNA, each of which directs the incorporation of a particular amino acid into a protein during protein synthesis or causes protein synthesis to start or stop.

genetic drift: a change in the allele frequencies of a small population purely by chance.

genetic engineering: the modification of the genetic material of an organism, usually using recombinant DNA techniques.

genetic recombination: the generation of new combinations of alleles on homologous chromosomes due to the exchange of DNA during crossing over.

genetically modified organism (GMO): a plant or animal that contains DNA that has been modified or that has been obtained from another species.

genital herpes: a sexually transmitted disease, caused by a virus, that can cause painful blisters on the genitals and surrounding skin.

genomic imprinting: a form of epigenetic control by which a given gene is expressed in an offspring only if the gene has been inherited from a specific parent; the copy of the gene that was inherited from the other parent is usually not expressed.

genotype (jēn'-ō-tīp): the genetic composition of an organism; the actual alleles of each gene carried by the organism.

genus (jē'-nus): in Linnaean classification, the taxonomic rank composed of related species. Closely related genera make up a family.

geographic isolation: reproductive isolation that arises when species do not interbreed because a physical barrier separates them.

germination: the growth and development of a seed, spore, or pollen grain.

ghrelin (grel'-in): a peptide hormone secreted by the stomach that acts via the hypothalamus to stimulate hunger.

gibberellin (jib-er-el'-in): one of a group of plant hormones that stimulates seed germination, fruit development, flowering, and cell division and elongation in stems.

gill: in aquatic animals, a branched tissue richly supplied with capillaries around which water is circulated for gas exchange.

gland: a cluster of cells that are specialized to secrete substances such as sweat, mucus, enzymes, or hormones.

glia: cells of the nervous system that provide nutrients for neurons, regulate the composition of the interstitial fluid in the brain and spinal cord, modulate communication between neurons, and insulate axons, thereby speeding up the conduction of action potentials. Also called *glial cells.*

glomeromycete: a member of the fungus clade Glomeromycota, which includes species that form mycorrhizal associations with plant roots and that form bush-shaped branching structures inside plant cells.

glomerular capsule: the cup-shaped portion of the renal corpuscle that surrounds the glomerulus and captures blood filtrate.

glomerulus (glō-mer'-ū-lus): a dense network of thin-walled capillaries, located within the renal corpuscle of each nephron of the kidney, where blood pressure forces water and small solutes, including wastes and nutrients, through the capillary walls into the nephron.

glucagon (gloo'-ka-gon): a hormone, secreted by the pancreas, that increases blood sugar by stimulating the breakdown of glycogen (to glucose) in the liver.

glucocorticoid (gloo-kō-kor'-tik-oid): a class of hormones, released by the adrenal cortex in response to the presence of ACTH, that makes energy available to the body by stimulating the synthesis of glucose.

glucose: the most common monosaccharide, with the molecular formula $C_6H_{12}O_6$; most polysaccharides, including cellulose, starch, and glycogen, are made of glucose subunits covalently bonded together.

glycerol (glis'-er-ol): a three-carbon alcohol to which fatty acids are covalently bonded to make fats and oils.

glycogen (glī-kō-jen): a highly branched polymer of glucose that is stored by animals in the muscles and liver and metabolized as a source of energy.

glycolysis (glī-kol'-i-sis): reactions, carried out in the cytoplasm, that break down glucose into two molecules of pyruvic acid, producing two ATP molecules; does not require oxygen but can proceed when oxygen is present.

glycoprotein: a protein to which a carbohydrate is attached.

goiter: a swelling of the thyroid gland, caused by iodine deficiency, that affects the functioning of the thyroid gland and its hormones.

Golgi apparatus (gōl'-jē): a stack of membranous sacs, found in most eukaryotic cells, that is the site of processing and separation of membrane components and secretory materials.

gonad: an organ where reproductive cells are formed; in males, the testes, and in females, the ovaries.

gonadotropin-releasing hormone (gō-na-dō-trō'-pin; GnRH): a hormone produced by the neurosecretory cells of the hypothalamus, which stimulates cells in the anterior pituitary to release follicle-stimulating hormone (FSH) and luteinizing hormone (LH). GnRH is involved in the menstrual cycle and in spermatogenesis.

gonorrhea (gon-uh-rē′-uh): a sexually transmitted bacterial infection of the reproductive organs; if untreated, can result in sterility.

gradient: a difference in concentration, pressure, or electrical charge between two regions.

grana: stacks of thylakoid membranes that form disks that surround the thylakoid space within the chloroplast.

grassland: a biome, located in the centers of continents, that primarily supports grasses; also called a *prairie*.

gravitropism: growth with respect to the direction of gravity.

gray matter: the outer portion of the brain and inner region of the spinal cord; composed largely of neuron cell bodies, which give this area a gray color in preserved tissue.

greenhouse effect: the process in which certain gases such as carbon dioxide and methane trap sunlight energy in a planet's atmosphere as heat; the glass in a greenhouse causes a similar warming effect. The result, global warming that causes climate change, is being enhanced by the production of these gases by humans.

greenhouse gas: a gas, such as carbon dioxide or methane, that traps sunlight energy in a planet's atmosphere as heat; a gas that participates in the greenhouse effect.

ground tissue system: a plant tissue system, consisting of parenchyma, collenchyma, and sclerenchyma cells, that makes up the bulk of a leaf or young stem, excluding vascular or dermal tissues. Most ground tissue cells function in photosynthesis, support, or carbohydrate storage.

growth factor: small molecules, usually proteins or steroids, that bind to receptors on or in target cells and enhance their rate of cell division or differentiation.

growth hormone: a hormone, released by the anterior pituitary, that stimulates growth, especially of the skeleton.

growth rate: a measure of the change in population size per individual per unit of time.

guanine (G): a nitrogenous base found in both DNA and RNA; abbreviated as G.

guard cell: one of a pair of specialized epidermal cells that surrounds the central opening of a stoma in the epidermis of a leaf or young stem and regulates the size of the opening.

gymnosperm (jim′-nō-sperm): a nonflowering seed plant, such as a conifer, gnetophyte, cycad, or gingko.

gyre (jīr): a roughly circular pattern of ocean currents, formed because continents interrupt the flow of the current; rotates clockwise in the Northern Hemisphere and counterclockwise in the Southern Hemisphere.

habitat fragmentation: the process by which human development and activities produce patches of wildlife habitat that may not be large enough to sustain minimum viable populations.

habituation (heh-bich-oo-ā′-shun): a type of simple learning characterized by a decline in response to a repeated stimulus.

hair cell: a type of mechanoreceptor cell found in the inner ear that produces an electrical signal when stiff hair-like cilia projecting from the surface of the cell are bent. Hair cells in the cochlea respond to sound vibrations; those in the vestibular system respond to motion and gravity.

hair follicle (fol′-i-kul): a cluster of specialized epithelial cells located in the dermis of mammalian skin, which produces a hair.

hammer: the first of the small bones of the middle ear that link the tympanic membrane (eardrum) with the oval window of the cochlea; also called the *malleus*.

haploid (hap′-loid): referring to a cell that has only one member of each pair of homologous chromosomes.

Hardy–Weinberg principle: a mathematical model proposing that, under certain conditions, the allele frequencies and genotype frequencies in a sexually reproducing population will remain constant over generations.

heart: a muscular organ responsible for pumping blood within the circulatory system throughout the body.

heart attack: a severe reduction or blockage of blood flow through a coronary artery, depriving some of the heart muscle of its blood supply.

heart rate: the number of cardiac cycles (heartbeats) per minute.

heartwood: older secondary xylem that usually no longer conducts water or minerals, but that contributes to the strength of a tree trunk.

heat of fusion: the energy that must be removed from a compound to transform it from a liquid into a solid at its freezing temperature.

heat of vaporization: the energy that must be supplied to a compound to transform it from a liquid into a gas at its boiling temperature.

Heimlich maneuver: a method of dislodging food or other obstructions that have entered the airway.

helix (hē′-liks): a coiled, spring-like secondary structure of a protein.

helper T cell: a type of T cell that helps other immune cells act against antigens.

hemocoel (hē′-mō-sēl): a cavity within the bodies of certain invertebrates in which a fluid, called hemolymph, bathes tissues directly; part of an open circulatory system.

hemodialysis (hē-mō-dī-al′-luh-sis): a procedure that simulates kidney function in individuals with damaged or ineffective kidneys; blood is diverted from the body, artificially filtered, and returned to the body.

hemoglobin (hē′-mō-glō-bin): the iron-containing protein that gives red blood cells their color; binds to oxygen in the lungs and releases it in the tissues.

hemolymph: in animals with an open circulatory system, the fluid that is located within the hemocoel and that bathes all the body cells, therefore serving as both blood and interstitial fluid.

hemophilia: a recessive, sex-linked disease in which the blood fails to clot normally.

herbivore (erb′-i-vor): literally, "plant-eater"; an organism that feeds directly and exclusively on producers; a primary consumer.

hermaphrodite (her-maf′-ruh-dit′): an organism that possesses both male and female sexual organs. Some hermaphroditic animals can fertilize themselves; others must exchange sex cells with a mate.

hermaphroditic (her-maf′-ruh-dit′-ik): possessing both male and female sexual organs. Some hermaphroditic animals can fertilize themselves; others must exchange sex cells with a mate.

heterotroph (het′-er-ō-trōf′): literally, "other-feeder"; an organism that eats other organisms; a consumer.

heterozygous (het′-er-ō-zī′-gus): carrying two different alleles of a given gene; also called *hybrid*.

hindbrain: the posterior portion of the brain, containing the medulla, pons, and cerebellum.

hinge joint: a joint at which the bones fit together in a way that allows movement in only two dimensions, as at the elbow or knee.

hippocampus (hip-ō-kam′-pus): a part of the forebrain of vertebrates that is important in emotion and especially learning.

histamine (his′-ta-mēn): a substance released by certain cells in response to tissue damage and invasion of the body by foreign substances; promotes the dilation of arterioles and the leakiness of capillaries and triggers some of the events of the inflammatory response.

homeobox gene (hō′-mē-ō-boks): a sequence of DNA coding for a transcription factor protein that activates or inactivates many other genes that control the development of specific, major parts of the body.

homeostasis (hōm-ē-ō-stā′-sis): the maintenance of the relatively constant internal environment that is required for the optimal functioning of cells.

hominin: a human or a prehistoric relative of humans; the oldest known hominin is *Sahelanthropus*, whose fossils are more than 6 million years old.

homologous chromosome: a chromosome that is similar in appearance and genetic information to another chromosome with which it pairs during meiosis; also called *homologue*.

homologous structures: structures that may differ in function but that have similar anatomy, presumably because the organisms that possess them have descended from common ancestors.

homologue (hō′-mō-log): a chromosome that is similar in appearance and genetic information to another chromosome with which it pairs during meiosis; also called *homologous chromosome*.

homozygous (hō-mō-zī′-gus): carrying two copies of the same allele of a given gene; also called *true-breeding*.

hormone: a chemical that is secreted by one group of cells and transported to other cells, whose activity is influenced by reception of the hormone.

host: the prey organism on or in which a parasite lives; the host is harmed by the relationship.

human immunodeficiency virus (HIV): a pathogenic virus that causes acquired immune deficiency syndrome (AIDS) by attacking and destroying the immune system's helper T cells.

human papillomavirus (pap-il-lo′-ma; HPV): a virus that infects the reproductive organs, often causing genital warts; causes most, if not all, cases of cervical cancer.

humoral immunity: an immune response in which foreign substances are inactivated or destroyed by antibodies that circulate in the blood.

Huntington disease: an incurable genetic disorder, caused by a dominant allele, that produces progressive brain deterioration, resulting in the loss of motor coordination, flailing movements, personality disturbances, and eventual death.

hybrid: an organism that is the offspring of parents differing in at least one genetically determined characteristic; also used to refer to the offspring of parents of different species.

hybrid infertility: a postmating reproductive isolating mechanism that arises when hybrid offspring (offspring of parents of two different species) are sterile or have low fertility.

hybrid inviability: a postmating reproductive isolating mechanism that arises when hybrid offspring (offspring of parents of two different species) fail to survive.

hydrogen bond: the weak attraction between a hydrogen atom that bears a partial positive charge (due to polar covalent bonding with another atom) and another atom (oxygen, nitrogen, or fluorine) that bears a partial negative charge; hydrogen bonds may form between atoms of a single molecule or of different molecules.

hydrologic cycle (hī-drō-loj′-ik): the biogeochemical cycle by which water travels from its major reservoir, the oceans, through the atmosphere to reservoirs in freshwater lakes, rivers, and groundwater, and back into the oceans. The hydrologic cycle is driven by solar energy. Nearly all water remains as water throughout the cycle (rather than being used in the synthesis of new molecules).

hydrolysis (hī-drol′-i-sis): the chemical reaction that breaks a covalent bond by means of the addition of hydrogen to the atom on one side of the original bond and a hydroxyl group to the atom on the other side; the reverse of dehydration synthesis.

hydrophilic (hī-drō′-fil′-ik): pertaining to molecules that dissolve readily in water, or to molecules that form hydrogen bonds with water; polar.

hydrophobic (hī-drō-fō′-bik): pertaining to molecules that do not dissolve in water or form hydrogen bonds with water; nonpolar.

hydrostatic skeleton (hī-drō-stat′-ik): in invertebrate animals, a body structure in which fluid-filled compartments provide support for the body and change shape when acted on by muscles, which alters the animal's body shape and position or causes the animal to move.

hydrothermal vent community: a community of unusual organisms, living in the deep ocean near hydrothermal vents, that depends on the chemosynthetic activities of sulfur bacteria.

hypertension: arterial blood pressure that is chronically elevated above the normal level.

hypertonic (hī-per-ton′-ik): referring to a solution that has a higher concentration of solute (and therefore a lower concentration of free water) than has the cytosol of a cell.

hypha (hī′-fuh; pl., hyphae): in fungi, a thread-like structure that consists of elongated cells, typically with many haploid nuclei; many hyphae make up the fungal body.

hypocotyl (hī′-pō-kot-ul) hook: the part of the embryonic shoot located below the attachment point of the cotyledons but above the root.

hypothalamus: (hī-pō-thal′-a-mus): a region of the forebrain that controls the secretory activity of the pituitary gland; synthesizes, stores, and releases certain peptide hormones; and directs autonomic nervous system responses.

hypothesis (hī-poth′-eh-sis): a proposed explanation for a phenomenon based on available evidence that leads to a prediction that can be tested.

hypotonic (hī-pō-ton′-ik): referring to a solution that has a lower concentration of solute (and therefore a higher concentration of free water) than has the cytosol of a cell.

immigration (im-uh-grā′-shun): migration of individuals into an area.

immune system: a system of cells, including macrophages, B cells, and T cells, and molecules, such as antibodies and cytokines, that work together to combat microbial invasion of the body.

imperfect flower: a flower that is missing either stamens or carpels.

implantation: the process whereby the early embryo embeds itself within the lining of the uterus.

imprinting: a type of learning in which an animal acquires a particular type of information during a specific sensitive phase of development.

incomplete dominance: a pattern of inheritance in which the heterozygous phenotype is intermediate between the two homozygous phenotypes.

incomplete flower: a flower that is missing one of the four floral parts (sepals, petals, stamens, or carpels).

indeterminate growth: growth in plants that continues to elongate and produce new leaves and branches throughout their lives.

indirect development: a developmental pathway in which an offspring goes through radical changes in body form as it matures.

induced pluripotent stem cell (ploo-rē-pō′-tent; iPSC): a type of stem cell produced from nonstem cells by the insertion or forced expression of a specific set of genes that cause the cells to become capable of unlimited cell division and to be able to be differentiated into many different cell types, possibly any cell type of the body.

induction: the process by which a group of cells causes other cells to differentiate into a specific tissue type.

inductive reasoning: the process of creating a generalization based on many specific observations that support the generalization, coupled with an absence of observations that contradict it.

inflammatory response: a nonspecific, local response to injury to the body, characterized by the phagocytosis of foreign substances and tissue debris by white blood cells and by the walling off of the injury site by the clotting of fluids that escape from nearby blood vessels.

ingestion: the movement of food into the digestive tract, usually through the mouth.

inhalation: the act of drawing air into the lungs by enlarging the chest cavity.

inheritance: the genetic transmission of characteristics from parent to offspring.

inhibiting hormone: a hormone, secreted by the neurosecretory cells of the hypothalamus, that inhibits the release of specific hormones from the anterior pituitary.

inhibitory postsynaptic potential (IPSP): an electrical signal produced in a postsynaptic cell that makes the resting potential more negative and, hence, makes the neuron less likely to fire an action potential.

innate (in-āt′): inborn; instinctive; an innate behavior is performed correctly the first time it is attempted.

innate immune response: nonspecific defenses against many different invading microbes; the innate response involves phagocytic white blood cells, natural killer cells, the inflammatory response, and fever.

inner cell mass: in human embryonic development, the cluster of cells, on the inside of the blastocyst, that will develop into the embryo.

inner ear: the innermost part of the mammalian ear; composed of the bony, fluid-filled tubes of the cochlea and the vestibular apparatus.

inorganic: describing any molecule that does not contain both carbon and hydrogen.

insertion: the site of attachment of a muscle to the relatively movable bone on one side of a joint.

insertion mutation: a mutation in which one or more pairs of nucleotides are inserted into a gene.

insight learning: a type of learning in which a problem is solved by understanding the relationships among the components of the problem rather than through trial and error.

insulin: a hormone, secreted by the pancreas, that lowers blood sugar by stimulating many cells to take up glucose and by stimulating the liver to convert glucose to glycogen.

integration: the process of adding up all of the electrical signals in a neuron, including sensory inputs and postsynaptic potentials, to determine the output of the neuron (action potentials and/or synaptic transmission).

integument (in-teg′-ū-ment): in plants, the outer layers of cells of the ovule that surround the female gametophyte; develops into the seed coat.

intensity: the strength of stimulation or response.

intercalated disc: junctions connecting individual cardiac muscle cells that serve both to attach adjacent cells to one another and to allow electrical signals to pass between cells.

intermediate filament: part of the cytoskeleton of eukaryotic cells that is composed of several types of proteins and probably functions mainly for support.

intermembrane space: the fluid-filled space between the inner and outer membranes of a mitochondrion.

internal fertilization: the union of sperm and egg inside the body of the female.

interneuron: in a neural network, a nerve cell that is postsynaptic to a sensory neuron and presynaptic to a motor neuron. In actual circuits, there may be many interneurons between individual sensory and motor neurons.

internode: the part of a stem between two nodes.

interphase: the stage of the cell cycle between cell divisions in which chromosomes are duplicated and other cell functions occur, such as growth, movement, and acquisition of nutrients.

interspecific competition: competition among individuals of different species.

interstitial cell (in-ter-sti'-shul): in the vertebrate testis, a testosterone-producing cell located between the seminiferous tubules.

interstitial fluid: fluid that bathes the cells of the body; in mammals, interstitial fluid leaks from capillaries and is similar in composition to blood plasma, but lacking the large proteins found in plasma.

intertidal zone: an area of the ocean shore that is alternately covered by water during high tides and exposed to the air during low tides.

intracellular digestion: the chemical breakdown of food within single cells.

intraspecific competition: competition among individuals of the same species.

intrinsically disordered proteins: proteins or segments of proteins with no stable secondary or tertiary structure.

intron: a segment of DNA in a eukaryotic gene that does not code for amino acids in a protein; see also *exon*.

invasive species: organisms with a high biotic potential that are introduced (deliberately or accidentally) into ecosystems where they did not evolve and where they encounter little environmental resistance and tend to displace native species.

inversion: a mutation that occurs when a piece of DNA is cut out of a chromosome, turned around, and reinserted into the gap.

invertebrate (in-vert'-uh-bret): an animal that lacks a vertebral column.

ion (ī-on): a charged atom or molecule; an atom or molecule that either has an excess of electrons (and, hence, is negatively charged) or has lost electrons (and is positively charged).

ionic bond: a chemical bond formed by the electrical attraction between positively and negatively charged ions.

iris: the pigmented muscular tissue of the vertebrate eye that surrounds and controls the size of the pupil, through which light enters the eye.

islet cell: a cell in the endocrine portion of the pancreas that produces either insulin or glucagon.

isolated system: in thermodynamics, a hypothetical space where neither energy nor matter can enter or leave.

isolating mechanism: a morphological, physiological, behavioral, or ecological difference that prevents members of two species from interbreeding.

isotonic (ī-sō-ton'-ik): referring to a solution that has the same concentration of solute (and therefore the same concentration of free water) as has the cytosol of a cell.

isotope (ī'-suh-tōp): one of several forms of a single element, the nuclei of which contain the same number of protons but different numbers of neutrons.

Jacob syndrome: a set of characteristics typical of human males possessing one X and two Y chromosomes (XYY); most XYY males are phenotypically normal, but XYY males tend to be taller than average and to have a slightly increased risk of learning disabilities.

J-curve: the J-shaped growth curve of an exponentially growing population in which increasing numbers of individuals join the population during each succeeding time period.

joint: a flexible region between two rigid units of an exoskeleton or endoskeleton, allowing for movement between the units.

karyotype: a preparation showing the number, sizes, and shapes of all of the chromosomes within a cell.

K-selected species: species that typically live in a stable environment and often develop a population size that is close to the carrying capacity of that environment. *K*-selected species usually mature slowly, have a long life span, produce small numbers of fairly large offspring, and provide significant parental care or nutrients for the offspring, so that a large percentage of the offspring live to maturity.

kelp forest: a diverse ecosystem consisting of stands of tall brown algae and associated marine life. Kelp forests occur in oceans worldwide in nutrient-rich cool coastal waters.

keratin (ker'-uh-tin): a fibrous protein in hair, nails, and the epidermis of skin.

keystone species: a species whose influence on community structure is greater than its abundance would suggest.

kidney: one of a pair of organs of the excretory system that is located on either side of the spinal column; the kidney filters blood, removing wastes and regulating the composition and water content of the blood.

kin selection: a type of natural selection that favors traits that enhance the survival or reproduction of an individual's relatives, even if the traits reduce the fitness of the individuals bearing them.

kinetic energy: the energy of movement; includes light, heat, mechanical movement, and electricity.

kinetochore (ki-net'-ō-kor): a protein structure that forms at the centromere regions of chromosomes; attaches the chromosomes to the spindle.

kinetoplastid: a member of a protist group characterized by distinctively structured mitochondria. Kinetoplastids are mostly flagellated and include parasitic forms such as *Trypanosoma*, which causes sleeping sickness. Kinetoplastids are part of a larger group known as euglenozoans.

kingdom: the second broadest taxonomic category, consisting of related phyla. Related kingdoms make up a domain.

Klinefelter syndrome: a set of characteristics typically found in individuals who have two X chromosomes and one Y chromosome; these individuals are phenotypically males but are usually unable to father children without the use of artificial reproductive technologies, such as in vitro fertilization. Men with Klinefelter syndrome may have several female-like traits, including broad hips and partial breast development.

Krebs cycle: a cyclic series of reactions, occurring in the matrix of mitochondria, in which the acetyl groups from the pyruvic acids produced by glycolysis are broken down to CO_2, accompanied by the formation of ATP and electron carriers; also called the citric acid cycle.

labium (pl., labia): one of a pair of folds of skin of the external structures of the mammalian female reproductive system.

labor: a series of contractions of the uterus that result in birth.

lactation: the secretion of milk from the mammary glands.

lacteal (lak-tēl'): a lymph capillary; found in each villus of the small intestine.

lactic acid fermentation: anaerobic reactions that convert the pyruvic acid produced by glycolysis into lactic acid, using hydrogen ions and electrons from NADH; the primary function of lactic acid fermentation is to regenerate NAD$^+$ so that glycolysis can continue under anaerobic conditions.

lactose (lak'-tōs): a disaccharide composed of glucose and galactose; found in mammalian milk.

lactose intolerance: the inability to digest lactose (milk sugar) because lactase, the enzyme that digests lactose, is not produced in sufficient amounts; symptoms include bloating, gas pains, and diarrhea.

lactose operon: in prokaryotes, the set of genes that encodes the proteins needed for lactose metabolism, including both the structural genes and a common promoter and operator that control transcription of the structural genes.

large intestine: the final section of the digestive tract; consists of the colon and the rectum, where feces are formed and stored.

larva (lar'-vuh; pl., larvae): an immature form of an animal that subsequently undergoes metamorphosis into its adult form; includes the caterpillars of moths and butterflies, the maggots of flies, and the tadpoles of frogs and toads.

larynx (lar'-inks): the portion of the air passage between the pharynx and the trachea; contains the vocal cords.

late-loss population: a population in which most individuals survive into adulthood; late-loss populations have a convex survivorship curve.

lateral bud: a cluster of meristem cells at the node of a stem; under appropriate conditions, it grows into a branch.

lateral meristem: a meristem tissue that forms cylinders parallel to the long axis of roots and stems; normally located between the primary xylem and primary phloem (vascular cambium) and just outside the phloem (cork cambium); also called *cambium*.

law of conservation of energy: the principle of physics that states that within any isolated system, energy can be neither created nor destroyed, but can be converted from one form to another; also called the first law of thermodynamics.

law of independent assortment: the independent inheritance of two or more traits, assuming that each trait is controlled by a single gene with no influence from gene(s) controlling the other trait; states that the alleles of each gene are distributed to the gametes independently of the alleles for other genes; this law is true only for genes located on different chromosomes or very far apart on a single chromosome.

law of segregation: the principle that each gamete receives only one of each parent's pair of alleles of each gene.

laws of thermodynamics: the physical laws that define the basic properties and behavior of energy.

leaf: an outgrowth of a stem, normally flattened and photosynthetic.

leaf primordium (pri-mor'-dē-um; pl., primordia): a cluster of dividing cells, surrounding a terminal or lateral bud, that develops into a leaf.

learning: the process by which behavior is modified in response to experience.

legume (leg'-ūm): a member of a family of plants characterized by root swellings in which nitrogen-fixing bacteria are housed; includes peas, soybeans, lupines, alfalfa, and clover.

lens: a clear object that bends light rays; in eyes, a flexible or movable structure used to focus light on the photoreceptor cells of the retina.

leptin: a peptide hormone released by fat cells that helps the body monitor its fat stores and regulate weight.

less developed country: a country that has not completed the demographic transition; usually has relatively low income and educational level for most of its population, with high birth rates and sometimes fairly high death rates, resulting in moderate to rapid population growth.

leukocyte (loo'-kō-sīt): any of the white blood cells circulating in the blood.

lichen (lī'-ken): a symbiotic association between an alga or cyanobacterium and a fungus, resulting in a composite organism.

life history: the characteristic survivorship and reproductive features of a species, particularly when and how often reproduction occurs, how many offspring are produced, how many resources are provided to each offspring, and what proportion of the offspring survive to maturity.

life table: a data table that groups organisms born at the same time and tracks them throughout their life span, recording how many continue to survive in each succeeding year (or other unit of time). Various parameters such as sex may be used in the groupings. Human life tables may include many other parameters (such as socioeconomic status) used by demographers.

ligament: a tough connective tissue band connecting two bones.

light reactions: the first stage of photosynthesis, in which the energy of light is captured in ATP and NADPH; occurs in thylakoids of chloroplasts.

lignin: a hard material that is embedded in the cell walls of vascular plants and that provides support in terrestrial species; an early and important adaptation to terrestrial life.

limbic system: a diverse group of brain structures, mostly in the lower forebrain, that includes the thalamus, hypothalamus, amygdala, hippocampus, and parts of the cerebrum and is involved in basic emotions, drives, behaviors, and learning.

limnetic zone: the part of a lake in which enough light penetrates to support photosynthesis.

linkage: the inheritance of certain genes as a group because they are parts of the same chromosome. Linked genes do not show independent assortment.

lipase (lī'-pās): an enzyme that catalyzes the breakdown of lipids such as fats into their component fatty acids and glycerol.

lipid (li'-pid): one of a number of organic molecules containing large non-polar regions composed solely of carbon and hydrogen, which make lipids hydrophobic and insoluble in water; includes oils, fats, waxes, phospholipids, and steroids.

littoral zone: the part of a lake, usually close to the shore, in which the water is shallow and plants find abundant light, anchorage, and adequate nutrients.

liver: an organ with varied functions, including bile production, glycogen storage, and the detoxification of poisons.

lobefin: fish with fleshy fins that have well-developed bones and muscles. Lobefins include two living clades: the coelacanths and the lungfishes.

local hormone: a general term for messenger molecules produced by most cells and released into the cells' immediate vicinity. Local hormones, which include prostaglandins and cytokines, influence nearby cells bearing appropriate receptors.

locus (pl., loci): the physical location of a gene on a chromosome.

logistic population growth: population growth characterized by an early exponential growth phase, followed by slower growth as the population approaches its carrying capacity, and finally reaching a stable population at the carrying capacity of the environment; this type of growth generates a curve shaped like a stretched-out letter "S."

long-day plant: a plant that will flower only if the length of uninterrupted darkness is shorter than a species-specific critical period; also called a *short-night plant*.

long-term memory: the second phase of learning; a more-or-less permanent memory formed by a structural change in the brain, brought on by repetition.

lung: in terrestrial vertebrates, one of the pair of respiratory organs in which gas exchange occurs; consists of inflatable chambers within the chest cavity.

luteinizing hormone (loo'-tin-īz-ing; LH): a hormone produced by the anterior pituitary that stimulates testosterone production in males and the development of the follicle, ovulation, and the production of the corpus luteum in females.

lymph (limf): a pale fluid found within the lymphatic system; composed primarily of interstitial fluid and white blood cells.

lymph node: a small structure located on a lymph vessel, containing macrophages and lymphocytes (B and T cells). Macrophages filter the lymph by removing microbes; lymphocytes are the principal components of the adaptive immune response to infection.

lymphatic capillary: the smallest vessel of the lymphatic system. Lymphatic capillaries end blindly in interstitial fluid, which they take up and return to the bloodstream.

lymphatic system: a system consisting of lymph vessels, lymph capillaries, lymph nodes, and the thymus, spleen, tonsils, and bone marrow. The lymphatic system helps protect the body against infection, carries fats from the small intestine to blood vessels, and returns excess fluid and small proteins to the blood circulatory system.

lymphocyte (lim'-fō-sit): a type of white blood cell (natural killer cell, B cell, or T cell) that is important in either the innate or adaptive immune response.

lysosome (lī'-sō-sōm): a membrane-bound organelle containing intracellular digestive enzymes.

macronutrient: a nutrient required by an organism in relatively large quantities.

macrophage (mak'-rō-fāj): a type of white blood cell that engulfs microbes and destroys them by phagocytosis; also presents microbial antigens to T cells, helping stimulate the immune response.

major histocompatibility complex (MHC): a group of proteins, normally located on the surfaces of body cells, that identify the cell as "self"; also important in stimulating and regulating the immune response.

Malpighian tubule (mal-pig'-ē-un): the functional unit of the excretory system of insects, consisting of a small tube protruding from the intestine; wastes and nutrients move from the surrounding blood into the tubule, which drains into the intestine, where nutrients are reabsorbed back into the blood, while the wastes are excreted along with feces.

maltose (mal'-tōs): a disaccharide composed of two glucose molecules.

mammal: a member of the chordate clade Mammalia, which includes vertebrates with hair and mammary glands.

mammary gland (mam′-uh-rē): a milk-producing gland used by female mammals to nourish their young.

marsupial (mar-soo′-pē-ul): a member of the clade Marsupialia, which includes mammals whose young are born at an extremely immature stage and undergo further development in a pouch, where they remain attached to a mammary gland; kangaroos, opossums, and koalas are marsupials.

mass extinction: a relatively sudden extinction of many species, belonging to multiple major taxonomic groups, as a result of environmental change. The fossil record reveals five mass extinctions over geologic time.

mass number: the total number of protons and neutrons in the nucleus of an atom.

mast cell: a cell of the immune system that releases histamine and other molecules used in the body's response to trauma and that are a factor in allergic reactions.

matrix: the fluid contained within the inner membrane of the mitochondrion.

mechanical digestion: the process by which food in the digestive tract is physically broken down into smaller pieces.

mechanical incompatibility: a reproductive isolating mechanism that arises when differences in the reproductive structures of two species make the structures incompatible and prevent interbreeding.

mechanoreceptor: a sensory receptor that responds to mechanical stimuli such as the stretching, bending, or dimpling of a part of the body.

medulla (med-ū′-luh): the part of the hindbrain of vertebrates that controls automatic activities such as breathing, swallowing, heart rate, and blood pressure.

megakaryocyte (meg-a-kar′-ē-ō-sīt): a large cell type in the bone marrow, which pinches off pieces of itself that enter the circulation as platelets.

megaspore: a haploid cell formed by meiotic cell division from a diploid megaspore mother cell; through mitotic cell division and differentiation, it develops into the female gametophyte.

megaspore mother cell: a diploid cell, within the ovule of a flowering plant, that undergoes meiotic cell division to produce four haploid megaspores.

meiosis (mī-ō′-sis): in eukaryotic organisms, a type of nuclear division in which a diploid nucleus divides twice to form four haploid nuclei.

meiosis I: the first division of meiosis, which separates the pairs of homologous chromosomes and sends one homologue from each pair into each of two daughter nuclei, which are therefore haploid.

meiosis II: the second division of meiosis, which separates the chromatids into independent chromosomes and parcels one chromosome into each of two daughter nuclei.

meiotic cell division: meiosis followed by cytokinesis.

melatonin (mel-uh-tōn′-in): a hormone, secreted by the pineal gland, that is involved in the regulation of circadian cycles.

memory B cell: a type of white blood cell that is produced by clonal selection as a result of the binding of an antibody on a B cell to an antigen on an invading microorganism. Memory B cells persist in the bloodstream and provide future immunity to invaders bearing that antigen.

memory T cell: a type of white blood cell that is produced by clonal selection as a result of the binding of a receptor on a T cell to an antigen on an invading microorganism. Memory T cells persist in the bloodstream and provide future immunity to invaders bearing that antigen.

menstrual cycle: in human females, a roughly 28-day cycle during which hormonal interactions among the hypothalamus, pituitary gland, and ovary coordinate ovulation and the preparation of the uterus to receive and nourish a fertilized egg. If pregnancy does not occur, the uterine lining is shed during menstruation.

menstruation: in human females, the monthly discharge of uterine tissue and blood from the uterus.

meristem cell (mer′-i-stem): an undifferentiated cell that remains capable of cell division throughout the life of a plant.

mesoderm (mēz′-ō-derm): the middle embryonic tissue layer, lying between the endoderm and ectoderm, and normally the last to develop; gives rise to structures such as muscles, the skeleton, the circulatory system, and the kidneys.

mesophyll (mez′-ō-fil): loosely packed, usually photosynthetic cells located beneath the epidermis of a leaf.

messenger RNA (mRNA): a strand of RNA, complementary to the DNA of a gene, that conveys the genetic information in DNA to the ribosomes to be used during protein synthesis; sequences of three bases (codons) in mRNA that specify particular amino acids to be incorporated into a protein.

metabolic pathway: a sequence of chemical reactions within a cell in which the products of one reaction are the reactants for the next reaction.

metabolic rate: the speed at which cellular reactions that release energy occur.

metabolism: the sum of all chemical reactions that occur within a single cell or within all the cells of a multicellular organism.

metamorphosis (met-a-mor′-fō-sis): in animals with indirect development, a radical change in body form from larva to sexually mature adult, as seen in amphibians (e.g., tadpole to frog) and insects (e.g., caterpillar to butterfly).

metaphase (met′-a-fāz): in mitosis, the stage in which the chromosomes, attached to spindle fibers at kinetochores, are lined up along the equator of the cell; also the approximately comparable stages in meiosis I and meiosis II.

microbe: a microorganism.

microbiome: populations of microorganisms (particularly bacteria) that reside in and on the bodies of animals. The largest human microbiome resides in the large intestine.

microfilament: part of the cytoskeleton of eukaryotic cells that is composed of the proteins actin and (in some cases) myosin; functions in the movement of cell organelles, locomotion by extension of the plasma membrane, and sometimes contraction of entire cells.

micronutrient: a nutrient required by an organism in relatively small quantities.

microRNA: small molecules of RNA that interfere with the translation of specific genes.

microspore: a haploid cell formed by meiotic cell division from a microspore mother cell; through mitotic cell division and differentiation, it develops into the male gametophyte.

microspore mother cell: a diploid cell contained within an anther of a flowering plant; undergoes meiotic cell division to produce four haploid microspores.

microtubule: a hollow, cylindrical strand, found in eukaryotic cells, that is composed of the protein tubulin; part of the cytoskeleton used in the movement of organelles, cell growth, and the construction of cilia and flagella.

microvillus (mī-krō-vi′-lus; pl., microvilli): a microscopic projection of the plasma membrane, which increases the surface area of a cell.

midbrain: during development, the central portion of the brain; contains most of an important relay center, the reticular formation.

middle ear: the part of the mammalian ear composed of the tympanic membrane, the auditory (Eustachian) tube, and three bones (hammer, anvil, and stirrup) that transmit vibrations from the auditory canal to the oval window.

mimicry (mim′-ik-rē): the situation in which a species has evolved to resemble something else, typically another type of organism.

mineral: an inorganic substance, especially one in rocks or soil, or dissolved in water. In nutrition, minerals such as sodium, calcium, and potassium are essential nutrients that must be obtained from the diet.

mineralocorticoid: a type of steroid hormone produced by the adrenal cortex that regulates salt retention in the kidney, thereby regulating the salt concentration in the blood and interstitial fluid.

minimum viable population (MVP): the smallest isolated population that can persist indefinitely and survive likely natural events such as fires and floods.

mitochondrion (mī-tō-kon′-drē-un; pl., mitochondria): an organelle, bounded by two membranes, that is the site of the reactions of aerobic metabolism.

mitosis (mī-tō′-sis): a type of nuclear division, used by eukaryotic cells, in which one copy of each chromosome (already duplicated during interphase before mitosis) moves into each of two daughter nuclei; the daughter nuclei are therefore genetically identical to each other.

mitotic cell division: mitosis followed by cytokinesis.

molecule (mol'-e-kūl): a particle composed of one or more atoms held together by chemical bonds; the smallest particle of a compound that displays all the properties of that compound.

molt: to shed an external body covering, such as an exoskeleton, skin, feathers, or fur.

monocot: short for monocotyledon; a type of flowering plant characterized by embryos with one seed leaf, or cotyledon.

monomer (mo'-nō-mer): a small organic molecule, several of which may be bonded together to form a chain called a polymer.

monosaccharide (mo-nō-sak'-uh-rīd): the basic molecular unit of all carbohydrates, normally composed of a chain of carbon atoms bonded to hydrogen and hydroxyl groups.

monotreme: a member of the clade Monotremata, which includes mammals that lay eggs; platypuses and spiny anteaters are monotremes.

more developed country: a country that has completed the demographic transition; usually has relatively high income and educational level for most of its population, with low birth and death rates that result in low or even negative population growth.

morula (mor'-ū-luh): in animals, an embryonic stage during cleavage, when the embryo consists of a solid ball of cells.

motor neuron: a neuron that receives instructions from sensory neurons or interneurons and activates effector organs, such as muscles or glands.

motor unit: a single motor neuron and all the muscle fibers on which it forms synapses.

mouth: the opening through which food enters a tubular digestive system.

multicellular: many-celled; most members of the kingdoms Fungi, Plantae, and Animalia are multicellular, with intimate cooperation among cells.

multiple alleles: many alleles of a single gene, perhaps dozens or hundreds, as a result of mutations.

muscle: an animal tissue composed of cells that are capable of contracting and thereby moving specific parts of the body.

muscle fiber: an individual muscle cell.

muscle tissue: tissue composed of one of three types of contractile cells (smooth, skeletal, or cardiac).

muscular dystrophy: an inherited disorder, almost exclusively found in males, in which defective dystrophin proteins cause the skeletal muscles to degenerate.

mutation: a change in the base sequence of DNA in a gene; often used to refer to a genetic change that is significant enough to alter the appearance or function of the organism.

mutualism (mū'-choo-ul-iz-um): a symbiotic relationship in which both participating species benefit.

mycelium (mī-sēl'-ē-um; pl., mycelia): the body of a fungus, consisting of a mass of hyphae.

mycorrhiza (mī-kō-rī'-zuh; pl., mycorrhizae): a symbiotic association between a fungus and the roots of a land plant that facilitates mineral extraction and absorption.

myelin (mī'-uh-lin): a wrapping of insulating membranes of specialized glial cells around the axon of a vertebrate nerve cell; increases the speed of conduction of action potentials.

myofibril (mī-ō-fī'-bril): a cylindrical subunit of a muscle cell, consisting of a series of sarcomeres, surrounded by sarcoplasmic reticulum.

myometrium (mī-ō-mē'-trē-um): the muscular outer layer of the uterus.

myosin (mī'-ō-sin): one of the major proteins of muscle, the interaction of which with the protein actin produces muscle contraction; found in the thick filaments of the muscle fiber; see also *actin*.

myosin head: the part of a myosin protein that binds to the actin subunits of a thin filament; flexion of the myosin head moves the thin filament toward the center of the sarcomere, causing muscle fiber contraction.

natural causality: the scientific principle that natural events occur as a result of preceding natural causes.

natural increase: the difference between births and deaths in a population. This number will be positive if the population is increasing and negative if it is decreasing.

natural killer cell: a type of white blood cell that destroys some virus-infected cells and cancerous cells on contact; part of the innate immune system's nonspecific internal defense against disease.

natural laws: basic principles derived from the study of nature that have never been disproven by scientific inquiry. Natural laws include the laws of gravity, the behavior of light, and the way atoms interact with one another.

natural selection: unequal survival and reproduction of organisms due to heritable differences in their phenotypes, with the result that better adapted phenotypes become more common in the population.

nearshore zone: the region of coastal water that is relatively shallow but constantly submerged and that can support large plants or seaweeds; includes bays and coastal wetlands.

nearsighted: the inability to focus on distant objects caused by an eyeball that is slightly too long or a cornea that is too curved.

negative feedback: a physiological process in which a change causes responses that tend to counteract the change and restore the original state. Negative feedback in physiological systems maintains homeostasis.

nephridium (nef-rid'-ē-um; pl., nephridia): an excretory organ found in earthworms, mollusks, and certain other invertebrates; somewhat resembles a single vertebrate nephron.

nephron (nef'-ron): the functional unit of the kidney, where blood is filtered and urine is formed.

nephron loop (loop of Henle; hen' -lē): a specialized portion of the tubule in birds and mammals that creates an osmotic concentration gradient in the fluid immediately surrounding it. This gradient allows the production of urine that is more osmotically concentrated than blood plasma.

nerve: a bundle of axons of nerve cells, bound together in a sheath.

nerve cord: a major nervous pathway consisting of a cord of nervous tissue extending lengthwise through the body, paired in many invertebrates and unpaired in chordates.

nerve net: a simple form of nervous system, consisting of a network of neurons that extends throughout the tissues of an organism such as a cnidarian.

nerve tissue: the tissue that makes up the brain, spinal cord, and nerves; consists of neurons and glial cells.

net primary production: the energy stored in the autotrophs of an ecosystem over a given time period.

neuromuscular junction: the synapse formed between a motor neuron and a muscle fiber.

neuron (noor'-on): a single nerve cell.

neurosecretory cell: a specialized nerve cell that synthesizes and releases hormones.

neurotransmitter: a chemical that is released by a nerve cell close to a second nerve cell, a muscle, or a gland cell and that influences the activity of the second cell.

neutral mutation: a mutation that does not detectably change the function of the encoded protein.

neutron: a subatomic particle that is found in the nuclei of atoms, bears no charge, and has a mass approximately equal to that of a proton.

neutrophil (nū'-trō-fil): a type of white blood cell that engulfs invading microbes and contributes to the nonspecific defenses of the body against disease.

nicotinamide adenine dinucleotide (NAD$^+$ or NADH): an electron carrier molecule produced in the cytoplasmic fluid by glycolysis and in the mitochondrial matrix by the Krebs cycle; subsequently donates electrons to the electron transport chain.

nicotinamide adenine dinucleotide phosphate (NADP$^+$ or NADPH): an electron carrier molecule used in photosynthesis to transfer high-energy electrons from the light reactions to the Calvin cycle.

nitrogen cycle: the biogeochemical cycle by which nitrogen moves from its primary reservoir of nitrogen gas in the atmosphere via nitrogen-fixing bacteria to reservoirs in soil and water, through producers and into higher trophic levels, and then back to its reservoirs.

nitrogen fixation: the process that combines atmospheric nitrogen with hydrogen to form ammonia (NH_3).

nitrogen-fixing bacterium: a bacterium that possesses the ability to remove nitrogen (N_2) from the atmosphere and combine it with hydrogen to produce ammonia (NH_3).

no-till: a method of growing crops that leaves the remains of harvested crops in place, with the next year's crops being planted directly in the remains of last year's crops without significant disturbance of the soil.

node: in plants, a region of a stem at which the petiole of a leaf is attached; usually, a lateral bud is also found at a node.

nodule: a swelling on the root of a legume or other plant that consists of cortex cells inhabited by nitrogen-fixing bacteria.

noncompetitive inhibition: the process by which an inhibitory molecule binds to a site on an enzyme that is distinct from the active site. As a result, the enzyme's active site is distorted, making it less able to catalyze the reaction involving its normal substrate.

nondisjunction: an error in meiosis in which chromosomes fail to segregate properly into the daughter cells.

nonpolar covalent bond: a covalent bond with equal sharing of electrons.

nonvascular plant: a plant that lacks lignin and well-developed conducting vessels. Nonvascular plants include mosses, hornworts, and liverworts.

norepinephrine (nor-ep-i-nef-rin′): a neurotransmitter, released by neurons of the sympathetic nervous system, that prepares the body to respond to stressful situations; also called *noradrenaline.*

northern coniferous forest: a biome with long, cold winters and only a few months of warm weather; dominated by evergreen coniferous trees; also called *taiga.*

notochord (nōt′-ō-kord): a stiff, but somewhat flexible, supportive rod that extends along the head-to-tail axis and is found in all members of the phylum Chordata at some stage of development.

nuclear envelope: the double-membrane system surrounding the nucleus of eukaryotic cells; the outer membrane is typically continuous with the endoplasmic reticulum.

nuclear pore complex: an array of proteins that line pores in the nuclear membrane and control which substances enter and leave the nucleus.

nucleic acid (noo-klā′-ik): an organic molecule composed of nucleotide subunits; the two common types of nucleic acids are ribonucleic acid (RNA) and deoxyribonucleic acid (DNA).

nucleoid (noo-klē-oid): the location of the genetic material in prokaryotic cells; not membrane enclosed.

nucleolus (noo-klē′-ō-lus; pl., nucleoli): the region of the eukaryotic nucleus that is engaged in ribosome synthesis; consists of the genes encoding ribosomal RNA, newly synthesized ribosomal RNA, and ribosomal proteins.

nucleotide: a subunit of which nucleic acids are composed; a phosphate group bonded to a sugar (deoxyribose in DNA), which is in turn bonded to a nitrogen-containing base (adenine, guanine, cytosine, or thymine in DNA). Nucleotides are linked together, forming a strand of nucleic acid, by bonds between the phosphate of one nucleotide and the sugar of the next nucleotide.

nucleotide substitution mutation: a mutation in which a single base pair in DNA has been changed.

nucleus (atomic): the central region of an atom, consisting of protons and neutrons.

nucleus (cellular): the membrane-bound organelle of eukaryotic cells that contains the cell's genetic material.

nutrient: a substance acquired from the environment and needed for the survival, growth, and development of an organism.

nutrient cycle: the pathways of a specific nutrient (such as carbon, nitrogen, phosphorus, or water) through the living and nonliving portions of an ecosystem; also called a *biogeochemical cycle.*

observation: in the scientific method, the recognition of and a statement about a specific phenomenon, usually leading to the formulation of a question about the phenomenon.

oil: a lipid composed of three fatty acids, some of which are unsaturated, covalently bonded to a molecule of glycerol; oils are liquid at room temperature.

oligotrophic lake: a lake that is very low in nutrients and hence supports little phytoplankton, plant, and algal life; contains clear water with deep light penetration.

ommatidium (ōm-ma-tid′-ē-um; pl., ommatidia): an individual light-sensitive subunit of a compound eye; consists of a lens and several receptor cells.

omnivore: an organism that consumes both plants and animals.

oogenesis (ō-ō-jen′-i-sis): the process by which egg cells are formed.

oogonium (ō-ō-gō′-nē-um; pl., oogonia): in female animals, a diploid cell that gives rise to a primary oocyte.

open circulatory system: a type of circulatory system found in some invertebrates, such as arthropods and most mollusks, that includes an open space (the hemocoel) in which blood directly bathes body tissues.

open ocean: that part of the ocean in which the water is so deep that wave action does not affect the bottom, even during strong storms.

operant conditioning: a laboratory training procedure in which an animal learns to perform a response (such as pressing a lever) through reward or punishment.

operator: a sequence of DNA nucleotides in a prokaryotic operon that binds regulatory proteins that control the ability of RNA polymerase to transcribe the structural genes of the operon.

operon (op′-er-on): in prokaryotes, a set of genes, often encoding the proteins needed for a complete metabolic pathway, including both the structural genes and a common promoter and operator that control transcription of the structural genes.

optic nerve: the nerve leading from the eye to the brain; it carries visual information.

order: in Linnaean classification, the taxonomic rank composed of related families. Related orders make up a class.

organ: a structure (such as the liver, kidney, or skin) composed of two or more distinct tissue types that function together.

organ system: two or more organs that work together to perform a specific function; for example, the digestive system.

organelle (or-guh-nel′): a membrane-enclosed structure found inside a eukaryotic cell that performs a specific function.

organic: describing a molecule that contains both carbon and hydrogen.

organic molecule: a molecule that contains both carbon and hydrogen.

organism (or′-guh-niz-um): an individual living thing.

organogenesis (or-gan-ō-jen′-uh-sis): the process by which the layers of the gastrula (endoderm, ectoderm, mesoderm) rearrange to form organs.

origin: the site of attachment of a muscle to the relatively stationary bone on one side of a joint.

osmolarity: a measure of the total number of dissolved solute particles in a solution.

osmoregulation: homeostatic maintenance of the water and salt content of the body within a limited range.

osmosis (oz-mō′-sis): the diffusion of water across a differentially permeable membrane, normally down a concentration gradient of free water molecules. Water moves into the solution that has a lower concentration of free water from a solution that has a higher concentration of free water.

osteoblast (os′-tē-ō-blast): a cell type that produces bone.

osteoclast (os′-tē-ō-klast): a cell type that dissolves bone.

osteocyte (os′-tē-ō-sīt): a mature bone cell.

osteoporosis (os′-tē-ō-por-ō′-sis): a condition in which bones become porous, weak, and easily fractured; most common in elderly women.

outer ear: the outermost part of the mammalian ear, including the external ear and auditory canal leading to the tympanic membrane.

oval window: the membrane-covered entrance to the cochlea.

ovary: (1) in animals, the gonad of females; (2) in flowering plants, a structure at the base of the carpel that contains one or more ovules and develops into the fruit.

overexploitation: hunting or harvesting natural populations at a rate that exceeds those populations' ability to replenish their numbers.

ovulation: the release of a secondary oocyte, ready to be fertilized, from the ovary.

ovule: a structure within the ovary of a flower, inside which the female gametophyte develops; after fertilization, it develops into the seed.

oxytocin (oks-ē-tō′-sin): a hormone, released by the posterior pituitary, that stimulates the contraction of uterine and mammary gland muscles.

ozone hole: a region of severe ozone loss in the stratosphere caused by ozone-depleting chemicals; maximum ozone loss occurs from September to early October over Antarctica.

ozone layer: the ozone-enriched layer of the upper atmosphere (stratosphere) that filters out much of the sun's ultraviolet radiation.

pacemaker: a cluster of specialized muscle cells in the upper right atrium of the heart that produce spontaneous electrical signals at a regular rate; the sinoatrial node.

pain receptor: a receptor cell that stimulates activity in the brain that is perceived as the sensation of pain; responds to very high or very low temperatures, mechanical damage (such as extreme stretching of tissue), and/or certain chemicals, such as potassium ions or bradykinin, that are produced as a result of tissue damage; also called *nociceptor*.

pancreas (pan′-krē-us): a combined exocrine and endocrine gland located in the abdominal cavity next to the stomach. The endocrine portion secretes the hormones insulin and glucagon, which regulate glucose concentrations in the blood. The exocrine portion secretes pancreatic juice (a mixture of water, enzymes, and sodium bicarbonate) into the small intestine; the enzymes digest fat, carbohydrate, and protein; the bicarbonate neutralizes acidic chyme entering the intestine from the stomach.

pancreatic juice: a mixture of water, sodium bicarbonate, and enzymes released by the pancreas into the small intestine.

parabasalid: a member of a protist group characterized by mutualistic or parasitic relationships with the animal species inside which they live. Parabasalids are part of a larger group known as the excavates.

paracrine communication: communication between cells of a multicellular organism in which certain cells release hormones that diffuse through the interstitial fluid to nearby cells and alter their activity.

parasite (par′-uh-sīt): an organism that lives in or on a larger organism (its host), harming the host but usually not killing it immediately.

parasympathetic division: the division of the autonomic nervous system that produces largely involuntary responses related to the maintenance of normal body functions, such as digestion; often called the *parasympathetic nervous system*.

parathyroid gland: one of four small endocrine glands, embedded in the surface of the thyroid gland, that produces parathyroid hormone, which (with calcitonin from the thyroid gland) regulates calcium ion concentration in the blood.

parathyroid hormone: a hormone released by the parathyroid gland that stimulates the release of calcium from bone.

parenchyma tissue (par-en′-ki-muh): A tissue formed from parenchyma cells that are alive at maturity, normally have thin cell walls, and carry out most of the metabolism of a plant. Most dividing meristem cells in a plant are parenchyma.

parthenogenesis (par-the-nō-jen′-uh-sis): an asexual specialization of sexual reproduction, in which a haploid egg undergoes development without fertilization.

passive transport: the movement of materials across a membrane down a gradient of concentration, pressure, or electrical charge without using cellular energy.

pathogen: an organism (or a toxin) capable of producing disease.

pathogenic (path′-ō-jen-ik): capable of producing disease; referring to an organism with such a capability (a pathogen).

pedigree: a diagram showing genetic relationships among a set of individuals, normally with respect to a specific genetic trait.

pelagic (puh-la′-jik): free-swimming or floating.

penis: an external structure of the male reproductive and urinary systems; serves to deposit sperm into the female reproductive system and deliver urine to the outside of the body.

peptide (pep′-tīd): a chain composed of two or more amino acids linked together by peptide bonds.

peptide bond: the covalent bond between the nitrogen of the amino group of one amino acid and the carbon of the carboxyl group of a second amino acid, joining the two amino acids together in a peptide or protein.

peptide hormone: a hormone consisting of a chain of amino acids; includes small proteins that function as hormones.

pericycle (per′-i-sī-kul): the outermost layer of cells of the vascular cylinder of a root.

periderm: the outer cell layers of roots and stems that have undergone secondary growth; consists primarily of cork cambium and cork cells.

periodic table: a chart first devised by Russian chemist Dmitri Mendeleev that includes all known elements and organizes them according to their atomic numbers in rows and their general chemical properties in columns (see Appendix II).

peripheral nervous system (PNS): in vertebrates, the part of the nervous system that connects the central nervous system to the rest of the body.

peristalsis: rhythmic coordinated contractions of the smooth muscles of the digestive tract that move substances through the digestive tract.

peritubular capillaries: a capillary network surrounding each kidney tubule that allows the exchange of substances between the blood and the tubule contents during reabsorption and secretion.

permafrost: a permanently frozen layer of soil, usually found in tundra of the Arctic or high mountains.

petal: part of a flower, typically brightly colored and fragrant, that attracts potential animal pollinators.

petiole (pet′-ē-ōl): the stalk that connects the blade of a leaf to the stem.

pH scale: a scale, with values from 0 to 14, used for measuring the relative acidity of a solution; at pH 7 a solution is neutral, pH 0 to 7 is acidic, and pH 7 to 14 is basic; each unit on the scale represents a tenfold change in H^+ concentration.

phagocyte (fā′-gō-sīt): a type of immune system cell that destroys invading microbes by using phagocytosis to engulf and digest the microbes. Also called a *phagocytic cell*.

phagocytosis (fa-gō-sī-tō′-sis): a type of endocytosis in which extensions of a plasma membrane engulf extracellular particles, enclose them in a membrane-bound sac, and transport them into the interior of the cell.

pharyngeal gill slit (far-in′-jē-ul): one of a series of openings, located just posterior to the mouth, that connects the throat to the outside environment; present (as some stage of life) in all chordates.

pharynx (far′-inks): in vertebrates, a chamber that is located at the back of the mouth, shared by the digestive and respiratory systems; in some invertebrates, the portion of the digestive tube just posterior to the mouth.

phenotype (fēn′-ō-tīp): the physical characteristics of an organism; can be defined as outward appearance (such as flower color), as behavior, or in molecular terms (such as glycoproteins on red blood cells).

pheromone (fer′-uh-mōn): a chemical produced by an organism that alters the behavior or physiological state of another member of the same species.

phloem (flō-um): a conducting tissue of vascular plants that transports a concentrated solution of sugars (primarily sucrose) and other organic molecules up and down the plant.

phospholipid (fos-fō-li′-pid): a lipid consisting of glycerol bonded to two fatty acids and one phosphate group, which bears another group of atoms, typically charged and containing nitrogen. A double layer of phospholipids is a component of all cellular membranes.

phospholipid bilayer: a double layer of phospholipids that forms the basis of all cellular membranes. The phospholipid heads, which are hydrophilic, face the watery interstitial fluid, a watery external environment, or the cytosol; the tails, which are hydrophobic, are buried in the middle of the bilayer.

phosphorus cycle (fos′-for-us): the biogeochemical cycle by which phosphorus moves from its primary reservoir—phosphate-rich rock—to reservoirs of phosphate in soil and water, through producers and into higher trophic levels, and then back to its reservoirs.

photic zone: the region of an ocean where light is strong enough to support photosynthesis.

photon (fō′-ton): the smallest unit of light energy.

photopigment (fō′-tō-pig-ment): a chemical substance in a photoreceptor cell that, when struck by light, changes shape and produces a response in the cell.

photoreceptor: a receptor cell that responds to light; in vertebrates, rods and cones.

photorespiration: a series of reactions in plants in which O_2 replaces CO_2 during the Calvin cycle, preventing carbon fixation; this wasteful process dominates when C_3 plants are forced to close their stomata to prevent water loss.

photosynthesis: the complete series of chemical reactions in which the energy of light is used to synthesize high-energy organic molecules, usually carbohydrates, from low-energy inorganic molecules, usually carbon dioxide and water.

photosystem: in thylakoid membranes, a cluster of chlorophyll, accessory pigment molecules, proteins, and other molecules that collectively capture light energy, transfer some of the energy to electrons, and transfer the energetic electrons to an adjacent electron transport chain.

phototropism: growth with respect to the direction of light.

phylogeny (fī-lah'-jen-ē): the evolutionary history of a group of species.

phylum (fī'-lum): in Linnaean classification, the taxonomic rank composed of related classes. Related phyla make up a kingdom.

phytochrome (fī'-tō-krōm): a light-sensitive plant pigment that mediates many plant responses to light, including flowering, stem elongation, and seed germination.

phytoplankton (fī'-tō-plank-ten): photosynthetic protists that are abundant in marine and freshwater environments.

pigment molecule: a light-absorbing, colored molecule, such as chlorophyll, carotenoid, or melanin molecules.

pilus (pl., pili): a hair-like protein structure that projects from the cell wall of many bacteria. Attachment pili help bacteria adhere to structures. Sex pili assist in the transfer of plasmids.

pineal gland (pī-nē'-al): a small gland within the brain that secretes melatonin; controls the seasonal reproductive cycles of some mammals.

pinna: a flap of skin-covered cartilage on the surface of the head that collects sound waves and funnels them to the auditory canal.

pinocytosis (pi-nō-sī-tō'-sis): the nonselective movement of extracellular fluids and their dissolved substances, enclosed within a vesicle formed from the plasma membrane, into a cell.

pioneer: an organism that is among the first to colonize an unoccupied habitat in the first stages of succession.

pit: an area in the cell walls between two plant cells where the two cells are separated only by a thin, porous cell wall.

pith: cells forming the center of a root or stem.

pituitary gland: an endocrine gland, located at the base of the brain, that produces several hormones, many of which influence the activity of other glands.

placenta (pluh-sen'-tuh): in mammals, a structure formed by a complex interweaving of the uterine lining and the embryonic membranes, especially the chorion; functions in gas, nutrient, and waste exchange between embryonic and maternal circulatory systems and also secretes the hormones estrogen and progesterone, which are essential to maintaining pregnancy.

placental (pluh-sen'-tul): referring to a mammal possessing a complex placenta (that is, species that are not marsupials or monotremes).

plankton: microscopic organisms that live in marine or freshwater environments; includes phytoplankton and zooplankton.

plant hormone: a chemical produced by specific plant cells that influences the growth, development, or metabolic activity of other cells, typically some distance away in the plant body.

plaque (plak): a deposit of cholesterol and other fatty substances within the wall of an artery.

plasma: the fluid, noncellular portion of the blood.

plasma cell: an antibody-secreting descendant of a B cell.

plasma membrane: the outer membrane of a cell, composed of a bilayer of phospholipids in which proteins are embedded.

plasmid (plaz'-mid): a small, circular piece of DNA located in the cytoplasm of many bacteria; usually does not carry genes required for the normal functioning of the bacterium, but may carry genes, such as those for antibiotic resistance, that assist bacterial survival in certain environments.

plasmodesma (plaz-mō-dez'-muh; pl., plasmodesmata): a cell-to-cell junction in plants that connects the cytosol of adjacent cells.

plasmodium (plaz-mō'-dē-um): a slug-like mass of cytoplasm containing thousands of nuclei that are not confined within individual cells.

plastid (plas'-tid): in plant cells, an organelle bounded by two membranes that may be involved in photosynthesis (chloroplasts), pigment storage, or food storage.

plate tectonics: the theory that Earth's crust is divided into irregular plates that are converging, diverging, or slipping by one another; these motions cause continental drift, the movement of continents over Earth's surface.

platelet (plāt'-let): a cell fragment that is formed from megakaryocytes in bone marrow; platelets lack a nucleus; they circulate in the blood and play a role in blood clotting.

play: behavior that seems to lack any immediate function and that often includes modified versions of behaviors used in other contexts.

pleated sheet: a form of secondary structure exhibited by certain proteins, such as silk, in which many protein chains lie side by side, with hydrogen bonds holding adjacent chains together.

pleiotropy (ple'-ō-trō-pē): a situation in which a single gene influences more than one phenotypic characteristic.

polar body: in oogenesis, a small cell, containing a nucleus but virtually no cytoplasm, produced by both the first meiotic division (of the primary oocyte) and the second meiotic division (of the secondary oocyte).

polar covalent bond: a covalent bond with unequal sharing of electrons, such that one atom is relatively negative and the other is relatively positive.

pollen: the male gametophyte of a seed plant; also called a *pollen grain*.

pollen grain: the male gametophyte of a seed plant.

pollination: in flowering plants, when pollen grains land on the stigma of a flower of the same species; in conifers, when pollen grains land within the pollen chamber of a female cone of the same species.

polygenic inheritance: a pattern of inheritance in which the interactions of two or more functionally similar genes determine phenotype.

polymer (pah'-li-mer): a molecule composed of three or more (perhaps thousands) smaller subunits called monomers, which may be identical (for example, the glucose monomers of starch) or different (for example, the amino acids of a protein).

polymerase chain reaction (PCR): a method of producing virtually unlimited numbers of copies of a specific piece of DNA, starting with as little as one copy of the desired DNA.

polypeptide: a long chain of amino acids linked by peptide bonds. A protein consists of one or more polypeptides.

polyploid (pahl'-ē-ploid): having more than two copies of each homologous chromosome.

polysaccharide (pahl-ē-sak'-uh-rīd): a large carbohydrate molecule composed of branched or unbranched chains of repeating monosaccharide subunits, normally glucose or modified glucose molecules; includes starches, cellulose, and glycogen.

pons: a portion of the hindbrain, just above the medulla, that contains neurons that influence sleep and the rate and pattern of breathing.

population: all the members of a particular species within a defined area, found in the same time and place and actually or potentially interbreeding.

population bottleneck: the result of an event that causes a population to become extremely small; may cause genetic drift that results in changed allele frequencies and loss of genetic variability.

population cycle: regularly recurring, cyclical changes in population size.

post-anal tail: a tail that extends beyond the anus and contains muscle tissue and the most posterior part of the nerve cord; found in all chordates at some stage of development.

positive feedback: a physiological mechanism in which a change causes responses that tend to amplify the original change.

posterior pituitary: a lobe of the pituitary gland that is an outgrowth of the hypothalamus and that releases antidiuretic hormone and oxytocin.

postmating isolating mechanism: any structure, physiological function, or developmental abnormality that prevents organisms of two different species, once mating has occurred, from producing vigorous, fertile offspring.

postsynaptic neuron: at a synapse, the nerve cell that changes its metabolic activity or its electrical potential in response to a chemical (the neurotransmitter) released by another (presynaptic) cell.

postsynaptic potential (PSP): an electrical signal produced in a postsynaptic cell by transmission across the synapse; it may be excitatory (EPSP), making the cell more likely to produce an action potential, or inhibitory (IPSP), tending to inhibit the production of an action potential.

potential energy: "stored" energy including chemical energy (stored in molecules), elastic energy (such as stored in a spring), or gravitational energy (stored in the elevated position of an object).

prairie: a biome, located in the centers of continents, that primarily supports grasses; also called *grassland*.

precapillary sphincter (sfink'-ter): a ring of smooth muscle between an arteriole and a capillary that regulates the flow of blood into the capillary bed.

predation (pre-dā′-shun): the act of eating another living organism.

predator: an organism that eats other organisms.

prediction: in the scientific method, a statement describing an expected observation or the expected outcome of an experiment, assuming that a specific hypothesis is true.

premating isolating mechanism: any structure, physiological function, or behavior that prevents organisms of two different species from exchanging gametes.

pressure-flow mechanism: the process by which sugars are transported in phloem; the movement of sugars into a phloem sieve tube causes water to enter the tube by osmosis, while the movement of sugars out of another part of the same sieve tube causes water to leave by osmosis. The resulting pressure gradient causes the bulk movement of water and dissolved sugars from the end of the sieve tube into which sugar is transported (a source) toward the end of the sieve tube from which sugar is removed (a sink).

presynaptic neuron: a nerve cell that releases a chemical (the neurotransmitter) at a synapse, causing changes in the electrical activity or metabolism of another (postsynaptic) cell.

prey: organisms that are eaten, and often killed, by another organism (a predator).

primary consumer: an organism that feeds on producers; an herbivore.

primary electron acceptor: a molecule in the reaction center of each photosystem that accepts an electron from one of the two reaction center chlorophyll *a* molecules and transfers the electron to an adjacent electron transport chain.

primary growth: growth in length and development of the initial structures of plant roots and shoots; results from cell division of apical meristems and differentiation of the daughter cells.

primary oocyte (ō′-ō-sīt): a diploid cell, derived from the oogonium by growth and differentiation, that undergoes meiotic cell division, producing the egg.

primary spermatocyte (sper-ma′-tō-sīt): a diploid cell, derived from the spermatogonium by growth and differentiation, that undergoes meiotic cell division, producing four sperm.

primary structure: the amino acid sequence of a protein.

primary succession: succession that occurs in an environment, such as bare rock, in which no trace of a previous community is present.

primate: a member of the mammalian clade Primates, characterized by the presence of an opposable thumb, forward-facing eyes, and a well-developed cerebral cortex; includes lemurs, monkeys, apes, and humans.

prion (prē′-on): a protein that, in mutated form, acts as an infectious agent that causes certain neurodegenerative diseases, including kuru and scrapie.

producer: a photosynthetic organism; an autotroph.

product: an atom or molecule that is formed from reactants in a chemical reaction.

profundal zone: the part of a lake in which light is insufficient to support photosynthesis.

progesterone (prō-ge′-ster-ōn): a hormone, produced by the corpus luteum in the ovary, that promotes the development of the uterine lining in females.

prokaryote (prō-kar′-ē-ōt): an organism whose cells are prokaryotic (their genetic material is not enclosed in a membrane-bound nucleus and they lack other membrane-bound organelles); bacteria and archaea are prokaryotes.

prokaryotic (prō-kar-ē-ot′-ik): referring to cells of the domains Bacteria or Archaea. Prokaryotic cells have genetic material that is not enclosed in a membrane-bound nucleus; they also lack other membrane-bound organelles.

prokaryotic fission: the process by which a single bacterium divides in half, producing two identical offspring.

prolactin: a hormone, released by the anterior pituitary, that stimulates milk production in human females.

promoter: a specific sequence of DNA at the beginning of a gene, to which RNA polymerase binds and starts gene transcription.

prophase (prō′-fāz): the first stage of mitosis, in which the chromosomes first become visible in the light microscope as thickened, condensed threads and the spindle begins to form; as the spindle is completed, the nuclear envelope breaks apart, and the spindle microtubules invade the nuclear region and attach to the kinetochores of the chromosomes. Also, the first stage of meiosis: In meiosis I, the homologous chromosomes pair up, exchange parts at chiasmata, and attach to spindle microtubules; in meiosis II, the spindle re-forms and chromosomes attach to the microtubules.

prostaglandin (pro-stuh-glan′-din): a family of modified fatty acid hormones manufactured and secreted by many cells of the body.

prostate gland (pros′-tāt): a gland that produces part of the fluid component of semen; prostatic fluid is basic and contains a chemical that activates sperm movement.

protease (prō′-tē-ās): an enzyme that digests proteins.

protein: a polymer composed of amino acids joined by peptide bonds.

protist: a eukaryotic organism that is not a plant, animal, or fungus. The term encompasses a diverse array of organisms and does not represent a monophyletic group.

protocell: the hypothetical evolutionary precursor of living cells, consisting of a mixture of organic molecules within a membrane.

proton: a subatomic particle that is found in the nuclei of atoms; it bears a unit of positive charge and has a relatively large mass, roughly equal to the mass of a neutron.

protonephridium (prō-tō-nef-rid′-ē-um; pl., protonephridia): the functional unit of the excretory system of some invertebrates, such as flatworms; consists of a tubule that has an external opening to the outside of the body, but lacks an internal opening within the body. Fluid is filtered from the body cavity into the tubule by a hollow cell at the end of the tubule, such as a flame cell in flatworms, and released outside the body.

protostome (prō′-tō-stōm): an animal with a mode of embryonic development in which the coelom is derived from splits in the mesoderm; characteristic of arthropods, annelids, and mollusks.

protozoan (prō-tuh-zō′-an; pl., protozoa): a nonphotosynthetic, single-celled protist.

proximal tubule: the initial part of the renal tubule; in mammals, most reabsorption occurs here.

pseudocoelom (soo′-dō-sēl′-ōm): in animals, a "false coelom," that is, a space or cavity, partially but not fully lined with tissue derived from mesoderm, that separates the body wall from the inner organs; found in roundworms.

pseudoplasmodium (soo′-dō-plaz-mō′-dē-um): an aggregation of individual amoeboid cells that form a slug-like mass.

pseudopod (soo′-dō-pod): an extension of the plasma membrane by which certain cells, such as amoebas, locomote and engulf prey.

puberty: a stage of development characterized by sexual maturation, rapid growth, and the appearance of secondary sexual characteristics.

pubic lice: arthropod parasites that can infest humans; can be transmitted by sexual contact.

pulmonary circuit: the pathway of blood from the heart to the lungs and back to the heart.

Punnett square method: a method of predicting the genotypes and phenotypes of offspring in genetic crosses.

pupa (pl., pupae): a developmental stage in some insect species in which the organism stops moving and feeding and may be encased in a cocoon; occurs between the larval and the adult phases.

pupil: the adjustable opening in the center of the iris, through which light enters the eye.

quaternary structure (kwat′-er-nuh-rē): the complex three-dimensional structure of a protein consisting of more than one peptide chain.

question: in the scientific method, a statement that identifies a particular aspect of an observation that a scientist wishes to explain.

***r*-selected species:** species that typically live in rapidly changing, unpredictable environments and usually do not have population sizes that approach carrying capacity. *r*-selected species usually mature rapidly, have a short life span, produce a large number of small offspring, and provide little parental care, so most offspring die before reaching maturity.

radial symmetry: a body plan in which any plane along a central axis will divide the body into approximately mirror-image halves. Cnidarians and many adult echinoderms exhibit radial symmetry.

radioactive: pertaining to an atom with an unstable nucleus that spontaneously breaks apart or decays, with the emission of radiation.

radiolarian (rā-dē-ō-lar′-ē-un): a member of a protist group characterized by pseudopods and typically elaborate silica shells. Radiolarians are largely aquatic (mostly marine) and are part of a larger group known as rhizarians.

rain shadow: a local dry area, usually located on the downwind side of a mountain range that blocks the prevailing moisture-bearing winds.

random distribution: the distribution characteristic of populations in which the probability of finding an individual is equal in all parts of an area.

reabsorption: the process by which cells of the renal tubule of the nephron remove water and nutrients from the filtrate within the tubule and return those substances to the blood.

reactant: an atom or molecule that is used up in a chemical reaction to form a product.

reaction center: two chlorophyll *a* molecules and a primary electron acceptor complexed with proteins and located near the center of each photosystem within the thylakoid membrane. Light energy is passed to one of the chlorophylls, which donates an energized electron to the primary electron acceptor, which then passes the electron to an adjacent electron transport chain.

receptor: (1) a protein, located in a membrane or the cytoplasm of a cell, that binds to specific molecules (for example, a hormone or neurotransmitter), triggering a response in the cell, such as endocytosis, changes in metabolic rate, cell division, or electrical changes; (2) a cell that responds to an environmental stimulus (chemicals, sound, light, pH, and so on) by changing its electrical potential.

receptor-mediated endocytosis: the selective uptake of molecules from the interstitial fluid by binding to a receptor located at a coated pit on the plasma membrane and pinching off the coated pit into a vesicle that moves into the cytosol.

receptor potential: an electrical potential change in a receptor cell, produced in response to the reception of an environmental stimulus (chemicals, sound, light, heat, and so on). The size of the receptor potential is proportional to the intensity of the stimulus.

receptor protein: a protein, located in a membrane or the cytosol of a cell, that binds to specific molecules (for example, a hormone or neurotransmitter), triggering a response in the cell, such as endocytosis, changes in metabolic rate, cell division, or electrical changes.

recessive: an allele that is expressed only in homozygotes and is completely masked in heterozygotes.

recognition protein: a protein or glycoprotein protruding from the outside surface of a plasma membrane that identifies a cell as belonging to a particular species, to a specific individual of that species, and in many cases to one specific organ within the individual.

recombinant DNA: DNA that has been altered by the addition of DNA from a different organism, typically from a different species.

recombination: the formation of new combinations of the different alleles of each gene on a chromosome; the result of crossing over.

rectum: the terminal portion of the vertebrate digestive tube where feces are stored until they are eliminated.

reflex: a simple, stereotyped movement of part of the body that occurs automatically in response to a stimulus.

regeneration: the regrowth of a body part after loss or damage; also, asexual reproduction by means of the regrowth of an entire body from a fragment.

regulatory gene: in prokaryotes, a gene encoding a protein that binds to the operator of one or more operons, controlling the ability of RNA polymerase to transcribe the structural genes of the operon.

regulatory T cell: a type of T cell that suppresses the adaptive immune response, especially by self-reactive lymphocytes, and appears to be important in the prevention of autoimmune disorders.

releasing hormone: a hormone, secreted by the hypothalamus, that causes the release of specific hormones by the anterior pituitary.

renal artery: the artery carrying blood to each kidney.

renal corpuscle: the portion of a nephron in which blood filtrate is collected from the glomerulus by the cup-shaped glomerular capsule.

renal cortex: the outer layer of the kidney, in which the largest portion of each nephron is located, including renal corpuscle and the distal and proximal tubules.

renal medulla: the layer of the kidney just inside the renal cortex, in which loops of Henle produce a highly concentrated interstitial fluid, allowing the production of concentrated urine.

renal pelvis: the inner chamber of the kidney, in which urine from the collecting ducts accumulates before it enters the ureter.

renal tubule (toob′-ūl): the tubular portion of a nephron composed of the proximal tubule, the nephron loop, and the distal tubule. Urine is formed from the blood filtrate as it passes through the tubule.

renal vein: the vein carrying blood away from each kidney.

renin: in mammals, an enzyme that is released by the kidneys when blood pressure falls. Renin catalyzes the formation of angiotensin, which causes arterioles to constrict, thereby elevating blood pressure.

replacement level fertility (RLF): the average number of offspring per female that is required to maintain a stable population.

repressor protein: in prokaryotes, a protein encoded by a regulatory gene, which binds to the operator of an operon and prevents RNA polymerase from transcribing the structural genes.

reproductive isolation: the failure of organisms of one population to breed successfully with members of another; may be due to premating or postmating isolating mechanisms.

reptile: a member of the chordate group that includes the snakes, lizards, turtles, alligators, birds, and crocodiles.

reservoir: the major source and storage site of a nutrient in an ecosystem, normally in the abiotic portion.

resource partitioning: the coexistence of two species with similar requirements, each occupying a smaller niche than either would if it were by itself; a means of minimizing the species' competitive interactions.

respiration: in terrestrial vertebrates, the act of moving air into the lungs (inhalation) and out of the lungs (exhalation); during respiration, oxygen diffuses from the air in the lungs into the circulatory system, and carbon dioxide diffuses from the circulatory system into the air in the lungs.

respiratory center: a cluster of neurons, located in the medulla of the brain, that sends rhythmic bursts of nerve impulses to the respiratory muscles, resulting in breathing.

respiratory membrane: within the lungs, the fusion of the epithelial cells of the alveoli and the endothelial cells that form the walls of surrounding capillaries.

respiratory system: a group of organs that work together to facilitate gas exchange—the intake of oxygen and the removal of carbon dioxide—between an animal and its environment.

resting potential: an electrical potential, or voltage, in unstimulated nerve cells; the inside of the cell is always negative with respect to the outside.

restriction enzyme: an enzyme, usually isolated from bacteria, that cuts double-stranded DNA at a specific nucleotide sequence; the nucleotide sequence that is cut differs for different restriction enzymes.

restriction fragment: a piece of DNA that has been isolated by cleaving a larger piece of DNA with restriction enzymes.

restriction fragment length polymorphism (RFLP): a difference in the length of DNA fragments that were produced by cutting samples of DNA from different individuals of the same species with the same set of restriction enzymes; fragment length differences occur because of differences in nucleotide sequences, and hence in the ability of restriction enzymes to cut the DNA, among individuals of the same species.

reticular formation (reh-tik′-ū-lar): a diffuse network of neurons extending from the hindbrain, through the midbrain, and into the lower reaches of the forebrain; involved in filtering sensory input and regulating what information is relayed to conscious brain centers for further attention.

retina (ret′-in-uh): a multilayered sheet of nerve tissue at the rear of camera-type eyes, composed of photoreceptor cells plus associated nerve cells that refine the photoreceptor information and transmit it to the optic nerve.

rhizarian: a member of Rhizaria, a protist clade. Rhizarians, which use thin pseudopods to move and capture prey and which often have hard shells, include the foraminiferans and the radiolarians.

ribonucleic acid (RNA) (rī-bō-noo-klā′-ik; RNA): a molecule composed of ribose nucleotides, each of which consists of a phosphate group, the sugar ribose, and one of the bases adenine, cytosine, guanine, or uracil; involved in converting the information in DNA into protein; also the genetic material of some viruses.

ribosomal RNA (rī-bō-sō′-mul; rRNA): a type of RNA that combines with proteins to form ribosomes.

ribosome (rī'-bō-sōm): a complex consisting of two subunits, each composed of ribosomal RNA and protein, found in the cytoplasm of cells or attached to the endoplasmic reticulum, that is the site of protein synthesis, during which the sequence of bases of messenger RNA is translated into the sequence of amino acids in a protein.

ribozyme: an RNA molecule that can catalyze certain chemical reactions, especially those involved in the synthesis and processing of RNA itself.

RNA polymerase: in RNA synthesis, an enzyme that catalyzes the bonding of free RNA nucleotides into a continuous strand, using RNA nucleotides that are complementary to those of the template strand of DNA.

rod: a rod shaped photoreceptor cell in the vertebrate retina, sensitive to dim light but not involved in color vision; see also *cone*.

root: the part of a plant body, normally underground, that provides anchorage, absorbs water and dissolved nutrients and transports them to the stem, produces some hormones, and in some plants serves as a storage site for carbohydrates.

root cap: a cluster of cells at the tip of a growing root, derived from the apical meristem; protects the growing tip from damage as it burrows through the soil.

root hair: a fine projection from an epidermal cell of a young root that increases the absorptive surface area of the root.

root pressure: pressure within a root caused by the transport of minerals into the vascular cylinder, accompanied by the entry of water by osmosis.

root system: all of the roots of a plant.

round window: a flexible membrane at the end of the cochlea opposite the oval window that allows the fluid in the cochlea to move in response to movements of the oval window.

rubisco: in the carbon fixation step of the Calvin cycle, the enzyme that catalyzes the reaction between ribulose bisphosphate (RuBP) and carbon dioxide, thereby fixing the carbon of carbon dioxide in an organic molecule; short for ribulose bisphosphate carboxylase.

rumen fungus: a member of the fungus clade Neocallimastigomycota, whose members have swimming spores with multiple flagella. Rumen fungi are anaerobic and most live in the digestive tracts of plant-eating animals.

ruminant (roo'-min-ant): an herbivorous animal with a digestive tract that includes multiple stomach chambers, one of which contains cellulose-digesting bacteria, and that regurgitates the contents ("cud") of the first chamber for additional chewing ("ruminating").

S-curve: the S-shaped growth curve produced by logistic population growth, usually describing a population of organisms introduced into a new area; consists of an initial period of exponential growth, followed by a decreasing growth rate, and finally, relative stability around a growth rate of zero.

sac fungus: a member of the fungus clade Ascomycota, whose members form spores in a saclike case called an ascus.

saccule: a patch of hair cells in the vestibule of the inner ear; bending of the hairs of the hair cells permits detection of the direction of gravity and the degree of tilt of the head.

sapwood: young secondary xylem that transports water and minerals in a tree trunk.

sarcomere (sark'-ō-mēr): the unit of contraction of a muscle fiber; a subunit of the myofibril, consisting of thick and thin filaments, bounded by Z lines.

sarcoplasmic reticulum (sark'-ō-plas'-mik re-tik'-ū-lum; SR): the specialized endoplasmic reticulum in muscle cells; forms interconnected hollow tubes. The sarcoplasmic reticulum stores calcium ions and releases them into the interior of the muscle cell, initiating contraction.

saturated: referring to a fatty acid with as many hydrogen atoms as possible bonded to the carbon backbone (therefore, a saturated fatty acid has no double bonds in its carbon backbone).

savanna: a biome that is dominated by grasses and supports scattered trees; typically has a rainy season during which most of the year's precipitation falls, followed by a dry season during which virtually no precipitation occurs.

science: the organized and systematic inquiry, through observation and experiment, into the origins, structure, and behavior of our living and nonliving surroundings.

scientific method: a rigorous procedure for making observations of specific phenomena and searching for the order underlying those phenomena.

scientific name: the two-part Latin name of a species; consists of the genus name followed by the species name.

scientific theory: an explanation of natural phenomena developed through extensive and reproducible observations; more general and reliable than a hypothesis.

scientific theory of evolution: the theory that modern organisms descended, with modification, from preexisting life-forms.

sclera: a tough, white connective tissue layer that covers the outside of the eyeball and forms the white of the eye.

sclerenchyma tissue (skler-en'-ki-muh): a tissue formed from sclerenchyma cells with thick, hardened cell walls. Sclerenchyma cells usually die as they mature and generally support or protect the plant body.

scrotum (skrō'-tum): in male mammals, the pouch of skin containing the testes.

second law of thermodynamics: the principle of physics that states that any change in an isolated system causes the quantity of concentrated, useful energy to decrease and the amount of randomness and disorder (entropy) to increase.

second messenger: an intracellular chemical, such as cyclic AMP, that is synthesized or released within a cell in response to the binding of a hormone or neurotransmitter (the first messenger) to receptors on the cell surface; brings about specific changes in the metabolism of the cell.

secondary consumer: an organism that feeds on primary consumers; a type of carnivore.

secondary growth: growth in the diameter and strength of a stem or root due to cell division in lateral meristems and differentiation of their daughter cells.

secondary oocyte (ō'-ō-sīt): a large haploid cell derived from the diploid primary oocyte by meiosis I.

secondary spermatocyte (sper-ma'-tō-sīt): a large haploid cell derived from the diploid primary spermatocyte by meiosis I.

secondary structure: a repeated, regular structure assumed by a protein chain, held together by hydrogen bonds; for example, a helix.

secondary succession: succession that occurs after an existing community is disturbed—for example, after a forest fire; secondary succession is much more rapid than primary succession.

secretin: a hormone produced by the small intestine that stimulates the production and release of digestive secretions by the pancreas and liver.

secretion: the process by which cells of the tubule of the nephron remove wastes from the blood, actively secreting those wastes into the tubule.

seed: the reproductive structure of a seed plant, protected by a seed coat; contains an embryonic plant and a supply of food for it.

seed coat: the thin, tough, and waterproof outermost covering of a seed, formed from the integuments of the ovule.

segmentation (seg-men-tā'-shun): an animal body plan in which the body is divided into repeated, typically similar units.

selectively permeable: the quality of a membrane that allows certain molecules or ions to move through it more readily than others.

self-fertilization: the union of sperm and egg from the same individual.

semen: the sperm-containing fluid produced by the male reproductive tract.

semicircular canal: in the inner ear, one of three fluid-filled tubes, each with a bulge at one end containing a patch of hair cells; movement of the head moves fluid in the canal and consequently bends the hairs of the hair cells.

semiconservative replication: the process of replication of the DNA double helix; the two DNA strands separate, and each is used as a template for the synthesis of a complementary DNA strand. Consequently, each daughter double helix consists of one parental strand and one new strand.

semilunar valve: a valve located between the right ventricle of the heart and the pulmonary artery, or between the left ventricle and the aorta; prevents the backflow of blood into the ventricles when they relax.

seminal vesicle: in male mammals, a gland that produces a basic, fructose-containing fluid that forms part of the semen.

seminiferous tubule (sem-i-ni'-fer-us): in the vertebrate testis, a series of tubes in which sperm are produced.

senescence: in plants, a specific aging process, typically including deterioration and the dropping of leaves and flowers.

sense organ: a multicellular structure that includes both sensory receptor cells and accessory structures that assist in the detection of a specific stimulus; examples include the eye and ear.

sensory neuron: a nerve cell that responds to a stimulus from the internal or external environment.

sensory receptor: a cell (typically, a neuron) specialized to respond to particular internal or external environmental stimuli by producing an electrical potential.

sepal (sē'-pul): one of the group of modified leaves that surrounds and protects a flower bud; in dicots, usually develops into a green, leaflike structure when the flower blooms; in monocots, usually similar to a petal.

septum (pl., septa): a partition that separates the fungal hypha into individual cells; pores in septa allow the transfer of materials between cells.

Sertoli cell: in the seminiferous tubule, a large cell that regulates spermatogenesis and nourishes the developing sperm.

severe combined immune deficiency (SCID): a disorder in which no immune cells, or very few, are formed; the immune system is incapable of responding properly to invading disease organisms, and the individual is very vulnerable to common infections.

sex chromosome: either of the pair of chromosomes that usually determines the sex of an organism; for example, the X and Y chromosomes in mammals.

sex-linked: referring to a pattern of inheritance characteristic of genes located on one type of sex chromosome (for example, X) and not found on the other type (for example, Y); in mammals, in almost all cases, the gene controlling the trait is on the X chromosome, so this pattern is often called X-linked. In X-linked inheritance, females show the dominant trait unless they are homozygous recessive, whereas males express whichever allele, dominant or recessive, is found on their single X chromosome.

sexual reproduction: a form of reproduction in which genetic material from two parent organisms is combined in the offspring; usually, two haploid gametes fuse to form a diploid zygote.

sexual selection: a type of natural selection that acts on traits involved in finding and acquiring mates.

sexually transmitted disease (STD): a disease that is passed from person to person by sexual contact; also known as *sexually transmitted infection (STI)*.

shoot system: all the parts of a vascular plant exclusive of the root; usually aboveground. Consists of stem, leaves, buds, and (in season) flowers and fruits; functions include photosynthesis, transport of materials, reproduction, and hormone synthesis.

short-day plant: a plant that will flower only if the length of uninterrupted darkness exceeds a species-specific critical period; also called a *long-night plant*.

short tandem repeat (STR): a DNA sequence consisting of a short sequence of nucleotides (usually two to five nucleotides in length) repeated multiple times, with all of the repetitions side by side on a chromosome; variations in the number of repeats of a standardized set of 13 STRs produce DNA profiles used to identify people by their DNA.

short-term memory: a memory that lasts only a brief time, usually while a specific neuronal circuit is active or while a change in biochemical activity temporarily strengthens specific synapses.

sickle-cell anemia: a recessive disease caused by a single amino acid substitution in the hemoglobin molecule. Sickle-cell hemoglobin molecules tend to cluster together, distorting the shape of red blood cells and causing them to break and clog capillaries.

sieve plate: in plants, a structure between two adjacent sieve-tube elements in phloem, where holes formed in the cell walls interconnect the cytoplasm of the sieve-tube elements.

sieve-tube element: in phloem, one of the cells of a sieve tube.

simple diffusion: the diffusion of water, dissolved gases, or lipid-soluble molecules through the phospholipid bilayer of a cellular membrane.

simple epithelium: a type of epithelial tissue, one cell layer thick, that lines many hollow organs such as those of the respiratory, digestive, urinary, reproductive, and circulatory systems.

sink: in plants, any structure that uses up sugars or converts sugars to starch, and toward which phloem fluids will flow.

sinoatrial (SA) node (sī'-nō-āt'-rē-ul nōd): a small mass of specialized muscle in the wall of the right atrium; generates electrical signals rhythmically and spontaneously and serves as the heart's pacemaker.

skeletal muscle: the type of muscle that is attached to and moves the skeleton and is under the direct, normally voluntary, control of the nervous system; also called *striated muscle*.

skeleton: a supporting structure for the body, on which muscles act to change the body configuration; may be external or internal.

small intestine: the portion of the digestive tract, located between the stomach and large intestine, in which most digestion and absorption of nutrients occur.

smooth muscle: the type of muscle that surrounds hollow organs, such as the digestive tract, bladder, and blood vessels; not striped in appearance (hence the name "smooth") and normally not under voluntary control.

social learning: learning that is influenced by observation of, or interaction with, other animals, usually of the same species.

sodium-potassium (Na⁺-K⁺) pump: an active transport protein that uses the energy of ATP to transport Na⁺ out of a cell and K⁺ into a cell; produces and maintains the concentration gradients of these ions across the plasma membrane, such that the concentration of Na⁺ is higher outside a cell than inside, and the concentration of K⁺ is higher inside a cell than outside.

solute: a substance dissolved in a solvent.

solution: a solvent containing one or more dissolved substances (solutes).

solvent: a liquid capable of dissolving (uniformly dispersing) other substances in itself.

somatic nervous system: that portion of the peripheral nervous system that controls voluntary movement by activating skeletal muscles.

source: in plants, any structure that actively synthesizes sugar, and away from which phloem fluid will be transported.

spawning: a method of external fertilization in which male and female parents shed gametes into water, and sperm must swim through the water to reach the eggs.

speciation: the process of species formation, in which a single species splits into two or more species.

species (spē'-sēs): the basic unit of taxonomic classification, consisting of a population or group of populations that evolves separately from other populations. In sexually reproducing organisms, a species can be defined as a population or group of populations whose members interbreed freely with one another under natural conditions but do not interbreed with members of other populations.

specific heat: the amount of energy required to raise the temperature of 1 gram of a substance by 1°C.

sperm: the haploid male gamete, normally small, motile, and containing little cytoplasm.

spermatid: a haploid cell derived from the secondary spermatocyte by meiosis II; differentiates into the mature sperm.

spermatogenesis: the process by which sperm cells form.

spermatogonium (pl., spermatogonia): a diploid cell, lining the walls of the seminiferous tubules, that gives rise to a primary spermatocyte.

spermatophore: a package of sperm formed by the males of some invertebrate animals; the spermatophore can be inserted into the female reproductive tract, where it releases its sperm.

sphincter muscle: a circular ring of muscle surrounding a tubular structure, such as the esophagus, stomach, or intestine; contraction and relaxation of a sphincter muscle controls the movement of materials through the tube.

spinal cord: the part of the central nervous system of vertebrates that extends from the base of the brain to the hips and is protected by the bones of the vertebral column; contains the cell bodies of motor neurons that form synapses with skeletal muscles, the circuitry for some simple reflex behaviors, and axons that communicate with the brain.

spindle: an array of microtubules that moves the chromosomes to opposite poles of a cell during mitotic and meiotic cell division.

spindle microtubule: one of the microtubules organized in a spindle shape that separate chromosomes during meiotic and meiotic cell division.

spiracle (spi'-ruh-kul): an opening in the body wall of insects through which air enters the tracheae.

spleen: the largest organ of the lymphatic system, located in the abdominal cavity; contains macrophages that filter the blood by removing microbes and aged red blood cells, and lymphocytes (B and T cells) that reproduce during times of infection.

spongy bone: porous, lightweight bone tissue in the interior of bones; the location of bone marrow. Compare with *compact bone*.

spontaneous generation: the proposal that living organisms can arise from nonliving matter.

sporangium (spor-an'-jē-um; pl., sporangia): a structure in which spores are produced.

spore: (1) in plants and fungi, a haploid cell capable of developing into an adult without fusing with another cell (without fertilization); (2) in bacteria and some other organisms, a stage of the life cycle that is resistant to extreme environmental conditions.

sporophyte (spor'-ō-fīt): the multicellular diploid stage in the life cycle of a plant; produces haploid, asexual spores through meiosis.

stabilizing selection: a type of natural selection that favors the average phenotype in a population.

stamen (stā'-men): the male reproductive structure of a flower, consisting of a filament and an anther, in which pollen grains develop.

starch: a polysaccharide that is composed of branched or unbranched chains of glucose molecules; used by plants as a carbohydrate-storage molecule.

start codon: the first AUG codon in a messenger RNA molecule.

startle coloration: a form of mimicry in which a color pattern (in many cases resembling large eyes) can be displayed suddenly by a prey organism when approached by a predator.

stem: the portion of the plant body, normally located aboveground, that bears leaves and reproductive structures such as flowers and fruit.

stem cell: an undifferentiated cell that is capable of dividing and giving rise to one or more distinct types of differentiated cell(s).

sterilization: a generally permanent method of contraception in which the pathways through which the sperm (vas deferens) or egg (oviducts) must travel are interrupted; the most effective form of contraception.

steroid: a lipid consisting of four fused carbon rings, with various functional groups attached.

steroid hormone: a class of hormones whose chemical structure (four fused carbon rings with various functional groups) resembles cholesterol; steroids, which are lipids, are secreted by the ovaries and placenta, the testes, and the adrenal cortex.

stigma (stig'-muh): the pollen-capturing tip of a carpel.

stirrup: the third of the small bones of the middle ear that link the tympanic membrane (eardrum) with the oval window; the stirrup is directly connected to the oval window; also called the *stapes*.

stoma (stō'-muh; pl., stomata): an adjustable opening in the epidermis of a leaf or young stem, surrounded by a pair of guard cells, that regulates the diffusion of carbon dioxide and water into and out of the leaf or stem.

stomach: the muscular sac between the esophagus and small intestine where food is stored and mechanically broken down and in which protein digestion begins.

stop codon: a codon in messenger RNA that stops protein synthesis and causes the completed protein chain to be released from the ribosome.

stramenopile: a member of Stramenopila, a large protist clade. Stramenopiles, which are characterized by hair-like projections on their flagella, include the water molds, the diatoms, and the brown algae.

strand: a single polymer of nucleotides; DNA is composed of two strands wound about each other in a double helix; RNA is usually single-stranded.

stratified epithelium: a type of epithelial tissue composed of several cell layers, usually strong and waterproof; mostly found on the surface of the skin.

stroke: an interruption of blood flow to part of the brain caused by the rupture of an artery or the blocking of an artery by a blood clot. Loss of blood supply leads to rapid death of the area of the brain affected.

stroma (strō'-muh): the semifluid material inside chloroplasts in which the thylakoids are located; the site of the reactions of the Calvin cycle.

structural gene: in the prokaryotic operon, the genes that encode enzymes or other cellular proteins.

style: a stalk connecting the stigma of a carpel with the ovary at its base.

subclimax: a community in which succession is stopped before the climax community is reached; it is maintained by regular disturbance—for example, a tallgrass prairie maintained by periodic fires.

substrate: the atoms or molecules that are the reactants for an enzyme-catalyzed chemical reaction.

succession (suk-seh'-shun): a structural change in a community and its nonliving environment over time. During succession, species replace one another in a somewhat predictable manner until a stable, self-sustaining climax community is reached.

sucrose: a disaccharide composed of glucose and fructose.

sugar: a simple carbohydrate molecule, either a monosaccharide or a disaccharide.

sugar-phosphate backbone: a chain of sugars and phosphates in DNA and RNA; the sugar of one nucleotide bonds to the phosphate of the next nucleotide in a DNA or RNA strand. The bases in DNA or RNA are attached to the sugars of the backbone.

surface tension: the property of a liquid to resist penetration by objects at its interface with the air, due to cohesion between molecules of the liquid.

survivorship curve: the curve that results when the number of individuals of each age in a population is graphed against their age, usually expressed as a percentage of their maximum life span.

survivorship table: a data table that groups organisms born at the same time and tracks them throughout their life span, recording how many continue to survive in each succeeding year (or other unit of time). Various parameters such as gender may be used in the groupings. Human life tables may include many other parameters (such as socioeconomic status) used by demographers.

sustainable development: human activities that meet current needs for a reasonable quality of life without exceeding nature's limits and without compromising the ability of future generations to meet their needs.

symbiosis: a relationship between species in which the two or more species share a close, long-term physical association.

sympathetic division: the division of the autonomic nervous system that produces largely involuntary responses that prepare the body for stressful or highly energetic situations; often called the *sympathetic nervous system*.

sympatric speciation (sim-pat'-rik): the process by which new species arise in populations that are not physically divided; the genetic isolation required for sympatric speciation may be due to ecological isolation or chromosomal aberrations (such as polyploidy).

synapse (sin'-aps): the site of communication between nerve cells. At a synapse, one cell (presynaptic) releases a chemical (the neurotransmitter) that changes the electrical potential or metabolism of the second (postsynaptic) cell.

synaptic cleft: in a synapse, a small gap between the presynaptic and postsynaptic neurons.

synaptic communication: communication between cells of an animal in which nerve cells affect the activity of other cells by releasing chemicals called neurotransmitters across a small gap separating the ending of a nerve cell from a target cell (usually another nerve cell, a muscle cell, or an endocrine cell).

synaptic terminal: a swelling at the branched ending of an axon, where the axon forms a synapse.

syphilis (si'-ful-is): a sexually transmitted bacterial infection of the reproductive organs; if untreated, can damage the nervous and circulatory systems.

systematics: the branch of biology concerned with reconstructing phylogenies and with naming clades.

systemic circuit: the pathway of blood from the heart through all the parts of the body except the lungs and back to the heart.

systolic pressure (sis'-tal-ik): the blood pressure measured at the peak of contraction of the ventricles; the higher of the two blood pressure readings.

T cell: a type of lymphocyte that matures in the thymus. Some types of T cells recognize and destroy specific foreign cells or substances; other types of T cells regulate the activity of other cells of the immune system.

T-cell receptor: a protein receptor, located on the surface of a T cell, that binds a specific antigen and triggers the immune response of the T cell.

T tubule: a deep infolding of the plasma membrane of a muscle cell; conducts the action potential inside the cell.

taiga (tī'-guh): a biome with long, cold winters and only a few months of warm weather; dominated by evergreen coniferous trees; also called *northern coniferous forest*.

taproot system: a root system, commonly found in dicots, that consists of a long, thick main root and many smaller lateral roots that grow from the main root.

target cell: a cell on which a particular hormone exerts its effect.

taste bud: a cluster of taste receptor cells and supporting cells that is located in a small pit beneath the surface of the tongue and that communicates with the mouth through a small pore.

taxonomy (tax-on'-uh-mē): the branch of biology concerned with naming and classifying organisms.

tectorial membrane (tek-tor'-ē-ul): one of the membranes of the cochlea in which the hairs of the hair cells are embedded. In sound reception, movement of the basilar membrane relative to the tectorial membrane bends the hairs.

telomere (tēl'-e-mēr): the nucleotides at the end of a chromosome that protect the chromosome from damage during condensation, and prevent the end of one chromosome from attaching to the end of another chromosome.

telophase (tēl'-ō-fāz): in mitosis and both divisions of meiosis, the final stage, in which the spindle fibers usually disappear, nuclear envelopes re-form, and cytokinesis generally occurs. In mitosis and meiosis II, the chromosomes also relax from their condensed form.

temperate deciduous forest: a biome having cold winters and warm summers, with enough summer rainfall for trees to grow and shade out grasses; characterized by trees that drop their leaves in winter (deciduous trees), an adaptation that minimizes water loss when the soil is frozen.

temperate rain forest: a temperate biome with abundant liquid water year-round, dominated by conifers.

template strand: the strand of the DNA double helix from which RNA is transcribed.

temporal isolation: reproductive isolation that arises when species do not interbreed because they breed at different times.

tendon: a tough connective tissue band connecting a muscle to a bone.

terminal bud: meristem tissue and surrounding leaf primordia that are located at the tip of a plant shoot or a branch.

territoriality: the defense of an area in which important resources are located.

tertiary consumer (ter'-shē-er-ē): a carnivore that feeds on other carnivores (secondary consumers).

tertiary structure (ter'-shē-er-ē): the complex three-dimensional structure of a single peptide chain; held in place by disulfide bonds between cysteines.

test cross: a breeding experiment in which an individual showing the dominant phenotype is mated with an individual that is homozygous recessive for the same gene. The ratio of offspring with dominant versus recessive phenotypes can be used to determine the genotype of the phenotypically dominant individual.

testis (pl., testes): the gonad of male animals.

testosterone: in vertebrates, a hormone produced by the interstitial cells of the testis; stimulates spermatogenesis and the development of male secondary sex characteristics.

tetrapod: an organism descended from the first four-limbed vertebrate. Tetrapods include all extinct and living amphibians, reptiles (including birds), and mammals.

thalamus: the part of the forebrain that relays sensory information to many parts of the brain.

therapeutic cloning: the production of a clone for medical purposes. Typically, the nucleus from one of a patient's own cells would be inserted into an egg whose nucleus had been removed; the resulting cell would divide and produce embryonic stem cells that would be compatible with the patient's tissues and therefore would not be rejected by the patient's immune system.

thermoreceptor: a sensory receptor that responds to heat or cold.

thick filament: in the sarcomere, a bundle of myosin that interacts with thin filaments, producing muscle contraction.

thigmotropism: growth in response to touch.

thin filament: in the sarcomere, a protein strand that interacts with thick filaments, producing muscle contraction; composed primarily of actin, plus the accessory proteins troponin and tropomyosin.

threatened species: all species classified as critically endangered, endangered, or vulnerable.

threshold: the electrical potential at which an action potential is triggered; the threshold is usually about 10 to 20 mV less negative than the resting potential.

thrombin: an enzyme produced in the blood as a result of injury to a blood vessel; catalyzes the production of fibrin, a protein that assists in blood clot formation.

thylakoid (thī'-luh-koid): a disk-shaped, membranous sac found in chloroplasts, the membranes of which contain the photosystems, electron transport chains, and ATP-synthesizing enzymes used in the light reactions of photosynthesis.

thymine (T): a nitrogenous base found only in DNA; abbreviated as T.

thymosin (thī'-mō-sin): a hormone, secreted by the thymus, that stimulates the maturation of T lymphocytes of the immune system.

thymus (thī'-mus): an organ of the lymphatic system that is located in the upper chest in front of the heart and that secretes thymosin, which stimulates maturation of T lymphocytes of the immune system.

thyroid gland: an endocrine gland, located in front of the larynx in the neck, that secretes the hormones thyroxine (affecting metabolic rate) and calcitonin (regulating calcium ion concentration in the blood).

thyroid-stimulating hormone (TSH): a hormone, released by the anterior pituitary, that stimulates the thyroid gland to release hormones.

thyroxine (thī-rox'-in): a hormone, secreted by the thyroid gland, that stimulates and regulates metabolism.

tight junction: a type of cell-to-cell junction in animals that prevents the movement of materials through the spaces between cells.

tissue: a group of (normally similar) cells that together carry out a specific function; a tissue may also include extracellular material produced by its cells.

tissue system: a group of two or more tissues that together perform a specific function.

tonsil: a patch of lymphatic tissue, located at the entrance to the pharynx, that contains macrophages and lymphocytes; destroys many microbes entering the body through the mouth and stimulates an adaptive immune response to them.

trachea (trā'-kē-uh): in terrestrial vertebrates, a flexible tube, supported by rings of cartilage, that conducts air between the larynx and the bronchi.

tracheae (trā'-kē): the respiratory organ of insects, consisting of a set of air-filled tubes leading from openings called spiracles and branching extensively throughout the body.

tracheid (trā-kē-id): an elongated cell type in xylem, with tapered ends that overlap the tapered ends of other tracheids, forming tubes that transport water and minerals. Pits in the cell walls of tracheids allow easy movement of water and minerals into and out of the cells, including from one tracheid to the next.

trans fat: a type of fat, produced during the process of hydrogenating oils, that may increase the risk of heart disease. The fatty acids of trans fats include an unusual configuration of double bonds that is not normally found in fats of biological origin.

transcription: the synthesis of an RNA molecule from a DNA template.

transfect: to introduce foreign DNA into a host cell; usually includes mechanisms to regulate the expression of the DNA in the host cell.

transfer RNA (tRNA): a type of RNA that binds to a specific amino acid, carries it to a ribosome, and positions it for incorporation into the growing protein chain during protein synthesis. A set of three bases in tRNA (the anticodon) is complementary to the set of three bases in mRNA (the codon) that codes for that specific amino acid in the genetic code.

transformation: a method of acquiring new genes, whereby DNA from one bacterium (normally released after the death of the bacterium) becomes incorporated into the DNA of another, living bacterium.

transgenic: referring to an animal or a plant that contains DNA derived from another species, usually inserted into the organism through genetic engineering.

translation: the process whereby the sequence of bases of messenger RNA is converted into the sequence of amino acids of a protein.

translocation: a mutation that occurs when a piece of DNA is removed from one chromosome and attached to another chromosome.

transpiration (trans'-per-ā-shun): the evaporation of water through the stomata, chiefly in leaves.

transport protein: a protein that regulates the movement of water-soluble molecules through the plasma membrane.

trial-and-error learning: a type of learning in which behavior is modified in response to the positive or negative consequences of an action.

trichomes: projections from the epidermal cells of some plants. Trichomes may absorb water, form a hairy coating on leaves, or aid in seed dispersal.

trichomoniasis (trik-ō-mō-nī'-uh-sis): a sexually transmitted disease, caused by the protist *Trichomonas*, that causes inflammation of the mucous membranes that line the urinary tract and genitals.

triglyceride (trī-glis'-er-īd): a lipid composed of three fatty acid molecules bonded to a single glycerol molecule.

trisomy 21: see *Down syndrome*.

trisomy X: a condition of females who have three X chromosomes instead of the normal two; most such women are phenotypically normal and are fertile.

trophic level: literally, "feeding level"; the categories of organisms in a community, and the position of an organism in a food chain, defined by the organism's source of energy; includes producers, primary consumers, secondary consumers, and so on.

tropical deciduous forest: a biome, warm all year-round, with pronounced wet and dry seasons; characterized by trees that shed their leaves during the dry season (deciduous trees), an adaptation that minimizes water loss.

tropical rain forest: a biome with evenly warm, evenly moist conditions year-round, dominated by broadleaf evergreen trees; the most diverse biome.

tropical scrub forest: a biome, warm all year-round, with pronounced wet and dry seasons (drier conditions than in tropical deciduous forests); characterized by short, deciduous, often thorn-bearing trees with grasses growing beneath them.

tropism: directional growth in response to an environmental stimulus.

true-breeding: pertaining to an individual all of whose offspring produced through self-fertilization are identical to the parental type. True-breeding individuals are homozygous for a given trait.

tube cell: the outermost cell of a pollen grain, containing the sperm. When the pollen grain germinates, the tube cell produces a tube penetrating through the tissues of the carpel, from the stigma, through the style, and to the opening of an ovule in the ovary.

tundra: a biome with severe weather conditions (extreme cold and wind, and little rainfall) that cannot support trees.

turgor pressure: pressure developed within a cell (especially the central vacuole of plant cells) as a result of osmotic water entry.

Turner syndrome: a set of characteristics typical of a woman with only one X chromosome; women with Turner syndrome are sterile, with a tendency to be very short and to lack typical female secondary sexual characteristics.

tympanic membrane (tim-pan'-ik): the eardrum; a membrane that stretches across the opening of the middle ear and transmits vibrations to the bones of the middle ear.

unicellular: single-celled; most members of the domains Bacteria and Archaea and the kingdom Protista are unicellular.

uniform distribution: the distribution characteristic of a population with a relatively regular spacing of individuals, commonly as a result of territorial behavior.

unsaturated: referring to a fatty acid with fewer than the maximum number of hydrogen atoms bonded to its carbon backbone (therefore, an unsaturated fatty acid has one or more double bonds in its carbon backbone).

upwelling: an upward flow that brings cold, nutrient-laden water from the ocean depths to the surface.

urea (ū-rē'-uh): a water-soluble, nitrogen-containing waste product of amino acid breakdown; one of the principal components of mammalian urine.

ureter (ū'-re-ter): a tube that conducts urine from a kidney to the urinary bladder.

urethra (ū-rē'-thruh): the tube leading from the urinary bladder to the outside of the body; in males, the urethra also receives sperm from the vas deferens and conducts both sperm and urine (at different times) to the tip of the penis.

urinary system: the organ system that produces, stores, and eliminates urine. The urinary system is critical for maintaining homeostatic conditions within the bloodstream. In mammals, it includes the kidneys, ureters, bladder, and urethra.

urine: the fluid produced and excreted by the urinary system, containing water and dissolved wastes, such as urea.

uterine tube: the tube leading from the ovary to the uterus, into which the secondary oocyte (egg cell) is released; also called the *oviduct*, or, in humans, the *Fallopian tube*.

uterus: in female mammals, the part of the reproductive tract that houses the embryo during pregnancy.

utricle: a patch of hair cells in the vestibule of the inner ear; bending of the hairs of the hair cells permits detection of the direction of gravity and the degree of tilt of the head.

vaccine: an injection into the body that contains antigens characteristic of a particular disease organism and that stimulates an immune response appropriate to that disease organism.

vagina: the passageway leading from the outside of a female mammal's body to the cervix of the uterus; serves as the receptacle for semen and as the birth canal.

variable: a factor in a scientific experiment that is deliberately manipulated in order to test a hypothesis.

variable region: the part of an antibody molecule that differs among antibodies; the ends of the variable regions of the light and heavy chains form the specific binding site for antigens.

vas deferens (vaz de'-fer-enz): the tube connecting the epididymis of the testis with the urethra.

vascular bundle: a strand of xylem and phloem in leaves and stems; in leaves, commonly called a *vein*.

vascular cambium: a lateral meristem that is located between the xylem and phloem of a woody root or stem and that gives rise to secondary xylem and phloem.

vascular cylinder: the centrally located conducting tissue of a young root; consists of primary xylem and phloem, surrounded by a layer of pericycle cells.

vascular plant (vas'-kū-lar): a plant that has conducting vessels for transporting liquids; also called a tracheophyte.

vascular tissue system: a plant tissue system consisting of xylem (which transports water and minerals from root to shoot) and phloem (which transports water and sugars throughout the plant).

vein: in vertebrates, a large-diameter, thin-walled vessel that carries blood from venules back to the heart; in plants, a vascular bundle in a leaf.

ventricle (ven'-tre-kul): the lower muscular chamber on each side of the heart that pumps blood out through the arteries. The right ventricle sends blood to the lungs; the left ventricle pumps blood to the rest of the body.

venule (ven'-ūl): a narrow vessel with thin walls that carries blood from capillaries to veins.

vertebral column (ver-tē'-brul): a column of serially arranged skeletal units (the vertebrae) that protect the nerve cord in vertebrates; the backbone.

vertebrate: an animal that has a vertebral column.

vesicle (ves'-i-kul): a small, temporary, membrane-bound sac within the cytoplasm.

vessel: in plants, a tube of xylem composed of vertically stacked vessel elements with heavily perforated or missing end walls, leaving a continuous, uninterrupted hollow cylinder.

vessel element: one of the cells of a xylem vessel; elongated, dead at maturity, with thick lateral cell walls for support but with end walls that are either heavily perforated or missing.

vestibular apparatus: part of the inner ear, consisting of the vestibule and the semicircular canals, involved in the detection of gravity, tilt of the head, and movement of the head.

vestigial structure (ves-tij'-ē-ul): a structure that is the evolutionary remnant of structure that performed a useful function in an ancestor, but is currently either useless or used in a different way.

villus (vi'-lus; pl., villi): a finger-like projection of the wall of the small intestine that increases its absorptive surface area.

viroid (vī'-roid): a particle of RNA that is capable of infecting a cell and of directing the production of more viroids; responsible for certain plant diseases.

virus (vī'-rus): a noncellular parasitic particle that consists of a protein coat surrounding genetic material; multiplies only within a cell of a living organism (the host).

vitamin: one of a group of diverse chemicals that must be present in trace amounts in the diet to maintain health; used by the body in conjunction with enzymes in a variety of metabolic reactions.

vitreous humor (vit´-rē-us): a clear, jelly-like substance that fills the large chamber of the eye between the lens and the retina; helps to maintain the shape of the eyeball.

vocal cords: a pair of bands of elastic tissue that extend across the opening of the larynx and produce sound when air is forced between them. Muscles alter the tension on the vocal cords and control the size and shape of the opening, which in turn determines whether sound is produced and what its pitch will be.

vulnerable species: a species that is likely to become endangered unless conditions that threaten its survival improve.

waggle dance: a symbolic form of communication used by honeybee foragers to communicate the location of a food source to their hive mates.

warning coloration: bright coloration that warns predators that the potential prey is distasteful or even poisonous.

water mold: a member of a protist group that includes species with filamentous shapes that give them a superficially fungus-like appearance. Water molds, which include species that cause economically important plant diseases, are part of a larger group known as the stramenopiles.

wax: a lipid composed of fatty acids covalently bonded to long-chain alcohols.

weather: short-term fluctuations in temperature, humidity, cloud cover, wind, and precipitation in a region over periods of hours to days.

wetlands: a region (sometimes called a marsh, swamp, or bog) in which the soil is covered by, or saturated with, water for a significant part of the year.

white matter: the portion of the brain and spinal cord that consists largely of myelin-covered axons and that gives these areas a white appearance.

wildlife corridor: a strip of protected land linking larger areas. Wildlife corridors allow animals to move freely and safely between habitats that would otherwise be isolated by human activities.

work: energy transferred to an object, usually causing the object to move.

working memory: the first phase of learning; short-term memory that is electrical or biochemical in nature.

X chromosome: the female sex chromosome in mammals and some insects.

xylem (zī-lum): a conducting tissue of vascular plants that transports water and minerals from root to shoot.

Y chromosome: the male sex chromosome in mammals and some insects.

yolk: protein-rich or lipid-rich substances contained in eggs that provide food for the developing embryo.

yolk sac: one of the embryonic membranes of reptiles (including birds) and mammals. In reptiles, the yolk sac is a membrane surrounding the yolk in the egg; in mammals, it forms part of the umbilical cord and the digestive tract but does not contain yolk.

Z disk: a fibrous protein structure to which the thin filaments of skeletal muscle are attached; forms the boundary of a sarcomere. Also called *Z-line*.

zona pellucida (pel-oo´-si-duh): a clear, noncellular layer between the corona radiata and the egg.

zooplankton: nonphotosynthetic protists that are abundant in marine and freshwater environments.

zygomycete: a fungus species formerly placed in the now-defunct taxonomic group Zygomycota. Zygomycetes, which include the species that cause fruit rot and bread mold, do not constitute a true clade and are now distributed among several other taxonomic groups.

zygosporangium (zī´-gō-spor-an-jee-um): a tough, resistant reproductive structure produced by some fungi, such as bread molds; encloses diploid nuclei that undergo meiosis and give rise to haploid spores.

zygote (zī´-gōt): in sexual reproduction, a diploid cell (the fertilized egg) formed by the fusion of two haploid gametes.

ANSWERS TO THINK CRITICALLY, EVALUATE THIS, MULTIPLE CHOICE, AND FILL-IN-THE-BLANK QUESTIONS

Chapter 1

Think Critically

Figure Captions

Figure 1-3 The bun is made from wheat, a photosynthetic organism that can capture sunlight directly. The meat came from a cow, which feeds on photosynthetic organisms and fuels its body with energy stored from photosynthesis.

Figure 1-9 Of all the animals, plant-eaters have access to the largest amount of energy because they feed on plants, which capture the energy directly from sunlight. The huge size of some herbivores is also an adaptation for reaching leaves on tall trees.

Figure 1-10 Global climate change

How Do We Know That? Controlled Experiments Provide Reliable Data

Anything that could have gotten through the gauze might possibly have produced the maggots, or they could have come from eggs that were in the meat before it was placed in the jars. An experiment to support the hypothesis that flies produce maggots would be to use Redi's experimental setup with meat in each of two gauze-covered jars, but place flies in one jar and not the other.

Multiple Choice

1. b; **2.** c; **3.** a; **4.** d; **5** a

Fill-in-the-Blank

1. stimuli; energy, materials; complex, organized; evolve
2. atom; cell; tissues; population; community; ecosystem
3. scientific theory; hypothesis; scientific method
4. evolution; natural selection
5. deoxyribonucleic acid, DNA; genes

Chapter 2

Think Critically

Figure Captions

Figure 2-1 The mass number of H is 1; the mass number of He is 4.

Figure 2-2 Atoms with outer shells that are not full become stable by filling (or emptying) their outer shells.

Figure 2-3 Heat from the fire excites electrons into higher energy levels. When the electrons spontaneously revert to their original stable level, they give off light as well as heat.

Figure 2-9 No. The hydrophobic oil exerts no attraction for the ions in salt, so the salt would remain in solid crystals.

Figure 2-10 The water drop would spread out on clean glass because of adhesion to the glass and cohesion among the water molecules. On an oil-covered slide, the droplet would round up due to hydrophobic interactions.

Figure 2-11 There is more empty space between the molecules in ice than between molecules of liquid water, so ice is less dense and floats.

How Do We Know That? Radioactive Revelations

Fluid-filled space occupies a far larger portion of the brain of the Alzheimer's patient, indicating a significant loss of neurons.

Evaluate This

Health Watch: Free Radicals—Friends and Foes?

Eating dark chocolate by itself is unlikely to reverse high blood pressure. If Thomas added a 6-oz chocolate bar (about 1000 Calories) to his regular daily diet, he could gain 50 pounds over 6 months, which would likely worsen his high blood pressure. Thomas should maintain a healthy weight, gradually increase his exercise, and eat lots of fruits and vegetables. In addition, it would be okay for him to add a far smaller amount of dark chocolate daily.

Multiple Choice

1. d; **2.** a; **3.** d; **4.** b; **5.** d

Fill-in-the-Blank

1. protons, neutrons; electrons, electron shells
2. ion; positive; ionic
3. isotopes; elements; radioactive
4. inert; reactive; share
5. polar; hydrogen; cohesion

Chapter 3

Think Critically

Figure Captions

Figure 3-1 Hydrogen cyanide is a polar molecule, because the nitrogen atom exerts a much stronger pull on carbon's electrons than does the hydrogen atom.

Figure 3-8 During hydrolysis of sucrose, water is split; a hydrogen from water is added to the oxygen from glucose (that formerly linked the two subunits), and the remaining OH from water is added to the carbon (that formerly bonded to oxygen) of the fructose subunit.

Figure 3-14 Other amino acids with hydrophobic functional groups are glycine, alanine, valine, isoleucine, methionine, tryptophan, and proline.

Figure 3-16 Heat energy can break hydrogen bonds and disrupt a protein's three-dimensional structure. This prevents the protein from carrying out its usual function(s).

Figure 3-22 Triglycerides are broken apart by hydrolysis reactions.

Figure 3-27 As lipids, steroids are soluble in the phospholipid-based cell membranes and can cross them to act inside the cell.

Evaluate This

Health Watch: Fake Foods

The doctor should do the following:

- Emphasize the importance of losing weight and checking the calories in food. Sugar-free cakes and donuts will likely have at least as many calories as the regular type.
- Explain that a sweet tooth can (and should) be tamed by gradually cutting back on sweets.
- Suggest the patient get more exercise.
- Provide standard advice for pre-diabetes patients (this information is beyond the scope of this chapter but is available online on many reputable Web sites).

Health Watch: Cholesterol, *Trans* Fats, and Your Heart

The doctor should do the following:

- Do a blood test for high LDL cholesterol; this could cause partial artery blockage that would deprive the heart of adequate oxygen during exercise and cause chest pain.
- Recommend that the patient lose weight.
- Ask about the patient's exercise regimen (if any) and recommend that the patient try a variety of exercise classes to find one she enjoys.
- Ask if her diet includes a lot of saturated fat; if so, strongly recommend she switch to oil.
- Ask if she smokes, which contributes to heart disease; if so, encourage cessation.
- Suggest additional tests that are used to evaluate arterial health and explain how obesity damages the heart (use reputable Web sites to research this information).

Multiple Choice

1. c; **2.** c; **3.** a; **4.** d; **5** a

Fill-in-the-Blank

1. monomer, polymers; polysaccharides; hydrolysis; (any three) cellulose, starch, glycogen, chitin
2. hydrogen bond, hydrogen and disulfide bonds, hydrogen bond, peptide bond
3. dehydration, water; amino acids; primary; helix, pleated sheet; denatured
4. ribose sugar, base, phosphate; adenosine triphosphate (ATP); adenine, guanine, cytosine, thymine; deoxyribonucleic acid (DNA), ribonucleic acid (RNA); phosphate
5. oil, wax, fat, steroids, cholesterol, phospholipid

Chapter 4
Think Critically
Figure Captions

Figure 4-8 Fluid would not move upward because the beating of the flagella would direct fluid straight out from the cell membranes. Mucus and trapped particles would accumulate in the trachea.

Figure 4-10 Condensation allows the chromosomes to become organized and separated from one another so that a complete copy of genetic information can be distributed to each of the daughter cells that results from cell division.

Figure 4-14 The fundamentally similar composition of membranes allows them to merge with one another. This allows molecules in vesicles to be transferred from one membrane-enclosed structure (such as endoplasmic reticulum) to another (such as the Golgi apparatus). The material can be exported from the cell when the vesicle merges with the plasma membrane.

Figure 4-15 If lysosomal enzymes were active at a pH found in the cytoplasm, the enzymes would break down the membranes of the endoplasmic reticulum, Golgi, and the vesicles exposed to the enzymes.

How Do We Know That? The Search for the Cell

The light micrograph provides overall views of the structures in relationship to one another, and it also allows you to see the living cell, undistorted by preservation techniques. You can observe how the cilia beat and how they move the cell. In the SEM of the intact cell, you can observe its overall three-dimensional shape and the fact that it is completely covered with cilia. The TEM provides a more diagrammatic view of the mitochondria with a clearer image of the internal organization and folded cristae (see Fig. 4-17). The SEM of mitochondria shows that the internal membranes create confined spaces separate from the fluid inside this organelle.

Earth Watch: Would You Like Fries with Your Cultured Cow Cells?

Your graph projections will differ somewhat based on different trend estimation lines. However, China's per person meat consumption if current trends continue will still not exceed that of the United States in 2050, but it will be similar to that of the UK. The United States and UK will increase slightly; India will remain stable. China currently consumes the most total meat; in 1980, the United States exceeded China in total meat consumption.

Multiple Choice

1. a; **2.** b; **3.** b; **4.** d; **5.** b

Fill-in-the-Blank

1. phospholipids, proteins; phospholipid, protein
2. microfilaments, intermediate filaments, microtubules; microtubules; microtubules; microfilaments; intermediate filaments
3. ribosomes, endoplasmic reticulum, nucleolus, Golgi apparatus, cell wall, messenger RNA
4. rough endoplasmic reticulum; vesicles, Golgi apparatus; carbohydrate; plasma membrane
5. mitochondria, chloroplasts, extracellular matrix, nucleoid, cilia, cytoplasm

6. mitochondria, chloroplasts; double, ATP, size
7. cell walls; nucleoid; plasmids; sex pili

Chapter 5
Think Critically
Figure Captions

Figure 5-6 The distilled water made the solution hypotonic to the blood cells, causing enough water to flow in to burst their fragile cell membranes.

Figure 5-7 The rigid cell wall of plant cells counteracts the pressure exerted by water entering by osmosis, so although the cell would stiffen from internal water pressure, it would not burst.

Figure 5-8 No. Actively transporting water across a membrane against its concentration gradient would waste energy because the water would simply diffuse (osmose) back through the membrane.

Figure 5-12 Exocytosis uses cellular energy, whereas diffusion occurs passively. During exocytosis, materials are expelled without passing directly through the plasma membrane, allowing the cell to eliminate materials that are too large to pass through membranes.

How Do We Know That? The Discovery of Aquaporins

The control eggs would have shrunk very slightly. Because they swelled slightly in distilled water, it is clear that they are somewhat permeable to water, and they would have lost some water by osmosis in the hypertonic solution. The eggs with aquaporins inserted into their plasma membranes would have shrunken considerably and would be much smaller than the control eggs because water can flow either way through aquaporins, and it would have flowed out into the hypertonic environment by osmosis.

Health Watch: Membrane Fluidity, Phospholipids, and Fumbling Fingers

It is adaptive to feel enhanced pain when parts of the body are in danger of being damaged by the cold, because this will stimulate urgent behavior to warm up the affected body region.

Case Study Revisited: Vicious Venoms

Venom phospholipases are injected to injure and help immobilize the prey, whereas phospholipases in the digestive tract break down membrane phospholipids into nutrients that can be absorbed.

Multiple Choice

1. c; **2.** b; **3** b; **4** c; **5** a

Fill-in-the-Blank

1. phospholipids; receptor, recognition, enzymes, attachment, transport
2. selectively permeable; diffusion; osmosis; aquaporins; active transport
3. channel, carrier; simple, lipids
4. adhesive junctions, tight junctions, gap junctions; plasmodesmata
5. simple diffusion, simple diffusion, facilitated diffusion, facilitated diffusion
6. exocytosis; yes; vesicles

Chapter 6
Think Critically
Figure Captions

Figure 6-1 Yes, but this would be a boring roller coaster because each successive "hill" would need to be much lower than the previous one.

Figure 6-4 Glucose breakdown is exergonic; photosynthesis is endergonic.

Figure 6-7 Both parts of the coupled reaction occur with a loss of useable energy in the form of heat.

Figure 6-8 No, only exergonic reactions can occur spontaneously after the activation energy is surmounted.

Case Study Revisited: Energy Unleashed

Excess heat in the runner's body stimulates responses that reduce heat, an example of feedback inhibition. This same principle is at work when the end product of a metabolic process inhibits an enzyme involved in its production.

Evaluate This

Health Watch: Lack of an Enzyme Leads to Lactose Intolerance

He would suspect lactose intolerance, which would be even more likely if the child's parents were of East Asian, West African, or Native American origin. If tests confirmed his suspicions, he might suggest that the child reduce lactose-containing foods to a level she can tolerate and that the parents try giving her special formulations of dairy products that have lactase added to them, or lactase pills that can be taken prior to a meal.

Multiple Choice

1. b; **2.** a; **3.** d; **4.** b; **5.** d

Fill-in-the-Blank

1. created, destroyed; kinetic, potential
2. less; entropy
3. exergonic; endergonic; exergonic; endergonic
4. adenosine triphosphate; adenosine diphosphate, phosphate; energy
5. proteins; catalysts, activation energy; active site
6. inhibiting; competitive

Chapter 7
Think Critically

Figure Captions

Figure 7-5 If only red light hit the leaf, much less light energy would be gathered from chlorophyll *b* and essentially none from the carotenoids, so photosynthesis and its resulting O_2 production would decline significantly. No oxygen would be generated if only infrared light was present because there are no infrared-capturing pigments in chloroplasts. Shining green light on the leaf would substantially reduce O_2 production because neither chlorphyll *a* nor *b* would absorb it. Most green light is reflected from the leaf.

Figure E7-1 In cool, moist conditions, evaporation is not a problem, so C_3 plants can leave their stomata open, allowing adequate CO_2 to enter and O_2 to diffuse out. The C_3 pathway is more energy efficient than the C_4 pathway; C_4 uses one extra ATP per CO_2 molecule (to regenerate PEP). Thus, when CO_2 is abundant and photorespiration is not a problem, C_3 plants produce sugar at lower energy cost, and they outcompete C_4 plants.

Earth Watch: Biofuels—Are Their Benefits Bogs?

It is reasonable to assume that algal and/or cellulose biofuels will gradually (or rapidly) replace corn. Corn prices would be expected to drop and stabilize at a lower price than they are currently. Other scenarios are possible, however, and any scenario with a reasonable rationale is correct.

Multiple Choice

1. a; **2.** b; **3.** a; **4.** b; **5.** d

Fill-in-the-Blank

1. stomata, oxygen (O_2), carbon dioxide (CO_2); water loss (evaporation); chloroplasts, mesophyll
2. red, blue, violet; green; carotenoids; photosystems, thylakoid
3. reaction center; primary electron acceptor molecule; electron transport chain; hydrogen ions (H^+); chemiosmosis
4. water (H_2O), carbon dioxide (CO_2); Calvin cycle; carbon fixation
5. rubisco, oxygen (O_2); photorespiration; C_4 pathway, CAM (or crassulacean acid metabolism) pathway
6. ATP, NADH, Calvin; RuBp (or ribulose bisphosphate); G3P (glyceraldehyde-3-phosphate), glucose

Chapter 8
Think Critically

Figure Captions

Figure 8-3 Glycolysis produces a net of two NADH and two ATP molecules.

Figure 8-6 Without oxygen, electrons would be unable to continue entering the electron transport chain, and no further ATP would be produced.

Figure 8-11 NAD^+ would become unavailable for further glycolysis or cellular respiration.

Evaluate This

Health Watch: How Can You Get Fat by Eating Sugar?

Hypothesis: Colin is eating many more carbohydrates than he did previously to stay satisfied. Questions: What is he eating instead of fat? Has he decreased his average daily caloric intake? Has he increased his exercise? Recommendations: Eat a lot of fruits and vegetables; include some healthy fats from foods like avocados and nuts. Avoid refined carbohydrates, count calories, exercise regularly, and gradually increase daily exercise.

Case Study Revisited: Raising a King

Jeremy does not need to worry about a child inheriting his disorder, because mitochondrial mutations are only inherited from the mother.

Multiple Choice

1. d; **2** a; **3.** b; **4.** d; **5.** b

Fill-in-the-Blank

1. glycolysis, cellular respiration; cytosol, mitochondria; aerobic
2. anaerobic; glycolysis, two; fermentation, NAD^+
3. ethanol (alcohol), carbon dioxide; lactic acid; lactate fermentation
4. matrix, intermembrane space, concentration gradient; chemiosmosis; ATP synthase
5. Krebs; acetyl CoA; two; NADH, $FADH_2$ (order not important)

Chapter 26

Think Critically

Figure Captions

Figure 26-1 One possibility is that the variation necessary for selection has never arisen. (If no members of the species by chance gain the ability to discriminate between their own chicks and cuckoo chicks, then selection has no opportunity to favor the novel behavior.) Another possibility is that the cost of the behavior is relatively low. (If parasitism by cuckoos is rare, a parent that feeds any begging chick in its nest is, on average, much more likely to benefit than suffer.)

Figure 26-24 If females do indeed gain any benefits from their mates, those benefits would necessarily be genetic (as the male provides no material benefits). Male fitness may vary, and to the extent that this fitness can be passed to offspring, females would benefit by choosing the most fit males. If a male's fitness is reflected in his ability to build and decorate a bower, females would benefit by preferring to mate with males that build especially good bowers.

Figure 26-25 Canines forage mainly by smell; mandrills are mostly visual foragers. Modes of sexual signaling are affected not only by the nature of the information to be encoded, but also by the sensory biases and sensitivities of the species involved. Communication systems may evolve to take advantage of traits that originally evolved for other functions.

Multiple Choice

1. c; **2.** a; **3.** b; **4.** a; **5.** d

Fill-in-the-Blank

1. genes, environment; stimulus; innate
2. energy, predators; practice, skills; adult; brains
3. habituation, repeated; imprinting; sensitive period
4. aggressive; displays, injuring (wounding, damaging); weapons (such as fangs, claws), larger
5. territoriality (territorial behavior); mate, raise young, feed, store food; male; same species
6. For pheromones; any of the following advantages are correct: long lasting, use little energy to produce, are species specific, don't attract predators, may convey messages over long distances. Any of the following disadvantages are correct: cannot convey changing information, convey fewer different types of information. For visual displays, any of the following advantages are correct: instantaneous, can change rapidly, many different messages can be sent, quiet. Any of the following disadvantages are correct: make animals conspicuous to predators, generally ineffective in darkness or dense vegetation, require that recipient be in visual range (close by).

Chapter 27

Think Critically

Figure Captions

Figure 27-3 Many variables interact in complex ways to produce real population cycles. Weather, for example, affects the lemmings' food supply and thus their ability to survive and reproduce. Predation of lemmings is influenced by both the number of predators and the availability of other prey, which in turn is influenced by multiple environmental variables.

Figure 27-11 Emigration relieves population pressure in an overpopulated area, spreading the migrating animals into new habitats that may have more resources. Human emigration within and between countries is often driven by the desire or need for more resources, although social factors—such as wars and religious or racial persecution—also fuel human emigration. (This subjective question can lead to discussion of the extent to which overpopulation may drive human emigration.)

Figure 27-18 When fertility exceeds RLF, there are more children than parents. As the additional children mature and become parents themselves, this more numerous generation produces still more children, and so on, in a positive feedback cycle.

Figure 27-19 U.S. population growth resembles the rapidly rising "exponential" phase of the S-curve. Stabilization will require some combination of reduction in immigration rates and birth rates. An increase in death rates is less likely, but cannot be ruled out entirely. People

often have fewer children during recessions, so the "great recession" of 2008 through 2014 probably reduced the U.S. birth rate temporarily.

Earth Watch: Boom-and-Bust Cycles Can Be Bad News

In the short term (while a bloom is occurring), educating people about the dangers of the bloom (for example, don't eat shellfish from the affected area) and/or destroying the bloom, if possible, are the only realistic alternatives. In the long run, preventing blooms provides both human and ecological health benefits. Investigate the causes of and remedies for HABs, for example, at the mouth of the Mississippi River. What social and economic costs would be required to prevent blooms?

Earth Watch: Have We Exceeded Earth's Carrying Capacity?

Answers will vary, but they should consider the following questions: What are the ecological and economic impacts of producing the product in its native country? Of shipping the product overseas? What domestic products could substitute for the imported product? Would the domestic product have a smaller ecological impact than the imported product?

Multiple Choice

1. b; **2.** c; **3.** a; **4.** d; **5.** c

Fill-in-the Blank

1. survivorship curves; early-loss; late-loss
2. exponential; no; J-curve; no
3. carrying capacity; logistic, S-
4. clumped; uniform; random
5. births, immigrants, deaths, emigrants; increases

Chapter 28

Think Critically

Figure Captions

Figure 28-6 Monarch caterpillars store toxic chemicals from the milkweeds they eat, so they would likely kill or at least sicken birds or other predators that might eat them. However, the caterpillar would still be dead. The bold stripes of monarch caterpillars probably evolved as a warning to predators, advertising that they are toxic. When a predator has eaten and been sickened by one monarch caterpillar, it would probably not want to eat another. The evolution of bright colors would make it easier for predators to learn to avoid monarch caterpillars. This would enhance survival of the monarchs.

Figure 28-7 Many predators hunt by detecting odors, sounds, or even electric fields, in addition to, or instead of, sighting their prey visually.

Figure 28-8 Ancestors of these organisms that happened to slightly resemble their surroundings would be a bit less likely to be eaten, so they would be slightly more likely to reproduce and leave offspring. Chance mutations that increased their camouflage would enhance their survival and reproduction even more, eventually resulting in the modern, superb camouflage.

Figure 28-16 Fire has been a natural part of the forest environment for many thousands of years. Some forest plants might directly depend on fire for reproduction (for example, opening cones to release seeds) or might benefit from clearing out the trees, which lets sunlight hit the ground and reduces competition for water and nutrients. Fire might maintain some forests in permanent, or recurring, subclimax stages.

Health Watch: Parasitism, Coevolution, and Coexistence

Mosquitoes, even those of the same species, have some genetic variability, including having differences in their preferred time and place of feeding. For simplicity, let's assume that the bed nets are 100% effective, and that people are never bitten while sleeping beneath the net. A mosquito that flew about, especially inside houses, earlier in the day would have the opportunity to feed on people before they went to bed beneath a net. These "early" mosquitoes would reproduce more often than the rest of the mosquito population, passing their genes for early feeding on to their offspring. Eventually, one would expect that early mosquitoes would dominate the population, rendering bed nets ineffective.

Case Study Revisited: The Fox's Tale

If the ecosystem is severely degraded, for example by overgrazing that almost completely eliminates native vegetation, then it would be difficult for succession to restore the original community. This is especially true on islands, which may be separated by many miles from sources of native seeds. If invasive species are introduced simultaneously with overgrazing, then the bare soil would provide an opening for seeds of invasive plants to sprout and possibly take over permanently.

Multiple Choice

1. a; **2.** d; **3.** c; **4.** d; **5.** b

Fill-in-the- Blank

1. natural selection; coevolution
2. carnivores, herbivores; camouflage
3. competitive exclusion
4. warning coloration, startle coloration, Batesian mimicry, aggressive mimicry
5. mutualism (or symbiosis), parasitism, predation, mutualism
6. succession; primary succession; secondary succession; climax; subclimax

Chapter 29

Think Critically

Figure Captions

Figure 29-2 On land, high productivity is supported by optimal temperatures for plant growth, a long growing season, and plenty of moisture, such as is found in rain forests. Lack of water limits desert productivity. In aquatic ecosystems, high productivity is supported by an abundance of nutrients and adequate light, such as is found in estuaries. Lack of nutrients limits the productivity of the open ocean, even in well-lit surface waters.

Figure 29-8 Humanity's need to grow crops to feed our growing population has led to the fixing of nitrogen for fertilizer using industrial processes. Additionally, large-scale livestock feedlots generate enormous amounts of nitrogenous waste. Nitrogen oxides are also generated when fossil fuels are burned in power plants, vehicles, and factories, and when forests are burned. Consequences include the overfertilization of lakes and rivers and the creation of dead zones in coastal waters that receive excessive nutrient runoff from land. Another important consequence is acid deposition, in which nitrogen oxides formed by combustion produce nitric acid in the atmosphere; this acid is then deposited on land.

Figure 29-14 Global temperatures would not begin to decline immediately. CO_2 stays in the atmosphere for years, providing a long lag time before its contribution to the greenhouse effect would decline significantly. Further, there are other greenhouse gases, such as methane, produced by human activities. Finally, large amounts of CO_2 are stored in the oceans; no one really knows how much of this CO_2 might be emitted into the atmosphere.

How Do We Know That: Monitoring Earth's Health

It isn't a trivial task to "eyeball" a trend line (scientists use computer programs). Further, not all trends are linear: the yearly increase in atmospheric CO_2 concentrations, for example, has been getting larger over time. Nevertheless, if you draw a straight line through the data for Arctic sea ice and, say, the last 25 years for CO_2 concentrations, you will find that the data predict the Arctic to become ice-free sometime in the 2050s, and CO_2 concentrations to have doubled by about 2070—both probably within your lifetime. Actually, if major changes in human activities do not occur, these effects may happen sooner. For example, ice reflects more than half of the sunlight that hits it, whereas open water absorbs more than 90%. Therefore, as Arctic sea ice declines in area, more open water exists, which absorbs sunlight, heating the water and melting more ice, creating even more open water, which warms up even more, and so on, so the decline in sea ice may accelerate. On the other hand, if people use more renewable energy and less fossil fuel energy, then CO_2 levels may eventually stabilize or even drop, slowing down or reversing the loss of ice.

Evaluate This

Health Watch: Biological Magnification of Toxic Substances

Refer Victoria to the "food" tab on the U.S. Food and Drug Administration's Web site for information on the mercury content of seafoods. She will find that catfish and salmon have the least mercury; light meat tuna (mostly from skipjack) have intermediate amounts; and white meat tuna (from albacore) have the most. Other websites can help to explain why. Assuming that the fish live in water of similar mercury content, there are two major factors that contribute to the amount of mercury in fish: (1) Their average trophic level: the lower the level, the less mercury. (2) Their age when they are eaten: on average, older fish have eaten more prey, and have had more chance to accumulate mercury. Most catfish in your supermarket are farmed fish, eaten at about 2 years old, that feed at a low trophic level (algae, aquatic plants, insects and crayfish). Salmon are mostly 2 to 4 years old when eaten (farmed salmon are eaten when younger, and have less mercury), and feed at a moderately low trophic level (mollusks, small fish, and crustaceans that feed on phytoplankton). Skipjack tuna are typically eaten when 2 to 3 years old, and feed at a somewhat higher trophic level than salmon do. Albacore tuna are eaten when 2 to 4 years old, and feed at a still higher trophic level. Albacore are also extremely active, and eat a great deal of food—as much as 25% of their body weight daily—which exposes them to a higher total dose of mercury.

Multiple Choice

1. c; **2.** a; **3.** d; **4.** d; **5.** c

Fill-in-the-Blank

1. sunlight, photosynthesis; nutrients, nutrient cycles
2. autotrophs, producers; net primary production
3. trophic levels; food chain; food webs
4. 10
5. heterotrophs, consumers; herbivores, primary consumers; carnivores, secondary consumers; detritivores, decomposers
6. nitrogen-fixing bacteria, denitrifying bacteria; ammonia, nitrate
7. atmosphere, oceans; CO_2 (carbon dioxide); limestone, fossil fuels

Chapter 30

Think Critically

Figure Captions

Figure 30-8 Nutrients are abundant in tropical rain forests, but they are not stored in the soil. The optimal temperature and moisture of tropical climates allow plants to make such efficient use of nutrients that nearly all nutrients are stored in plant bodies, and to a lesser extent, in the bodies of the animals they support. These growing conditions support a vast array of plants, and these, in turn, provide a wealth of habitats and food sources for diverse animals.

Figure 30-18 Tropical deciduous forests have a dry season in which the soil has little moisture. Temperate deciduous forests have freezing winter weather, in which soil moisture becomes frozen and unavailable to the trees. In both cases, dropping the leaves reduces the trees' water loss at a time of year when the water cannot be replaced by absorbing water from the soil.

Figure 30-27 Coastal ecosystems have an abundance of the two limiting factors for life in water: nutrients and light to support photosynthetic organisms. Both upwelling from ocean depths and runoff from the land can provide nutrients, depending on the location of the ecosystem. The shallow water in these areas allows adequate light to penetrate to support rooted plants and/or anchored algae, which in turn provide food and shelter for a wealth of marine life.

Earth Watch: Plugging the Ozone Hole

Ozone depletion would lead to higher UV radiation, which would reduce photosynthesis. Less photosynthesis means that less CO_2 would be removed from the atmosphere. More CO_2 remaining in the atmosphere would increase the greenhouse effect, leading to more global warming and other changes in climate. Increased CO_2 in the atmosphere would also cause more CO_2 to dissolve in the oceans, increasing ocean acidification.

Multiple Choice

1. c; **2.** b; **3.** d; **4.** a; **5.** c

Fill-in-the-Blank

1. seasons; ocean currents *or* the presence of the ocean; rain shadow
2. suitable temperatures, availability of liquid water; light, nutrients, suitable temperature

3. tropical rain forests; coral reefs

4. littoral zone; phytoplankton, zooplankton; limnetic zone, profundal zone; oligotrophic; eutrophic; wetlands

5. phytoplankton; chemosynthesis, hydrogen sulfide; high pressure

Chapter 31

Think Critically

Figure Captions

Figure 31-5 Any rare organism faces a greater chance of extinction in a small reserve. For example, large carnivores need a large prey population to support them (see discussion of energy pyramids in Chapter 29), which in turn needs a large area of suitable habitat. Large herbivores are likely to be rare for similar reasons; for example, it takes a very large area of vegetation to support a population of elephants. A chance event (storm, fire, disease) may well kill all of the members of such a population in a small reserve. The effect on the ecosystem will depend on which species disappear. The loss of large predators, as in Yellowstone, may cause a cascading effect in which herbivore populations skyrocket, to the detriment of populations of at least some plants and the animals that depend on them.

Figure 31-8 A small reserve will have small populations of many organisms, especially large, predatory animals. Small populations typically lose genetic diversity through genetic drift (see Chapter 16). As genetically diverse organisms migrate through corridors, they help to reduce genetic drift and maintain genetic diversity.

Earth Watch: Whales—The Biggest Keystones of All?

In the absence of whaling, whale populations would be expected to increase. If the whale pump hypothesis is correct, then iron, nitrogen, and perhaps other nutrients in surface waters should increase, which should increase populations of phytoplankton and perhaps krill.

Earth Watch: Saving Sea Turtles

With a low turtle population, food supplies were probably abundant. Listing leatherbacks as endangered and enforcing other protection measures meant that they were much less likely to be killed in fishing nets. When turtle nesting beaches in Florida were protected, people no longer disturbed the nests and eggs were no longer collected. Abundant food, less predation by fishing, and protected nesting sites greatly increased turtle survival and reproduction, allowing exponential population growth (see Chapter 27). Exponential growth cannot continue indefinitely. Density-dependent factors usually slow down population growth in long-lived species such as sea turtles. These factors might include increasing natural predation, for example, by gulls and raccoons learning that the beaches with large numbers of turtle nests are easy sources of food during turtle nesting season. As turtle populations increase, food supplies in the ocean might also become depleted.

Multiple Choice

1. a; **2.** b; **3.** a; **4.** d; **5.** b

Fill-in-the-Blank

1. genetic, species, ecosystem; genetic
2. ecosystem services; provisioning services, regulating services, cultural services, supporting services
3. ecological economics
4. habitat destruction, overexploitation, invasive species, pollution, global warming; habitat destruction
5. minimum viable population; habitat fragmentation; wildlife corridors
6. sustainable

CREDITS

Photo Credits

Unit Openers: Unit 1: Volker Steger/Christian Bardele/Science Source;

Unit 4: Rodger Klein/WaterFrame/AGE Fotostock;

Chapter 1 opener: Misha Hussain/Reuters; 1-CO-inset: Frederick A. Murphy/CDC; 1-1: Mary Martin/Biophoto Associates/Science Source; 1-2: Melba Photo Agency/Alamy; 1-4: Rido/Shutterstock; 1-5: Terry Audesirk; 1-6a: Dr. Tony Brain/Science Source; 1-6b: Terry Audesirk; 1-6c: Eric Baccega/AGE Fotostock; 1-7: NASA; 1-8: Penny Tweedie/Alamy; 1-9: Jose Maria Farfagl/Wenn Photos/Newscom; 1-12: John Durham/Science Source; Have You Ever Wondered? box: Joel Sartore/Getty Images

Chapter 2 opener: Air Photo Service/ABACAUSA.COM/Newscom; 2-4b: Piotr Sosnowski; 2-8a: Basil/Shutterstock; 2-8b: Danita Delimont/Alamy; 2-8c: Terry Audesirk; 2-10: Renn Sminkey/Pearson Education, Inc.; 2-12: Vicky Kasala/SuperStock; E2-1a: National Institutes of Health; E2-2a–b: Science Source; E2-3: Hunor Kristo/Fotolia; E2-4-1-2: Terry Audesirk

Chapter 3 opener: Terry Audesirk; 3-9a: Jeremy Burgess/Science Source; 3-10a: Mike Norton/Shutterstock; 3-10b: Jeremy Burgess/Science Source; 3-10c: Biophoto Associates/Science Source; 3-11: Terry Audesirk; 3-12a: Tracy Morgan/DK Images; 3-12b: B G Smith/Shutterstock; 3-12c: Xiaodong Ye/iStock/Getty Images; 3-18: Fotokostic/Shutterstock; 3-23a: Sylvie Bouchard/Fotolia; 3-23b: Terry Audesirk; 3-24a-b: Terry Audesirk; 3-25: Tischenko Irina/Shutterstock; E3-1: Terry Audesirk; E3-3: GJLP/Science Source; E3-4-1: VersusStudio/Fotolia; E3-4-2: Valua Vital/Fotolia

Chapter 4 opener: Matt Dunham/AP Images; E4-1-a1: Cecil H. Fox/Science Source; E4-1-a2: The Project Gutenberg Literary Archive Foundation; E4-1b: The Print Collector/Alamy; E4-1c: Pacific Northwest National Laboratory; E4-2a: M. I. Walker/Science Source; E4-2b: SPL/Science Source; E4-2c: CNRI/Science Source; E4-2d: Science Source; UN-1: Stacie Kirsch/Electron Microscopy Sciences; 4-3b-c: Science Source; 4-3d: John Cardamone Jr./Biological Photo Service; 4-3e: Proceedings of the National Academy of Sciences; 4-6b: Steve Gschmeissner/Science Source; 4-7b: Jennifer Waters/Science Source; 4-8a: Don W. Fawcett/Science Source; 4-8b: Charles Daghlian/Science Source; 4-8c: David M. Phillips/Science Source; 4-9b: Dr. Elena Kiseleva/Science Source; 4-10: Melba/AGE Fotostock; E4-3: Toby Melville/Reuters; 4-11: Oscar L. Miller Jr.; 4-12b, bottom: Don W. Fawcett/Science Source; 4-12b, top: MedImage/Science Source; 4-13: Meredith Carlson/Biophoto Associates/Science Source; 4-16b: Walter Dawn/Science Source; 4-17: The Keith R. Porter Endowment for Cell Biology; 4-18: Robin Treadwell/Science Source; 4-19: Biophoto Associates/Science Source

Chapter 5 opener: Fred LaBounty/Alamy; E5-1: Ted Kinsman/Science Source; E5-3: El Pais Photos/Newscom; E5-4a: Maarten J. Chrispeels and Peter Agre. Elsevier; 5-6a: David M. Phillips/Science Source; 5-6b: Amar/Phanie/AGE Fotostock; 5-6c: David M. Phillips/Science Source; 5-7a-b: Nigel Cattlin/Science Source; 5-9b: Don W. Fawcett/Science Source; 5-10b-1-3: The Company of Biologists Ltd; 5-11b: Eric V. Grave/Science Source; 5-11c: SPL/Science Source; 5-12: Linda Hufnagel; 5-14a,c: Don W. Fawcett/Science Source; 5-14b: Claude and Goodenough. *The Journal of Cell Biology*; 5-14d: Biology Pics/Science Source; 5-15a: Justin Schwartz; 5-15b: American College of Physicians; 5-15b inset: Larry F Jernigan/Getty Images

Chapter 6 opener: Lucas Jackson/Reuters; 6-1: David Wall/Alamy; 6-3: Terry Audesirk; 6-5a: Terry Audesirk; Have You Ever Wondered? box right: Cathy Keifer/Shutterstock; Have You Ever Wondered? box left: Bioglow/REX/AP Images; E6-2: Terry Audesirk; 6-14: Terry Audesirk

Chapter 7 opener: Detlev van Ravenswaay/Science Source; 7-2a-b: Jeremy Burgess/Science Source; 7-3a: Haveseen/Shutterstock; 7-3c: John Durham/Science Source; 7-3d: Robin Treadwell/Science Source; 7-6: Terry Audesirk; E7-1 left: Terry Audesirk; E7-1 center: Martin Haas/Shutterstock; E7-1 right: Terry Audesirk; E7-2 left: Mathisa/Shutterstock; E7-2 center, right: Terry Audesirk; E7-4 inset: Eric Gevaert/Shutterstock; E7-4: Beawiharta/Reuters

Chapter 8 opener: University of Leicester/Rex Fe/AP Images; 8-CO-inset: The Print Collector/Glow Images; 8-4: CNRI/Science Source; 8-8: Mara Zemgaliete/Fotolia; E8-3 left: Tassii/Getty Images; E8-3 right: William Leaman/Alamy; 8-10: Walter Bieri/EPA/Newscom; 8-12: Terry Audesirk; 8-13: Rui Vieira/PA Wire/AP Images

Science Source; 28-13a: Jany Sauvanet/Science Source; 28-13b: WILDLIFE GmbH/Alamy; 28-13c: Science Source; E28-2: Centers for Disease Control and Prevention (CDC); 28-14a: Terry Audesirk; 28-14b: Carol Buchanan/Dreamstime; 28-15a: Tish1/Shutterstock; 28-15b: Jörn Friederich/imageBROKER/ Alamy; 28-15c: Tom Mangelsen/Nature Picture Library; 28-16a left: Greg Vaughn/Alamy; 28-16a right: Steffen Foerster/Shutterstock; 28-16b left: Phil Farnes/Science Source; 28-16b right: Jim Zipp/Science Source; 28-19: Michael P. Gadomski/Science Source

Chapter 29 opener: Oksana Perkins/Shutterstock; 29-10: NASA; 29-11: Monica Schroeder/Science Source; 29-12: Peter M. Miller/Science Source; 29-15a-b: USGS Information Services; E29-3: NASA; E29-4: NASA; E29-5: Newscom; 29-16: NOAA, 29-17: Accent Alaska/Alamy

Chapter 30 opener: Florian Kopp/Imagebroker/AGE Fotostock; E30-1a-b: NASA; 30-8 top left: Ricardo Arnaldo/Alamy; 30-8 top center: Schafer/Hil/Getty Images; 30-8 top right: Wilie Davis/Shutterstock; 30-8 bottom David Noton/ Alamy; 30-9 top left: EcoPrint/Shutterstock; 30-9 top center: Federico Rizzato/ Fotolia; 30-9 top right: Dirk Freder/iStockphoto/Getty Images; 30-9 bottom: iStockphoto/Getty Images; 30-10a: Vladimir Wrangel/Shutterstock; 30-10b: Louise A Heusinkveld/Alamy; 30-11a: Terry Audesirk; 30-11b: Tom Mchugh/ Science Source; 30-12: George H.H. Huey/Alamy; 30-13a: Tom Mchugh/ Science Source; 30-13b: Craig K. Lorenz/Science Source; 30-14: Siegfried Modola/ Reuters; 30-15: PhotoShot; 30-16 bottom left: Olivier Le Queinec/Dreamstime; 30-16 bottom center: Eric Gevaert/Shutterstock; 30-16 bottom right: Alan Scheer/Shutterstock; 30-16 top: Bill Brooks/Alamy; 30-17: Terry Audesirk; 30-18 top left: Paultessier/Istockphoto/Getty Images; 30-18 center left: Fbosse/ Istockphoto/Getty Images; 30-18 bottom left: Blakisu/Istockphoto/Getty Images; 30-18 right: Aleksander Bolbot/Shutterstock; 30-19 top left: Istockphoto/Getty Images; 30-19 center left: Mark Wallace/Alamy; 30-19 bottom left: Stockcam/Getty Images; 30-19 right: Alamy; 30-20 top left: Tom/Pat Leeson/ Science Source; 30-20 top right: Science Source; 30-20 bottom: Top-Pics Tbk/ Alamy; 30-21: Bill Brooks/Alamy; 30-22 top left: Larry Trupp/Alamy; 30-22 top center: Dmitry Deshevykh/Istockphoto/Getty Images; 30-22 top right: Science Source; 30-22 bottom: Lisa Dearing/Alamy; 30-24: Michael P. Gadomski/ Science Source; Have You Ever Wondered? box: Nastenok/Shutterstock; 30-27a: Vince Bucci/Istockphoto/Getty Images; 30-27b: Universal Images Group/ SuperStock; 30-27c: NHPA/SuperStock; 30-27d: Vlad61/Shutterstock; 30-28 top: Wildlife Gmbh/Alamy; 30-28 bottom left: WILDLIFE GmbH/Alamy; 30-28 bottom center: National Geographic Stock; 30-28 bottom right: Jan Hinsch/ Science Source; 30-29 top left: Greg Rouse; 30-29 top center: Image Quest Marine; 30-29 top right: Peter Batson/Image Quest Marine; 30-29 bottom: Craig R. Smith; 30-30 left: Newscom; 30-30 right: American Association for the Advancement of Science (AAAS)

Chapter 31 opener: Charles Nolder/Alamy; 31-1: Danish Ismail/Reuters; 31-2a: Strmko/Istockphoto/Getty Images; 31-2b: Robert Harding World Imagery; E31-1: AGE Fotostock; UN-1: Mark Gurney/Smithsonian/Sipa Usa/Newscom; 31-4: NASA; 31-5: Bruno Locatelli; 31-6a: Mark Smith/Science Source; 31-6b: Franz Pagot/Alamy; 31-7a: Ed Reschke/Getty Images; 31-7b: Tom Nevesely/Age fotostock; 31-7c: Reinhard Dirscherl/Alamy; 31-8: Instituto de Pesquisas Ecologicas; 31-8 inset: Luiz Claudio Marigo/Nature Picture Library; E31-2a: Age fotostock/ SuperStock; E31-2b: Doug Perrine/Nature Picture Library; 31-9a-b: Dr. George Naderman; 31-10a: Keith Dannemiller/Alamy; 31-10b: Steve Bly/Alamy; 31-12: Michael S. Nolan/Agefoto Stock/AGE Fotostock

Text Credits

p. 4: Theodosius Dobzhansky (1900–1975); p. 14: CBS Inc,; p. 15: Villarreal, Luis; p. 17: Max Delbruck, from *Transactions of The Connecticut Academy of Arts and Sciences,* vol. 18, Dec. 1949; p. 26: Loren Eiseley, *The Immense Journey,* p. 15 (Vintage Books, 1959); p. 54: Robert Hooke (1635–1703);

p. 493: *On the Origin of Species,* by Charles Darwin, published on 24 November 1859; p. 493: Data from Krebs, C. J., Kenney, A. J., Gilbert, S., Danell, K., Angerbjorn,A.,Erlinge,S.,Bromley,R.G.,Shank, C. & Carriere, S. 2002 Synchrony in lemming and vole populations in the Canadian Arctic. *Can. J. Zool.* 80, 1323–1333; Figure 27-4: Data from the U.S. Fish and Wildlife Service and the Center for Biological Diversity; Figure 27-8: Data from Connell, J.H. 1961. Effects of competition, predation by Thais lapillus and other factors on natural populations of the barnacle Balanus balanoides. *Ecological Monographs* 31:61–104. ©Copyright by the Ecological Society of America; Figure 27-10: Data from Utida, S. 1957. Cyclic fluctuations of population density intrinsic to the host -parasite system. *Ecology* Figure 27-13: Data in part (a) from Arias, E. 2014. National Vital Statistics Reports 63 (7); Figure 27-16: Data from Centers for Disease Control and Prevention. 2008 National Vital Statistics Reports; Figure 27-17: Data from the United States Census Bureau, International Data Base; Figure 27-18: Data from the United States Census Bureau, International Data Base; Figure 27-19: Data from the United States Census Bureau, Population Division; Figure 28-1: Data from The Struggle for Existence, G. F. Gause, 1934, Dover Phoenix Editions Dover Books on Biology, Edition 1, G.F. Gause @2003 p.102; Figure 28-2: Data from MacArthur, R.H. 1958. Population ecology of some warblers of Northeastern coniferous forest. *Ecology* 39:599–619;

Figure 29-14: Dr. Pieter Tans, NOAA/ESRL (www.esrl.noaa.gov/gmd/ccgg/trends/) and Dr. Ralph Keeling, Scripps Institution of Oceanography (scrippsco2.ucsd.edu/); p. 558: The Washington Post Company; Figure 30-4: Korner, Christian, Spehn, Eva M., Global Mountain Biodiversity Assessment. 2002 DIVERSITAS (UNESCO and UNEP); Figure 31-3: Data from The World Wildlife Fund, the Zoological Society of London, and the Global Footprint Network, 2010. The Living Planet Report; p. 594: Caring for the Earth: A Strategy for Sustainable Living. 1991. Gland, Switzerland: Published in partnership by IUCN, UNEP, and WWF; p. 599: Who Will Care for the Earth?, Annual Report 1993: IUCN, International Union for Conservation of Nature & Natural Resources, 1994; p. 686: Kevin Sack, 60 Lives, 30 Kidneys, All Linked, February 18, 2012, *New York Times;* p. 692: *The Rime of the Ancient Mariner,* Samuel Taylor Coleridge; p. 733: *Romeo and Juliet* by William Shakespeare; p. 835: Song of the Flower XXIII by Khalil Gibran, 1914; p. 874: U.S. Supreme Court, NIX v. HEDDEN, 149 U.S. 304 (1893) 149 U.S. 304 NIX et al. v. HEDDEN, Collector. No. 137. May 10, 1893; p. 874: Arkansas Code, Title 1, Chapter 4, Section 1-4-115. Title 1. General Provisions. Chapter 4. State Symbols, Motto, Etc. Acts 1987, No. 255, § 1; p. 877: Ecology and Adaptation edited by Lisa Gould, M.L. Sauther: refs for lemurs as primary pollinators and seed dispersers in Madagascar; p. 877: African Trees May Be Tied to Lemurs' Fate, by John Roach for National Geographic News, July 26, 2004: lemurs as primary seed dispersers on Madagascar;

INDEX

Citations followed by *b* refer to material in boxes; citations followed by *f* refer to material in figures or illustrations; and citations followed by *t* refer to material in tables.